UNITED STATES
and CANADA

A REGIONAL GEOGRAPHY

UNITED STATES
and CANADA

A REGIONAL GEOGRAPHY

Alfred J. Wright

THE OHIO STATE UNIVERSITY

Second  Edition

New York

APPLETON-CENTURY-CROFTS, INC.

November 7, 1956
019

$7.00

' HC103
, W92
1956
Copy 2

HC103
W92
1956

To

H. T. W.

Preface

THE FIRST EDITION of this book appeared early in 1948 when the United States and Canada had assumed positions of leadership in the postwar world. The wartime evolution had left its imprint upon the life of both nations. Billions of dollars spent for new industrial and commercial facilities resulted in new combinations of productive factors, on the farm, in the mine, and in the factory. What were then believed to be emergency changes in the economy have, in many instances, proved to be accepted practices. The increased birth rate and the redistribution of population brought about fundamental changes, not only in the place of economic activity but in its manner as well.

In the development of both countries a regionalism related to the physical conditions of the landscape persists, but the works of man tend increasingly to blur the delineation of these traditional regions. Increasingly, as the years pass, the United States and Canada have sought through legislation to gain some of the advantages which their natural development has denied them. Neither can legislate an increased endowment of resources, but each can and does secure for itself the benefits of markets, carrying trade, and processes. Despite the tremendous flow of trade across their common boundary, they are two nations with distinct economies. Although crop associations may cross the border, the economy under which each is grown and marketed is distinctive for each nation. In determining geographic regions it must be kept in mind that they are not just productive regions but consuming areas as well. The international boundary is a geographic limit of major importance.

In order that the student may become familiar with some of the forces which are modifying the economy of both nations, the agriculture, mineral

vii

industries, manufacturing, and commerce of Canada and the United States are summarized in the first five chapters. It is highly desirable that the student have before him a large physiographic diagram such as that of Lobeck or Raisz. The awareness of the distribution of the physical and human facts involved in this regionalism is by no means solely a visual concept.

The events of the past quarter century have done much to confront students of economic geography with the acceleration of change in livelihood processes and patterns. At the same time, these years have witnessed a growing body of factual material concerned with the bonds which develop among industries and with the community of which they are a part.

It will be apparent to those familiar with the earlier edition that this is a thorough revision, involving new maps, charts, and illustrations, as well as extensive textual rewriting. Every effort has been made to present the most recent statistical data. Most extensive rewriting has been done for those regions in which manufacturing has experienced the greatest changes, as in the Middle Atlantic Littoral, the South, the Middle West, Pacific Coast, and southern Canada.

It is a pleasure to acknowledge the help of many persons who, in one way or another, have aided in the preparation of this book. With the exception of one map by E. Willard Miller, Pennsylvania State University, all maps are new and, unless otherwise credited, were prepared by Henry L. Hunker.

Appreciation is tendered to George F. Deasy and Phyllis R. Greiss, Pennsylvania State University; to Guy-Harold Smith, Robert M. Basile, and Henry L. Hunker, The Ohio State University; to the reference staff of the W. O. Thompson Memorial Library; and to those who have made helpful suggestions while using the first edition. While gratefully acknowledging these aids, the writer assumes full responsibility for errors in fact or in interpretation.

Columbus, Ohio   A. J. W.

Contents

Part Three

GEOGRAPHIC REGIONS OF CANADA, ALASKA, AND HAWAII

Part Four

PROSPECT

List of Tables

List of Illustrations

INTRODUCTION

CHAPTER 1

INTRODUCTION

THIS BOOK discusses the economic geography of that portion of North America occupied almost wholly by English-speaking peoples. It is based upon the viewpoint expressed in Dr. Isaiah Bowman's statement that economic geography is the study of "the timeless creative experiment." From this point of view Anglo-America is seen as a grouping or arrangement of general economic activities and regions allocated in such a way that both the individual economies and the pattern or the areal organization of the whole are subject to change. As changing activities and demands are imposed upon environmental conditions, the economic regionalism of America is constantly being altered.

Economic Regions and Economic Change. The dynamic nature of economic geography is recognized by more people than ever before. The events of the past few decades have made us realize that even though political boundaries remain the same and the physical environment is essentially stable, the economy of the several regions and the use of natural resources are being modified continually. It is now generally recognized that our economy can never be static, that we cannot expect any single environmental factor or any particular activity to become a permanent basis of prosperity. Our traditional attitude toward "abundance" and "isolation," manifested in the creation of barriers to the free exchange of raw materials, comes to be more widely questioned at a time when our industry is increasingly dependent upon materials not found within our borders, and when the accumulation of stockpiles is practiced.

These changes are continuous, but they are greatly accelerated and, therefore, are more obvious during a time of war. Then new industries

3

emerge, others cease; additional resources are exploited and new centers of production arise. With these changes there come extensive rearrangements of trade relations, involving the development of new routes and means of transportation. Some of these changes are temporary, but many more have permanent effect.

The rapidity with which economic changes have taken place in North America, and the close relation that these developments have had to the physical environment, make the study of our economic geography particularly interesting. As Dr. O. E. Baker stated: "Perhaps nowhere else and at no other time has a great civilization been shaped so rapidly, so simply, and so directly out of the fat of the land." More than one section of our country has seemed to reach a geographical climax only to witness the beginning of another.

Resources-Population Ratio. In reviewing the past half-century of historic-economic developments in the United States, Professor C. O. Sauer of the University of California has said that the two most important events were (1) the passing of free farm lands, and (2) the mass production of Ford's Model T automobile, the first car manufactured in the United States that was cheap enough for millions to purchase. Lands which belonged to the public domain and were given away or sold at a nominal price were for over a century an important element in our economy. The existence of undeveloped lands for exploitation gave hope of an increased prosperity for the nation and an opportunity for self-advancement for the individual. The free lands offered outlets which prevented serious overpopulation of any one district. The abundance and the fertility of the land have, perhaps more than any other one environmental factor, differentiated the economy of the United States from that of western Europe. Even the vast difference in wages for unskilled labor between the United States and Europe is primarily due, not to any difference in the virtues of the individual or of the government, but to the different ratios of resources to men. If the worker and his family did not like the wages or working conditions in eastern United States, they could "Go West" and take up some of the cheap land on the frontier.

Vertical Frontier. The free lands were of great advantage to us in all but one respect: their existence tempted people to think of our land as inexhaustible and thus encouraged waste. As long as there were lands to be opened, we were inclined to squander the grass, trees, soil, minerals, and animals as new areas were occupied.

Naturally the passing of this frontier has deeply affected the economic attitudes of the nation. We have had to develop more intensive methods of farming, learn to practice conservation, revise our view of the nation's future, and seek a new basis of national prosperity. For some people the intellectual adjustment has been painful or impossible. Since our expanding markets have been based largely on an expanding nation, those people can see little value in foreign trade (*Fig.* 1-1).

They believe that with the disappearance of the physical frontier the door to opportunity is closed. They have overlooked the fact that a new frontier, which has been aptly termed the "vertical frontier," has taken the place of the other; and that this

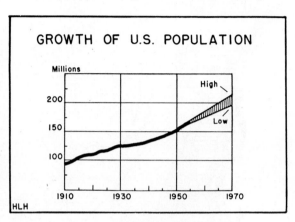

FIGURE 1-1

No matter which of the two estimates of population increase for the 1955-1970 period is achieved, this chart reflects an extraordinary change in the base of the nation's economy.

does not require new territory, but merely increased ingenuity and perseverance in working toward a higher standard of living for a large proportion of the population.

The Model T Ford mentioned by Sauer is a symbol of the opening of this new type of frontier. It stands for many aspects of the new economy: mass production and the concentration of industrial wage earners, cheap transportation, and powered machinery for all sorts of enterprises. Such changes give rise to new problems which must be solved by generations yet unborn.

Field of Economic Geography. Since economic geography deals with and correlates aspects of both economics and of geography, and has as its field the areal expression and consideration of all the factors of production, it must always recognize changes in the relative values of these factors.

This can be illustrated by reference to a particular economic region, the Corn Belt. Table 1-1, on page 8, indicates the factors involved in the economy of this district:

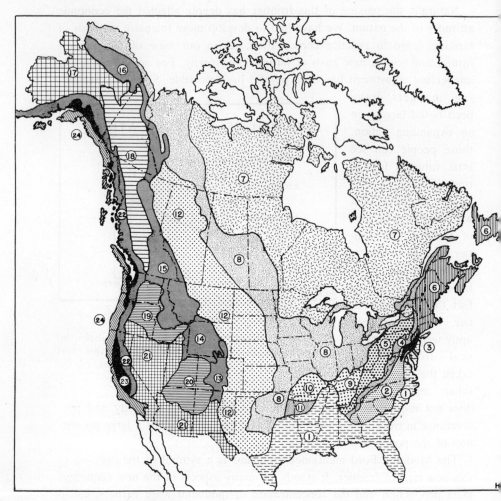

FIGURE 1-2: *Physiographic Provinces, United States and Canada*
(1) Atlantic and Gulf Coastal Plain, (2) Older Appalachians, (3) Triassic Lowland,
(4) New or Folded Appalachians, (5) Appalachian Plateau, (6) New England-
Maritime, (7) Laurentian Upland, (8) Central Lowland, (9) Interior Low Plateaus,
(10) Ozark, (11) Ouachita, (12) Great Plains, (13) Southern Rockies, (14) Middle
Rockies, (15) Northern Rockies, (16) Arctic Rockies, (17) Central Alaskan Uplands
and Plains, (18) Interior Plateaus, (19) Columbia Plateau, (20) Colorado Plateau,
(21) Basin and Range, (22) Sierra-Cascade-Coast Mountains, (23) Pacific Troughs,
(24) Pacific Coast Ranges. (*After* LOBECK)

6

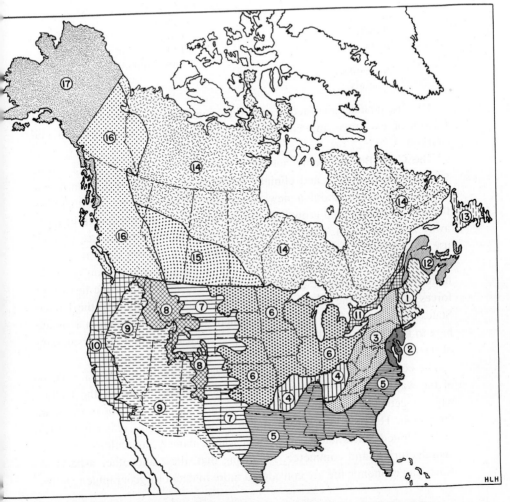

FIGURE 1-3: Geographic Regions, United States and Canada

(1) New England, (2) Middle Atlantic Littoral, (3) Appalachian Highlands, (4) Central Highlands, (5) The South, (6) The Middle West, (7) Western Great Plains, (8) Rocky Mountains, (9) Intermontane Area, (10) Pacific Valleys and Ranges, (11) St. Lawrence Valley, (12) The Maritimes, (13) Newfoundland, (14) Laurentian Upland, (15) Prairie Plains, (16) Pacific Mountains and Valleys, (17) Alaska.

TABLE 1-1

Natural Factors Of Environment	*Economic Factors Of Production*
Situation	Labor
Climate	Capital
Relief	Entrepreneur
Soil	Government
Vegetation	
Minerals	

This list includes the factors of production. To these must be added the factors of exchange and consumption, which include transportation and markets.

The Corn Belt economy has been derived logically from its favorable situation, soil, terrain, and climate. Corn dominated the region until new influences brought about a new equilibrium. Prominent among these influences were the rapid growth of urban centers and the movement of labor away from the farm. City markets gradually changed the nature of land use. The declining farm labor made mechanization of farm work necessary.

Economic geography, its phenomena so subject to change, can never be mere description of static conditions. It is necessarily a dynamic history of forces in action, "the timeless creative experiment." In dividing the United States and Canada into regions convenient for study, the attempt is made here to keep the regionalism as simple as is consistent with an understanding of the diversity of activities which characterize these subdivisions.

The economic geography of a country treats of the distributional aspects of the ways in which its population makes its living. Some of the factors which together give character to the economic activity are not inherent in the region. The next four chapters of this book take up the major industries of the United States and Canada as a whole, namely, agriculture, mining, manufacturing, and commerce. Following that, these and other aspects of American economic life are considered more in detail by geographic regions.

Major Geographic Regions. There are several ways in which the United States and Canada may be divided into regions convenient for treatment. From the teacher's viewpoint, geographic regions become useful concepts only if the component factors of each region, both human and physical, can be readily identified and differentiated from those of other regions (*Figs.* 1-2, 1-3).

This type of region is one where availability of resources and environmental conditions are relatively uniform throughout, permitting the development of an over-all socioeconomic homogeneity. Several such regions have emerged and are generally recognized, such as the Middle West and the South.

The regions into which the United States and Canada have been divided have varying degrees of this regional quality. Within each of them are distinctive groupings of economic activities, a few of which lead to further regional subdivision. In the chapters which follow, economic activities of the American people are first considered broadly; then, in Part II, they are treated as component elements of the 17 geographic regions (*Fig.* 1-3).

Despite the unfortified nature of the international boundary, it is the most significant environmental factor in the regions which it separates. It delineates the extent of the respective national markets. This fact becomes more obvious as depressions and times of neutrality or of war rock the normal stability of economic regionalism. Canada and the United States are therefore treated separately, although at times and at places the role of the international border is distinctly passive.

An appraisal of the foundations of Anglo-America's well-being shows that the door of opportunity is still wide open.

Part One

GENERAL ECONOMIC ACTIVITIES

CHAPTER 2

AGRICULTURE AND AGRICULTURAL REGIONS

CHARACTERISTICS AND TRENDS

Westward Movement of the Frontier. Within a century and a half of agricultural conquest of North America, the frontier moved from the Atlantic Coast to the Pacific. Man's attempt to put this continent under the plow constituted a movement that may never occur again in all history. Across the eastern third of the continent the movement was slow because the population was numerically inadequate for the herculean task of clearing the forest, one of the largest and densest in the world (*Fig.* 2-1). The Appalachian Highland also interposed an obstacle to easy conquest. Midland America with its expansive plains and treeless prairies was brought under cultivation much more rapidly. By 1800 the increasing population of the eastern states was finding its relatively meager agricultural resources more and more inadequate. In addition, the high tide of European immigration provided a steady stream of settlers who sought out the fertile farm land along the frontier. Also, the government's policy of public land disposition had become increasingly favorable for settlement; so, too, was the policy of internal improvements, which dispelled isolation by the construction of roads, canals, and railroads.

Geographic Specialization. With each new physical province encountered by these pioneer farmers in their westward migration, they had to learn about the characteristics of the soils and climate which would affect crops (*Figs.* 2-2, 2-6). As a result of trial and error there evolved in each region an agriculture suited more nearly to the physical environment and the economic conditions than in any other important farming area of the world.

13

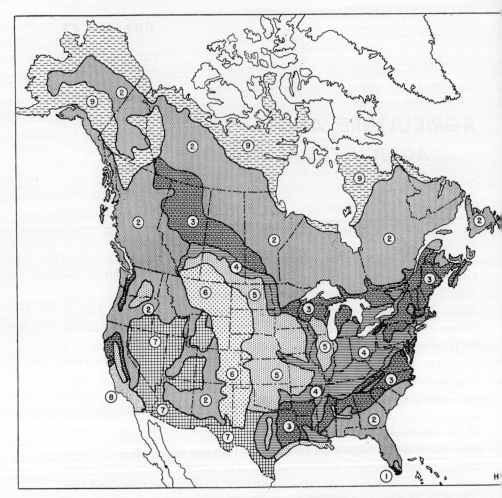

FIGURE 2-1: *Vegetation Regions, United States and Canada*

(1) Grass, (2) Needleleaf Evergreen Trees, (3) Mixed Broadleaf Deciduous and Needleleaf Evergreen Trees, (4) Broadleaf Deciduous Trees, (5) Prairie, (6) Short-grass, (7) Broadleaf Evergreen and Broadleaf Deciduous Dwarf Shrubform, (8) Broadleaf Evegreen Shrubform, (9) Tundra. (*After* KUCHLER)

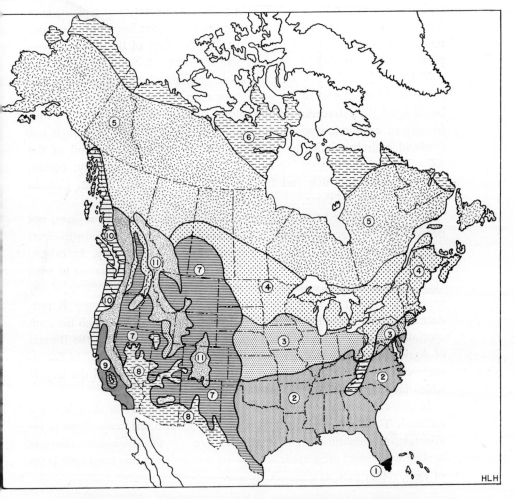

FIGURE 2-2: *Types of Climate, United States and Canada*

(1) Tropical Savannas, (2) Humid Subtropical, (3) Humid Continental, Long Summers, (4) Humid Continental, Short Summers, (5) Sub-Arctic, (6) Tundra (desert), (7) Steppe, (8) Desert, (9) Mediterranean, (10) Marine West Coast, (11) Highlands. (*After* TREWARTHA)

Geographic specialization brought about changes in the economy more rapidly than is common in areas where a traditional and self-sufficing agriculture is well established. Within each of the great crop regions, man found it necessary to adapt his crops to the limitations imposed by nature, and, so far as he knew how, tried to take advantage of the economic opportunities for farming in his particular environment.

The amazing diversity of geographic specialization is a phenomenon found in no other part of the world, not even in Europe as a whole. It is based upon the extraordinary diversity of physical conditions and the uniformity of economic opportunity and of social conditions. Although not confined entirely within the boundaries of the United States, all of the following major crop-growing regions do exist within the country: cotton, corn, wheat, hay, truck and fruit, grazing, and irrigated crops. Canada shares in several of these.

It must be realized that these are essentially rural land-use regions, not necessarily single economic regions. Some of them are highly industrialized and agriculture is far from being dominant in the economy. In others, mining is the principal source of income. It is an oversimplification to term even the predominantly rural areas as "economic regions" because of the varying physical and economic conditions under which one crop is produced. The concept is therefore of relatively large regions in which the crop specialty of rural land gives title to the whole. A recent map by the Bureau of Agricultural Economics, *Types of Farming Areas in the United States,* embraces more than five hundred separate regions, based upon the way in which farmers make their living from agriculture.[1]

In this chapter only the major lineaments of the agricultural regions are outlined. They are introduced early in the book, along with chapters on minerals, manufacturing, and commerce because the subsequent chapters dealing with broad geographic regions are treated from this functional point of view, rather than as a mosaic of small regions.

Mechanization. In nearly all of the important crop regions of the United States and Canada, the agricultural goal has been the maximum yield per man engaged, rather than the maximum yield per acre which prevails in countries with greater pressure of population upon agricultural resources. In the gratification of human wants, this is wholly desirable. It has pro-

---

[1] *Generalized Types of Farming in the United States,* Agric. Inform. Bull. No. 3 (Washington, February, 1950); *Types of Farming in Canada,* Pub. No. 825, Farmers Bulletin 157 (Ottawa, December, 1949).

FIGURE 2-3: *Planting Peas in Southern New Jersey*

This is a modern version of stoop labor on one of the largest farming operations in the Middle Atlantic Littoral. For the industrial aspect of this farm see *Fig.* 8-2. (*Steelways*, American Iron and Steel Institute)

moted the mechanization and the industrialization of agriculture in Canada and the United States.

The substitution of powered machinery for human labor has been facilitated by the nature of crops which are grown and by the nature of the terrain. The advent of the first farm tractor and the wheat combine made a permanent change in the agricultural practices of the wheat lands of the interior; the transformation of eastern agriculture waited for lighter tractors and smaller combines. It got them. The cotton-growing parts of the South are still waiting for the widespread use of mechanical cotton pickers, thus far restricted to the plains of Texas westward to California where all bolls on the cotton plant ripen at the same time. Thus in the 1951 picking season some 7,000 mechanical cotton pickers and 15,000 mechanical strippers were used on farms which grow cotton. With their use, 17 per cent of the total cotton crop was mechanically harvested. The portion of the crop thus harvested in 1950 was 8 per cent; in 1947 it was 2 per cent. It is in such areas that economic and social changes are greatest. Yet in the rich delta lands of the Mississippi alluvial plains only 5 per cent of the 1950 crop was mechanically harvested. The number of bales of cotton picked in California and the delta lands were approximately the same.

Even rice, potatoes, and sugar beets are produced in America by methods quite different from those prevailing in the Old World. These and other so-called "stoop" labor crops are subject to increasing mechanization (*Fig.* 2-3).[2]

TABLE 2-1: *Mechanization and Size of Farms in the United States*

	1910	*1920*	*1930*	*1940*	*1950*
TRACTORS	1,000	246,000	920,000	1,545,000	3,619,000
MILKING MACHINES	12,000	55,000	100,000	175,000	637,000
NO. OF FARMS USING COMBINES	1,000	4,000	61,000	190,000	714,000
CORN PICKERS		10,000	50,000	110,000	456,000
NO. OF FARMS IN U.S.	6,361,502	6,448,343	6,288,648	6,096,799	5,379,043
AVE. SIZE OF FARMS	138.1 acres	148.2	156.9	174.	215.2

SOURCE: Bureau of the Census.

Conditions in Canadian agriculture are similar, although the extent and the variety of crops are less. The trend toward mechanization of Canadian agriculture has developed more recently than in the United States.

Tenancy. For one reason or for a combination of reasons, agriculture in the United States particularly has been characterized by a relatively high rate of tenant farming. It varies by agricultural regions and it may appear in one of several forms, perhaps the best known is share-cropping. It is the result of forces not all of which have to do with the price of farmland. Tenancy may be so important a consideration in the farm economy as to virtually dictate what land will be cropped, what will be grown, and the manner of production. It has become one device by which agricultural entrepreneurs secure the way of life they desire.

Generally, the rate of tenant farming is relatively high where the farmland is expensive. The land must be productive enough to support the owner and the tenant. Maine has a low tenancy rate; the land is relatively low in price and in productivity. Illinois has a much higher rate; the land is more costly and of greater productivity.

In the following table, the proportion of part-time farm workers is

---

[2] *Migratory Labor in American Agriculture* (Report to the President, Washington, 1951).

given by Census divisions; the Census does not report them by major crop regions.

TABLE 2-2: Proportion of Farm Workers Employed for Two Months or Less

Region	Per cent, 1939	Per cent, 1950
NEW ENGLAND	5	25
MIDDLE ATLANTIC	11	11
E. NORTH CENTRAL	12	13
W. NORTH CENTRAL	16	21
SOUTH ATLANTIC	4	25
E. SOUTH CENTRAL	20	47
W. SOUTH CENTRAL	13	34
MOUNTAIN	13	10
PACIFIC	7	17

SOURCE: *Migratory Labor in American Agriculture* (Report to the President, Washington, 1951).

Migratory Labor. In some parts of the United States and Canada the intensification of agriculture has earned the doubtful distinction of being described as "factories in the field." This does not mean establishing factories in rural areas. In essence it means the passing of farming as a "way of life." A large part of the laborers in such districts are aptly termed "adrift on the land." No large agricultural section of the United States is entirely free from this practice of considering field hands as completely dissociated from the farm as is factory labor, but the Pacific valleys are the principal centers where this distinction is made.

Although the majority of the hired agricultural workers in the United States are part-time, only one in 14 is migratory. They perform about 5 per cent of the man-days of work and are employed on but 2 per cent of the total farms. Yet owing to the conditions under which they live and work, migratory labor is widely regarded as a problem.[3] Many of these farms are called "captive" farms and depend upon large processors or upon labor contractors to supply them with both labor and market.

[3] A Rio Grande farmer who raises 50 bales of cotton may save $1,000 annually by employing "wet backs" or Mexicans of illegal entry, an estimated 400,000 of whom enter the United States each year. In contrast, about 190,000 Mexicans enter this country legally under contract each year. Labor contractors deliver "labor service," not simply a man to do a job. Hence, it is customary to have perhaps ten times as many men sent to do a job as are needed. For a short time during World War II the Farm Security Administration by mechanization reduced the need for imported farm labor.

TABLE 2-3: United States Population, 1900-1950

YEAR	TOTAL	RURAL	URBAN	NO. PERSONS ON FARMS
1950	150,697,361	61,769,897	88,927,464	24,335,000
1940	131,669,275	57,245,573	74,423,702	29,047,000
1930	122,775,046	53,820,223	68,954,823	29,450,000
1920	105,710,620	51,552,647	54,157,973	31,559,000
1910	91,972,266	49,973,334	41,998,932	32,077,000
1900	75,994,575	45,834,654	30,159,921	——

SOURCE: Bureau of the Census.

Government. The government has in effect become an active partner in agriculture, first through the Agricultural Adjustment Administration program, and subsequently through the Production Marketing Administration program. These Acts have affected the agricultural sections of the United States; Canadian legislation has been similar but not quite so extensive. The effects have by no means been uniform, but in general the government has sought to retire submarginal farm land and to regulate price changes in farm crops so that they will ordinarily show a profit for the careful farmer.

Agricultural-industrial Relationships. In both countries it has been generally true that farm labor could and would advance up the so-called "agricultural ladder," from farm hand and tenant, to owner-operator, and perhaps absentee owner. The declining rural farm population characteristic of most important agricultural sections manifests an interruption of this process (*Fig.* 2-4). The rise of manufacturing has to a large extent depended upon the rural population for labor. The farms from which these laborers have come have been important consumers of factory goods. Probably no other nation can approach the extent of this farm market. There is a third aspect of this farm-factory relationship, and that is the production of raw materials for factory consumption; this bond is strengthened as chemistry enables the nation to produce its own substitutes for some raw materials formerly imported.

The present industrialization of Canada is manifesting a similar effect upon agriculture there.

REGIONALISM

The specialization in agriculture by regions in the United States and in Canada results in a diversified but not self-sufficing agricultural economy which is regionally interdependent (*Fig.* 2-5). The growth of regional

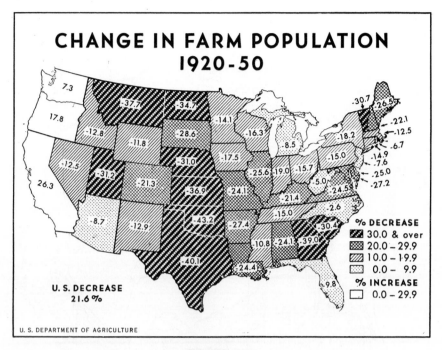

CHANGE IN FARM POPULATION
1920-50

U. S. DECREASE
21.6%

% DECREASE
30.0 & over
20.0 – 29.9
10.0 – 19.9
0.0 – 9.9

% INCREASE
0.0 – 29.9

U. S. DEPARTMENT OF AGRICULTURE

FIGURE 2-4

Those who have long thought of farming as a way of life should study this map. No major livelihood escapes the impact of this fundamental change in American agriculture. Agriculture accounts for a declining proportion of the nation's net product as well as employment.

specialization has been beneficial to agriculture. It has enabled the bulk of most crops to be grown under conditions approaching the optimum, although there have been instances where the movement of a crop has been away from the area in which optimum conditions prevail.

Mechanization has been fostered in the specialized-crop regions, thus lowering the production costs (*Fig.* 2-3). Mechanization has also made the economic goal the maximum yield per man employed, thus permitting the regular cropping of drier and more distant lands than would be possible with hand labor. Mechanization may put a premium upon certain plant characteristics and thus promote their use such as hybrid corn and single beet seeds.

Agricultural regionalism has increased the amount and influenced the direction of commerce. In most instances there have been widespread and important social and economic changes consequent to crop specialization. The monetary returns from a crop may be so timed as to give rise to special

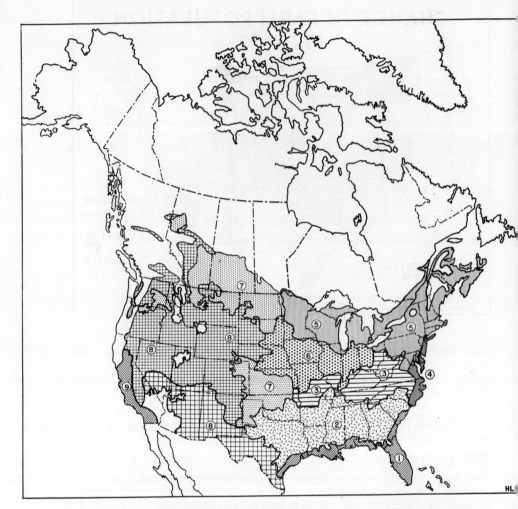

FIGURE 2-5: *Agricultural Regions, United States and Canada*

(1) Humid Subtropical Crops, (2) Cotton Belt, (3) General Farming, (4) Middle Atlantic Truck, (5) Hay and Dairy, (6) Corn Belt, (7) Wheat Belt, (8) Range Livestock, (9) Dry Subtropical Crops. (After *Generalized Types of Farming in the United States,* Agric. Inform. Bull. 3, Washington, 1950, and *Types of Farming in Canada,* Farmers Bulletin 157, Ottawa, 1949)

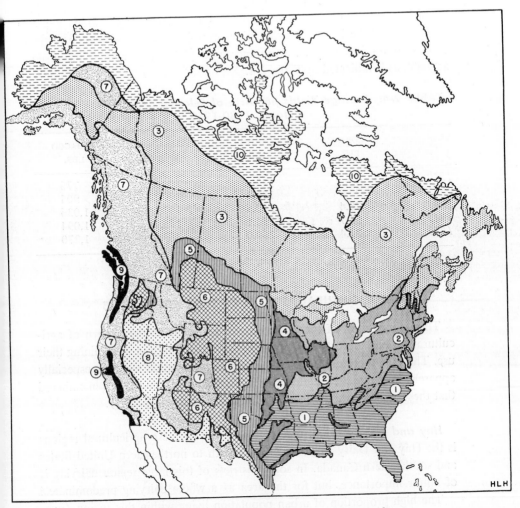

FIGURE 2-6: Soils, United States and Canada

(1) Red and Yellow Soils, (2) Gray-brown Podzolic, (3) Podzols, (4) Prairie, (5) Chernozems, (6) Brown, (7) Mountain and Undifferentiated Valley Soils, (8) Siero-zem and Desert Soils, (9) Pacific Valley Soils, (10) Tundra. (*After* U.S. Dept. of Agriculture, Miscel. Pub. 260, 1937, p. 12, and *Canadian Regions,* D. F. PUTNAM, ed., New York, 1952, p. 30)

credit systems, as for example in the old Cotton Belt. In all specialized agricultural regions a narrower range of labor skills is required, labor demand is more seasonal, and migratory workers are more common.

Since 1930 the increased production of major crops in Canada and the United States has resulted from increased yields rather than increased acreage, as is indicated in Table 2-4.

TABLE 2-4: Average Yields per Acre of Selected Crops in the United States, 1930-1950

YEAR	CORN BU.	COTTON LBS.	POTATOES BU.	TOBACCO LBS.
1930	20.5	157.1	109.5	776
1935	24.0	185.1	109.2	905
1940	28.4	252.5	133.1	1,036
1945	32.7	254.1	155.1	1,094
1950	37.4	269.0	253.0	1,270

SOURCE: Special Report, *Business Week*, July 4, 1953.

AGRICULTURAL REGIONS OF THE UNITED STATES

Throughout most of the United States and Canada the pattern of agricultural regions suggests the importance of temperature in determining their use. There is, therefore, a general east-west orientation which is especially apparent in the eastern half of the United States. It must be remembered that these regions are bordered by transition zones (*Fig.* 2-5).

Hay and Dairy Region. One of the largest of these agricultural regions is the Hay and Dairy Region, common both to northeastern United States and southeastern Canada. In some districts of this large region dairying is of minor importance, but for the area as a whole dairying predominates.

The high proportion of urban population living within this region (one-half of Canada's and one-fourth of the United States') has been conducive to the development of dairying. The greater accessibility of the eastern half of this region to large fluid-milk markets has enabled dairymen to devote themselves primarily to supplying this demand. But the western half of the area includes less perishable products, such as butter, cheese, and condensed milk. The great influx of summer visitors to the Hay and Dairy Region makes the market for fresh milk very seasonal in some districts, and therefore encourages the manufacture of milk products at other times. The great permissive factor in the farm economy of the area is hay and pasture. Most of this region has a climate favorable to grass. Throughout New England, the Middle Atlantic, and the upper Lakes States hay and natural pasture constitute the principal land use. Either thin soils, poor drainage, steep slopes, or short growing season, or a combination of them discourage crop agriculture.

Corn Belt. The geographical and agricultural heart of the continent is the Corn Belt of the United States. This is the only large area of the United States which exhibits such a high proportion of cropped land per square mile.

It is in reality a good general farming region with no more than half of its cropped land devoted to the growing of corn. The corn is fed to swine and to beef animals, with minor amounts to dairy cattle, sheep, and poultry. Illinois is the only state which sells an important part of its corn crop for other than feeding purposes, growing at least 3,000 bushels of corn per square mile. However, there are other areas where corn occupies almost as large a proportion of the cropped land as any other crop. Some of them lie in the southern states, east of the Mississippi River. Cropped land here constitutes a smaller proportion of the whole area in farms, than in the Corn Belt.[4]

Most farmers practice a regular rotation of the main crops such as: corn, wheat, or oats, and alfalfa or clover. Specialty crops are grown in many districts; tobacco, sweet corn, tomatoes, soybeans, and truck crops. Dairying and poultry are increasing in importance, especially in the more highly urbanized part of the region east of the Mississippi River. In no part of the region is there anything like "industrialized corn growing" exclusively, the equivalent of developments found in cotton and wheat production.

Perhaps the outstanding quality of Corn Belt farming is its general prosperity. The broad gently-rolling-to-flat plains of western Ohio, Indiana, Illinois, Iowa, eastern Nebraska, northern Missouri, and southern Minnesota support probably the most independent and prosperous farm population of similar extent in all the world. The prosperity of the rural population has given rise to active trading centers and to manufacturing. To the north are the Great Lakes and on the south the Ohio River. Cutting across it from north to south is the Mississippi. These water routes have served the Corn Belt as routes to market. Just east of this major agricultural region lie the major gateways across the Appalachians utilized by the great freight-

[4] John C. Weaver, "Changing Patterns of Cropland Use in the Middle West," *Economic Geography*, Vol. 30, No. 1 (Jan., 1954), pp. 1-47.

carrying railroads which serve this area. Certainly one of the most important aspects of the region is its accessibility to the northern and eastern port cities.

This accessibility has contributed much to the emergence of commerce and manufacturing in the Corn Belt. Despite the fact that the level terrain, the climate, the fertility of soil, and the inclination of farmers combine to make this a highly successful corn-growing region, the dominant economy of many parts of the area tends to make the name, Corn Belt, inappropriate. Yet in many areas the types of industry, such as the processing of corn and meat packing, are functionally related to the raising of corn.

General Farming Belt. Like the term Corn Belt, the name given this region does not quite do justice to the present-day type of rural land use. It is the second region thus far cited which has considerable amount of hilly land. Lying immediately south of the Corn Belt of the Mississippi Valley, and south of the Hay and Dairy Belt of the northern Appalachians, it partakes of the economy of both northern neighbors. It embraces the hill country of the Ozark Highland, the Interior Low Plateaus south of the Ohio River, crosses the Appalachian Highlands, and extends eastward to Chesapeake Bay. The critical natural environmental factor in the economy of this great region is unquestionably its rough topography. Wherever hills cease to be dominant in the landscape, some specialized land use interrupts the prevailing tendency toward self-sufficiency in agriculture, based primarily upon corn and winter wheat.

As far as climate is concerned, all but the higher portions are similar to the Corn Belt. Many of the lowland areas and broad valleys are important for corn. The most notable agricultural areas include the Kentucky Blue Grass, the Nashville Basin in Tennessee, the Shenandoah Valley, and the southeastern counties of Pennsylvania.

A specialty that is found in many districts throughout this area is tobacco. The varieties and the conditions under which it is grown vary with the district. The Coastal Plain and Piedmont of Virginia and North Carolina produces mostly a flue-cured tobacco. The central Kentucky Blue Grass area raises burley. The Pennyroyal district in western Kentucky and Tennessee grows a dark fire-cured tobacco. Fields may range from a "patch" of a few acres to farms devoted mainly to tobacco. Tobacco is a dependable cash crop, one that can be stored until the price rises, and one crop that has resisted mechanization and crop diversification.

Tobacco auctions are as regionally specialized as the tobacco plant. Tobacco fits into the farm program of such diverse farming areas as the lower Connecticut Valley, southern Wisconsin, the Carolina Piedmont, and the St. Lawrence Valley.

Cotton Belts. Nearly one-sixth of the area of the United States is embraced in the Cotton Belt. Unlike the Hay and Dairy, and the Wheat regions, the climate of the cotton-growing region permits the cultivation of a wide variety of crops. Few areas in the South have such a high proportion of the land devoted to the major crop as in the wheat areas or even in the western portion of the Corn Belt.

Historically, the boundaries of the cotton-growing South have been almost wholly defined by climate; but changes in cropping have been taking place which have modified the location of the Cotton Belt. Generally the northern boundary follows the average summer isotherm of 77°F. and 200 frost-free days. The western limit has been moving progressively westward and has now reached, without the benefit of irrigation, the 18-inch isohyet. The southern limit is approximately the 10-inch isohyet of autumn precipitation, generally some fifty miles inland from the Gulf coast. In the east poor drainage and inferior soils keep cotton from reaching the Atlantic. Within this large region there are many districts in which cotton does not dominate the farm landscape, particularly in the southeast.

After nearly a century and a half of cotton farming, the "system" under which it is grown has made the farmers among the least prosperous and independent in America. Cotton growing is an exacting type of agriculture. It has a long work year, a maximum of hand labor and a dependence upon commercial credit. It has so modified the sources of credit and the outlets for distribution are so specialized that it is very difficult for the small cotton farmer to break away from the cotton system.

Widespread ravages by the cotton boll weevil and the effects of the Second World War gave powerful impetus to crop changes in the cotton-growing South. Industrial payrolls at scores of new plants and shipyards, stoppage of imported vegetable oils into the United States, migration of both white and Negro labor to northern factories, and the greatly increased purchasing power of many southern families, have been strong factors in bringing about a diversification of land use in the Cotton Belt. Relative independence was made possible for thousands of southern farm laborers; the Cotton Belt is less than ever a one-industry region.

The introduction of new types of cotton which permit mechanization has enabled cotton production to enter some of the valleys of southern New Mexico, Arizona, and California. None of these western valleys is properly a part of the Cotton Belt as generally delineated.

Subtropical Crops Regions. This is a specialized crops region which is found widely dispersed over the southern and southwestern periphery of the United States. In its humid aspects, its largest extent borders the Gulf of Mexico.

More than three-fourths of a wide belt of Coastal Plain which fronts upon the Gulf is forest cut-over land, or swamp. In it are many "oases" of intensive agriculture where sugar cane, rice, citrus fruit, or early vegetables are produced for distant markets. The less desirable land, a very large part of the total area, is devoted to grazing livestock, or is unused. There is too much autumn rain for cotton.

Another subtropical area lies along the Pacific Coast south of San Francisco. It is not so restricted to the coast as that along the Gulf. It includes the valleys of the Coast Ranges, much of the Central Valley of California, and a portion of the arid interior of southern California. It is by no means uniformly utilized for agriculture. Although it contains larger arable regions than are found along the Gulf of Mexico, a smaller proportion of its total area can be used. Half or more of its area is mountainous.

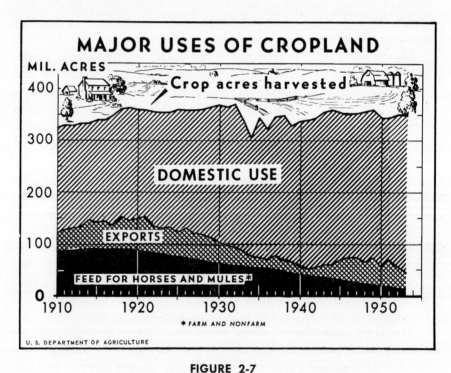

FIGURE 2-7

This chart should be compared with *Fig.* 1-1.

Its expensive irrigated lands are much more densely populated than along the Gulf coast. The Gulf South is surfeited with labor, while the south Pacific coastal area is deficient in labor and must rely on large numbers of migrant laborers.

Wheat and Small Grains Belts. There are three main wheat-growing regions in the United States. What have long been known as the Spring and Winter Wheat regions are separated by the unproductive sand hills of western Nebraska. The third major wheat region is on the eastern Columbia Plateau of Washington and is known as the Palouse country.

North of the Nebraska sand hills is the spring-sown wheat area, embracing much of the Dakotas, Minnesota and eastern Montana. This wheat region crosses the international boundary into southern Saskatchewan, Alberta, and Manitoba. Although natural conditions are comparable on both sides of the border, the role played by wheat in the economy of the respective countries is quite different. One, by law, has been able to protect its market; the other has not.

The southeastern margin of the Spring Wheat region in the United States is characterized by competition with corn. In Canada the low temperatures and poor soils form its northern and eastern limits, respectively. Aridity determines the western boundary in both countries. The Winter Wheat region has an eastern boundary with competition from corn and cotton; low summer rainfall again marks the western boundary.

The Palouse wheat region of the Columbia Plateau is a third important wheat region. The loessal soils of this rolling aeolian plain are very productive and winter rains are adequate for both winter and spring wheat. This is more of a one-crop area than any wheat district farther east.

No matter where wheat is grown in these three regions of United States and one of Canada, its production has tended to become a specialized industry rather than a way of life as found in the Corn Belt. Mechanization of all phases of wheat growing, land abandonment in the parts afflicted by wind erosion, and gradual diversification of farming practices characterize all four wheat regions.

Range Livestock Region. There is a vast domain of western land which has an economy that is based upon range livestock. The principal variations in this economy include (1) seasonal grazing, migratory in such areas as the Great Basin, Columbia Basin, and the Sierra Nevada foothills; (2) seasonal grazing, nonmigratory, in such areas as Nebraska's sand hills, the northern Great Plains, and central Texas; (3) upland summer grazing in areas some of which are migratory and some nonmigratory, including semi-deserts of the southwest for the former, and the Rio Grande basins for the latter.

AGRICULTURAL REGIONS OF CANADA

Reference to *Fig.* 2-5 indicates that Canada shares with the United States several of these agricultural regions. They constitute a relatively narrow east-west belt across southern Canada.

Most extensive of these regions is the Hay and Dairy Belt which embraces most of the densely populated Ontario-St. Lawrence lowlands, the Maritimes, and some of the central lowland of Canada. The Range Livestock Belt crosses the border both east and west of the Rocky Mountains.

Reference has been made to the international character of the Spring Wheat region. The number of relatively small, specialized agricultural districts in the basins between the Canadian Rockies and the coastal mountains is not as great as in the corresponding portion of the United States but it is a similar type of economy.

The two countries have an agricultural regionalism which is both complementary and competitive. With the rapid industrialization of Canada which has taken place since 1940 the agricultural-industrial relationships are becoming more like those of the southern neighbor.

BIBLIOGRAPHY

BARGER, Harold and H. H. LANDSBERG, *American Agriculture, 1899-1939: A Study of Output, Employment, and Productivity* (New York, National Bureau of Economic Research, 1942).

BROWN, Ralph H., *Historical Geography of the United States* (New York, Harper and Brothers, 1948).

Climate and Man: The Yearbook of Agriculture (U.S. Dept. of Agriculture, Washington, 1941).

DAVIS, Joseph S., "Our Amazing Population Upsurge," *Journal of Farm Economics,* Vol. 31 (Nov., 1949), pp. 765-778.

—— "Our Changed Population Outlook and Its Significance," *American Economic Review,* Vol. 42, No. 3 (June, 1952), pp. 306-308.

DOUGLAS, E. M., *Boundaries, Area, Geographic Centers, and Altitudes of the United States,* Bulletin 817 (U.S. Geological Survey, Washington, 1939).

Farmers in a Changing World; The Yearbook of Agriculture (U.S. Dept. of Agriculture, Washington, 1940).

PATTON, Robert D., *The American Economy* (Chicago, Scott, Foresman and Co., 1953).

PAULLIN, C. O. and J. K. WRIGHT, eds., *Atlas of the Historical Geography of the United States* (Washington and New York, Carnegie Institution and the American Geographical Society, 1932).

PEFFER, E. Louise, *The Closing of the Public Domain* (Stanford, Calif., Stanford University Press, 1951).

PUTNAM, Donald F., Editor, *Canadian Regions* (New York, Thomas Y. Crowell Co., 1952).

REUSS, L. A., H. H. WOOTEN and F. J. MARSCHNER, *Inventory of Major Uses of Land in the United States, 1945*, Miscel. Pub. 663 (U.S. Dept. of Agriculture, Washington, 1948).

Soils and Men: The Yearbook of Agriculture (U.S. Dept. of Agriculture, Washington, 1938).

TAYLOR, Griffith, *Canada* (London, Methuen and Co., Ltd., 1947).

Trees; The Yearbook of Agriculture (U.S. Dept. of Agriculture, Washington, 1949).

Types of Farming in Canada, Publ. No. 825 (Farmers Bulletin 157, Ottawa, 1949).

WEAVER, John C., "Crop-Combination Regions in the Middle West," *Geographical Review*, Vol. 44, No. 2 (April 4, 1954), pp. 175-200.

ZIMMERMANN, Erich W., *World Resources and Industries* (New York, Harper and Brothers, 1951).

CHAPTER 3

MINERAL RESOURCES
AND INDUSTRIES

RESOURCES

Mineral Endowment. The United States has been for many years the world's principal producer and consumer of mineral raw materials. The experience of supplying needed minerals and their products during the five years of the Second World War brought to the attention of Congress and to laymen everywhere the question of adequacy of resources. It was not enough for United States interests to own mineral industries in foreign lands; the diversion of shipping space and of men during the emergency was critical.

No nation is self-sufficient in the minerals needed in today's industrial life. The United States and Canada together are superlatively well endowed with mineral resources, even with some of those most recently in demand, e.g., titanium and uranium. But as industrial nations, they are forced to go to many parts of the world to obtain some 27 minerals needed in their industrial processes. For some years the United States has been stockpiling many of these needed mineral raw materials. Several of the minerals in short supply are produced in the United States or Canada but not in quantities to meet the demand.

Perhaps the most surprising aspect of the war situation was the change from the status of surplus-producing to that of deficiency. The resources of the United States and of Canada were strained to meet the demand for some minerals during World War II; the manpower shortage and the added expense and time lag in raising the output of mining properties conspired to make them deficient for the emergency. Copper, for instance, fell from an export surplus to a 37 per cent deficiency; lead from a virtual adequacy to a 40 per cent deficiency; zinc from virtual adequacy to 36 per cent deficiency. Zinc, copper, and lead alone accounted for more than half of the dollar value of the United States' mineral imports during the war. Although serious in Canada, the shortage was perhaps not so critical due to the fact that Canadian industry was related closely to that in the United States, and the joint demand was attuned somewhat more closely to Canadian resources than was the case with the United States. It is probably true that Canadian manufacturing was more nearly in line with its resource endowment than it had been previously.

TABLE 3-1: *Imports of Certain Raw Materials by the United States, 1937 and 1951*

(1000 metric tons)

Commodity	1937	1951
ALUMINUM	20.3	148.
BAUXITE	515.6	2875.3
CHROME	251.	595.1
COBALT	0.7	5.3
COPPER	206.4	505.6
IRON ORE	2481.2	10366.2
LEAD	14.5	192.3
LUMBER	661.1	541.4
NICKEL	49.4	86.5
RUBBER, NATURAL	601.1	780.3
TIN	89.7	62.3
WOOD PULP	2172.7	2218.5
WOOL (CLEAN)	99.3	182.2
ZINC	37.7	327.7

SOURCE: *Minerals Yearbook, 1937* and *1951* (U.S. Dept. of the Interior, Washington).

TABLE 3-2: *Top Foreign Sources of Iron Ore Imports into the United States, 1953*

	Tons
CHILE	2,363,401
SWEDEN	2,097,522
VENEZUELA	1,949,868
CANADA	1,841,633
PERU	844,481
LIBERIA	720,440
BRAZIL	458,282
MEXICO	241,636

SOURCE: *Annual Report,* Lake Carriers' Association, 1953, p. 79.

TABLE 3-3: Principal Ferro-Alloys Used by Steel Industry

Commodity	Reason for Use	Typical Applications	Prewar Average			Wartime Average		
			Per Cent of World Production Produced in U.S.	Per Cent of World Production Consumed in U.S.	Chief Sources of United States Supply	Per Cent of World Production Produced in U.S.	Per Cent of World Production Consumed in U.S.	Chief Sources of United States Supply
CHROMIUM	Small amounts improve hardening qualities; more than 10% prevents rust	Tools; machinery parts; stainless and heat- and acid-resisting steels	Insignificant	35	Africa, Cuba, Greece, New Caledonia, Oceania	5	50	Africa, Cuba Greece, New Caledonia, Oceania
COBALT	Holds cutting edge at high temperatures. Improves electrical qualities	High-speed cutting tools; permanent magnet steel	None	10	Canada, Belgian Africa, Australia	5	50	Utah, Canada, Belgian Africa, Fr. Morocco
MANGANESE	Small amounts remove gases from steel; 1 to 2% increases strength and toughness; 12% imparts great toughness and resistance to abrasion	Small amounts present in all steels; 1 to 2% used in rails; 12% or more for frogs and switches and dredge bucket teeth	Insignificant	20	Russia, Gold Coast, Brazil, India	5	30	Gold Coast, Brazil, India, Cuba
MOLYBDENUM	Increases strength, ductility, and resistance to shock.	Tools; machinery parts; tubing for air-plane fuselage	80	40	United States	90	75	United States
NICKEL	Increases toughness, stiffness, strength, and ductility. In large amounts resists heat and acids	Tools; machinery parts; stainless steels; heat- and acid-resisting steels	Insignificant	50	Canada, Norway, New Caledonia	Insignificant	75	Canada, Cuba, New Caledonia
TUNGSTEN	Retains hardness and toughness at high temperature	High-speed cutting tools; magnets	10	20	China, British Malaya, United States	25	40	United States, Bolivia, China, Argentina, Brazil
VANADIUM	Increases strength, ductility, and resiliency	Tools; springs; machinery parts	15	25	United States, Peru, Rhodesia	50	75	United States, Peru, South West Africa

SOURCE: *Steel Facts*, March, 1947. These are the principal metals added to carbon steel in order to make a steel with certain qualities as indicated above.

The experts differ, even those charged with policy-making for mineral conservation, as to the extent of the United States' reserves. Conflicting and sometimes alarming views have been expressed.

TABLE 3-4: Position of the United States with Respect to Selected Minerals

I. VIRTUAL LONG-TIME SELF-SUFFICIENCY ASSURED

Bituminous coal and lignite	Helium
Anthracite	Magnesite
Natural gas	Nitrates
Magnesium	Phosphate rock
Molybdenum	Potash
Fluorspar	Salt
(metallurgical)	Sulfur

II. COMPLETE OR VIRTUALLY COMPLETE DEPENDENCE ON FOREIGN SOURCES

    a. *Small or remote expectations of improving position through discovery*

Chromite	Tin
Ferro-grade manganese	Industrial diamonds
Nickel	Asbestos (spinning quality)
Platinum metals	

    b. *Good expectation of improving position through discovery*

Cobalt	Graphite (flake)

III. PARTIAL DEPENDENCE UPON FOREIGN SOURCES

    a. *Good expectation of improving position through discovery or improvement in techniques.*

Petroleum	Cadmium
Arsenic	Copper
Bismuth	Iron Ore
Lead	Tungsten
Mercury	Zinc

    b. *Little hope of improving position through discovery*

Antimony
Vanadium
Highgrade bauxite

SOURCE: "Mineral Position of the United States," J. A. Krug, in A. B. Parsons, ed., *Seventy-five Years of Progress in the Mineral Industry, 1871-1946* (New York, 1947).

Commerce in Minerals. The United States and Canada have been favored with adequate resources of both iron and bituminous coal. The timing of the commercial extraction of these two basic resources of industry has not been the same in the two nations, however. Owing in part to geographical location and in part to the character of the iron ore and the coal, there has been an active commerce between the two countries in both of these commodities. The capital of each one has been invested in the coal or the iron of the other. The shift from exclusively high-grade ore to taconite and jasper ore with lower iron content has not diminished this commerce across the border.

The foreseeable shortage in the high-grade ore of the Mesabi region has been one factor in accounting for the importation of ore from Venezuela, Labrador, Liberia, and Chile by United States' steel makers. Neither iron ore nor coal alone locates the iron-making industry. They form a major frame of reference for its location, however. In North America both iron and coal move toward the market for iron and steel products. The Great Lakes play an important part in bringing ore to the industrial cities of the lower Great Lakes states.

CHARACTERISTICS OF MINERAL INDUSTRIES

Mining, quarrying, and their associated industries in the United States and in Canada employ fewer wage earners than either agriculture or manufacturing. Owing to their geographical segregation, minerals constitute a large part of the domestic commerce of the two countries. Coal and iron account for the major part of this mineral tonnage. In the sparsely populated western half of the United States, the mineral industry dominates the economy of many areas. In the Superior Upland and the Appalachian Plateau, mining dominates many areas. The Atlantic and Gulf coast plains and the Pacific province have but little mining activity.

Mining in the United States and in Canada reflects the relatively high cost of labor. Mechanization has proceeded in all aspects of mining, from the extraction of the mineral to its subsequent handling and processing. This has meant the abandonment of many small workings and revolutionary changes in mining procedure.

Strip mining has been used in copper and iron mining for a long time. Its use in coal mining has been more recent; the trend to strip mining is unmistakable. The ratio of permissable overburden to minable coal is constantly changing as power shovels increase in size and as the market for coal increases in and near the areas where stripping can be carried on (*Fig.* 3-1).

Changes in the character of the ores used have caused a shift in the mining centers of a number of minerals. Other shifts have occurred because of recent discoveries of petroleum, iron, phosphate, copper, and magnesium. In some cases old workings have been reopened, as new techniques made profitable the rejuvenation of the property. Deficiencies arising from a state of war frequently caused renewed activity in mining properties.

FIGURE 3-1: *Strip Coal Mine, Kanawha Section, Appalachian Plateau*

Pictured here is the huge shovel for removing the overburden; a smaller shovel follows this one to mine the coal. (Ohio Development Commission)

COAL INDUSTRY

The fuels are especially important among the minerals. The work force in coal mining in the United States is the largest in the mineral industries. In 1920 there were 884,000 in anthracite and bituminous coal mining; in 1952 there were 400,000. This is due in part to increased mechanization of the industry and in part due to the decline in the amount of coal mined. Since 1946 the output of coal in the United States has declined from 630.6 million tons to 440 million tons in 1953, less than was mined in 1912.

In 1952, for the first time, petroleum was more important than coal as a source of energy in the United States. Canadian use of oil in home heating increased more rapidly than in the United States; in 1953, three-fifths of all Canadian homes were heated by oil.

This swing to oil and gas heat is not the result of coal scarcity. Despite the 32 billion tons that have been mined in the United States, only about 3 per cent of the nation's coal reserves have been used. Some of the choicest seams, however, have been mined out.

Canada has found it economical to purchase coal from the United States rather than to further develop its own important reserves known to exist, much of it probably of lower grade than the coal Canada now imports from the United States.

Appalachian Fields. The industrial cities of the lower Great Lakes region, the Middle Atlantic, and the New England states absorb about 70 per cent of the bituminous output of the great Appalachian bituminous and anthracite fields (*Fig.* 3-2).

The principal bituminous field of the Applachian Highlands is the famous Pittsburgh seam of western Pennsylvania and eastern Ohio. This seam covers an area of 2,500 square miles and averages seven feet in thickness. A second important seam is the Pocahontas, embracing some 300 square miles in West Virginia, which averages about the same thickness as the Pittsburgh seam. Both of these seams are persistent and lie at relatively shallow depths. Individual mining districts produce the Connellsville coking coal, the Kanawha gas coal, and the Pocahontas smokeless steam coal. The virtual monopoly of Connellsville coal for coke making was broken by the perfection of the by-product method of coke making.

Farther south in the Appalachians are the eastern Kentucky, the Tennessee, and the Alabama coal areas. The proportion of "captive" coal mines—that is, owned by a manufacturing concern—is much lower in these southern fields; the fluctuations in mining activity are greater among these southern Appalachian coal mines than in the northern.

Anthracite coal was once highly desired as a domestic fuel because of its cleanliness and long-burning quality. It has never been a dominant industrial or railroad fuel, except for the eastern railroads which owned anthracite mines. The producing area lies within a few counties of northeastern Pennsylvania in the newer or folded Appalachians. Despite its excellence as a solid fuel, the cost of mining the folded, faulted, and generally thin seams has discouraged its use. Apartment dwellers generally are more interested in a cheaper fuel for central heating.

The long history of strikes and lockouts which characterizes the anthracite mining industry also tended to discourage its use as a domestic fuel. This hard coal does not lend itself to by-product manufacture. Competition with oil, gas, and raw and processed bituminous coal has seriously retarded anthracite sales. In 1930 there were 212,000 employed in mining this coal and quarrying slate. In 1940 it was 118,000; in 1950 it was 95,000. Population of the four anthracite counties in 1940 was 1,150,000; in 1950 it was 1,015,000; and the estimated population for 1960 is 955,000. It is unlikely that anthracite will share the predicted increase in coal mined.

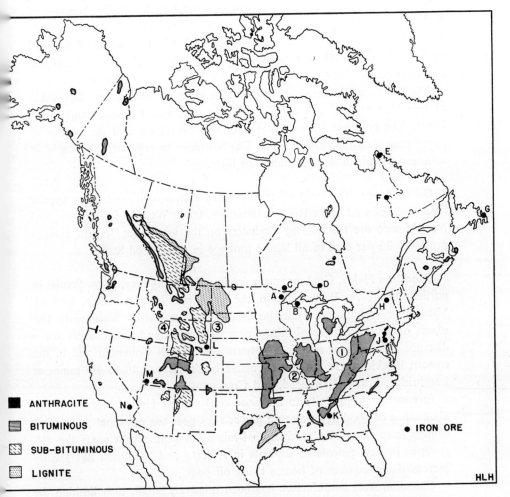

FIGURE 3-2: Coal and Iron Resources, United States and Canada

Coal: (1) Appalachian, (2) Interior, (3) Great Plains, (4) Rocky Mountain. *Iron:* (A) Mesabi, (B) Michigan, (C) Steep Rock, (D) Michipicoten, (E) Ungava, (F) Burnt Creek, (G) Wabana, (H) Adirondack, (J) Cornwall, (K) Birmingham, (L) Hartville, (M) Cedar City-Iron Mountain, (N) Eagle Mountain. (*Mineral Yearbook,* 1952)

Interior Fields of the United States. The Eastern Interior field lies in Illinois, southwestern Indiana, and in northwestern Kentucky. Because of its location and generally high quality, it ranks after the Appalachian field in production, but the relatively high ash and sulphur content of the coal makes it less desirable for coking purposes. It is a satisfactory steam and domestic coal.

The Western Interior field lies in southern Iowa, southeastern Nebraska, eastern Kansas, and extends through Missouri into Arkansas and Oklahoma. The coal seams are shallow for the most part, and the coal is of lower rank than the eastern fields. The Northern Interior field is located in southern Michigan and produces but little.

Other Areas. The only other important commercial coal fields appear both east and west of the Rocky Mountains. Utah, Wyoming, Colorado, and New Mexico are the leading producers on the west side; [1] North Dakota produces 96 per cent of all lignite tonnage in the United States.

Canadian Fields. Coal measures are found near Sydney, Nova Scotia, in northeastern New Brunswick, in the Western Plains province, and on Vancouver and Queen Charlotte Islands in the Pacific Southwest. The seams of good coking coal mined near Sydney extend under water for a distance of a mile or more. In Alberta and British Columbia and in the eastern Rockies there are several active fields. Among these are mines at Lethbridge, Frank, Bankhead, and Crowsnest.

In general, propinquity to the good coals of the United States and the abundance of good hydroelectric power sites near the principal population centers have retarded Canadian coal mining. Within recent years the discoveries of new petroleum deposits in Alberta and Manitoba has greatly increased the number of homes using oil heat.

Canadian steel manufacture has been relatively small, thus limiting the amount of coke consumed; much of this coke was made from U.S. coal.

PETROLEUM

Districts. The production of petroleum in the United States in 1953 was the greatest on record, 2,359,000,000 barrels; for Canada it also was a peak year with 60,864,500 barrels. For the first time coal was superseded by oil as the most important mineral fuel in the United States. Natural

[1] In comparison with West Virginia's 122,610,000 net tons, and Pennsylvania's 89,215,000 (bituminous), Utah's 6,160,000, Colorado's 4,636,000, and Wyoming's 6,000,000 tons appear to be minor.

FIGURE 3-3: *Trenche Power Plant, St. Maurice River, Quebec*

An inexhaustible resource of the Canadian Shield is water power such as this plant represents. (Shawinigan Water and Power Co.)

gas has had an even greater proportional increase, amounting to 8,425 billion cubic feet consumed in the United States in 1953. These sets of production figures represent about two-thirds of the world's total for that year. The known reserves in the United States are estimated to be second only to those of the Near East.

Production of petroleum is found in about half of the forty-eight states; the bulk of it comes from the western states, with Texas by far the major producer, 37 per cent. California ranks second with 16 per cent, Oklahoma 11 per cent, Illinois 10 per cent, and Louisiana 8 per cent.

The 1953 decision of the Congress to recognize state claims to the so-called tideland oil reserves, within certain distances of the Gulf and Pacific shores, has enabled drilling to increase in the shallow Gulf of Mexico coastal waters. Some of the man-made "islands" or drilling platforms are 60 miles offshore.

Canada has produced crude oil in the general area of Edmonton, Alberta, for several years. Since 1950 the number of producing wells in this area has greatly increased. Saskatchewan has produced some, and Norman Wells in the northern plains of the Mackenzie River was active for a time during and after World War II.

Although oil is still produced in the nation's first oil district in western Pennsylvania, it is but a fraction of the former yield. Eastern and northwestern Ohio, northern Indiana, central Michigan, and northern West Virginia have long since passed their peak of production. Secondary recovery methods are being employed in some of these oil districts with results that barely keep the industry active. The great depths to which some western wells have penetrated are unknown in these eastern fields.[2] Southern Illinois and Indiana experienced a revival in their production in the early 1940's.

Commerce in Oil. Since oil production in the United States and Canada is generally far from consuming centers, its commerce is very important. By ocean tanker, pipeline, river barge, and railroad tanker, oil moves from the great production centers of Texas, Oklahoma, and Kansas to the cities of the northeastern and lower Lake states. Despite the importance of this trade, there was no through pipeline until World War II brought about the construction of "Big Inch," followed by "Little Inch" a few months later. They were abandoned a year after hostilities ended; natural gas from Texas fields now flows through them. Recently other and more direct oil pipelines have been built from Texas to the middle Atlantic port cities.

Natural Gas. Somewhat less than one-half of the natural gas produced in the United States in 1950 was obtained jointly with petroleum. Formerly most of the gas came from the Appalachian fields; now it comes from Texas, New Mexico, Oklahoma, Kansas, Mississippi, Arkansas, and Louisiana. Most of the reserves are believed to be in these states. More recently gas wells have been opened in the Rocky Mountain states and in California.

IRON-MINING INDUSTRY

Production and Reserves. In the production and in the consumption of iron ore, no other country approaches the tonnage of the United States.[3] Most of this tonnage of ore comes from the Mesabi district in Minnesota, 65 per cent. Michigan is second with 17 per cent; Alabama produces 10 per cent; New York 4 per cent; Pennsylvania 2 per cent; and Wisconsin 1.6 per cent (*Fig.* 3-2).

---

[2] Trend in drilling depth: 1924, 7,319 feet; 1935, 12,785 feet; 1953, 19,000 feet.
[3] In 1950 the United States consumed 103,998,000 net tons of iron ore; U.S.S.R. followed with 35,000,000 tons; Great Britain 15,358,000 tons; and Canada 5,635,000 tons.

**FIGURE 3-4: *Drilling Blast Holes in Taconite Rock,
near Mountain Iron, Minnesota***

The tree-covered dirt bank at the top of the picture is the glacial overburden covering the flint-hard taconite iron formation on which the drills are working. (United States Steel Corp.)

Canada buys iron ore from the United States when the price is lower. Canadian iron mines are at Steep Rock Lake, some hundred miles north of the Mesabi iron district. Recently iron ore began coming from southwestern Labrador, by way of the St. Lawrence River. Bell Island, in Conception Bay, in the Maritimes of southeastern Canada mines iron ore for furnaces at St. Johns.

At the rate of ore consumption during World War II, the high-grade ore of the Mesabi district would be exhausted within a decade or so. Reserves of lower grade ore nearby promise several generations with ore for the future (*Fig.* 3-4).[4]

[4] In the Adirondacks, mining by open-pit methods has increased since the war. While the ore body is large, it is relatively low grade; the rock is very hard and more difficult to mine than Mesabi ore. Treatment of the black magnetic ore is complicated; the final product is a high-grade sinter comparable to fine Swedish ores.

The Ford Motor Company combined with Cleveland Cliffs Company to mine and process hematite jasper in northern Michigan.

The new Grace Mine near Morgantown and old Cornwall Mine near Lebanon, Pennsylvania, are the largest producers near the Atlantic seaboard. In 1953, ore was shipped from: Mesabi, 78 per cent; Menominee, 4.78; Gogebic, 4.61; Marquette, 5.87; Cuyuna, 2.84; and Vermillion, 1.37.

Transportation. The distribution of the principal iron-mining districts has been indicated. The importance of the Great Lakes in the shipment of this ore is apparent in *Fig.* 5-7. The lakes serve as a great concentrating base, gathering in ore and limestone for shipment to the furnaces and then serving as distributors of steel products to other Lake cities and for export. Railroads move only a small part of the iron ore from the western end of Lake Superior to the cities of the lower Great Lakes. With the recent increase in the ore-handling capacity of Escanaba, more iron ore goes by rail to this port. The establishment of ore stock piles at Lower Lake ports and at interior manufacturing cities has been based upon the economical ore boats. Iron mining has become so mechanized that men play only a small part in the industry. Some of the open-pit mines and the power shovels are the world's largest. The ore docks and the ore boats are on the same scale.

The iron-mining districts of eastern Texas, near Birmingham, Alabama, in the central Rockies of Utah and Wyoming, and in the Sierra Nevadas of California produce but a minor part of the nation's total ore. For reasons of economy, or for blending, the United States has long imported iron ore from Chile, Cuba, and Sweden; within recent years ore has been imported from Venezuela, Liberia, and Canada.

Ferro-alloys. Before iron can be made into steel, carbon must be added in measured amounts. To this carbon steel must be added one or more of the alloying minerals. All steel contains carbon; it is not regarded as a ferro-alloy. The addition of a certain amount of vanadium will give springiness, tungsten will give hardness, and molybdenum will give toughness to steel. Although the amount of these mineral raw materials added to each ton of steel is small, their uninterrupted supply is vital. Technological improvements require new tools, operated at high speeds. Machines and factories are designed with these quality steels in mind. A modern steel-making nation is dependent upon these ferro-alloys as new technological demands are made.

In only two (molybdenum and vanadium) is the United States reasonably well endowed. In the former this country has more or less of a monopoly; in the latter, domestic production is some 50 per cent of the country's needs. Canada produces most of the world's nickel and some cobalt. In all other ferro-alloys, both countries must depend upon imports (see Table 3-3) for varying proportions of their needs. Production of many of these alloying metals is derived from by-products of other mines, particularly copper.

NONFERROUS MINERAL INDUSTRY

Copper. Functionally, as the leading carrier of electrical energy, copper may be classed as a basic metal in modern industry, ranking next to iron in amount used. During the half-century or more of United States dominance in world copper production, the mining of copper has experienced great shifts in its major centers. During the middle of the nineteenth century, Michigan's Keweenaw Peninsula achieved world dominance.

The next important copper mining district was Butte, Montana, where in 1879 work began on the "richest hill on earth." The industry next shifted to the second greatest concentration of copper workings in the world, central and southern Arizona. In 1950 Arizona produced 44 per cent of the nation's total, Utah 31 per cent, and Montana, New Mexico, Michigan, and Nevada accounted for 22 per cent. Within recent years the Butte and the Keweenaw copper districts have undergone extensive modernization with a view toward increasing output; new mines have been opened in Arizona and Nevada.

Copper ore often has less than 3 per cent metallic content, as against 50 per cent for iron ore. Hence, enormous tonnages move from the mines to the concentrators or smelters where 99 per cent of the waste is removed. Obviously these smelters are located as near the mines as possible. But most copper mines do not operate continuously throughout the year, whereas the smelter must process huge tonnages and operate day and night. Hence the smelter must draw upon more than one mine to secure the required tonnage; there is also a desirable blending of the different ores. Thus from Bingham Canyon copper mines in Utah, the ore is hauled by rail nearly twenty miles northward to smelters at Arthur and Magma. The copper refineries which finish the purification may be located near the smelters or near the port city markets. Examples of the former are: Great Falls, Montana; El Paso, Texas; Inspiration, Arizona; Tacoma, Washington; and Garfield, Utah. Examples of port locations are near New York and Baltimore.

Shifting demand for copper and the indestructibility of copper scrap sometimes combine to plague the copper mines with a surplus of copper. In 1950, however, the import of copper, principally from Chile, amounted to 40 per cent of domestic consumption.

Canada's principal copper mines are in the Sudbury (primarily nickel mines), Noranda, and Rouyn districts in Quebec, and Flin Flon on the Manitoba-Saskatchewan border. Alaska has had one important copper mine at Kennicott. Until World War II, the abundance of copper in the

United States made Canadian mines marginal in the former market; in 1950 Canada ranked third in copper production.

Lead and Zinc. The United States produced in 1950 about one-fourth of the world's output of lead (418,809 short tons), and one-third of the zinc (623,375 short tons). Missouri (Tri-state District) and Idaho (Coeur d'Alene District) lead all other lead-producing states by a wide margin; Utah ranks third. Canada's production is about one-third that of the United States (*Fig.* 3-5).

The principal zinc-producing states in 1954 are Idaho (87,890 short tons), Montana (67,678), Arizona (60,480), New Jersey (55,029), and Colorado (45,776). The Tri-state area of Missouri-Oklahoma-Kansas is a major producer of both lead and zinc. Canada's zinc production is about one-fourth that of the United States. The principal districts are the Kimberly, British Columbia, near Flin Flon, Manitoba, Noranda in Quebec, and Buchans in Newfoundland. There is only one mine, Treadwell-Yukon, in Alaska, just over the Canadian border at Keno.

Aluminum. Aluminum is one of the newer of the industrial metals. Since 1920 each decade has witnessed a great increase in the amount of aluminum used in the United States and Canada, and the use of steel, lead, zinc, and copper was somewhat less, proportionally. The Second World War necessitated a great increase in primary aluminum production. Immediately after the war, domestic consumption dropped, and with it primary production. The Korean War gave another impetus to the consumption and production of this light metal.

The manufacture of aluminum is functionally decentralized. The three basic operations of this industry are (1) mining and delivery to the processing plant of the ore or bauxite, (2) production of alumina from the bauxite, (3) the reduction of alumina to aluminum. This last step requires a great deal of electric power, and cheap power sites have played an important part in the location of the reduction plants.

Most of the ore comes from Surinam or Jamaica mines, with Arkansas supplying the major part of domestic tonnage. The principal alumina plants are at East St. Louis, Illinois; Lister Hill and Mobile, Alabama; Baton Rouge, Louisiana; Hurricane Creek, Arkansas; and Corpus Christi, Texas.

The principal aluminum plants are at Massena and Niagara Falls, New York; Alcoa, Tennessee; Baden, North Carolina; Chalmette, Louisiana; Jones Mills, Arkansas; Point Comfort, Texas; Troutdale, Oregon; Spokane and Vancouver, Washington. Such a distribution of plants bespeaks the

FIGURE 3-5: *Lead Mine, Flat River District, Missouri*

The lead-mining landscape represented here is one of despoliation. For many years this has been a major lead producer in the United States. (Missouri Division of Resources and Development. MASSIE Photo)

differing location factors in the processes of manufacturing primary aluminum. Domestic facilities in 1952 were one million tons or five times greater than in 1931.

Canada's aluminum industry includes integrated plants on both the Atlantic and Pacific coasts. The Arvida plant on the Saguenay River in eastern Quebec is one of the two largest in the world. Bauxite is brought by ship from company mines in British Guiana to Quebec, requiring only a short rail haul. A substantial part of the aluminum is converted into semifabricated articles or consumers' goods within the Arvida mills.

The Pacific installation is in British Columbia's coastal mountains at Kitimat. There a river was reversed to provide power, and a huge powerhouse cut out of the base of the mountain. This integrated plant doubles the Canadian aluminum refining capacity. Unlike the United States, Canada has a fabricating capacity only about one-fourth as great as its ingot capacity.

Despite the $30 per ton tariff imposed upon Canadian aluminum coming into the United States, Canadian costs are low enough to permit competition with domestic producers in United States' markets.

Magnesium. Magnesium, lightest of the structural metals now in production, is in a stage of development comparable to that of aluminum in 1939. Primary metal production rose from 3,300 tons in 1939 to a peak of 180,600 tons in 1943. The new plants which permitted such an increase in production were in each case larger than the single big producer in 1939. In 1950 there were three large plants in operation, the original one at Midland, Michigan, and a new one on the Gulf coast, and one in southern California.

Despite enormous war stocks and scrap, magnesium production in 1951 was 38,500 tons, with increases in view. As with aluminum, the use of power is a very important factor in magnesium reduction and the electrolytic process has thus far been the dominant one.

Other Light Metals. One of the outstanding developments of the past fifty years has been the emergence of a group of metals which prior to the turn of the century were scientific curiosities. Two of these have long since been in commercial production, aluminum and magnesium. Others of these light metals have not yet attained the same status, but titanium, particularly, has increased in importance; a new plant is being erected in northern Ohio. In the production of atomic energy zirconium is used in the purification process.

PRECIOUS METALS

Industry has relatively little direct use for the precious metals. Even certain types of diamonds have greater industrial utility than precious metals.[5]

Gold. The annual gold production of the United States and its territories is 14 per cent of the world's output. Canada's production is somewhat greater. The chief gold-mining districts are near the western foothills of the Sierra Nevada in California, Lead in South Dakota, Cripple Creek and the San Juan Mountains in Colorado, and Fairbanks and the Seward Peninsula in Alaska. The chief Canadian mines are in Ontario's Porcupine and Kirkland Lake districts.

Silver. The United States ranks second among the nations as a silver producer, accounting for slightly more than one-fourth of the world's ton-

[5] During the Second World War, a comparatively small Detroit plant made war goods under unusually heavy guard, the reason: $18 million in silver electric wiring was being used instead of copper, worth perhaps $700.

nage.[6] Silver mines are seldom very large enterprises. Most of the silver is mined jointly with copper, lead, zinc or gold, with silver usually the more profitable commodity in the mining enterprise. The Sunshine Mine, Coeur d'Alene district in Idaho, is the principal silver producer in the United States. In Canada, Cobalt led in silver for many years; recently the production of silver is mostly from base metals in British Columbia.

FERTILIZER MINERALS

Less spectacular in their role are the mineral raw materials used in the manufacture of fertilizers and in the chemical industries. Three of the minerals used in commercial fertilizers are phosphorus, potassium, and nitrogen; nearly all of the production takes place in the United States and consumption is local.

Potash. Prior to the 1930's, the United States was dependent upon imports from Germany for much of its potash. At that time there were discoveries made of abundant and high-grade potash deposits near Carlsbad, New Mexico. The country is presently supplied by the domestic deposits; Searles Lake in California ranks next to New Mexico in potash tonnage. The reserves are not great.

Phosphorus. A second mineral plant food is phosphorus, a mineral long known to be abundant in the United States. Peninsular Florida and the Highland Rim of Tennessee now supply the greater part of the domestic market. The greatest reserves of phosphorus are located in the middle Rocky Mountain province; distant though they are from the greater part of the domestic market, these deposits have been worked for the Intermontane agricultural districts. Synthetic detergents are in part responsible for increased use of phosphorus from near Pocatello and Soda Springs, Idaho, and Silver Bow, Montana. The new Hungry Horse and Idaho Falls dams sell power to some of these companies.

Nitrogen. Nitrogen was long imported from the natural deposits in northern Chile for the American market. Its extraction from the air has superseded most of the natural product. A number of power centers manufacture nitrogen for fertilizer: Hopewell, Virginia; Omaha, Nebraska; Orange, Texas, and South Point, Ohio.

---

[6] 1950 production—United States: gold—100 metric tons; silver—1100 metric tons
Canada: gold—150 metric tons; silver— 550 metric tons

OTHER MINERALS

Sulphur. Sulphur has a greater variety of industrial uses than the fertilizer minerals noted above. The United States is well supplied with sulphur deposits, producing more than three-fourths of the world's tonnage. The greatest producing districts are along the Gulf of Mexico in eastern Texas and in western Louisiana. By forcing superheated water into the sulphur-bearing rock, molten sulphur is brought to the surface where it solidifies in bins provided for that purpose.

Reportedly only 16 per cent of about 200 sulphur-bearing domes have been developed to date. This is in part owing to the swampy location, but primarily because of the limited market. For instance, one of the most recent deposits to be worked is at Bay St. Elaine in Louisiana's tidewater marshlands. Operations here are completely amphibious. Pumping from barges, the sulphur is run in molten state by pipeline to insulated barges for delivery to the storage points. Similar operations are at Garden Island Bay and Grand Ecaille, now producing 1.3 million tons yearly.

Salt. The three main sources of salt in the United States are brines pumped from deep in the earth, thick beds of rock salt as in the Lake Erie district, and the curious "islands" or underground salt domes extending westward from New Orleans over the Gulf coastal prairies. Other important districts are in California and in Utah where the waters of Great Salt Lake are evaporated. The increased activity in the chemical industries has been important in the extraction of salt brines especially from central Michigan south to West Virginia.

Sand and Gravel. The humble sand and gravel deposits found in so many parts of the country and under so many conditions constitute an important commercial mineral resource. One of the most densely populated sections of the United States, the upper Mississippi Valley and the Great Lakes Basin, has extensive deposits of sand and gravel of glacial origin. On many a farm the least productive field has become a source of gravel and sand for local highway construction.

The more spectacular aspect of sand is the use made of it in the manufacture of glass. Only the purest silica sand is used for the manufacture of clear glass. The location-value of the two factors in glass making, fuel and pure sand, have varied during the history of the industry. In Colonial days the relatively pure sands of the Atlantic Coastal Plain attracted an important glass industry, using charcoal from local wood as the fuel. As the industry was able to free itself from the hand labor involved in making glass by the invention of machines, the fuel factor rose in importance. The westward trek of the industry was largely due to the use of natural gas found in quantity in the upper Ohio Valley. Sandstone of desirable quality has become an important source of glass sand; it has enabled the industry to expand with the westward-moving market to the Mississippi Valley.

Clay. The clay industry is a rapidly growing phase of manufacturing as new uses are found for this common material. The mining industry is divided into several categories, based upon the nature of the clay. The "miscellaneous" clays are widespread, every state but one engages in this branch of the industry. Ohio and Illinois each produce more than two million tons annually; more than one million tons are produced in North Carolina, Georgia, Pennsylvania, California, Texas, New York, Michigan, and Alabama. More than 90 per cent of the mining operations are captive. A very great variety of tile and brick is made from these clays.

Another type of clay mined in great quantity is fire clay. Like the miscellaneous clays, it is low priced, $3 per ton. It is also widely distributed, but four states produce most of the fire clays; Ohio leads, followed by Pennsylvania, Missouri, and Indiana. The market is for refractories and heavy-clay products.

A third category is ball clay, used in the pottery industry, including white-wear, high-grade tile, paper filler, and enamels. Tennessee ranks first in the production of ball clays, followed by Kentucky, Maryland, Mississippi, and New Jersey.

A fourth type of clay is kaolin. This is much more costly than the tonnage clays mentioned above. Georgia leads in production, followed by South Carolina and Pennsylvania. This white china clay is used in coating paper, dinnerware, and parts for jet engines.

Stone, Cement, and Slate. Companion resources with clay in the non-metallic construction materials are stone, raw materials of cement, and slate. The least common of these three materials is slate; it is also the least varied in its uses. The common building stones found in important quantities in the United States and Canada are granite, limestone, sandstone, and marble. The principal granite-quarrying districts are near Barre, Vermont, in the southern Appalachian Highland, and in central Wisconsin.

Limestones are widely distributed and of many different qualities. The principal uses are for fertilizer, road construction, as a flux in iron making, and for building construction. The principal quarries for limestone destined for iron making are in the Appalachian Highlands of Pennsylvania, northern and central Ohio, and the northern portion of the lower peninsula of Michigan. The traffic in this limestone in the United States is exceeded on no other routes in the world. The greatest center for the quarrying of fine building stone is in south central Indiana, near Bedford and Bloomington. This fine stone hardens after exposure to the air, has splendid coloring, and lends itself to decorative and artistic uses as well as a building veneer. Many other districts quarry limestone for building purposes, but none has the fame of Indiana's product.

Sandstone is not so important commercially, but it has an extensive market for grinding rolls and is used for much building construction. Northern and eastern Ohio have long quarried sandstone for grinding purposes. Some sandstones are prized for glass making.

Cement is manufactured from local limestone in most of the 48 states. The largest concentrations are near the great population centers: Pennsylvania, Ohio, Illinois, Michigan, and Missouri.

SUMMARY

There is little to give continuity or regionalism to the inventory of mineral resources of the United States and Canada. The commerce in these minerals is tremendous. The Great Lakes commerce is largely minerals, and several railroads derive most of their operating revenue from the transportation of mineral raw materials. A system of pipelines has been developed to a high degree to carry oil and gas. The distribution of certain minerals is over some of the longest sea routes known.

The freeing of mineral wealth from the rock or foreign material has given rise to important industries, which, as techniques change or ore bodies are found, tend to migrate. The importance of the location of mineral raw materials is diminishing in its locational value for most industries. On the whole, both the United States and Canada have been exceedingly fortunate in the abundance, variety, and location of the mineral resources upon which has been predicated the economy of the past century and a half.

But minerals are wasting assets. Despite new discoveries and secondary recovery methods, some of them will be exhausted within the foreseeable future. Conservation of a mineral is difficult so long as its price is relatively low. The unwelcome problems of a declining heritage have engendered many types of control schemes upon the mineral hierarchy, by no means all of which conserve the mineral in question.

BIBLIOGRAPHY

BATEMAN, Alan M., "Geographical Factors in the Utilization of Mineral Deposits," *Proceedings of the United Nations Scientific Conference on the Conservation and Utilization of Resources,* Vol. 2 (1951), pp. 13-16.

BERNARD, Merrill, "The Appraisal of Water Resources in the United States," *Proceedings of the United Nations Scientific Conference on the Conservation and Utilization of Resources,* Vol. 4 (1951), pp. 55-64.

DAVIS, John, "Natural Gas in North America," *Canadian Geographical Journal,* Vol. 46, No. 5 (May, 1953), pp. 182-200.

DEWHURST, J. F., and others, *America's Needs and Resources* (New York, Twentieth Century Fund, 1955).

FORBES, J. M., "Iron Ore," *Minerals Yearbook, 1951* (U. S. Dept. of the Interior, Washington), pp. 668-695.

HOLBROOK, E. M., "Oil From the Earth," *Canadian Geographical Journal,* Vol. 39, No. 4 (Oct., 1949), pp. 135-153.

INGALLS, Philip C., "Williston Basin: Today's Most Exciting Oil Producing Province," *The Oil and Gas Journal,* Vol. 51 (1952).

KESO, Edward E. and HUBER Self, "The Magnesium Industry," *Economic Geography,* Vol. 25, No. 4 (Oct., 1949), pp. 296-313.

MEYER, H. M. and G. N. GREENSPOON, "Copper," *Minerals Yearbook, 1951* (U. S. Dept. of the Interior, Washington), pp. 521-556.

MILLER, E. Willard, "Some Aspects of the United States Mineral Self-Sufficiency," *Economic Geography,* Vol. 23, No. 12 (April, 1947), pp. 77-84.

PARSONS, James J., "The Geography of Natural Gas in the United States," *Economic Geography,* Vol. 26, No. 3 (July, 1950), pp. 162-178.

PUTNAM, P. C., *Energy in the Future* (New York, D. Van Nostrand Co., 1953).

SMITH, Guy-Harold, ed., *Conservation of Natural Resources* (New York, John Wiley and Son, Inc., 1950).

VOSKUIL, Walter H., *Minerals in World Industry* (New York, McGraw-Hill Book Co., Inc., 1955).

Water in Industry (Report of the President's Materials Policy Committee, Washington, 1952), Vol. V.

WHITE, A. G., A. T. COUMBE, D. S. COLBY, and E. M. SEELEY, "Petroleum," *Minerals Yearbook, 1951* (U.S. Dept. of the Interior, Washington), Vol. 2, pp. 318-439.

YOUNG, W. H., R. L. ANDERSON, and E. M. HALL, "Coal," *Minerals Yearbook, 1952* (U.S. Dept. of the Interior, Washington), Vol. 2, pp. 44-180.

CHAPTER 4

MANUFACTURING AND
MANUFACTURING DISTRICTS

INTRODUCTION

Manufacturing—an Urbanizing Factor. Historically, commerce is an older factor than manufacturing in the urbanization of Anglo-America. However, in both the United States and in Canada, the rise of cities began so late in the world's history that the period of commercial urbanization was relatively short in duration.

Even in the United States, the first manufacturing was once an industry conducted in homes and therefore not a potent factor in urbanization. This period lasted until the factory system was introduced in New England at the close of the eighteenth century. Home industries responded to the change in manufacturing procedure variously, depending upon the nature of the commodity made. Cotton textiles and shoes were the first to become factory enterprises. Thus began the concentration of factory workers and those whose livelihood depended upon the satisfaction of the wants of these workers—the complete economic city.

Not all cities in the United States or in Canada have grown because of manufacturing activities. No one of the ten "industrial districts" as set up by the Bureau of the Census has failed to show some growth in population since their delineation in 1930, but some individual cities have failed to keep pace with the national increase in manufacturing. This applies particularly to the eastern states.

The statistics of urban growth shown in *Table* 4-1 and *Table* 4-2 suggest but a part of the interrelationship between urban centers and manufacturing in the United States and Canada (*Figs.* 4-1, 4-2). During the first 150 years of the existence of North American colonies, urbanization was slow

54

and the growth of manufactures was relatively slow. Since the middle of the nineteenth century both have accelerated. This rapidity of growth of cities has served to stimulate manufacturing; this is in part owing to the increased market for factory goods, but another factor is the imbalance in the labor force which promotes mechanization not only in agriculture, but in other pursuits as well.

TABLE 4-1: Growth of the Ten Largest Cities in the United States, 1920-1950

City	1920	1930	1940	1950	Metropolitan district, 1950
NEW YORK	5,620,048	6,930,446	7,454,995	7,891,957	12,296,117
CHICAGO	2,701,705	3,376,438	3,396,808	3,620,962	5,495,364
PHILADELPHIA	1,823,779	1,950,961	1,931,334	2,071,605	3,671,048
LOS ANGELES	576,673	1,238,043	1,504,277	1,970,358	4,367,911
DETROIT	993,673	1,568,662	1,623,452	1,849,568	3,016,197
BALTIMORE	733,826	804,874	859,100	949,708	1,337,373
CLEVELAND	796,841	900,429	878,336	914,808	1,465,511
ST. LOUIS	772,897	821,960	816,048	856,796	1,681,281
WASHINGTON	437,571	486,869	663,091	802,178	1,464,089
BOSTON	748,060	781,188	770,816	801,444	2,369,986

SOURCE: Bureau of the Census. All of these cities except Los Angeles are in the Manufacturing Belt. The tendency of suburban cities to grow even at the expense of the major city is demonstrated by a comparison of population of the nuclear cities with that of the metropolitan district. A century ago the largest cities were: New York, Boston, Philadelphia, New Orleans, Cincinnati, Brooklyn, St. Louis, and Albany.

TABLE 4-2: Growth of the Ten Largest Cities in Canada, 1920-1950

City	1920	1930	1940	1950	Metropolitan district, 1950
MONTREAL	618,506	818,577	903,007	1,021,520	1,395,400
TORONTO	521,893	631,207	667,457	675,754	1,117,470
VANCOUVER	163,220	246,593	275,353	344,833	530,728
WINNIPEG	179,087	218,785	221,960	235,710	354,069
HAMILTON	114,151	155,547	166,337	208,321	259,685
OTTAWA	107,843	126,872	154,951	202,045	281,908
QUEBEC	95,193	130,594	150,757	164,016	274,827
EDMONTON	58,821	79,197	93,817	159,631	173,075
CALGARY	63,305	83,761	88,904	129,060	139,105
WINDSOR	38,591	63,108	105,311	120,049	157,672

SOURCE: Census of Canada. Edmonton and Calgary were not classed as Census Metropolitan Areas until 1941. Prior estimates of the population of the metropolitan districts of these two cities are based upon data from local subdivisions.

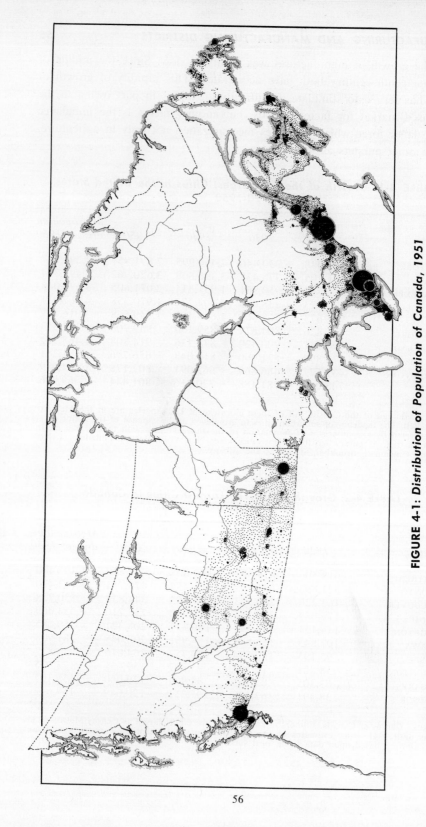

FIGURE 4-1: *Distribution of Population of Canada, 1951*

A dot represents 1,000 people but the population of each of the fifteen metropolitan areas is shown by a disc proportionate in area to the dot.
(Dominion Bureau of Statistics, Ottawa)

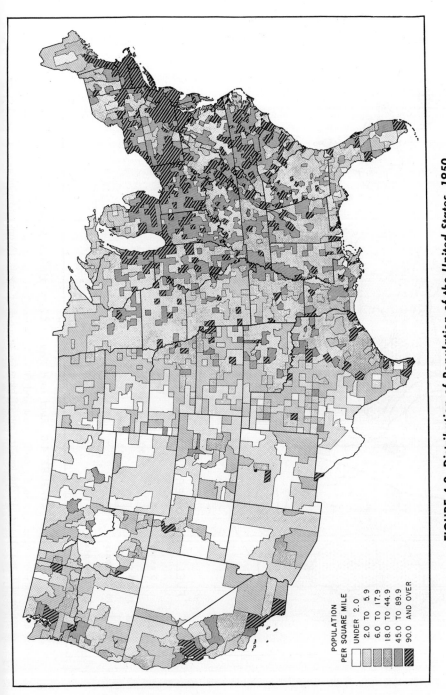

FIGURE 4-2: *Distribution of Population of the United States, 1950*

This map shows the population per square mile by counties. (Bureau of Census)

POPULATION
PER SQUARE MILE

UNDER 2.0
2.0 TO 5.9
6.0 TO 17.9
18.0 TO 44.9
45.0 TO 89.9
90.0 AND OVER

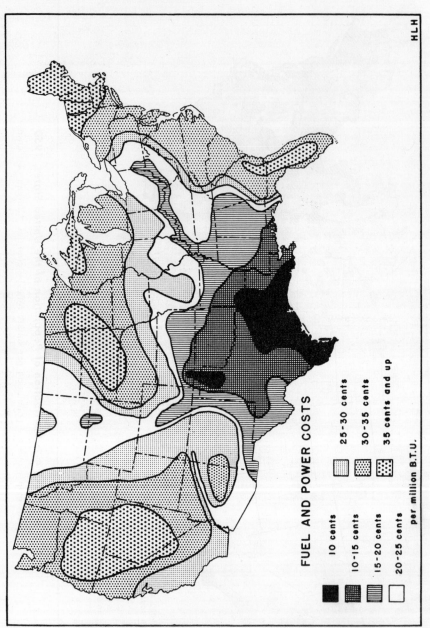

HLH

FUEL AND POWER COSTS

■ 10 cents	▨ 25-30 cents
▨ 10-15 cents	▨ 30-35 cents
▤ 15-20 cents	▨ 35 cents and up
☐ 20-25 cents	

per million B.T.U.

FIGURE 4-3: *Fuel and Power Costs, United States*

The availability of cheap fuel in the Gulf Coast and Ohio Valley regions, as shown on this map, should be studied in connection with the changes in the localization of manufacturing since 1940. (Monsanto Chemical Co.)

FACTORS IN THE LOCALIZATION OF INDUSTRY

Urbanization of the United States and Canada is intimately related to the factors governing the location of manufacturing industries. This is true though some industries may not have been rationally located, even at the period of their establishment. By many devices and by the evolution of the economy they have remained in production.

Raw Materials. The American resources of coal, iron, copper, and petroleum include some of the world's most important deposits, yet they have not, by themselves, localized important industries or cities. Agricultural raw materials such as cotton, wheat, wool, and corn are not important location factors for industry.

Power. In countries of such great areas as the United States and Canada, where population numbers have been inadequate to develop the resources without the aid of machinery, the use of powered equipment in the mine, field, factory, and in transportation has been imperative.[1] Both countries have coal in quantity and of a quality satisfactory for most uses. The United States mines most of the coal used in both countries, owing to accessibility. For certain uses, coal south of the border is more satisfactory and is regularly shipped across the Great Lakes, nearly all of it crosses Lake Erie.

The bituminous coal of the Appalachian Plateaus has contributed much to urbanization and industrialization in the Central Plains and in parts of the plateaus which have east-west access to markets by means of the corridors afforded by the Appalachian drainage.

The direct use of water power was an early urbanizing factor, but the period of this type of utilization was not long in either country. Water-power sites were particularly important in New England and along the Fall Line between the Piedmont and the Coastal Plain before the advent of hydroelectricity. The indirect use of water power as hydroelectricity has become important in several sections, among them are the southern Appalachians, St. Lawrence Valley, Niagara Falls, and the Pacific Northwest.

For such industries as require very great amounts of heat or power, such as electricity, aluminum, iron, coke, clay, and cement, the prospect for using atomic power may be more imminent than is now apparent.

---

[1] The United States has an area of 3,628,130 square miles and a population of 156,981,000 (1952). Canada has a population of 14,430,000 and an area of 3,577,163 square miles.

Present atomic production centers are for military uses, with the single exception of an experimental unit near Pittsburgh [2] (*Fig.* 4-3).

Labor. Labor in adequate quantities, either unskilled and relatively low cost, or skilled and high cost, is increasingly important as a factor of industrial location. Industries which primarily seek such labor are termed labor-oriented. During the early years of World War II, the federal government issued a map which showed the adequacy of labor for industrial purposes in every state. The purpose of this map was to aid in locating the new government-financed industrial facilities. The war gave labor increased locational importance which has not been dissipated during the postwar years. Generally speaking, the greatest potential labor pool in America is undoubtedly the relatively dense rural population in the hill country of the central and southern Appalachians and the Central Highlands.

Industrial plant facilities in the United States have been almost completely rebuilt since 1928. The number of man-hours worked in our economy during 1952 was about the same as in 1928; although the labor force is greater, the individual worker puts in a shorter working day. The output per worker is higher than in 1928.

Market. Technological advances have tended to weaken the importance of raw materials and power in the location of an industry. Market and labor supply are increasing in importance.[3] This is especially true of those industries which have a high value added by the manufacturing process, for instance in the manufacture of machine tools and many types of industrial machinery. It is also dominant, but for a different reason, in many lines of consumption goods including utilities where the value added is relatively low.

The practices of subcontracting and of integration, both forward and backward, have complicated the role of market as a location factor for some industries. This is owing to the increase in the number of parts suppliers and in materials producers. But broadly speaking, the market for factory goods in America has been characterized by its homogeneity, its regional specialization, and its primarily domestic nature. If our major crops were to be grown uniformly over the arable portion of the country,

    [2] S. H. Schurr and Jacob Marshall, *Economic Aspects of Atomic Power* (Princeton Univ. Press, Princeton, 1950); Walter Isard and V. Whitney, *Atomic Power: An Economic and Social Analysis* (New York, 1952).

    [3] Chauncy D. Harris, "The Market as a Factor in the Localization of Industry in the United States," *Annals Assn. of American Geographers,* Vol. 44 (Dec., 1954), pp. 315-348.

the use of specialized, powered, agricultural machinery would be drastically reduced. Specialization has promoted mechanization by concentrating the markets for types of agricultural and other machinery.

Transportation. Transportation costs have risen with the cost of other goods and services. The cost of assembling materials and distributing the product is therefore of increasing moment to the manufacturer of most types of commodities. There has been marked relocation of the population, especially in the United States, with a consequent change in the market centers for many types of factory goods. For example, reclamation of dry lands and of wet lands not only gives rise to new population centers, but also creates a new market for the machines used in the reclamation and maintenance of these lands. Geographic shifts in population have also resulted from a recentralization of manufacturing industries, particularly in California, Texas and southern Ontario.

Government. The interest of the federal government in manufacturing is by no means something new. During the first administration, Alexander Hamilton, Secretary of the Treasury, advocated a "Federal City of Manufactures" in which most of the nation's factories would be concentrated and over which the federal government would exercise control and derive profits. Although the Congress did not bring this about, by example each generation since then has never been allowed to forget how manufactures promote the general welfare. The source of revenue which the sale of public lands so long provided has dwindled to the point where some substitute is sought.

Local communities looked in turn to canals, railroads, and finally the highways and motor trucks to increase their economic prospects. Not all communities profited from these changes in transportation and the effects of these improvements were not always lasting. For at least a quarter century Americans on both sides of the border have hoped for so-called "decentralization" (a better term for most of it is recentralization) of industry to give them local factory payrolls.

World War II gave much impetus to this growth of industry in nonindustrial areas. It also greatly increased the information available concerning industrial movement. On subsequent pages some account will be taken of the vigor of industrial growth in each Census division as it reflects the depression, World War II, and the postwar period.[4]

---

[4] D. B. Creamer, *Is Industry Decentralizing?* (Philadelphia, 1937); Glenn McLaughlin, *Areal Growth in Manufacturing* (Pittsburgh, 1934); Alfred J. Wright,

As a part of the government's active interest in manufacturing, the device of Certificate of Necessity was used to speed up the manufacture of certain commodities needed in national defense. These Certificates were granted to the firms which manufactured such commodities and were considering plant expansion. The Certificates permit a fast tax write-off. Their number and value constitute a means for measuring industrial facilities increase.

TABLE 4-3: *Geographic Distribution of the Number and Cost of Industrial Facilities with Certificates of Necessity, September 30, 1953*

State	Number	Cost ($1,000)
OHIO	1509	$1,400,064
CALIFORNIA	1423	1,114,862
MICHIGAN	1217	1,054,758
PENNSYLVANIA	1193	2,216,282
NEW YORK	1119	864,570
ILLINOIS	966	898,058
NEW JERSEY	781	476,199
MASSACHUSETTS	474	125,381
INDIANA	440	634,713

SOURCE: *Business Week.*

CHARACTERISTICS OF UNITED STATES' AND CANADA'S MANUFACTURING

The influence of far-flung and varied resources, relatively sparse and scattered population, and the relative absence of political restrictions, may be observed in the types of industry which have come to dominate the American scene. One characteristic is the three-fold relationship which manufacturing has with agriculture: (1) both the United States and Canadian farmer is a consumer of factory products in the home and upon his farm to a degree surpassed nowhere; (2) he supplies the factories with many of their raw materials; and (3) an important part of the farm population is absorbed into the ranks of factory workers. This characteristic interrelationship between manufacturing and agriculture is a distinguishing feature of American industry.

A second characteristic of American industry is the complex division of

"Recent Changes in the Concentration of Manufacturing" *Annals Assn. of American Geographers,* Vol. 35 (1945), pp. 144-166; W. Blair Stewart, "Shifts in the Geographical and Industrial Pattern of Economic Activity," *Amer. Econ. Review,* Vol. 36 (1946), pp. 36-51; John W. Alexander, "Industrial Expansion in the United States, 1939-1947," *Economic Geography,* Vol. 28, No. 2 (April, 1952), pp. 95-104.

labor. A third characteristic is the relatively high degree of value added by the manufacturing process. In the United States the gross value of factory products for 1950 was about $180 billion; after deducting purchased materials and labor, the factory output or the net value was $89,675,779. This means little until comparison is made with other leading manufacturing nations. Great Britain and West Germany together have an estimated 20 million wage earners; but the United States has only 16 million. Yet with 20 per cent greater number of industrial wage earners in Great Britain and Germany together, the amount which the manufacturing process adds to the value of the factory products of these two is only about two-thirds that of the United States. All three countries stress manufacturing, yet the manner in which the factors of production are combined for profit in manufacturing differs markedly.

A fourth characteristic naturally follows from the others: American manufacturing differs from that of other major manufacturing countries in that increased roundaboutness of processing gives rise to a more extensive consumption of power.

Another distinguishing characteristic in a sense conditions the others, manufactures of both the United States and Canada have developed primarily for a domestic market.

The United States has forged ahead of all other countries in manufacturing, both relatively and absolutely. With roughly 7 per cent of the world's population and 6 per cent of its land area, the United States does about 35 per cent of the world's manufacturing.[5] Although the United States is by no means the only nation to do so, no other equals it in the extent to which

[5] In 1950 the manufacturing industries in the United States consumed the following proportions of the world's production of selected commodities:

Per Cent	
64	petroleum
50	nickel
49	tin
50	copper
52	pig iron
42	lead
50	zinc
20	cotton
21	wool
39	coal
40	chromium
49	aluminum
33	natural rubber

It must be remembered that the United States' economy for 20 years had been operating under certain controls which regulated the consumption of raw materials. Natural rubber has had one of the tightest controls. *Recent Changes in Production, Supplement to World Economic Report, 1950-51* (United Nations, 1952).

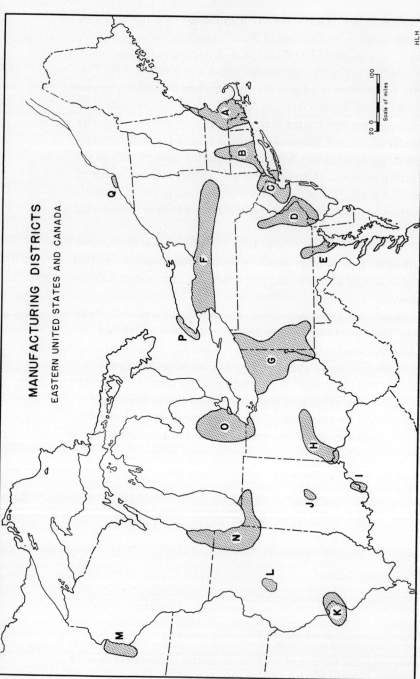

MANUFACTURING DISTRICTS
EASTERN UNITED STATES AND CANADA

Scale of miles
20 0 100

HLH

FIGURE 4-4

Despite the industrial growth on the Gulf and Pacific coasts and in the South Atlantic states, there has been relatively little change in the concentration of value-added-by-manufacturing in eastern United States and Canada since 1940. These centers constitute the so-called Manufacturing Belt: (A) Boston-Blackstone Valley, (B) Connecticut Valley, (C) New York, (D) Delaware Valley, (E) Baltimore, (F) Mohawk Valley-Lake Plain, (G) Pittsburgh-Cleveland, (H) Cincinnati-Dayton-Columbus, (I) Louisville, (J) Indianapolis, (K) St. Louis, (L) Peoria, (M) Minneapolis-St. Paul, (N) Chicago, (O) Detroit, (P) Hamilton-Toronto, (Q) Montreal.

manufactured goods and manufacturing facilities are at present being used to aid friendly nations.

AREAL ORGANIZATION OF MANUFACTURING IN THE UNITED STATES AND CANADA

Bases for Assessing Distribution. The position that manufacturing now holds in the economy of both countries makes it imperative that this industry be accorded a careful and detailed appraisal. No one factor will serve as an absolute basis for measuring the amount of manufacturing productivity in an individual district. Various single factors such as wage earners, gross value and net value of the product, wages paid, and the horsepower of prime movers have been used as bases for mapping the distribution of manufacturing in both countries. Only the net value (or value added by manufacturing) measures industrial productivity.

The choice of this base for appraisal rests upon two advantages. In the first place there is no duplicated value, as would be the case if gross value were used, since, from the value of output from each factory, there has been subtracted costs of all goods purchased. In the second place, the base is weighted in proportion to the several factors of production used, since net value is not a factor of production but is the product (measured in dollars) resulting from production. With such a base, for instance, the declining employment but increasing production in Youngstown's steel mills will be accurately shown. A weighted base is particularly necessary in nations such as these where the factoral proportion in manufacturing is changing so rapidly.

Manufacturing Belt. Unlike agriculture or forestry, manufacturing does not display the same areal uniformity of land use, yet the Manufacturing Belt is a term commonly used to designate the section having the greatest concentration of industrial centers in this country (*Fig.* 4-4). Manufacturing is not as simple as agriculture; it does not consist simply of adding value to given raw materials within a single establishment. The manufacture of most products is divided among several plants, each specializing in one or more stages of production, the materials passing from one plant to another until the processing is finally completed.

Several industrialized districts which collectively make up the United States Manufacturing Belt are easily identifiable and generally known. They lie for the most part east of the Mississippi and north of the Ohio and Potomac rivers. They cross into Canada at two points: the Ontario Peninsula and the upper St. Lawrence Valley. The Swedish geographer, Sten De Geer, first mapped this phenomenon and termed it a belt, about a generation ago.

Except for the Mohawk Valley-Lake Plain lowland in central New York, the Folded Appalachians Province separates the eastern and western portions of the Manufacturing Belt. The eastern portion is approximately twice as old as the western, and it is more nearly continuous. It embraces southern New England, the cities of the Middle Atlantic Littoral, and some important penetrations along the valleys of the eastern Appalachians. The greater age of these industrial districts has subjected them to greater industrial selection. The industries have in many instances, been adjusted to a remote as well as the local environment. The industrial structure of any given eastern industrial district has changed with the times; and the bonds among the urban clusters have likewise changed. The heavy hand of the past lies upon most of these eastern centers: in the older districts the buildings and the site locations are often less well adapted to the needs of the incumbents than they were to the early occupants.

TABLE 4-4: Percentage Increase in Value Added by Manufacturing, 1947-1952

CALIFORNIA	74.2
MICHIGAN	59.4
OHIO	57.8
INDIANA	50.
ILLINOIS	39.4
PENNSYLVANIA	39.3
NEW JERSEY	38.
NEW YORK	35.5
MASSACHUSETTS	26.7
UNITED STATES	45.7

SOURCE: Bureau of the Census.

Although the states of the United States Manufacturing Belt did not display a percentage increase in net value comparable to California, theirs is a percentage of a larger amount.

On the other hand, the western portion of this Belt is not only half the age of its eastern counterpart, but the timing of its development has been such as to give it a different areal framework. Water-power sites were important for only a relatively short period, hence the pattern of industrial centers so characteristic of the older East is not apparent here. The rapidity with which canal, railroad, and highway transport succeeded pioneer travel gave little time for any crystallization of the distribution of cities. Coal and iron were not only closer but in greater abundance. The immediate market of the eastern industrial centers was the eastern Appalachian Highlands primarily a large region with fairly dense population, but with much rough and inaccessible terrain. The immediate market of the western portion of the Manufacturing Belt has been to some extent the same Appalachians in the east and southeast, but in addition the great Central Lowlands, arable, accessible, relatively densely populated, and likewise endowed with some industrial raw materials. This western portion has no equivalent of the great middle Atlantic port cities, but the Great Lakes and Mississippi ports have compensated for this in a sense.

The western portion of the Manufacturing Belt is composed of several outstanding industrialized districts. Oldest and one of the largest of these agglomerations is the Pittsburgh-Cleveland-Detroit-peninsular-Ontario-city group. Another large concentration is the Chicago area with attenuations extending along Lake Michigan's south and west shores. Another is the Miami Valley in southwestern Ohio, and not far distant is the Indianapolis group. There are, in addition towns with just a few industries which lie among the larger concentrations of industry.

Canadian industrial agglomerations are chiefly in the Ontario peninsula and in the Montreal area. These manufacturing centers form a portion of the Manufacturing Belt. Montreal stands essentially alone, a nucleus for the growing industry of the upper and middle St. Lawrence Valley.

Canada has a larger proportion of its industry in the East; the Vancouver-Victoria district is the principal outlier of Canadian manufacturing.

There are other important concentrations of industry in both countries not included in the Belt. The Pacific coast has two main concentrations about Los Angeles and San Francisco, with smaller ones on Puget Sound and on the lower Columbia River. The southern Piedmont in the Carolinas and Georgia is a growing industrial region of great importance. The Gulf Coast of Texas is another detached industrial area of growing significance.

Effects of World War II. Whereas World War I cast the United States and Canada in the role of food producers for the Allies, the adoption of Lend-Lease and the demands of participation in World War II made both countries tremendously important producers of factory goods. It is still difficult for us to realize what the expenditure of approximately $20 billion by the federal government for increased manufacturing facilities in the United States alone has done to our total industrial establishment. It contributed to an increased industrial capacity of about 40 per cent. It nearly doubled the number of wage earners. Perhaps more important, it put factories in areas hitherto primarily rural. It also gave rise to a great variety of emergency production techniques, many of which have become accepted practices, owing to the very high level of production which has prevailed since 1945.

The geographical distribution of these new government-financed industrial facilities favored the western part of the Manufacturing Belt and two western states. In order of facility-increase, the states are: Ohio, Pennsylvania, Michigan, Illinois, New York, California, Texas, and Indiana. It must not be assumed that this represents all of the increased industrial capacity built during the five war years. Private capital went into increased capacity, accounting for some 22 per cent of the total increase; most of these private funds went into manufacturing enterprises such as power generation and transmission, mining, and various types of transportation. An important part of the government financing went into what were believed to be "duration" plants or "war industries," but during the postwar years many of these plants have been converted to peacetime production and incorporated into the regular industrial establishment.

Although much of the private capital went into power developments, a very small part of the total increase in power capacity was privately financed. Such large installations as Shasta, Grand Coulee, Bonneville, Hoover, and the several installations in the Tennessee Valley were publicly financed.

Canada's increase in manufacturing during the war years was both absolutely and relatively great, although not comparable in amount with that in the United States. Here, too, the war effort brought about increased facilities in relatively nonindustrial areas as well as older centers. Canada also was able to incorporate a large proportion of these plants into her peacetime establishment. Co-operative efforts between Canada and the United States permitted Canada to use some of our patented processes; markets, too, were shared by the two neighbors. They jointly became an Arsenal for the Democracies. Partly as a result of the wartime experience, the Toronto industrial area now leads in Canadian manufacturing increase.

In order to gain some concept of the changes in the over-all distribution of manufactures since 1919, some attention will be given to the recentralization in the Northeastern states, the Middle West, the South, and the West. Each of these regions is delimited on the basis of Census divisions. Subsequent treatment of manufacturing as it relates to the economy of each geographic region of the United States and Canada follows in the appropriate chapters.

CHANGES BY MAJOR AREAS

Northeast. The ten states which comprise the industrial northeast include New England and the Middle Atlantic states (New York, Pennsylvania, and New Jersey). This is the older, eastern portion of the Manufacturing Belt. It remains one of the two most important industrial areas of the continent.

TABLE 4-5: *Percentage of Contribution by Each Census Geographic Division to the Total Wage Earners in Manufacturing Industries for the Years 1909, 1919, 1929, 1939 and 1949*

Census Divisions	*1909*	*1919*	*1929*	*1939*	*1949*
NEW ENGLAND	16.65	14.85	12.43	12.09	9.96
MIDDLE ATLANTIC	33.37	31.58	28.99	28.52	27.04
EAST NORTH CENTRAL	22.88	26.35	28.76	27.84	29.21
WEST NORTH CENTRAL	5.67	5.35	5.36	4.85	5.55
SOUTH ATLANTIC	10.02	8.99	10.32	12.51	11.81
EAST SOUTH CENTRAL	3.96	3.62	4.27	4.54	4.68
WEST SOUTH CENTRAL	3.09	3.14	3.37	3.33	4.05
MOUNTAIN	1.14	1.2	1.16	.09	1.04
PACIFIC	3.22	4.78	5.33	5.44	6.66
Total	100.00	100.00	100.00	100.00	100.00

SOURCE: Bureau of the Census.

TABLE 4-6: *Percentage of Contribution by Each Census Geographic Division to the Total Value Added by Manufacture for the Years 1909, 1919, 1929, 1939, 1949*

Census Divisions	*1909*	*1919*	*1929*	*1939*	*1949*
NEW ENGLAND	13.99	12.9	10.38	9.84	8.3
MIDDLE ATLANTIC	34.97	33.67	32.08	29.29	27.5
EAST NORTH CENTRAL	25.53	28.42	31.67	31.53	32.6
WEST NORTH CENTRAL	6.59	5.42	5.72	5.52	5.8
SOUTH ATLANTIC	6.93	7.42	7.64	9.05	9.3
EAST SOUTH CENTRAL	3.45	2.65	2.82	3.36	3.8
WEST SOUTH CENTRAL	2.85	2.91	2.92	3.34	4.1
MOUNTAIN	1.59	1.25	1.09	1.01	1.1
PACIFIC	4.10	5.15	5.68	6.46	7.6
Total	100.00	100.00	100.00	100.00	100.00

SOURCE: Bureau of the Census.

1919-1939. The Bureau of the Census measures the amount of manufacturing activity on three bases: (1) value added by manufacturing (net value); (2) wages paid; (3) and the number of wage earners employed. On these three bases, expressed as a proportion of the national total, New England declined in manufacturing during this twenty-year period. In Massachusetts and Connecticut where four-fifths of the manufacturing took place, the decline was the greatest.

The Middle Atlantic states fared somewhat better, yet New York, Pennsylvania, and New Jersey failed to maintain their proportion of the nation's manufacturing on the same three bases. New Jersey declined less than the other states.

New Facilities, 1939-1945. War contracts and the construction of new plant facilities during Lend-Lease and World War II did not alter the general trend downward of New England's manufacturing. Compared with the 12 per cent of the nation's value-added which New England had in 1939, the 4.5 per cent of total new facilities is relatively low. No other Census division received so low a proportion of war facilities, expressed in terms of its value-added in 1939.

In other words, New England did the bulk of its war-contract manufacturing in lines which its factories were already fitted to produce, products which would be susceptible of subcontracting in many instances.

New England's manufacturing activity in this period as a result of the depression, a world war, and government spending for new facilities did not change essentially from the period of 1919-1939.

Since 1945. The most recent Census information reveals that industrial New England at the beginning of the second half of the twentieth century shows a continued downward trend. New manufacturing did come to these states, notably electronics, chemicals, and rubber products, but the loss of established cotton, wool, and other employment was greater. Still greater losses were sustained during the floods of 1955.

The proportional decline in the net value of manufacturing for the Middle Atlantic states continued through 1950. All gained employment in electrical and electronic manufacture. Pennsylvania gained an important increase in primary steel and other manufactures in the lower Delaware Valley. This, together with recent industrial increases in Pittsburgh and northern New Jersey may halt the relative decline by the 1960 Census.

East North Central. The five states (Ohio, Indiana, Illinois, Michigan, and Wisconsin) comprising this division have long been characterized by a balanced economy. That is to say the number of wage earners engaged in

FIGURE 4-5: *North American Aviation Plant, Columbus*

From Ohio the manufacture of aircraft spread to the Atlantic and Pacific coasts. In a sense it was the "return of a native" when the federal government built several huge plants for the manufacture of aircraft during World War II. The one shown continues to manufacture airplanes in an expanded factory. (North American Aviation Co.)

agriculture, manufacturing, mining and quarrying, commerce, and the service industries are more or less in balance.

No other division rivals it in the close interrelationship between agriculture and manufacturing. The division was settled more than a century after the Atlantic seaboard, yet in little more than 80 years this western half of the Manufacturing Belt became the dominant part.

1919-1939. Taken as a whole, the division showed no great change in manufacturing activity during this twenty-year period. Greatest proportional gains were in Michigan, Illinois, and Wisconsin. These states experienced appreciable industrial movement, loosely termed decentralization, but more accurately recentralization. A marked regional shift took place in the manufacture of agricultural implements. The center of this important industry moved from Ohio to Wisconsin and Illinois. Another industry with important changes in its localization was the manufacture of automobiles. Originally it was a fairly well-dispersed type of industry, with perhaps two score cities having one or more automobile plants. The number of makes greatly declined, and as a consequence automobile manufacture was sharply localized in the Detroit area.

New Facilities, 1939-1945. This division received somewhat more than its share of new industrial facilities. It had 28 per cent of the total value added by manufacturing in 1929; it received 30 per cent of the nation's new plant facilities (*Fig.* 4-5). As compared with the New England and Middle Atlantic states this is a lion's share, yet in proportion to the net value in 1939, these east north central states were third from the bottom.

Conversion to War Work. In this connection it is worth while to recall how some of these midwestern plants were able to convert for war contracts. Outstanding was the automobile industry. For these manufacturers, conversion meant almost complete retooling, and considering the enormous size of some of their machine tools, this was a very important factor. An estimated 80 per cent of the machine tools used in the production of peacetime automobiles had to be put aside in heavy grease for the duration of the war.[6]

Since 1945. The changes in manufacturing activity in these states since the war is evident in Table 4-7. Ohio made the only significant gain, followed by Indiana (*Fig.* 4-6).

Southern States. This large area includes the South Atlantic division (Delaware, Maryland, Virginia, North and South Carolina, Georgia, and Florida), the East South Central (West Virginia, Kentucky, Tennessee, Alabama, and Mississippi), and the West South Central states (Louisiana, Arkansas, Oklahoma, and Texas).

Changes, 1919-1939. During this 20-year period all but four states in these three divisions increased their shares of the nation's manufacturing. Mississippi, Florida, Louisiana, and Arkansas declined. Lustiest growth was in Texas, the Carolinas, and Tennessee.

The variety of new industries established during this period was greater in Texas, Tennessee, and Alabama. The South Atlantic region greatly increased its cotton textiles, wood products including paper, and tobacco manufacturing. But the interior states gained substantially in knit goods, rubber tires, iron and steel, machinery, aluminum and chemical products including petroleum.

Increased facilities in these states include steel plants at Daingerfield and Houston, Texas; a tin smelter at Texas City, and magnesium plant at Free-

---

[6] In England the same industry was able to convert 80 per cent of its machine tools to war work. This sharp contrast is indicative of the degree to which this industry has become specialized in the United States.

FIGURE 4-6: *Standard Oil Refinery, Lima, Ohio*

An important example of the recentralization of manufacturing which has been taking place since 1940, is the petroleum-refining industry. One of the three main refining districts in the United States is the lower Great Lakes region where this catalytic cracking plant is located. (Standard Oil Co., Ohio)

TABLE 4-7: Value Added by Manufacture, 1952, and Rank by Value Added by Manufacture, 1952, 1951, and 1947, Fifteen Most Heavily Populated States, United States

State (Rank: Population)	Value Added by Mfgr. 1952 ($1,000)	Rank by Value Added by Manufacture		
		1952	*1951*	*1947*
NEW YORK	13,101,875	1	1	1
CALIFORNIA	6,960,932	6	6	7
PENNSYLVANIA	9,673,846	3	2	2
ILLINOIS	9,309,363	4	4	3
OHIO	10,033,105	2	3	4
TEXAS	3,185,658	11	11	11
MICHIGAN	8,284,675	5	5	5
NEW JERSEY	5,764,365	7	7	6
MASSACHUSETTS	4,270,674	9	9	8
NORTH CAROLINA	2,013,824	13	13	12
MISSOURI	2,351,377	12	12	13
INDIANA	4,464,882	8	8	9
GEORGIA	1,355,318	15	15	15
WISCONSIN	3,320,663	10	10	10
VIRGINIA	1,440,012	14	14	14

SOURCE: U.S. Dept. of Commerce, Bureau of the Census, *1952 Annual Survey of Manufactures, 1951 Annual Survey of Manufactures,* and *1947 Census of Manufactures.*

port; synthetic rubber plants at Port Neches, Lake Charles, Baytown, and Baton Rouge; aircraft at Tulsa and Oklahoma City; shipyards at New Orleans; and an increased oil refining capacity at several places.

New Facilities, 1939-1945. Between 1939 and 1945 twelve of the fifteen states in the South gained in population; their proportional increase was exceeded by only one Census division, the Pacific Coast. The only southern states which failed to gain in population were Arkansas, Kentucky, and Oklahoma. While each of the three Census Divisions in the South accounted for some 3 per cent of the nation's net value in manufacturing in 1939, the proportion of new industrial facilities increase was at least twice that.

The wartime employment in the South was in two principal groups of industry: (1) the old-established cotton and wool textiles, steel, aluminum, rubber, and chemical industries, and (2) the newly constructed ordnance, explosives, aircraft, aluminum, and steel plants and shipyards. Half of the money spent for these new facilities went into shipyards. In 1940 there were 7,500 employed in southern shipyards; in 1943 there were

200,000 employed in the industry. Of these 50,000 were in Mobile, 18,000 in New Orleans, 13,000 in Panama City, and 10,000 in Pascagoula.

Since 1945. Most southern states have not been able to maintain industrial employment at the wartime level; Texas has shown the highest employment. Since 1950 there have been some other bright spots, for instance the Atomic Energy Commission's installation near Aiken, South Carolina; the Kanawha Valley's ferro-alloy industry; Memphis with its diversified plants; Paducah's electrochemicals; Louisville's electrical appliance and aluminum industries; the "chemical coast" east of Houston; and Tennessee's paper industry (*Figs.* 4-7, 4-8).

Pacific Coast. For many years the Pacific coast cities were sometimes called "warehouses for eastern manufacturers." Only the relatively simple types of manufacturing were found on the coast. Like the eastern part of the Cotton Belt almost a century earlier, agriculture was dominant, and a profitable dominance it was. It furnished one of the chief bases for the early manufacturing; furthermore, the processing of agricultural products was continued as an important industry.

Shortage of industrial water supply retarded Los Angeles' bid for new industry early in the present century. Not until after World War I did the Los Angeles district gain much manufacturing. The greatest single impetus to West Coast manufacturing was the rise of petroleum refining. The Pacific Northwest undertook little beyond wood-products manufacture, wool textiles, and the food canning industries until World War II. An exception was the manufacture of aircraft which got its start in the Northwest in World War I.

1919-1939. This period witnessed an increase in manufacturing activity in California and Oregon; Washington failed to maintain its position in the nation. The most vigorously growing cities in the United States included the port cities of California. New manufactures in California included rubber tires, auto parts, earth-moving machinery, sugar and oil-refined products, furniture, and aircraft.

In the Pacific Northwest there was little change in the types of manufactured products. The aircraft industry struggled through several lean years until rearmament in Europe gave it a new lease on life.

New Facilities, 1939-1945. All three Pacific states gained substantially in population and industry between 1939 and 1945. California experienced the greatest numerical increase in the nation, 1,559,135, and the fourth largest proportional gain, 22 per cent.

Eighty per cent of California's war contracts were for aircraft and ships;

FIGURE 4-7: Burlington Mills, near Raleigh

This Wake County finishing plant is an example of the physical plant to which the bulk of cotton textile manufacture has gone. Spinning, weaving, and finishing have all come to the Carolina Piedmont. (North Carolina Dept. of Conservation and Development)

an even higher proportion was for these two items in Washington. Ninety per cent of Oregon's contracts were for ships. Diversification in manufactures during this period was much greater in California than either of the other two Pacific states.

As for new industrial facilities financed by the government, these states received 8 per cent, half again as great as their share of the nation's value added in 1939. Among the new industries in California thus financed were the following: magnesium reduction (using both dolomite and sea water), cement, shipyards, aircraft, machine shops, and tool plants.

The industrial districts of Oregon and Washington are similar in the nature of products and close enough geographically to warrant treatment as one region. New industrial facilities erected during the war were scarcely half those of California and were added principally for aluminum, ship, and aircraft manufacture. The shipyards were to Portland what the aircraft industry was to Seattle. Both the North Pacific and South Pacific coast industrial centers were dependent upon outside labor. Nearly every state in the union was represented in this labor force. Although most of the new

FIGURE 4-8: *Westinghouse Factory, near Raleigh*

Suggestive of the profound changes taking place in manufacturing in the South is this modern building. (North Carolina Dept. of Conservation and Development)

facilities were for the production of war goods, California experienced an important step in the evolution of its permanent industrial economy by maintaining many of these facilities.

Changes Since 1945. Although the Northwest has not maintained similarly high rates of industrial growth since World War II, California has continued its vigorous growth. The term "warehouse" no longer is descriptive of its industry, with a population of 10 million and ranking among the top ten industrial states, the amount of new industry is rivaled only by its diversity.

West North Central. Every state (Minnesota, North Dakota, South Dakota, Iowa, and Missouri) in this division lost population between 1940 and 1945. Although there was a slight decline in population in a few of the states of the Manufacturing Belt, the decline in the West North Central group was two to four times as great, proportionally. This is something of an anomaly when viewed in the light of public funds spent for new industrial facilities. With only 5 per cent of the net value of the nation's manufactures in 1939, these states received 10 per cent of all facilities increase. Missouri alone got about one-half of this increase, with Minnesota and

Kansas each receiving 20 per cent. Missouri is the most important industrial state in this division, yet it has declined, proportionately, since the war.

Mountain States. Between 1919 and 1939 the share of the nation's manufacturing contributed by the eight Mountain States (Montana, Idaho, Colorado, Wyoming, Arizona, New Mexico, Nevada, and Utah) declined in all but the last three named, where there was almost no change.

Copper refining declined somewhat during this twenty-year period owing to the depressed business conditions, but the government's policy of purchasing silver tended to prevent an even greater reduction in copper production, since the standard alloy for United States silver coins is nine parts silver and one part copper.

A large part of Mountain States' manufacturing is concerned with food processing (flour milling, sugar refining, canning, meat packing), industries which showed the minimum depression slump.

New Facilities, 1939-1945. Between 1939 and 1945 every Mountain State gained in population except Idaho and Montana. In other states the rate of gain was relatively high: in Arizona 40 per cent, Nevada 30 per cent, Utah 15 per cent, Wyoming 1.5 per cent, Colorado 3.5 per cent and New Mexico 0.5 per cent. Mining rather than manufacturing was the cause of this increase. Utah, with a population increase of 15 per cent, had the greatest increase in manufacturing.

The proportion of government financing of new facilities in Utah was relatively high, 5 per cent, with the award of war contracts correspondingly high. Largest of these facilities is the Geneva steel plant near Provo, where three blast furnaces were built to produce 1,150,000 tons of pig iron, nine open-hearth furnaces to pour 1,283,400 tons of steel ingots, and two rolling mills to produce 700,000 tons of plate and 20,000 tons of structural shapes yearly.

Since 1945. The Geneva steel plant was converted to peacetime production and the capacity increased somewhat, but the over-all picture of the Mountain States' manufacturing is not particularly bright. The production of magnesium, ordnance, and explosives, aircraft parts, and ship fittings has languished. The building of the world's fourth-largest dam at Hungry Horse will irrigate some 60,000 acres near Kalispell. Its power is to be the basis for the manufacture of electrometallurgical and electrochemical products. The least industrial of the Mountain States, New Mexico, alone showed an increased proportion of the nation's manufactures in 1951-1952.

BIBLIOGRAPHY

ALDERFER, E. B., and H. E. MICHL, *Economics of American Industry,* 2nd ed. (New York, McGraw-Hill Book Co., Inc., 1950).

ALEXANDER, John W., "Industrial Expansion in the United States, 1939-1947," *Economic Geography,* Vol. 28, No. 2 (April, 1952), pp. 95-104.

Basic Industrial Location Factors, Industrial Series No. 74 (Office of Domestic Commerce, U.S. Dept. of Commerce, Washington, 1947).

BLUE, D. D., "Aluminum," *Minerals Yearbook, 1951* (U.S. Dept. of the Interior, Washington), pp. 128-150.

DE CARLO, J. A., J. A. CORGAN, and M. M. OTERO, "Coke and Coal Chemicals," *Minerals Yearbook, 1951* (U.S. Dept. of the Interior, Washington), pp. 459-520.

Geographic Distribution of Industrial Facilities, 1941-1944 (Defense Plant Corporation, Washington, 1945).

HARRIS, C. D., "A Functional Classification of Cities in the United States," *Geographical Review,* Vol. 33 (1943), pp. 86-99.

HOOVER, E. M., *Location of Economic Activity* (New York, McGraw-Hill Book Co., Inc., 1948).

Industrial Location and Natural Resources (National Resources Planning Board, Washington, 1943).

Iron and Steel, War Changes in Industry Series (U.S. Tariff Commission, Washington, 1946).

LARKIN, J. E., "Iron and Steel Scrap," *Minerals Yearbook, 1951* (U.S. Dept. of the Interior, Washington), pp. 715-737.

MELCHER, N. B., J. M. FORBES, and J. C. O. HARRIS, "Iron and Steel," *Minerals Yearbook, 1951* (U.S. Dept. of the Interior, Washington), pp. 696-714.

WRIGHT, Alfred J., "Recent Changes in the Concentration of Manufacturing," *Annals Assn. of American Geographers,* Vol. 35 (1945), pp. 144-166.

CHAPTER 5

COMMERCE AND
COMMERCIAL ROUTES

BASIS AND ORIGIN OF AMERICAN COMMERCE

Meaning of Commerce. Commerce is the exchange of goods and service. The products of agriculture, mining, lumbering, and manufacturing are not all consumed by the people who produce them, nor even by the people within the area where they are produced. Not all, but most, of these commodities are sold or exchanged, transported, and then used or consumed by other people.

The growth of these major economic activities is dependent upon commerce. It is not only our large foreign trade, but our vastly greater domestic trade that puts the United States at the top of the world's commercial nations. Canada, with less than one-tenth the population of the United States, had, by mid-century, become the world's third-largest foreign trader. Before World War II Canada was first in per capita exports.

Specialization. Within its continental limits, the United States has specialized geographically to a degree equaled by no other nation. In this geographical division of labor lies the basis of our great commerce. Despite the relative homogeneity of the economic and social development of the United States, the unequal distribution of natural resources and the specialized livelihood regions noted above have given rise to a vast and complicated commercial structure in the economy. In a country characterized by great distances, fronting on two oceans, and with great natural diversity, such geographical specialization is possible only if freight costs are low.

Specialization results in greater skill, efficiency, and output per worker, and in consequence, a large surplus for exchange. At the same time specialization means less self-sufficiency within the group or the district. This naturally means a greater demand for the surplus products of another group or region. Increased production per worker, due to specialized skill, makes possible a rise in the standard of living. This results in greater and more diversified wants, and so a widening of the market. Thus, a mutually beneficial commerce grows along with an expanding agriculture and the evolution of industry.

Factory System. The industrial revolution invaded manufacturing long before it did agriculture, and it has influenced commerce in factory products to a greater degree, even though our farms usually provide a large part of the raw materials of industry. Industries with a raw material orientation, or with power, labor, or market orientation, have become established in their respective centers, thus increasing the amount of commerce. Examples of this may be seen in Akron, Detroit, Dayton, Schenectady, Youngstown, and Whiting. This factor is responsible for the increased range of commuting labor, common to many places in the United States and a few places in Canada.

RAILWAYS

Importance. The volume of domestic commerce in the United States and in Canada is expressed in well-nigh astronomical figures; it is greater than for all other nations combined. Approximately one-half of it is carried by railroads. There are two railroads in the United States with a greater freight ton-mileage than the total railroads in any foreign country.

Railroad Network. The fact that there are 224,511 miles of railroads in the United States is misleading in that it gives no account of multiple tracks or of the density of freight traffic. Likewise a standard railroad map fails to distinguish between the main and the branch lines. It does, however, indicate the geographical pattern of the railway net. Generally speaking, the lines east of the Mississippi River and north of the Ohio-Potomac rivers have the greatest multiple trackage, and the density of freight and passenger traffic is likewise much greater in this division (*Fig.* 5-1). The density of passenger traffic for the northeastern states is shown on a map by Raisz.[1] This type of map gives some perspective to railroad traffic; the pattern ceases to be just thin lines on a map.[2]

[1] Erwin Raisz, *Traffic Density for Eastern Railroads* (Cambridge, Geographical Institute, Harvard University, Map Series, 1941).
[2] Railroad mileage by states: Texas 16,221; Illinois 11,933; Pennsylvania 10,275; Iowa 8,949; Kansas 8,567; Ohio 8,462; Minnesota 8,365; Michigan 7,256; Missouri 6,973; Indiana 6,888, and Wisconsin 6,617.

FIGURE 5-1: *Railroad Map of the United States*
(Association of American Railroads)

FIGURE 5-2: *Union Station, Kansas City*

Something of the role the railroads have been playing in the American economy is suggested in this photograph of a modern terminal. Diesels have taken over, even on the coal-owning railroads. (Missouri Division of Resources and Development, MASSIE photo)

A departure from normal railroad traffic are the sea trains which regularly sail between New York and Galveston, Florida and Cuba, and the car ferries which cross Lake Michigan, Lake Erie, the Detroit River, Straits of Mackinac, and the principal Atlantic and Pacific ports.

Character of Freight. In 1951 the products of mines and quarries accounted for 28 per cent of the railroad freight revenue for the Class I railroads in the United States. Manufactured goods accounted for 50 per cent, agricultural commodities 7 per cent, and forest products 5.1 per cent of the traffic revenue of these roads. These are nation-wide proportions and represent no single railroad or system. Instead there is so much specialization by some railroads in the character of freight hauled, as to give rise to such expressions as "coal road" (Virginian), "iron road" (Bessemer and Lake Erie), and "potato road" (Bangor and Aroostook) (*Fig.* 5-3). The tonnage hauled has declined about one-third since 1930.

Although Canadian railroads function in much the same manner in the economy of that country, the pattern of the rail lines is different. Neither the Atlantic nor the Pacific coastal margins have comparable importance to the interior traffic. There is no Canadian equivalent of the rail traffic in the Gulf plains area. There is no equivalent of the great middle western crossing of north-south and east-west railroads. So many Canadians live within so few miles of the United States centers of population and industry that connecting railroads tend to dominate the rail traffic of Canada.

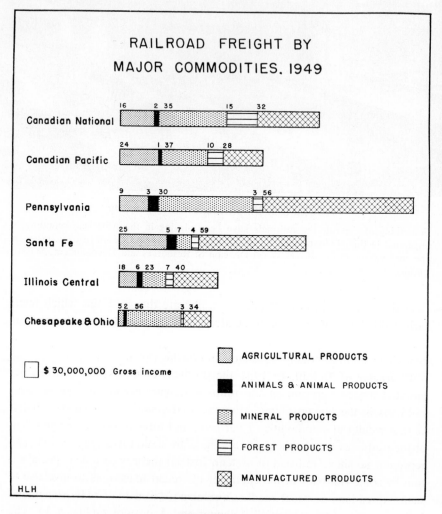

FIGURE 5-3

The proportion of freight revenue for each of the five principal groups of commodities carried by Class I railroads in the United States and Canada is shown on this chart. The scale of each bar is one-quarter inch per $30 million of gross revenue. (Data from Interstate Commerce Commission)

FIGURE 5-4: *Logging, Pacific Northwest*

The motor truck has enabled isolated or small stands of timber to be economically lumbered. This is also true of some mineral deposits, particularly copper in Nevada. (International Harvester Co.)

TRUCK TRANSPORTATION

World War I greatly promoted the use of the motor truck for interregional transportation. Since then the motor truck has steadily increased its share of the nation's commerce. Trucks have supplanted the railroad, both narrow- and standard-gauge, in certain mining and logging enterprises where the output is too small to justify building a railroad (*Fig. 5-4*). Railroads operate fleets of trucks to supplement the mainline hauls. Even such products as primary iron and steel are increasingly moved by truck. One of the half-dozen largest rolling mills in the United States now ships 80 per cent of its output by truck as against 20 per cent in 1935. In 1954 trucks hauled about 19 per cent of the domestic freight tonnage.

As industry has recentralized geographically and as subcontracting has increased, the motor truck has in some instances become an extension of the factory building. Parts and processes, by means of trucks, are linked with the parent plant. Refrigerated trucks, tank trucks, and other specialized types of truck units have blazed new trade routes. In peacetime and in war, truck lines freely cross the United States-Canadian boundary.

The five hundred or more specialized types of farming areas in the United States are possible only because transportation is available. For many of them the interregional as well as the local transportation is by means of motor trucks. In 1950 there were 2,100,000 trucks used in the operation of farms by farmers. This does not take into account the great numbers of trucks which serve the farmers' needs.

INLAND WATERWAYS

Mississippi River System. The rebirth of river transportation began in 1918 when Congress authorized the building of a small fleet of steel two-boats and barges with which to start services on the lower Mississippi and the Warrior River of Alabama to determine whether such transportation had any public appeal and could be successfully maintained. In 1954 this Federal Barge Line was sold to private interests, having demonstrated its public acceptance.

In the meantime, 9-foot navigation has been achieved between New Orleans and Pittsburgh, Chicago, and Minneapolis interrupted only in the upper Mississippi by ice during the winter. With the virtual completion of this 9,000-mile system, there has been a great development of traffic. In 1939, excluding the Great Lakes and car ferries, rivers accounted for 3.7 per cent of the total ton-miles in the United States. In 1953, with ton-miles doubled, their share was somewhat over 4 per cent. On the Mississippi system this amounted to about 42 million ton-miles.

TABLE 5-1: *Total Waterborne Commerce of the United States, 1953*
(2,000 lbs.)

Foreign	Domestic
IMPORTS, total—127,981,407	EXPORTS, total—706,151,204
IMPORTS, coastal ports—120,594,892	” , coastwise—188,757,641
” , Great Lakes, from Canada— 7,056,629	” , lakewise—188,621,385
” , ” ” ” overseas— 329,886	” , internal—224,957,448
EXPORTS, total—89,415,082	” , intra-port—47,902,038
” , coastal ports—63,780,288	” , local—54,659,693
” , Gt. Lakes to Canada— 25,415,354	” , intra-territory—1,252,999
” , ” ” ” overseas— 160,663	

SOURCE: *Report of the Chief of Engineers U.S. Army on Civil Works Activities,* 2 vols. (Washington, 1954), Vol. I, pp. 51-87.

Among the seasonal movements are fuel oil from New Orleans to Minneapolis and St. Paul; gasoline in bulk from Texas to Pittsburgh; hydrochloric acid in rubber-lined barges from Freeport, Texas to Cincinnati; Canadian wheat moving in bond from Chicago elevators to Galveston; molasses moving from New Orleans to Peoria for the manufacture of alcohol; styrene moving from Texas City to Cincinnati; vast tonnages of coal moving out of West Virginia and Kentucky to the power plants for the atomic energy installation near Portsmouth, Ohio, and to other cities; and new automobiles moving from Detroit to Houston (*Fig.* 5-5).

There are several reasons for the increase in this river trade. One is the rising cost of rail and truck transportation; another is the vast improvement in barges, towboats, and handling facilities on the rivers; and a final factor is the great increase in industrialization of river cities, all the way from Pittsburgh to Texas. Since 1941 nearly $1 billion in industrial facilities have been constructed along the Ohio and Mississippi alone, excluding the Intracoastal Waterway.

Ohio River System. In many ways the Ohio River traffic differs from that on the Mississippi. For one thing the Ohio traffic is to a marked degree fragmented, that is, it travels on the river but a relatively short distance. The barge lines on the Ohio have always been privately owned. The upstream traffic is less than the downstream traffic. Coal is the most important commodity in its commerce. And as against a few hundred vessels on the Mississippi, Ohio River cities are home ports to about 1,800 (*Fig.* 5-6).

Other Systems. The Gulf Intracoastal Waterway is in active operation from Corpus Christi to Carrabelle, Florida. Tows on this waterway are flexible, not the rigid tows used on the Mississippi and Ohio rivers. The Atlantic Waterway offers continuous inland navigation from New York to Miami, Florida. Its use is primarily by pleasure craft.

New port facilities are being added to some river cities. In 1953 the seven-mile stretch of the upper Mississippi known as Chain-of-Rocks has been canalized. Memphis has completed a million-dollar river-rail-truck terminal. St. Louis has doubled its port capacity. These improvements are a far cry from the floating wharf boat, the paved river bank with great chains imbedded for tying the river boat which prevailed until 1950.

There has been a marked increase in barge-load traffic which the shipper loads and the consignee unloads. On a sample load of grain from Havana, Illinois, to New Orleans the cost to the shipper by rail is $6.27 per ton; by barge it is $3. From Minneapolis it would be $17.69 by rail and $5.55

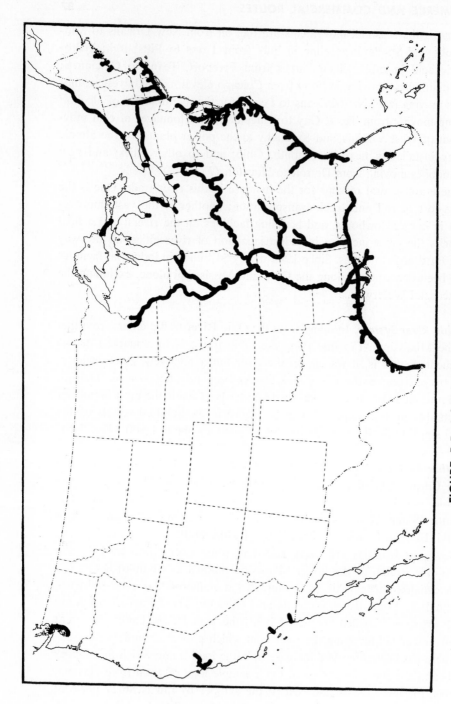

FIGURE 5-5: Inland Waterways, United States

This chart shows the waterways with a minimum channel depth of 9 feet.
(*After Goode's World Atlas*)

FIGURE 5-6: *Allied Ashland Tow on the Ohio River*

In this photograph the statistics are impressive. The towboat is 166 feet in length, has a 36-foot beam, 10.5-foot molded depth, and draws 7.5 feet. With a crew of 25, with radar and ship-to-shore communication, and with power from two 1,000 h.p. diesel engines driving twin screws, the tow maintains an average speed of eight miles an hour. The twelve oil-carrying barges, each of 9,000 barrels capacity, comprise a total of 108,000 barrels. In practice one or more of the barges is released at the river port, the towboat continuing on its way with the remaining barges, thereby avoiding a laying-up of the power plant while the cargo is discharged. The Ford Motor Company pioneered in the use of specially constructed vessels for the delivery of new automobiles. A recent innovation is the movement of molten sulphur in insulated barges from Texas ports to St. Louis chemical plants, a five-day run. (Ashland Refining Co.)

by barge. These are the costs levied on the shipper; allowance is not made for the century and more of public maintenance of the waterways.

The huge sums expended upon the Mississippi system in its entirety may be regarded as having several objectives: (1) to increase navigability and integrate waterborne commerce with the railroad and pipeline systems, (2) prevent floods by the control of tributary streams (Great Miami, Tennessee, and Muskingum projects are completed or nearly so), and (3) to aid in the conservation of water and land resources through water storage and erosion control, and the development of recreation facilities.

Great Lakes. The Great Lakes waterway curves southeast a thousand miles from the greatest source of iron ore on the continent to the greatest

FIGURE 5-7

The proportional tonnage in the commerce of principal bulk commodities on the Great Lakes system. (Based on a chart drawn for *Fortune* by BORIS ARTZYBASHEFF. Redrawn by E. WILLARD MILLER)

TABLE 5-2: Great Lakes Ports, 1953
(2,000 lbs.)

Port	total	Foreign (imports)		Exports		Domestic Lakewise	
		Canadian	overseas	Canadian	overseas	receipts	shipments
DULUTH-SUPERIOR	77,243,545	436,307	3,861	6,696,205	9,232	6,376,934	63,699,166
CHICAGO	32,281,685	822,521	94,063	971,382	84,170	16,374,788	4,084,680
TOLEDO	31,617,522	61,810	7,455	5,074,816	52,849	4,931,262	21,058,294
DETROIT	25,463,140	457,189	136,896	169,957	18,688	22,740,695	1,098,032
CLEVELAND	23,480,714	411,639	21,965	89,513	16,169	22,183,282	351,894
BUFFALO	22,008,987	1,617,908	3,305	587,741	3,152	16,562,222	1,903,290
INDIANA HARBOR	20,044,665	179,532	—	65,518	—	12,350,477	7,203,000
CONNEAUT	16,058,774	72,890	—	407,729	—	15,008,500	568,387
ASHTABULA	15,228,497	530,348	—	2,474,713	—	11,463,328	716,087
LORAIN	11,780,986	310,487	—	1,381,900	—	8,555,391	1,321,874
SANDUSKY	8,521,771	25	—	1,579,680	—	1,564	6,832,259
MILWAUKEE	8,165,023	447,776	10,186	12,774	25,155	6,337,842	1,319,873

SOURCE: *Report of the Chief of Engineers, U.S. Army, on Civil Works Activities*, 2 vols. (Washington, 1954), Vol. I, pp. 51-87.

FIGURE 5-8: *Ore Boat and Battery of Hulett Unloaders, Great Lakes*
This photograph shows the extraordinary developments in bulk transportation. Each shovel holds seventeen tons. (Wellman Engineering Co.)

steel-making centers. It lies between the greatest wheat fields of North America and the richest consumer population on any seaboard area in the world. From these lakes there are four routes by which smaller lake vessels can reach the oceans and thus carry cargoes between domestic and foreign ports: (1) St. Lawrence River and canals with a 14-foot channel, (2) New York State Barge Canal with a 12-foot channel, (3) Oswego section of the Barge Canal joining Lake Ontario with the Hudson River and (4) the Illinois Waterway linking the Chicago with the Illinois rivers, the Mississippi and the Gulf with a 9-foot channel (*Fig.* 5-5).

Using the Great Lakes there are 381 bulk carriers of which 332 fly the United States flag; 52 of them are of the self-unloading type.[3] A representative Great Lakes ore freighter of the larger class is about 600 feet in length, with the bridge and deck crew located in the bow, the engine and boiler room and engineer's and steward's quarters in the stern, and the vast cargo space extending unbroken from the forecastle to the boiler room bulkheads (*Fig.* 5-8).

In an ice-free season of eight months or less a carrier in its twenty round

[3] The combined carrying capacity of the Canadian and U.S. Lakes fleet (1953) was 5 million tons, 75.27 per cent United States, 24.73 per cent Canadian.

FIGURE 5-9: *Iron Ore Bridge, Great Lakes*

Seasonal movement on the Great Lakes necessitates stockpiling of iron ore and limestone on the lower Great Lakes margin. This giant ore bridge continues the economical work of the bulk freighter. For the scores of smaller ports without this expensive equipment, some bulk carriers have been equipped with self-unloading devices.
Most of these vessels carry limestone and coal which have a much wider market than
iron ore. (Wellman Engineering Co.)

trips will make the equivalent of two trips around the world. The average
turnaround time in an unloading port over a ten-year average is 11 hours
and 51 minutes; in a loading port the average time is 4 hours and 17
minutes. The profit varies with the number of trips made and the cargo
carried (*Fig.* 5-9). Half or more of the ore freighters return to the upper
Lakes with a cargo of bituminous coal from Lake Erie ports.

There are three major movements of traffic on the Lakes, for the most
part parallel with and in places within sight of the shoreline: (1) from
Lake Superior to lakes Erie and Michigan, (2) from Lake Erie to lakes
Michigan and Superior, (3) from Lake Michigan to Lake Erie. Since coal,
the principal commodity moving up the Lakes, adds up to about half the
tonnage of the down-lake movement of grain, ore and limestone, about half
of the vessels must return in ballast.

One hundred twenty-seven million ton-miles of cargo were carried by
the Lakes freighters of the United States from one domestic port to another, through the Soo Canals, while 17 million ton miles were carried from

United States ports to Canadian ports and overseas.[4] The Canadian fleet of some 200 vessels of all types carry several million tons between Canadian ports. Except during emergencies and by Congressional action, Canadian vessels do not move freight between United States ports.

Great Lakes Ports. On the United States side of the Great Lakes are most of the active ports; 64 of them handle more than 100,000 tons each season, but five of them handle most of the tonnage: Cleveland, Duluth-Superior, Toledo, Chicago, and Buffalo. Canadian ports are Fort William, Port Arthur, Sault Ste. Marie, Sarnia, and Port Colborne.

Other Ports. In a country as large as the United States, and with such a variety of physical features, commerce becomes a dominant consideration. The several ports are intimately related to these specialized regions of the interior. In only six of the ocean ports is the proportion of foreign trade greater than domestic; four of them are Atlantic ports, one is on the Gulf, and one on the Pacific. Of the twenty ports with a tonnage in excess of 10 million in commerce, ten are on the Gulf, six on the Atlantic, and four on the Pacific. Only the Atlantic ports have coastwise receipts greater than shipments. Only on the Pacific are the internal receipts as great as shipments (*Table* 5-3).

Exports dominate the foreign commerce of the Gulf ports. Internal trade is a more important part of their total commerce than with Atlantic ports. Although these tables of port commerce are included in this chapter, it is strongly urged that the student refer to them for each of the appropriate geographic regions (*Fig.* 1-3).

As agriculture has become geographically specialized and manufacturing areally concentrated, the principal ports have reflected this specialization. Only four of the Pacific ports move in excess of 10 million tons annually. As with the Gulf ports, internal receipts and shipments are an important part of the port function.

Internal and connecting waterways carry a large tonnage. For instance the St. Mary's Falls Canal between Lake Superior and Lake Huron bore a commercial tonnage in 1953 of 128,510,232 tons. The Detroit River moved 154,322,381 tons. The Cape Cod Canal had 13,529,380 tons. The Chicago Sanitary Canal had 14,924,536 tons. The New York State Barge Canal moved 4,497,231 tons. On the Mississippi River from Minneapolis to the Passes, in 1953 the commercial tonnage was 80,099,909 tons. By way of

---

[4] Iron ore, coal, wheat and limestone constitute 90 per cent of the total tonnage. Other commodities include sand, cement, lumber, newsprint, coke, petroleum, scrap iron and steel, dairy products, and miscellaneous metals and manufactured products including automobiles.

TABLE 5-3: Pacific Ports, 1953

1953 commerce Harbor	(2,000 lbs.) total	Foreign		Coastwise		Internal	
		imports	exports	receipts	shipments	receipts	shipments
LOS ANGELES	19,661,486	2,379,411	1,989,844	6,768,566	7,979,634	22,473	372,740
SAN FRANCISCO	37,748,789	3,559,530	2,808,437	12,981,897	11,212,457	7,150,597	
PORTLAND	11,716,650	144,186	1,144,759	5,905,858	667,453	1,816,345	1,371,406
VANCOUVER	1,367,713	14,849	273,499	18,213	107,448	781,609	152,625
LONGVIEW	2,323,979	5,856	615,529	167,149	160,091	1,302,500	63,873
TACOMA	4,736,121	502,729	603,247	719,043	216,695	1,152,410	804,256
SEATTLE	11,850,811	390,000	643,017	5,372,870	703,107	2,157,864	1,501,126

SOURCE: *Annual Report, Chief of Engineers, U.S. Army, on Civil Works Activities*, 2 vols. (Washington, 1954), Vol. I., pp. 64-74.

TABLE 5-4: Gulf Ports, 1953

1953 commerce Harbor	(2,000 lbs.) total	Foreign		Coastwise		Internal	
		imports	exports	receipts	shipments	receipts	shipments
1. TAMPA	9,061,058	652,477	1,986,510	3,580,297	1,454,166	65,836	346,841
2. MOBILE	13,127,633	4,050,956	1,152,343	565,015	1,760,075	1,542,330	2,148,465
3. NEW ORLEANS	36,691,253	4,467,317	6,025,374	702,218	5,998,371	12,385,120	7,601,059
4. BATON ROUGE	15,809,843	1,223,536	839,082	920,130	5,614,116	2,894,341	4,315,933
5. LAKE CHARLES	15,950,421	31,411	528,448	71,910	7,503,723	4,659,893	2,660,469
6. BEAUMONT	23,422,652	24,449	809,819	1,591,929	16,978,142	2,197,675	1,637,563
7. PORT ARTHUR	22,309,765	14,232	1,498,209	2,011,935	14,597,028	1,950,042	2,220,365
8. HOUSTON	44,263,704	1,609,832	4,678,825	677,682	20,417,806	3,376,252	5,754,307
9. TEXAS CITY	14,827,298	—	744,464	335,767	8,016,857	4,361,848	1,368,362
10. GALVESTON	5,112,576	348,449	2,347,250	57,005	1,430,026	484,614	445,232
11. FREEPORT	4,402,113	2,812	678,322	2,625	1,600,111	1,123,454	994,789
12. PORT ARANSAS	10,022,693	1,319	290,963	—	8,533,542	153,497	1,031,790
13. CORPUS CHRISTI	13,544,003	695,267	569,912	50,043	8,843,099	678,257	2,464,650

SOURCE: *Annual Report, Chief of Engineers, U.S. Army, on Civil Works Activities*, 2 vols. (Washington, 1954), Vol. I, pp. 64-74.

comparison, the Great Lakes system accounted for 127,383,073 tons, excluding trade between foreign ports.

TABLE 5-5: *Iron Ore Receipts, Great Lakes Ports, 1953*

(short tons)

CLEVELAND	17,210,459
CONNEAUT	14,876,304
ASHTABULA	11,562,955
GARY	8,800,000
LORAIN	8,051,051
INDIANA HARBOR	7,568,413
ERIE	4,360,788
DETROIT	4,286,452
SOUTH CHICAGO	4,196,865
TOLEDO	4,160,331
HURON	2,276,385

SOURCE: *Annual Report,* Lake Carriers' Association, 1953.

St. Lawrence Seaway. The Great Lakes have been open to ocean shipping for many years. The canals which by-passed the rapids of the International Section were capable of admitting vessels of no more than 14-foot draft, thus prohibiting most of the merchant fleet. However, international shipping did take place on the Great Lakes-St. Lawrence system. An estimated 2 per cent of the bulk trade on the Great Lakes reached the port of Montreal on the St. Lawrence River.

As with all of the narrow connecting waterways (Detroit River, St. Clair River, Soo Canals, and the Welland Canal), the proposed canals of the International Section would freeze before the Lakes; seven months of ice-free shipping is anticipated.

Granted shipping charges on the new waterway will be lower than on present rail-water routes, just what difference it will make in the commerce of the Middle West, the Middle-Atlantic Littoral, and New England is by no means clear. Whereas the five canals now in use are Canadian (Cornwall, Farrans Point, Morrisburg, Galop, and North Channel), the seaway canals (27 feet) will be on the south side of the border. It is anticipated that the commerce in iron ore from Labrador's new fields, and coal, petroleum, and grain from the Great Lakes ports will yield a toll revenue sufficient to retire the costs of construction and maintenance (*Fig.* 20-9).

TABLE 5-6: Atlantic Ports, 1953

1953 commerce Harbor	(2,000 lbs.) total	Foreign		Coastwise		Internal	
		imports	exports	receipts	shipments	receipts	shipments
1. BOSTON	18,076,260	4,756,747	234,147	10,993,829	817,694	3,916,931	4,114,081
2. NEW YORK	139,395,118	28,837,891	6,720,527	42,964,587	10,333,731	12,715,391	12,715,391
3. DELAWARE RIVER PORTS	73,432,216	25,550,577	1,696,194	21,685,600	8,316,448	12,715,391	12,715,391
4. BALTIMORE	41,807,753	16,537,107	4,837,359	7,026,494	1,402,157	1,349,331	2,366,578
5. NORFOLK	24,083,192	2,320,378	6,880,581	4,891,175	4,344,219	1,835,900	3,147,284
6. NEWPORT NEWS	12,250,616	553,184	6,608,624	5,592	4,481,210	512,369	89,637
7. CHARLESTON, S. C.	4,020,134	1,309,174	177,412	1,991,496	123,247	42,290	256,949
8. SAVANNAH	3,782,568	1,638,259	188,139	1,554,269	158,801	105,100	84,432
9. JACKSONVILLE	4,992,309	948,022	77,327	2,628,988	128,147	298,967	715,251

SOURCE: *Annual Report of the Chief of Engineers, U.S. Army, on Civil Works Activities*, 2 vols. (Washington, 1954), Vol. I, pp. 64-74.

FIGURE 5-10: *Tanker, Atlantic Coast*

This tanker for the transportation of liquid chemicals (caustics) is in service along the Atlantic Coast. The interior of all tanks is nickel. On the Pacific Coast a chemical manufacturer uses a barge fleet, each barge carries eleven cars of liquid chlorine on deck and 1,000 tons of liquid caustic soda below deck. (Dow Co.)

COASTAL WATERWAYS

In normal times the domestic trade of the United States accounts for about 90 per cent of the total trade. A significant portion of the tonnage is coastwise, a term which includes trade between the Atlantic, Gulf, and Pacific coasts, the mainland and the territories of Hawaii, Alaska, Puerto Rico, Canal Zone, and minor areas.

The intercoastal trade between the Atlantic and Pacific ports has profited most from the construction of the Panama Canal. In this trade the tonnage of petroleum and lumber have been in first or second place for virtually all of the canal period. In order of importance the other commodities, Atlantic-bound, include fish products, canned fruits and vegetables, copper, and furs. The smaller Pacific-bound tonnage is mainly manufactured and semi-manufactured goods.

Gulf-Atlantic Trade. This trade is likewise principally raw materials moving to Atlantic ports and includes phosphate, petroleum, copper, sulphur, lumber, cotton, naval stores, wheat, citrus fruit, and canned shrimp. To the Gulf ports from Middle Atlantic cities come steel and machinery for shipyards and oil fields, and a variety of manufactured products. Along with its great petroleum industry, the United States has built up a great transportation system. In addition to pipelines, it ships oil in 444 of its own tankers and in nearly 300 tankers operating under other flags; most of the tankers plying between Texas oil ports and the refining cities of the Middle Atlantic region (*Fig.* 5-10).

Traffic Between Atlantic Ports. The principal item in this trade between Atlantic ports is bituminous coal from the ports on Hampton Roads and Baltimore to the New England and Middle Atlantic cities. Steel from Baltimore moves both north and south to the ports of the Atlantic and Gulf coasts. Fruit and phosphate from Florida move to Middle Atlantic cities. Although the intracoastal waterway extends all along the Atlantic coast, its use south of Chesapeake Bay is primarily for pleasure craft.

AIRWAYS

Pre-World War II Status. When World War II broke out the United States and Canada were well served by commercial airways as domestic and foreign airlines of the United States flew more air miles than all of the major European-owned lines combined. Pan-American Airways had the most extensive international air service in the world, covering 98,582 route miles.

Development. With World War II, the Army established the Air Transport Command; in 1942 this service was flying 60,000 miles of route; in 1943 the number of planes and the number of trips flown were increased several hundred per cent. Its flying routes literally encircled the globe. The Navy likewise operated a tremendous air transport system, comparable in scope to the Army's.

This was a far cry from the experimental airway established by the Army in 1918, from New York to Washington, Chicago, and Cleveland. A combination plane-train transcontinental airway was established in 1929, with only daytime flying in the first, large trimotored transport planes. A lighted transcontinental route soon followed. Dawn-to-dusk flights, sleeper planes, and stratosphere planes followed in that order (*Fig.* 5-11).

The airways map of Canada and the United States reflects much the same continental pattern as the railroads. Notable exceptions are found in Alaska and northern Canada. Both maps show the critical nature of relief and

FIGURE 5-11: *Air Terminal, Pittsburgh*

It takes a great volume of air commerce to show a return on such a capital investment as is represented by this modern air terminal facility. Covering 1,600 acres, it is approximately fifteen miles from downtown Pittsburgh. This photograph was taken shortly before the terminal was opened for traffic. (Pittsburgh Chamber of Commerce)

climate in commerce. Although the rise in airline passengers, express, and freight traffic has been impressive, the effect upon the location of population centers is not apparent. Air commerce has made it easier for industry to recentralize some of its operations. The airplane has also found a place in agriculture, both in management and in moving commodities. In extensive agricultural and livestock operations it is an important factor.

Canada depends upon the airplane for linking the mining districts of the Laurentian shield with southern cities. Machinery and labor were flown in to open the iron mines and build the railroad from the iron fields of western Labrador to the St. Lawrence River. Alaska is heavily dependent upon the airplane for territorial commerce and for some trade with the United States. Intercontinental airline traffic has become commonplace throughout the New World and between the Old and the New.

PIPELINES

The use of pipelines for the transportation of petroleum began shortly after the discovery of the commercial use of petroleum. The major de-

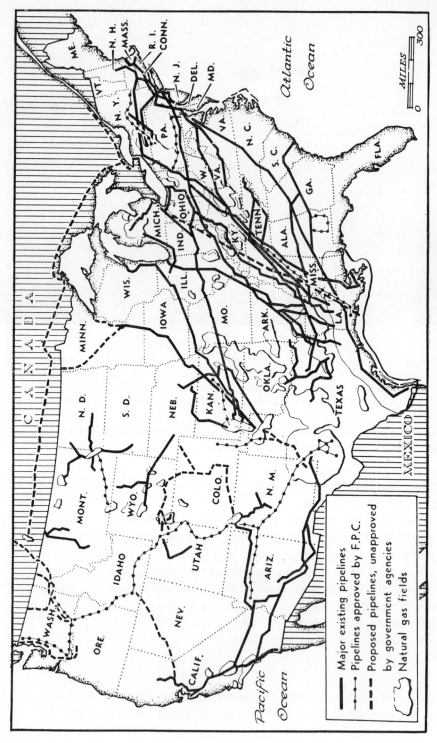

FIGURE 5-12: Gas Pipelines, United States, 1955

This complex of pipelines includes those approved by the Federal Power Commission but not yet completed and suggests the increasing importance of gas to manufacturing industries. (*New York Times* and LUCAS MANDITCH.)

velopment of pipelines occurred much later, however. From tank wagon to railroad tank car to pipeline to river and ocean tankers, petroleum successively cheapened its mode of transportation.

World War II drastically reduced the proportion of petroleum moving by ocean tanker and increased the proportion moved by rail, river barge, and by pipeline. The first transcontinental pipelines from the Texas oil fields to Middle Atlantic cities were constructed during the war, Big Inch and Little Inch. In 1947 these lines were given over to the transport of natural gas. The economical ocean tanker again dominates the flow of oil from Gulf ports to northeastern seaboard cities (*Fig.* 5-12).

Since the war, additional pipelines have been built both east and west of the Mississippi River. Some of them are for gasoline; most of these lie between Ohio and the Atlantic coastal cities with their great refineries. Even solids can be moved by pipeline. Powdered coal in water (slurry) is moved by pipeline from a bituminous mine near Cadiz, in eastern Ohio, to a power plant in Cleveland. Municipal water supplies are everywhere moved by pipelines.

Canada has built pipelines connecting the several Alberta oilfields with the Vancouver district on the Pacific, Lake Superior, and is constructing one to the St. Lawrence Valley.

AMERICA'S FOREIGN COMMERCE

United States Looks Abroad. Like other aspects of the economic geography of the United States, foreign trade reveals the fundamental character of the national economy. The United States has had the double advantage of being a new country with a surplus of raw materials and of food, and at the same time a mature country with its highly developed manufacturing industries. The economies of large-scale factory production have been possible because of the size and overwhelming dominance of domestic trade, which steadily expanded for more than a century. As a result of these economies, foreign markets have been opened to certain manufactures of the United States because of low price and/or high quality. The proportion of total trade classed as foreign has varied with the years, but it remains generally less than 10 per cent. Yet for each 1 per cent of foreign trade perhaps a million persons will be directly affected in the United States. World War II taught most Americans that national self-sufficiency is a myth. As dependence is placed upon distant sources for needed materials, the industrial shipping of the United States or Canada is increasingly vulnerable to enemy submarines.

TABLE 5-7: United States Foreign Trade, 1950

Exports ($1 million)		Imports ($1 million)	
MACHINERY	1800	COFFEE	1100
COTTON	1100	PAPER AND PRODUCTS	725
AUTOMOBILES	725	PETROLEUM PRODUCTS	575
CHEMICALS	655	RUBBER	450
PETROLEUM PRODUCTS	550	WOOL	425
TEXTILES	500	SUGAR	375
WHEAT-FLOUR	500	WOOD PRODUCTS	375
IRON-STEEL PRODUCTS	425	COPPER	250
COAL	265	FRUITS, NUTS, VEGETABLES	225
TOBACCO	250	VEGETABLE OILS	185

SOURCE: *National Industrial Conference Board, Yearbook, 1951* (New York), p. 430.

Nature and Extent of Foreign Trade. The nature of the exports and the imports of the United States reveals the double advantage the nation has in being an exporter of both raw materials and manufactured goods. Our foreign trade reflects the need that United States industry has for raw materials, partially manufactured and finished goods.

TABLE 5-8: Percentage Distribution of United States Imports and Exports, 1951

Area	Imports—1900 per cent	Imports—1951 per cent
EUROPE	51.8	18.6
ASIA	17.2	18.8
CANADA	4.7	20.8
SOUTH AMERICA	11.0	21.2
CENTRAL AMERICA AND MEXICO	10.6	11.1

Area	Exports—1900 per cent	Exports—1951 per cent
EUROPE	74.6	26.9
ASIA	4.8	14.9
CANADA	7.0	17.2
SOUTH AMERICA	2.8	13.8
CENTRAL AMERICA AND MEXICO	6.5	11.3

SOURCE: *Statistical Abstract of the United States, 1952* (U.S. Dept. of Commerce, Washington), p. 857. Hereafter cited as *Statistical Abstract*.

Geographical Distribution. Over the past fifty-year period there has been a change in the types of goods the United States wanted to buy and to sell; these changes are reflected in the shifting centers of our trade. As *Table* 5-8 above reveals, in half a century the proportion of our foreign trade which is with Europe has about halved, while that with Asia has doubled. Although the trade between the United States and South America has increased, it has been in no such spectacular fashion.

As a nation which exports 21 per cent of all world exports and imports 12 per cent of all world imports, the United States appears to be a foreign trader. But when these proportions are expressed in terms of our national product, the exports become 6.1 per cent and imports 4.1 per cent of the national product; the commerce of the United States is primarily domestic.

The United States and Canada did not escape the effects on foreign trade of the depression and two wars. In both countries trade is used as an instrument of foreign policy, but each of these two nations remains the other's best customer.

Underlying all of our concepts of international trade as a means of keeping the peace is an often-quoted remark: "Only the productive can be strong, and only the strong can be free." Periodically the Congress is forced to decide how much additional import trade is to be permitted in order that the productivity and strength of friendly countries may be increased. The stockpiling program for certain strategic raw materials which the Congress had authorized during World War II was given additional impetus by the "cold" war and the Korean conflict.

TABLE 5-9: Canadian Foreign Trade, 1950
($1,000 U.S.)

Country of origin of destination	Imports for consumption	Per cent of total	Domestic exports	Per cent of total
UNITED STATES	1,963,652	67.1	1,856,389	64.7
UNITED KINGDOM	372,546	12.7	433,069	15.1
VENEZUELA	80,431	2.7	23,461	.8
NEW ZEALAND	37,386		10,122	
AUSTRALIA	30,235		32,667	
MEXICO	30,149		16,242	
BRAZIL	25,972		14,566	
JAMAICA	17,586		6,907	
TRINIDAD AND TOBAGO	14,014		6,890	
COLOMBIA	12,298		13,645	

SOURCE: *Foreign Commerce Yearbook, 1950* (U.S. Dept. of Commerce, Washington), p. 297.

CANADA'S TRADE

Canada is a progressive new country with a large foreign trade per capita. The production of wheat, cheese, butter, meat, woodpulp, paper, gold, petroleum, nickel, uranium, and fish gives rise to a large surplus with which Canada buys from the United States such commodities as automobiles and parts, all kinds of machinery used in the extraction, transportation, and processing of her raw materials, agricultural implements, coal, textiles, iron, petroleum products, vegetables, and fruit.

BIBLIOGRAPHY

Annual Report of the Civil Aeronautics Board (Washington, 1953).

BALLERT, Albert G., "Major Ports and Commerce of the Great Lakes," *Michigan Business Review,* Vol. 4, No. 5, (Sept., 1952), pp. 26-32.

"Commercial Statistics, Water-borne Commerce of the United States, 1952," *Annual Report of the Chief of Engineers, U.S. Army, on Civil Works Activities,* 2 vols. (Dept. of the Army, Office of the Chief of Engineers, Washington, 1954).

Foreign Commerce Yearbook, 1952 (U.S. Dept. of Commerce, Washington).

ULLMAN, Edward L., "Railroad Pattern of the United States," *Geographical Review,* Vol. 39 (1949), pp. 242-256.

WILSON, G. Lloyd, *Transportation and Communication* (New York, Appleton-Century-Crofts, Inc., 1954).

Part Two

GEOGRAPHIC REGIONS OF CONTINENTAL UNITED STATES

CHAPTER 6

NEW ENGLAND

INTRODUCTION

NEW ENGLAND has been one of the readily identified regions of the United States, physically and culturally. This stems in part from its situation and in part from the time and manner of settlement (*Fig.* 6-1). For 300 years New Englanders have by trial and error sought to make a living from their own land and from more distant lands. This was by no means a one-way relationship. The Atlantic seaboard colonies were for many years an "Imperial Frontier" for certain western European nations. Men, money, and institutions found opportunities for investment in the New World. The westward movement in the United States made possible the same sort of economic opportunity for the older settlements on the Atlantic seaboard, including New England. To an important degree, this relationship continues.

Land of Contradictions. Superficially, New England would appear to be a land of contradictions. It has often been termed a hard land; resistant geologically and hard economically, with both attributes merited in large measure. Over a long period of time, any region, no matter what its natural endowments may be, will have its resources appraised and reappraised, not only in terms of the physical abundance or niggardliness of nature, but also in terms of its human resources and its changing position with respect to national and international economic conditions.

In New England both agriculture and manufacturing are on the decline. The decline of the former is measured in terms of specific places and crops;

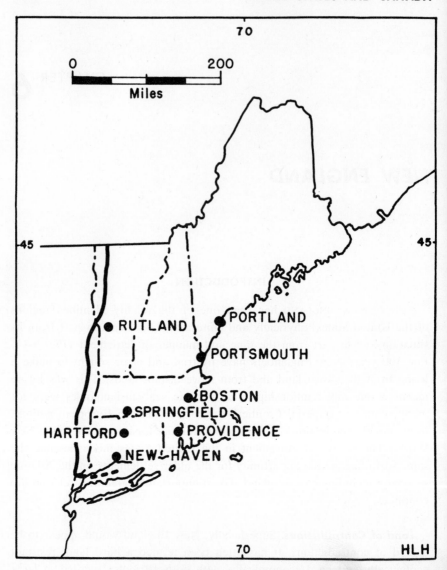

FIGURE 6-1: *New England*

the latter, in terms of particular concerns, and only occasionally as a considerable part of an entire industry. In many of the rural areas of the six New England states, the decline in population and in agricultural return has been at a decreasing rate for several decades. Even in the three northern states, life in the New England hills is staging a comeback, although manifestations of this revival are of a different nature.

Small Landscapes. New England has been described as a region of small landscapes. This might well be the keynote of a discussion of the area, for it is true of both the physical and the economic landscapes. These hills and valleys have over the years favored regional specialization both in agriculture and in manufacturing. An inspection of a physiographic map will reveal much that has profoundly affected the nature as well as the course of New England's economic development.[1]

LOWLANDS, HIGHLANDS, AND RIVERS

Lowlands. Significant in the life of this region have been the lowlands, which are here briefly sketched in their distribution and general characteristics. The coastal lowlands, which include the Boston Basin, the Narragansett Basin, the New Hampshire and Maine coastal lowlands, Cape Cod, and the Massachusetts islands, have become so associated with the life and times of New England as to require only a brief review here. Peripheral to the main block of the New England Upland, these lowlands have been attractive centers during the three centuries of white occupancy. Three-quarters of New England's population live on these narrow lowlands along the coast and in the Connecticut River Valley. The sandy flats of Cape Cod and the Massachusetts islands are of minor importance as population centers.

The attraction of these coastal lands has resulted not so much from extensive level and fertile areas, as from their situation adjacent to the mouths of the numerous rivers flowing generally southward from the upland, which makes up the major portion of New England.

Except for the Connecticut River Valley in its broad lower reaches, the interior lowlands of New England are not so densely populated as are the lowlands along the coast. The Champlain and Berkshire lowlands, and the remote Aroostook Valley in northern Maine have localized population in about that order of importance. Situation with respect to two of the three principal gateways to New England has given these interior lowlands economic advantages. With the Canadian provinces on the north and the northeast, the Atlantic on the east, the Hudson River, the Berkshires, and Lake Champlain on the west, there are only three feasible routes by which New England can be served by direct rail connections with the rest of the United States. These rail entries are by way of three natural corridors:

---

[1] Throughout this book frequent reference is made to A. K. Lobeck, *Physiographic Diagram of North America* (Geographical Press, Columbia University, New York, 1952). See also Erwin Raisz, *Landform Regions of United States,* and *Canada.* A student will do well to have these maps when studying this book.

the northern end of Lake Champlain, the northern end of the Berkshires, and the north shore of Long Island Sound.

Rugged Uplands. The physical backbone of New England is an ancient mountainous upland stretching from the Canadian border of Maine to the Hudson River highland. Though the northern and western sections are especially rugged, prolonged erosion by water and ice has reduced much of this former mountainous region to a subdued rolling hill country, above which rise the Green Mountains of Vermont, and White Mountains of New Hampshire, and such isolated hills as Monadnock, Greylock, and Katahdin.

Continental glaciation wrought notable changes in the terrain of New England. The highlands bore the brunt of glacial erosion; the lower areas to the south and east were mantled by the boulder-laden drift removed from the highlands.

Among these forested hills are found literally thousands of lakes of all sizes and degrees of attractiveness. The ice removed the soil in many places; in others it deposited so many boulders that cultivation is impossible. In the literature of the New England hill country reference is frequently made to "barrens"—a clearing in the woods where neither trees nor grass grew. Nearly everywhere the soil is thin and often poor, yet in many places the weathering of the glacial drift has yielded a soil which is suitable for agriculture.

Rivers. The derangement of New England's preglacial rivers by the ice made easy the development of water power during the first half of her industrial history. Waterfalls near the coast became the nuclei of early industrial centers, such as, Lowell, Lawrence, and Haverhill on the Merrimac River, and Pawtucket on the Blackstone. Although the streams of the northern New England upland have greater potential power, the accessibility of the lower courses of the Connecticut, Housatonic, Blackstone, and Merrimac, all below the 1,000-foot contour, has fostered more complete development.

Navigation on New England rivers is largely historical, although some traffic now moves on the lower Connecticut to Hartford, on the Thames to Norwich, on the Charles to Cambridge, on the Merrimac to Haverhill, on the Penobscot to Bangor, on the Kennebec to Augusta but only traffic in bulky materials, such as stone, sand, coal, and wood is in evidence today.

As land-trade routes the river valleys have lost little of their importance, for the modern, hard-surfaced roads have tended to follow them. The growth of rural population has been based in large part upon the increased accessibility of the New England rural dweller to the manufacturing cities and towns of the coastal lowlands, and this in turn has been made possible by cheap personal transportation by motor car. The key to the rejuvenation of life in New England's hills is the modern highway which makes it possible for the commuter to get to work quickly.

CLIMATE

Precipitation and Temperature. Reference to the climatic regions map in Chapter 2 will serve to orient the reader with respect to the climate of New England. Rainfall is a permissive factor in the New England environment as its amount and distribution make possible the production of practically all farm crops common to regions with similar temperature conditions. The average annual precipitation varies from 45 inches at places in the southern tier of states to 30 inches in the extreme north; a little more than half of it falls during the frost-free period. Extended droughts of a killing nature are not experienced.

Temperature is not so favorable to agriculture.[2] The growing season varies from something less than a hundred days in the three northern states to two hundred on the southern coast. The effect of altitude is clearly seen in the zoning of crops in the hill lands between the Champlain Lowland and the Aroostook Valley, where the direction of the slope is a decisive factor in land use.

Hazards of Climate. The lack of sunshine at haying time and occasional destructive hailstorms in the tobacco-growing areas of the lower Connecticut Valley are unfavorable features of the climate of New England.

Despite the relatively seasonal uniformity in the distribution of rainfall and the hundreds of natural reservoirs, floods which cause great damage and considerable loss of life occasionally occur in the spring. These floods are caused usually by the rapid melting of heavy snowfall at times of full streams. Snowfall of 100 inches has been known in the northern portions, although along the southern periphery it is not so heavy, averaging about 30 inches in Connecticut.

The three northern states lie north of the latitude of the Corn Belt, thus where corn is grown it must be for ensilage and not for grain. Although many crops are not regarded as commercially profitable in this latitude, potatoes, hay, clover, oats, and barley do mature here. The three southern

[2] P. W. Church, "A Geographical Study of New England Temperatures," *Geographical Review,* Vol. 26, No. 2 (April, 1936), pp. 283-292.

states produce corn in most sections and tobacco in the lower Connecticut Valley. Relief determines the length of growing season just as it does in the northern states. The "small landscapes" are matched by the related "micro-climates" of New England.

Favorable Aspects of Climate. The sale of New England's climate and scenery to tourists has been the region's most rapidly growing industry for several decades, and an examination of climate will reveal one reason for this phase of her economy. Because of the amount of snowfall in winter months, New England has been able to exploit the public's growing interest in winter sports. To her already large summer-tourist trade, drawn in part by mild summer temperatures, has been added a growing number of winter-sports enthusiasts, not only those who participate, but also the greater number who come for "atmosphere" and relaxation. The snow trains and ski trains, and the Dartmouth and Middlebury winter festivals have enjoyed growing popularity.

In traveling about the United States one hears comments from various localities, lauding the beauty of their autumn or their spring, as the case may be. The New Englander, perhaps not so articulate, thinks thus about all four seasons. More and more travelers share his enthusiasm and become transient guests of the province for winter sports, summer dwelling, or autumn coloring.

The relatively even distribution of precipitation has been a boon to the users of water power in New England. The thousands of glacier-formed ponds and lakes which serve as natural reservoirs also tend to minimize the fluctuation of stream levels.

The relation between the climate of New England and her extensive forests is a close one. Natural reforestation of the New England hills has been fostered by the withdrawal of man from many of the submarginal farms of the upland. Trees with a diameter of ten inches or more may be seen growing in the middle of a former secondary road, in the center of a tumble-down farmhouse, or in a formerly productive field. These climatically induced forest resources are a continuing asset to the region.

The hundreds of harbors of all sizes and degrees of importance are ice-free in winter (*Fig.* 6-2). Shipments of goods through New England ports the year round is ample evidence of the uninterrupted railroad service. Although highway maintenance is an expense not confined to these states, clearing the winter roads is a considerable task. If the owners of the many refurbished New England farmhouses were year-round dwellers rather than summer visitors, the demands for road service and schools would be greater.

FIGURE 6-2: *Boston*

Boston Harbor retains the same excellent physical features it has always had, but the port function has undergone a relative downward revision. The commerce through New England's port has failed to keep pace with that of Atlantic ports farther south. (American Air Lines, Inc.)

SOILS

Some aspects of the soils of New England are well known. Fiction writers perhaps have given more attention to these soils than to those of any other region in the United States. Their notoriety takes account of their reclamation from stones and boulders, of their thinness, of their passing from the hands of Yankees to foreign-born and sons of foreign-born. Surprisingly little is known of certain economic characteristics of these soils, that is, their importance to the man who buys them and to the state hoping to see them used for the ultimate advantage of society. Land that was valuable to one generation may be valueless to the next, with no decline of fertility, because more favorable supply centers have risen, or changes in consumption habits have lowered the prices of commodities which they are best fitted to produce.

As a result of abundant moisture, the entire region originally supported a forest. New England soils bear the expected relation to climate in a region where rainfall is relatively heavy and relatively uniform throughout the year, and where the evaporation rate is low even in summer.

A very large part of New England is covered with a thin, stony, light-textured soil which varies from a fine sandy loam to a silt loam. Nearly all soil groups are light in color and acid in reaction. In the northern forested section, the terrain in Maine is less mountainous than that of the other two states, and contains large areas of swamps. Conditions over much of New England have favored the development of the ashen, podzolic soils characteristic of the coniferous forest of the humid microthermal climates.

Intricate Soils Pattern. Here again the concept of small landscapes will apply to the pattern of New England's soils as well as to relief. The complexity of soil types arising from a variety of parent materials has been further complicated by glacial action. In judging the worth of the soils in New England, however, the physical and economic characteristics common to the major groups will suffice to outline their role in the several stages which have marked New England agriculture for the past century and a half.

Interior Lowland Soils. In small interior valleys and basins there are loams, varying in texture from a gravelly or sandy loam to a silt loam. In some places such soils are especially favorable for plant growth because of the presence of a particular mineral in the parent rock: lime in the western lowlands of Vermont, Massachusetts, and Connecticut, phosphatic material in the Aroostook Valley of northern Maine. The greater part of these soils is in good pasture.

Coastal Margin Soils. One of the densely populated soil provinces is the narrow strip of low sandy plain in southeastern Massachusetts. It is dotted with marshes and peat bogs, some of which are well adapted to cranberry culture. The lower Connecticut Valley has been so extensively enriched by alluvium and marine silts that it has become the principal agricultural district in all New England.

Mountain and Hill Soils. In the mountainous and hilly regions the soil is generally thin and bare rock is exposed in great patches, both on slopes and in the valleys. However, many of these slopes support an irregular pattern of fields from which fairly good crops were once harvested. The fertility has been exhausted generally and at present the yield is low. Many areas have been allowed to grow up in pasture or brush. The dairy industry has encouraged planting of forage crops in such regions.

POPULATION

Historical Changes. The contradictions mentioned as being characteristic of certain phases of New England's development are well exemplified in her population. Far from being a new *England,* today, it has the largest proportion of foreign-born of any part of the United States. Numerically it has more foreign-born residents than any but the Middle Atlantic and East North Central divisions. Although literature gives us a picture of the New England farmer as the typical inhabitant, he is in the minority as four-fifths of all the people are urban dwellers. Many New Englanders took a leading part in the peopling of the Middle and Far West; many more went to eastern cities. Abandonment of its farmland has been going on since 1850; yet today, its population is one of the densest in the nation: 142 persons per square mile, as against 53 for the United States as a whole.

Foreign-born. Not only does New England have a large proportion of foreign-born, but the percentage of New England foreign-born who are Canadians is six times that of the country as a whole. One out of every four of her foreign-born is Canadian, and half of these are French. Next in number are the Irish who are almost as numerous as the Canadians. The Italians are next, numbering only slightly less than the Irish. There are other stocks comprising the minor groups but they are neither so numerous nor so widely distributed as those named.

It is not enough to say that the proportion of foreign-born in the three southern states of New England is twice that of the three northern states. In the large cities of the former states they are found in very great numbers; for instance in 1950 they made up about 30 per cent of the population of the following cities: Fall River, Holyoke, New Bedford, New Britain, Woonsocket, Cambridge, Lowell, Bridgeport, Waterbury, Stamford, Pawtucket, Nashua, and Lewiston.

The type of New Englander associated with John G. Whittier and Sarah Orne Jewett is seldom encountered today because the foreign-born have found their way into even the remote areas of rural New England. Only about an eighth of all the people of foreign stock live in the three northern states, but nearly half the foreign-born farm population is in the north. The French in northern Maine, Vermont, and New Hampshire settled at the time of the Revolution. The small numbers found on farms in the southern states came down before the present century, usually to work in the textile mills. Italians are especially numerous on the farms of the lower Connecticut Valley and on the periphery of every city.

Distribution of Population. Within New England there are pronounced contrasts in the distribution of population. The contrast between the three northern and the three southern states is greater than between New England as a whole and the rest of the United States. The character of New

England's population is dominated by the three southern states which, with but one-fifth of the area, have four-fifths of the population. Population density in the northern group is only 34 inhabitants per square mile, whereas for the southern group it is 532. In the nation, Rhode Island ranks first, and Massachusetts and Connecticut rank third and fourth, respectively. All but four of the twenty-two New England cities with a population in excess of 50,000 are in the three southern states. These intra-New England contrasts in population are reflected in the regional character of her agriculture, manufacturing, fishing, and commerce.

TABLE 6-1: *Geographical Distribution of Population and Income in the United States, 1953*

	% total pop.	Population millions	% Increase pop. 1947-52	Income	% Nat. income
NEW ENGLAND [1]	6.1	9.5	5	$16.9	6.6
E. NO. CENTRAL	20.2	31.5	8	57.8	22.5
W. NO. CENTRAL	9.2	14.4	9	22.3	8.7
MID. ATLANTIC	22.3	34.7	8	66.4	25.8
SO. ATLANTIC	11.8	18.4	10	21.8	8.5
E. SO. CENTRAL	7.3	11.4	3	12.1	4.7
W. SO. CENTRAL	10.2	15.9	10	22.1	8.6
MOUNTAIN	3.	4.7	18	7.7	3.
PACIFIC	9.9	15.5	11	30.3	11.8

SOURCE: *Business Week,* Special Report, July 4, 1953.

[1] The Census geographic divisions comprise the following groups of states. New England—Maine, New Hampshire, Vermont, Connecticut, Massachusetts, and Rhode Island. East North Central—Ohio, Indiana, Illinois, Michigan, and Wisconsin. West North Central—Minnesota, Iowa, Missouri, North Dakota, South Dakota, Nebraska, and Kansas. Middle Atlantic—New York, Pennsylvania, and New Jersey. South Atlantic—Delaware, Maryland, West Virginia, Virginia, North Carolina, South Carolina and Georgia. East South Central—Kentucky, Tennessee, Mississippi and Alabama. West South Central—Arkansas, Louisiana, Texas and Oklahoma. Mountain—Montana, Idaho, Wyoming, Nevada, Utah, Colorado, New Mexico and Arizona. Pacific—Washington, Oregon, and California.

Population Movements. A review of the movement of population within New England and to points outside, unaccompanied by an explanation of the economic circumstances which attended them, would make the phenomenon seem bloodless and dispassionate. However, it seems wise to sketch the major aspects of the redistribution of New England's people before examining her agricultural and industrial economies.

The earliest population movement was caused by the attempt to occupy as much of their respective states as environmental conditions permitted and economic conditions warranted. The better lands of southern New England were more quickly occupied than the frontier areas to the north. The settling of the Connecticut Western Reserve in Ohio and the equally attractive portions of the upper Mississippi Valley began to make drains upon the population of these six states as early as 1850, but the abandonment of farmland in New England was not widespread before 1880. After 1880, New England had economic repercussions from these former citizens. As middle western farmers, they contributed to the production and export of an agricultural surplus which drove prices down, thus putting the New England farmer in a predicament from which he could extricate himself only by specialization or by migration. The migration slowed greatly after 1900, but only in specific districts did these hill lands show an increase in population.

The three northern states did not reach their maximum rural population until the period from 1850 to 1870. By 1880, 80 per cent of the towns in Vermont and 65 per cent of those in New Hampshire were declining in population; after 1900 the decline was at a decreasing rate. By 1930 only 64 per cent of the towns in Vermont were declining in population and only 49 per cent in New Hampshire. In the three southern states between 1840 and 1870 wage earners in agriculture decreased 40 per cent, while in industry the number increased 288 per cent.

The trans-Appalachian country was by no means the only attraction for New England farmers and townspeople. The rise of manufacturing in southern New England attracted and depended upon the labor of thousands of rural dwellers who sought an easier life. This has gone on for more than a century.

FORESTS IN THE NEW ENGLAND ECONOMY

Forests, a Mainstay. Along with water power, forests have always been one of the mainstays of New England's economy. Both have been stabilizing forces in industry and, along with other environmental factors, each has left its impress on at least one period in the economic life of these states. In nearly every section of New England, income from forest products has enabled farmers to pursue their subsistence agriculture and has constituted the major source for cash for scores of small towns and villages. Indirectly, the forest wealth of New England has been a force in freeing much of the area from the blight of isolation.

Relation to Maritime Activities. With the rise of the fishing industry and the temptation for New England men to take to the sea rather than struggle with their boulder-strewn fields, timber resources assumed a predominant position. Fishing led to an even greater use of wood in commercial shipping and shipbuilding. So far as this trade was concerned, the Napoleonic wars in Europe were very propitious. Commerce, logically and rather promptly, stimulated manufacturing, and New England's workshops supplied the local market and provided many of the products required by the emigrants who soon were to become a part of the westward migration. A foreign market hungry for timber and fish could also use the fabricated products of New England.

Farmland to Woodland. Reversion of farmland to woodland started just before the Civil War. About half of the privately-owned woodland in New England is in natural or improved wood lots and cut-over land with young growth. The Forest Service estimates that there is 15 per cent more forest land now than in 1860. It is a commentary on the woodland situation that, although New England has about 6 per cent of the total forest land in the United States, the area has a scant 2 per cent of the nation's stand of sawtimber. Seven-eighths of the original stand is gone.

Nearly 70 per cent of the area of New England is classed as woodland; although the bulk of this in in the three northern states, the three southern states have nearly half of their area in woodland, despite the density of population. Figures alone will not express the relative value of woodland in these two regions. In addition to quantity, the quality, accessibility, character of ownership, and potential uses of woodland areas for purposes other than industrial raw material, determine their value. The northern uplands contain by far the greater proportion of merchantable timber, probably 75 per cent.

Northern Forests. The northern forests produce the greater part of the pulpwood credited to New England. They support many large industrial establishments using wood, some of which own and systematically cut their renewing resource of timber. These forests are primarily in the belt of spruce, balsam fir, and northern hardwoods. Most of these northern forests which were at all accessible, were cut over in the early days for the pine and spruce, leaving the bulk of the hardwoods standing. White pine cut reached its peak in 1840, and the stand was nearly exhausted by 1870. With the re-establishment of the forest, it was cut over again. The most recent cutting for pulpwood has reduced the softwood stand to small diameter stock. The cuttings have not been uniform, but the greater part of the northern forest has substantially undergone this exploitation. Hardwoods have been left standing, especially in Maine, constituting an excellent forest cover predominantly deciduous in character.[3]

[3] For an account of the northern lumbering industry, see *Kennebec,* by R. P. T. Coffin (New York, Farrar and Rinehart, Inc., 1932).

Southern Forests. In the southern tier of states the forests are checkered with farms and villages. Most of the timber is owned by the small land holders. Hardwoods predominate and forests generally occupy the poorer soils and steeper slopes which, found unfit for cropping, have been allowed to revert to woodland. Because of their greater accessibility, the forests have long supplied the smaller industries with wood, and the farmers them-selves have cut some for use on the farm or for sale. For the most part, the forests have not been cut with a view toward forest maintenance, so today the trees are generally inferior and progressively deteriorating. It is in the southern states, however, that the recreation industry is most actively pro-moting the conservation of the remaining timber.

Forest Depletion. At the present time a great deal of timber enters New England from the virgin forests of the South and the Pacific Northwest at prices competitive with those of local producers. This increasing depend-ence upon imported wood is due partly to the ease with which great wood-using industries have been able to turn to other regions. However, the continued existence of the numerous but small industries depending directly upon nearby lumbering operations is out of the question. New England's lumbering industry is virtually gone from the land. The Census reports that since 1910 all lumber production decreased 65 per cent; that the number of wage earners decreased by 56 per cent; and that the total value of prod-ucts declined 44 per cent. These figures pertain only to the lumber industry and the industries directly connected with the further fabrication of the products of the sawmill, but there are other aspects of timberland as a re-source which require attention.

Wood Industries. Cutting spruce and other softwood for pulpwood began about 1890 and reached its peak just before World War I. In recent years it has fallen off, until now it is estimated that not more than half of the consumption of New England mills is from local sources.

On many of the northern upland farms a substantial part (20 per cent or more) of the income is from the sale of wood in some form, perhaps as logs for the sawmill, highway guard rails and bridge timbers, or is derived from maple sugar and syrup. Possibly the farmer can make some money in off seasons by renting his teams for use in the lumbering operations. This income makes it possible to carry on low-profit farming operations which could not be carried on otherwise.

New Englanders have learned by experience what this asset of forest land is really worth. New England forests were profitable during the exploitive stage. However, in contrast to the situation in the upper Great Lakes district and the Pacific Northwest, the forests were cut off to permit agriculture. Both the agriculture and the lumbering prospered so long as the exploitation of first-rate timber could continue; but both languished when, rather than take the second-best or reforest, New England industries bought timber from virgin areas in the South and West. It appears, therefore, that the rate at which New England farmers reforest their submarginal crop land and waste land is dependent, not so much upon the quantity or quality of her own forested land, as upon the rate of depletion of competing virgin forests elsewhere in the United States. The chief problem is the hazard of waiting for the timber to mature that must run the gauntlet of fires, taxes, and finally market. The New England Forestry Foundation deplores "clear cutting" which has contributed to the decline of the saw-timber reserve. Only 58 billion board feet reportedly is standing on New England's 31 million acres of woodland; most of her timberland has not recovered sufficiently to yield the 5,000 board feet per acre deemed the minimum for commercial use.

Progress is being made but not fast enough for full assurance that New England's future forest economy will keep pace with its needs. Forest resource management faces the fact that forest operations in these six states are small, most of them so small as to constitute the basic problem in forest management and conservation. Authorities tell us that growing trees is not enough; there is also much to be done in the way of improved handling and processing of the timber after it is grown.

Tourism. Meanwhile attempts to incorporate the forest into the economy of the New England farms by way of the tourist trade gives much promise. This may be the ultimate forest-use for much of New England. Aided by federal, state, and town purchases of forest preserves, the New England farmer allows more and more of his fields to grow into woodland.

A metropolitan Sunday supplement carries photographs of people skiing in Tuckerman Ravine on the southeastern slope of Mt. Washington. This is the heart of a 700,000 acre national forest area, which the federal government is gradually developing for the growing army of winter-sports enthusiasts. This great snowbowl, which owes its shape to glacial sculpture, holds a perfect surface of "corn" snow, ideal for skiing. This is but one of the meccas for which many thousands entrain from the principal New England and Middle Atlantic cities every winter. Be they participants or onlookers, the economic result is the same upon the railroads, the filling stations, and those who cater to their wants at the scene of their sport. It is a revival in the very parts of the upland most in need of it. Directly and indirectly these New England forest lands now may, and in many instances do, support more people better than was possible when lumbering was in its heyday.

But wintertime recreation by no means dominates the New England tourist industry. The practice of taking "paying guests" during the summer months is most important. Whereas the winter sports are localized at favored districts, the ubiquitous summer tourist knows no metes nor bounds save accessibility by highway. Forests, lakes, and the seacoast have served to make the recreation industry the greatest source of revenue of all in New England.

FISHING INDUSTRY

Favorable Factors. On the broad continental shelf which extends along the eastern margin of North America, the water is relatively shallow and cold. The minute floating plant and animal life of the ocean is very abundant in the cool waters of the Labrador Current which flows southward along this coast. Upon these tiny plants feed minute floating animals which form the principal food for small fish, which are eaten by larger fish. The shallow water supports an abundant plant life where light is able to penetrate.

Flowing northeastward along the Atlantic Coast is the Gulf Stream, a warm water current. Where the cold and warm currents mix, the plankton animals of the cold water meet the plankton plants of the warm water and provide one of the world's great fishing grounds. The men who fish these waters tend to become specialists in one or more kinds of fish, a consequence of the fact that cold waters tend to support great numbers of relatively few kinds of fish. Of the 80 species of edible fish found in these waters, the bulk of the commercial catch comprises haddock, redfish, flounder, cod, whiting, pollock, mackerel, and hake. These varieties constitute year-round harvest.

The relatively inhospitable agricultural lands which border the North Atlantic make fish a comparatively attractive resource. The hundreds of natural harbors along this coast and a nucleus of seafaring people have promoted a great fishing industry. For more than two hundred years the fishing industry operated from scores of harbors along this coast, from Labrador to Chesapeake Bay. Despite the existence of conditions that are favorable to the industry, New England has had its troubles in fishing.

Competition with other countries and the decline in the fish population are most serious. The longer runs necessary to secure desirable varieties and the rising cost of a day's run, have hurt several ports, particularly Boston (*Fig.* 6-2).

In the main the New England fishing industry is tariff-protected. World War II aggravated the problems of the industry by increasing the market and in consequence the filleting and freezing facilities of eastern Canada. Postwar imports of Canadian fish products reached an all-time high.

TABLE 6-2: Facilities and Employment in the New England Fishing Industry, 1949, Major Ports

Port	Number of vessels	Number of fishermen	Number of processing plants	Number of shore workers	Number of freezing plants
BOSTON	89	1000	55	2000	11
GLOUCESTER	248	2000	21	2300	6
NEW BEDFORD	208	1400	31	1200	3
PORTLAND	41	246	6	788	4

SOURCE: *Monthly Review*, Federal Reserve Bank of Boston, Vol. 32, No. 3, March, 1950.

In 1951 New England's fishing industry accounted for about 23 per cent of the nation's output of fish products. Boston, Gloucester, New Bedford and Portland turned out nearly all of the region's packaged-fish product. They landed about two-thirds of the weight and five-sixths of the value of all fish brought into New England's ports. The catch by states: Maine $14,988,000, New Hampshire $169,000, Massachusetts, $38,991,000, Rhode Island $2,229,000, Connecticut $2,157,000.

Ports. The Boston Fish Pier was the scene of the modern expansion of the fresh and frozen fish industry (*Fig.* 6-3). Improvements in the fishing technique and equipment, the filleting process, and the quick freezing process all redounded to Boston's advantage. Subsequent troubles have led to the integration of Boston's boat-owning and fishing interests; this has tended to make fishing more responsive to market conditions, particularly for haddock, Boston's principal fish. This city's relative specialization in haddock and cod proved to be something of a handicap when new varieties attained popularity.

Gloucester for years was the salt fish center of the world. Three-fourths of its population depended directly or indirectly upon the fishing industry. Foreign competition finally priced Gloucester out of the salt fish market.

FIGURE 6-3: *Fish Market, Boston*

Boston is the major port for New England fishing. (Fairchild Aerial Surveys, Inc.)

The once-discarded redfish found favor in United States' markets and has been the basis of Gloucester's comeback. In 1949 its 25,000 people were again able to surpass Boston in the volume of the catch and led all New England as a producer of food fish.

New Bedford, an old whaling port, has been a relative newcomer to New England fishing ports. Nine-tenths of the nation's catch of sea scallop comes to this port where storage and freezing capacity have greatly increased. Portland and Rockland have shared in the increase in redfish catch and preparation, although neither compares in importance with Gloucester.

Problems. After World War II the well-being of the New England fishing industry and its principal fishing ports declined. Greater investment in equipment, boats, longer trips, processing machinery, and a lethargic market have not been potent against imports from the Canadian Maritimes. Higher wages, declining fish population, internal conflicts between labor and management, and lack of a conservation program for the industry have combined to make the New England fishing industry vulnerable to the efforts of Canada, Iceland, and other northern fishing countries to exploit the United States market.

AGRICULTURE: GENERAL ASPECTS

Self-Containment. Although overshadowed by the manufacturing industries, agriculture in New England merits careful examination if for no other reason than that it is essentially self-contained. The relationship between the farms and the 20 million people within a hundred miles of Connecticut is not the same as that prevailing in the lower Lakes region and the Ohio Valley. New England farms do not supply any considerable part of the raw materials consumed by her factories, nor do they consume much of their output.

Changing Patterns of Land Use. Less than a quarter of the total land surface of these states is now in farms, and only a little over a third of this portion is classified as improved land used for crops and plowable pasture. Although the peak of land abandonment has long passed, Vermont, with the largest proportion of cropland in the northern group, reports decreases in her number of farms as follows: in comparison with each preceding Census period, the state had one per cent fewer farms in 1910, 11 per cent in 1920, and 27 per cent in 1930. Despite these data, agriculture has been experiencing some growth since World War II.

This seeming anomaly is explained by somewhat larger size of individual farms as mechanization and specialization proceed.[4] Rural living has been integrated with industrial employment. Part-time farms of several types have become commonplace in New England. The bulk of the farm market, however, remains within New England, three or four products to the contrary, notwithstanding.

AGRICULTURE IN NORTHERN NEW ENGLAND

Upland Areas. The altitude and interior location give to the northern uplands a shorter growing season than that in eastern and southern New England. Snowfall is heavier than along the coast or even on the Laurentian Upland northwest of the St. Lawrence River. Parts of the region have never made any attempt at commercial agriculture, such as one-third of northern Maine, which is virtually unoccupied. Subsistence farming together with the proceeds from the sale of wood products supports a sparse population on these extensive hilly areas. There has been no attempt at what might be called a self-contained mountain economy, although the fine

---

[4] Vermont: number of farms, 1935, was 27,061; in 1950 it was 19,043; acreage in farms, 1935, was 4,053,000; in 1950 it was 3,527,000. *Statistical Abstract, 1952,* p. 574.

balance required of the people who try to make a living here is suggestive of mountains. Maple sugar and syrup have given this region a reputation, but little income.

Although the commercial timber of these upland hills is depleted, pulp mills are supported in all three states by systematic cutting from planned reforestation areas. The mills have made possible the same sort of part-time subsistence farming that existed when the virgin timber was being cut. These conditions exist in all three states, but not to the same extent. Vermont agriculture has long fared better than that of New Hampshire or Maine. A greater degree of accessibility is the main difference, but somewhat better soils and superior pasture have been contributing factors. Corn and oats are grown for ensilage, but root crops and hay are likewise used for dairy feed during the indoor winter feeding. City markets are accessible by truck and rail, so the intensification and the fitting of the crops to the soil and climate have been possible because of income from dairy products. This opportunity is denied most of the farmers in the two eastern states of this upland.

Aroostook County. There are two districts that may be termed purely agricultural. One is the potato region of Aroostook County in northern Maine which extends from Houlton to Fort Kent, with its center at Presque Isle and Caribou. It lies in the rolling hill country of the Aroostook, Allegash, and St. John River valleys. While the ordinary farm raises from thirty to fifty acres of potatoes, it is not uncommon to find farms operating a thousand acres of land of which nearly half will be in potatoes. Originally this northern agricultural district grew potatoes in order to make starch which was sold to New England cotton textile mills. In later years the much higher yield (as compared with other potato districts) induced more and more farmers to specialize in potatoes; in 1951 just 90 per cent of the farm income was from the potato crop. The question is often asked, Is this specialization in potatoes an element of strength or of weakness in the districts' economy? The answer seems to lie in the increasing diversity of crops which is discernable. In 1940 Maine had 182,000 acres in potatoes; in 1951, it was 103,000. For the same years the total crop was 59,654,000 bushels and 45,835,000. Meanwhile all cattle, dairy cows, and hogs had increased somewhat.

Champlain Lowland. The other purely agricultural district is the western lowland of Vermont. The Champlain lowland is an extension of the St. Lawrence lowland, and in common with it, is generally covered with clay loam or clay soils of dark color. North of Burlington the soil is underlaid with limestone, and hay and clover grow abundantly. The tempering effect of

Lake Champlain makes possible the growing of corn for ensilage, and a silo is almost as common as a barn in the farm landscape. The major advantages of this lowland are the absence of stones and boulders, and the presence of low relief which permits fields and farms of ample size. Accessibility to fresh milk markets enables the farmers to take advantage of the natural factors favoring dairying. The co-operative creameries and milk plants of Vermont, however, have been hard pressed since 1928 to retain their market for cream, in the face of competition with lower Lakes states.

Specialty Areas. The future of agriculture in these northern states seems to be foreshadowed by what has taken place thus far. Frequently several small farms are operated under a single management. The potato economy persists, although turkeys, peas, dairy products, vegetables, and small grains are increasing in importance.

In addition to the Aroostook and Champlain agricultural areas, there are a number of smaller agricultural districts on the upland of New England where specialized farming merits attention. Blueberry farming in Maine is localized along the coast from Penobscot Bay to Eastport. Such holdings vary from a few acres owned by a fisherman, shopkeeper, or general farmer, to relatively large tracts. The berries are picked by men, women, and children who specialize in the work year after year. Blueberry farming in Maine, however, is not so much a type of farming as an annual exploitation of a wild crop.

Elsewhere the salvation of upland farming appears to rest on the degree of success attained in combining part-time farming with supplying the pulp mills, selling other wood products, boarding and entertaining tourists, and increasing the number of residence farms occupied by wage earners in industries within commuting distance.

AGRICULTURE IN SOUTHERN NEW ENGLAND

Contrasts with Northern Upland. Southern New England on the other hand, contrasts in most respects with this northern upland, with perhaps the minimum of tangible physical differences to account for this. There is little abandoned farm land in these states, yet marginal and submarginal land forms a considerable part of the landscape. This is the New England with which most of us are reasonably familiar.

Like the northern upland, the southern portion is also largely a dairying region, but with marked differences in its other farm activities. Perhaps the major difference is the greater importance of part-time farming in the southern region. Tobacco, sweet corn, apples, potatoes, eggs and chickens, and miscellaneous fruits and vegetables all lend themselves to part-time interests. The proximity of much of the southern upland to industrial centers promotes residence-farming and recreation-farming.

Connecticut Valley. The largest and the most important agricultural region in all New England is the Connecticut Valley (*Fig.* 6-4). For three centuries New Englanders have farmed this north-south trending valley which, in its economy, reflects the transition between the agriculture of the far northern countries to the broad fertile plain nearly 400 miles south. Not quite half of this valley is in farmland.

A fourth of all farm income in the six New England states is from the Connecticut Valley. For 1952 the 10,000 farms in the Massachusetts and Connecticut portions of the Connecticut Valley returned an agricultural income of $85 million, and the 12,000 farms in the New Hampshire and Vermont portion returned $40 million.[5] In the narrow northern half of this valley, the more generally self-sufficing agriculture has dairying as the principal specialty; other sources of income include poultry, maple sugar, and summer guests.

Farther south in the valley, tobacco, potatoes, onions and truck crops, poultry, and small fruits are produced. Generally, on these farms of the lower valley, the tobacco is grown on the more productive and level lower lands. On the more distant and hilly valley land, which lies beyond these river farms, more attention is given to potatoes, dairying, and poultry. In view of the presence of many industrialized cities of the lower valley, the production of truck crops, with its heavy labor demands, seems out of order. Tobacco, particularly, requires much labor. This crop is grown in a small district in Connecticut and Massachusetts, much of it under the shade of a type of cheesecloth. By means of this device growing conditions similar to those in Sumatra are achieved and wrapper leaf is successfully grown. Ten large corporations grow most of this shade tobacco, bringing in labor from Puerto Rico and from schools; some 15,000 seasonal workers are thus brought in to supplement the 5,000 year-round workers native to the district.[6]

For the most part Havana seedleaf tobacco is raised in Massachusetts, broadleaf tobacco on the east side of the river in Connecticut, and both

[5] *Monthly Review,* Federal Reserve Bank, Boston, November, 1953.

[6] This is the first agricultural region dependent upon outside labor thus far studied in this book; others will be referred to later. For the economic and social implications of this see *Migratory Labor in the United States,* (Report to the President, Washington, 1952).

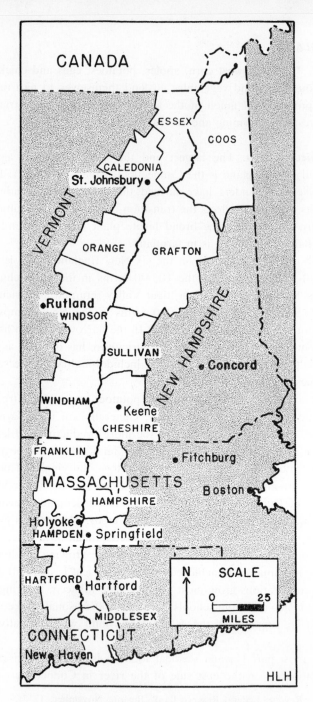

FiGURE 6-4: Connecticut River Valley

This is the agricultural heart of New England. Over expansion of tobacco production is being adjusted in part through the loss of fertile acres to industrial sites and urban development. It is one of the most highly industrialized areas of New England. Twenty-two of its 29 municipalities had a population increase of at least 20 per cent between 1940 and 1950; 18 had increases of 30 per cent or more. New England as a whole failed to hold its own in the nation's growth since 1950.

varieties on the west side in Connecticut. Most of the shade tobacco is grown in Hartford County, Connecticut. Although this tobacco is manufactured locally, the supply is greater than the local demand and the surplus leaf is exported regularly.

This same Hartford County in Connecticut, with Hampshire County to the north, also raises an important acreage of potatoes. These two counties raise half of the potato crop in the entire valley. The remaining acreage is scattered, with acre-yields generally about two-thirds that of Maine's Aroostook County where 475 bushels per acre is the average. However, the relatively stoneless soils of the lower Connecticut Valley permit the use of machinery in harvesting the potato crop, whereas Maine must still use much hand labor. The potato barns and root cellars which are common in Aroostook County are not generally found in the Connecticut Valley where most of the crop is marketed before winter.

Onions have been a specialty in the valley for many years, most of them grown in Franklin and Hampshire counties, Massachusetts. Since 1940, however, production of this crop has been curtailed by about 80 per cent, owing largely to the increased price of labor and to the ravages of a crop pest. Other truck crops are grown in the lower valley for the nearby large urban markets. Fruit is important only in Franklin County, Massachusetts (apples), and in Hartford County, Connecticut (apples and pears).

Dairying is an important source of farm income in virtually every county both north and south. The milk is sold fresh for the most part, but during the spring and early summer months, when yields are greater, the surplus milk is converted into dairy products.

Other Agricultural Specialty Districts. The cranberry-producing regions of southeastern Massachusetts are interspersed among the barren soils of Plymouth and Barnstable counties, and on the islands of Martha's Vineyard and Nantucket. There are two areas of concentration, one about the communities of Wareham and Carver in Plymouth County, the other at Harwich and Brewster on Cape Cod (*Fig. 6-5*).

Cultivation of the cranberry requires intensive preparation of the soil, including sanding of the bogs and control of the water to permit flooding at critical frost periods. The most important labor requirement is for harvesting, for which experienced hands must be used. Despite these requirements, mechanization is making inroads in the cranberry industry, particularly on the larger plantations.

Sweet corn is grown in a number of communities in southern Maine.

FIGURE 6-5: *Cranberry Bog, Cape Cod*

Stoop labor continues to be dominant in New England cranberry bogs. Note the large wooden scoop used in harvesting the berries. Cape Cod produces about two-thirds of the nation's crop. This is one reason for the relatively high cash receipts per acre of cropland and pasture in southern New England. (New England Council)

The cool summers keep the corn in the milk stage much longer than is possible in Ohio or Indiana where summers normally are warmer, thus reducing the speculative element in this crop. Field corn does not mature for grain in Maine, so sweet corn is a cash crop grown for the canneries and the fodder is used in silos.

Poultry farming is one of the most important specialties. It is often found in part-time farming combinations. Even in the fertile Connecticut Valley poultry is important throughout its length, generally most common to the foothills remote from the river. This region alone produced in 1952 some $17 million in poultry products, about half being from eggs.

The newest aspect of the New England poultry industry is the production of broilers for market. High meat prices and nationwide shortages of beef and pork during and since World War II gave this industry its start here; the per capita consumption of broilers increased by 50 per cent during the war years. Eastern Connecticut poultry men initiated the industry, but Maine led all New England in 1951 with a total of 21 million broilers most of which were produced in the Waldo County area. New Hampshire, Vermont, Rhode Island, and Massachusetts also share in this industry but on a smaller scale.[7]

Vegetable growing is a part of the farm economy in many New England communities. Small areas of specialized production are springing up in many places where good roads and the motor truck have opened up markets. The market garden of the horse-and-buggy days is being eased out of the picture by an intensified vegetable industry organized to serve the growing urban markets. The typical vegetable farm is not the specialized producer, but rather a small farm growing a variety of vegetables from the earliest to the latest, and employing besides the members of the family, one or more men the year round and a dozen or more during the rush months. Most of the itinerant workers speak English. Their quarters are generally little more than shelters. Just how much specialization within this industry can take place in New England is dependent upon many factors, over some of which New England has little or no control.

As with other commodities on New England farms, co-operative organizations have been formed to standardize the grades and aid in marketing the vegetables. The co-operative movement has achieved success among the asparagus growers about Concord, the market gardeners at Dighton, and the cranberry growers on Cape Cod.

BIBLIOGRAPHY

See bibliography at end of Chapter 7.

[7] The Boston Federal Reserve *Monthly Review* notes that the municipally-owned Belfast and Moosehead Railroad, running the 33 miles from Burnham Junction to Belfast in Waldo County, Maine, in 1945 hauled 796 carlots of poultry and animal feed; in 1951 it hauled 2,447 carlots, representing 50 per cent of its freight revenue.

MANUFACTURING IN
NEW ENGLAND

ANTECEDENTS OF MANUFACTURING

IT IS NO overstatement to say that the New England states constitute a manufacturing region, if it is understood that the term does not imply regional uniformity. Manufacturing industries are by no means common to all parts of the large area, but in terms of livelihood no more descriptive term can be used.

Persistence of Manufacturing. The amazing thing about New England has been the persistence of its industrial importance. It transcends all other aspects of the economy. Despite the many changes in transportation, in sources of industrial raw materials, shifting population, and changing markets, New England has remained one of the three most important industrial areas in the United States. Every phase of the American industrial evolution has been reflected in the economy of New England.

TABLE 7-1: New England Production: Agriculture and Manufacturing, 1950

($1 million)

Value of farm marketing	State	Value added by manufacturing
182	MAINE	407
64	NEW HAMPSHIRE	310
106	VERMONT	151
183	MASSACHUSETTS	3,200
23	RHODE ISLAND	564
156	CONNECTICUT	1,000

SOURCE: Bureau of the Census.

FIGURE 7-1: *Granite Quarry, near Barre, Vermont.*
(Rock of Ages Corp.)

Sequence of Economies. From the preceding chapter it is apparent that New England's manufacturing did not develop as a means of livelihood apart and distinct from her agriculture. On the surface, agriculture-industry relations appear weak indeed; New England farms produced but little in the way of raw materials for manufacturing and consumed but a minor part of the factory products. This was in contrast with factory beginnings in the trans-Appalachian west. Equally uninviting was the situation with respect to mineral raw materials; there was almost no metal and no coal; only wood, stone, and water. Yet from this environment New England has risen to an important position in the nation's manufacturing, a phenomenon which suggests an intriguing study in economic geography.

Handicapped in farming by relatively unfavorable land and climatic environment, New England turned to the sea. The Grand Banks off Nova Scotia offered a fishing region, approximately as large as Pennsylvania, and accessible from the scores of good harbors along the New England coast. The embayed coastline with many safe harbors, a gently sloping ocean floor, a broad continental shelf averaging less than sixty fathoms deep on which are a score of offshore fishing banks, and inland a wealth of lakes and streams suited to fish—all promoted fishing as a livelihood. Without these advantages there would have been meager profits in the carrying trade. These widely traveled men of the sea found markets and materials for New England's manufactured goods.

England's Attitude. The attitude of old England, in its policy of repression of manufactures in the New World, probably contributed directly to the rise of industry in the New England colonies. The emigration of trained operatives, the export of machinery and tools, and the export of machine designs all were prohibited after 1765. The War of 1812 stimulated manufacturing in New England by preventing the importation of factory goods and creating a wartime demand.

Dependence Upon Trade. Today the industrial structure of New England, having outgrown and supplanted the shipping and trading activities of earlier years, is yet dependent upon, and conditioned by, foreign trade as in few other industrial areas in the United States. No longer the mainstay of New England's economic life, foreign trade nevertheless is one of the fundamental supports of manufacturing, and its importance in this regard appears to be increasing.

Imported Raw Materials. Industrial New England is largely dependent upon outside materials. This is so partly because the local resources are exceedingly limited; partly because so many of the industries, originally founded on imports, still depend upon them; partly because any highly industrialized region, such as this one, must draw upon a widening circle of imports to meet the complex and exacting needs of modern manufacturing.

With manufacturing so largely based on the use of imported raw materials, imports have come to acquire an industrial character. For some of New England's manufacturing, this trade association has become of paramount locational significance.

STABILIZING FACTORS

Interdependence of Region and Factory. Out of the early start, in which commerce played so great a part, there arose certain advantages which have had a potent effect upon the subsequent development of the manufacturing industries. At least two of them have been cumulative in their influence. The first is the establishment of manufacturing centers and the trade routes which serve them in which the manufacturer himself, his labor, the railways or waterways which move his materials in and his products out, and the stores, banks, and even the good will of the community all set to work to make greater the advantages of a particular location. The interdependence of the region and the plant are recognized by the several groups of people concerned, and each group in its own way tries to make this manufacturing plant a permanent thing, thereby establishing to a considerable degree its own economic conditions. There are cases on record of New England communities actively sacrificing in various ways for the purpose of continuing a plant in operation. Early start may also give rise to the association of quality of products with the name of a company or the place of manufacture.

Human Factor. A second cumulative advantage to New England manufacturing has been the development of trained labor, some of it skilled. Association with skilled labor has been an industrial location factor. Community attachments for skilled laborers are often more substantial than for unskilled. Although most older industrial plants are said to have been located by chance, the fortuitous factor has a way of becoming rational when both factory and community co-operate in improving upon its regional bonds.

Manufacturing everywhere is dependent upon people for management, labor, and market. Manufactured products embody a great deal of labor, the amount varying with the type of commodity. The highly processed nature of New England's manufactures and the above-average dependence upon human labor are indicated by an appraisal of the several aspects of the manufacturing function. For instance, with but 6 per cent of the nation's population, New England has about 10 per cent of the wage earners and 11 per cent of the wages paid, yet has to buy only an estimated 7 per cent of the nation's total factory raw materials. Thus to a somewhat greater extent than other comparable areas, New England's factory products represent a high proportion of human services.

UPROOTING FORCES

In its development, New England has been subject to influences which tend to uproot industry as well as those which tend to hold it. Some of these factors continue to operate; thus there has been a continuing give-and-take, which has modified her industrial landscape. Among the uprooting forces, one of the most important is market. The westward movement of people away from the Atlantic seaboard usually placed New England producers at a disadvantage. Another is the mechanization of manufacturing which in certain instances nullified the advantage of trained labor in New England.

The size of water-power sites usually became inadequate as the factory units became larger. Introduction of new sources of power placed these states at a disadvantage. The junior senator from Massachusetts has recently stated that this is a most important factor in New England's loss of textile manufacture to the eastern South.

Coal, directly or indirectly, accounts for some 86 per cent of New England's industrial power needs. Annual importation of coal is approximately 30 million tons, nearly all of it from the Appalachian bituminous fields. This supplements the power developed on the lower Connecticut River, the Housatonic, Blackstone, Charles, Merrimack and the smaller Kennebec, Saco, Androscoggin, and Penobscot rivers. Although the use of coal has been something of an uprooting force in New England, manufacturing continues to be important at these river-power sites.

COTTON TEXTILE MANUFACTURING

It is, perhaps, understandable that the average person thinks of New England's manufacturing as textiles, primarily. Doubtless more columns of copy in the big eastern newspapers have been concerned with the problems of the textile industries than with the affairs of any or all of the other industries found there. As a matter of fact, the number of wage earners directly dependent upon textiles, or their closely related industries, is somewhat greater than that for any other group of industries in New England. However, the value added by, and the total income from, the manufacturing process is greater for items fashioned from metals than from all textiles. Metals, textiles, leather, and rubber constitute nearly three-fourths of all New England's industry.

Pioneers. Samuel Slater and a Providence financier began the manufacture of cotton at Pawtucket, Rhode Island, in 1790 (*Fig.* 7-2). The first complete cotton spinning and weaving mill in America was put in operation in 1813 at a waterfall on the Charles River near Waltham, Massachusetts. A decade later the power needs of more modern machines made this site inadequate, with the result that the more abundant power at the site of Lowell on the Merrimack superseded it. Shortly afterwards, mills at Lawrence, Manchester, and Nashua manufactured cotton at sites along the Merrimack. Within a few years Saco, Biddeford, and Lewiston in Maine had cotton mills. The Hadley Falls dam on the Connecticut River was instrumental in the development of Holyoke, founded as a cotton town but now better known for the manufacture of paper.

Introduction of Steam Power. Up to 1850 water power dominated New England's industrial needs, particularly in textile manufacturing. By 1870 steam-powered textile mills were being erected along the coast, using coal from the middle Appalachian fields. These new coastal centers included Newburyport, Salem, and Portsmouth in the north, and Newport, Bristol, and Warren in the south.

From the first venture of seventy-two spindles in 1790, the industry expanded during the ensuing century and a half to 1,600 establishments with more than 34 million active spindles. So far as New England is concerned, the location of cotton manufacture has changed but little, despite the changed source of power and the improvement in techniques. Industrially the two cotton manufacturing districts have remained distinct. The northern cities have larger mills and make standardized fabrics; while the southern group, centering in the Blackstone Valley, and in smaller and more numerous units, make somewhat higher grade textiles.

Distribution of Mills. Although the textile industry is important in every state in New England except Vermont, the principal centers are in Rhode Island, eastern Massachusetts, and southeastern New Hampshire. Approxi-

FIGURE 7-2: Cotton Mill, Pawtucket, Rhode Island

The first successful cotton textile mill in the United States is now a museum. The company operates today at Slaterville, North Carolina. Not far south of this old mill is a new industrial development bordering the Sound, with modern, one-story buildings and devoted primarily to metals manufacture. (Rhode Island Development Council)

mately 75 per cent of the wage earners and 90 per cent of the establishments are in Rhode Island and Massachusetts. The concentration of mills found in these areas is not characteristic of southern Piedmont mills; a much more open pattern of mill distribution obtains.

Bristol County, Massachusetts, and Providence County, Rhode Island, two highly specialized cotton districts, have half the total active cotton spindles in all New England. Here are located Fall River, New Bedford, Pawtucket, Taunton, and Woonsocket, all-time important names in United States cotton manufacturing. A third of the spindles are farther north in the lower Merrimack Valley. Lowell, Lawrence, Manchester, and Nashua, while dominant cotton cities in the past, are declining in importance today.

New England cotton manufacturing felt the effect of many changes and adjustments incidental to the extension of this local industry to other sections of the country in the 1880's. The extent to which an industry is geographically bound to the sources of its raw materials depends largely upon the loss of weight experienced in the process of manufacture. The loss of weight in ginning raw cotton averages but 10 per cent, and compression to a high density does not materially damage it. The cotton fiber, therefore, is relatively economical to ship; textiles are not a raw-material-oriented industry.

Plant Site and Form. Textile mills in New England are for the most part at river sites, generally built of brick and of from two to four stories in height. The remaining mills are close to tidewater and for the most part are more modern in construction and layout. Most of the idle spindles are found in the interior mills. Both the interior and coastal New England cotton textile mills are in sharp contrast with mills on the Carolina Piedmont, so far as appearance is concerned.

Rise of Southern Competition. The cost of cotton fiber was but one of several factors which brought the cotton textile industry to the Carolina Piedmont. Labor was the most important factor in the rise of southern textile manufacture. By 1904 the New England cotton mills and the southern mills were of about equal capacity. No other region in the United States or Canada has risen to challenge the leadership of these two cotton textile manufacturing districts (*Fig.* 7-3).

Between 1904 and the outbreak of World War I, the Piedmont mills of the South were increasing their capacity at the expense of the older New England mills. The flood of orders incidental to Allied purchases and our own wartime demands served to bring about a plant expansion in both the North and the South. The postwar deflation could not be weathered by certain New England mills living on borrowed time, so many failed.

The loss of the Oriental and South American markets, principally to Japan and Brazil, seriously affected American exports of cotton textiles. New England mills felt this loss more keenly than the Piedmont mills which had never enjoyed an important share of the export trade, due largely to their late start.

Foreign Competition in Cotton Fiber. During the years 1930-1945 the price of raw cotton was pegged (in effect) at about 9 cents per pound in the United States, and the old coffee-growing lands of southeastern Brazil were able to inaugurate a cotton-growing program of considerable importance. World War II aided

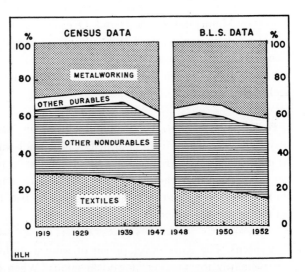

FIGURE 7-3: *Distribution of Employment, New England, 1919-1952*

This chart shows manufacturing shifts by major categories. With this decline in textile manufacturing, Fall River, New Bedford, Lowell, and Lawrence were particularly affected. (Federal Reserve Bank of Boston)

in this venture. What the ultimate effect of this will be upon the New England cotton factories remains to be seen. Thus far it has enabled Brazil to cut into the South American market of the United States.

WOOLEN AND WORSTED MANUFACTURING

Half of all the wool manufacturing establishments in the United States are in New England, although this industry on the basis of wage earners, ranks after both cotton and metals. Textiles made from wool may be woolens, worsteds, or knit goods. At first the woolens were widely made in the home; worsteds have been a factory-made product; knit goods have been both home- and factory-made.[1] At least 90 per cent of the wool processed in New England is used for the woolen and worsted types of goods.

The proportion of the woolen to the worsted mills varies considerably by individual states within New England. Only Rhode Island has more worsted than woolen mills. Approximately half of the woolen establishments are in eastern Massachusetts, with about half of the remainder shared by Maine and Rhode Island. Over a long period of time the worsted industry has shown a slow but steady increase in the number of establishments. Woolen mills on the other hand have shown a slow decline. There has been no change in the type or size of the mill to compensate for the decline in number.

Early Development. Wool manufacturing in New England has had a very different history from cotton. Because wool was cheaper than cotton, its use was more general. Wool was a local animal product then. The spinning of wool was a simpler task owing to the length of the fiber. Wool could be manufactured in most homes; cotton was the factory-made product during the early years.

Woolens. The early development of wool manufacture in New England was primarily the making of woolen goods. When yarn was prepared for weaving in the home the practice had been to card it. The transition of this yarn manufacture to a mill was brought about by the powered machinery of the fulling mill, developed in most communities to do the heavy work involved in finishing the home-woven fabric for tailoring into garments. By 1810 there were twenty-four small woolen mills in the United States, virtually all of them in the northeastern states, the largest employing 150 persons. But after the War of 1812, woolen mills appeared in many parts of the United States east of the Mississippi River.

The number of woolen mills in New England and elsewhere declined and their size increased about the time of the Civil War, when reciprocity with Canada enabled us to secure long staple wool for combing, and at a time when a power wool-combing machine was introduced from England. This encouraged the making of worsted goods. The dwindling supply of raw

---

[1] The operations required for the manufacture of woolen and worsted fabrics are similar, the essential difference being the greater density of the worsted yarn, its longer fibers, and the inability to use reclaimed fiber. A commentary upon the relation of this industry to the trade of New England is the fact that while manufacturing more than half the nation's wool, only 5 per cent of the commodities made from it are fabricated in New England.

cotton from the seceding states made some cotton manufacturers turn to wool for "the duration." The heavy demands during the war for worsted uniform cloth gave some of the mills a specialty they followed thereafter. When the reciprocal trade agreement with Canada ceased after 1868, Canadian manufacturing was hard hit and New England worsted mills would have suffered severely but for the perfection of wool-combing machinery which made it possible for them to use the shorter wool fiber from Argentina and other wool-exporting countries.

Worsteds. Worsteds did not become commercially important until after the invention in 1860 of power machinery for combing the wool. This work is too heavy for home manufacture. The proportion of worsted mills in New England has reflected the changes which have taken place in these two major divisions of the industry since that time. First one and then the other would be stimulated by some style or some price change caused by a war or by depressed business conditions. However, worsteds were the established leader by the turn of the century and have remained so. From the beginning, worsted mills have been larger establishments, have employed more people, and have made more standardized items than the more numerous but smaller woolen mills. Worsted mills are more localized than either cotton or woolens.

Worsted plants resemble cotton mills in the completeness of processing within one mill, but the former employ men primarily, the latter employ women. At first the worsted industry was at a disadvantage because of the requirement of relatively more men than women in the manufacturing processes. Like cotton mills, worsted mills have installed a greater proportion of labor-saving devices than have the woolen mills.

Sources of Wool. New England has in wool manufactures another industry which depends upon imported raw materials and a national market. Unlike cotton, wool continues to have its major processing region in New England. Only in the Middle Atlantic states has the manufacture of woolens and worsteds developed significantly. Although it was founded originally on local supplies of wool, the New England industry today buys wool not only from other regions of the United States but also from most of the other great wool-producing nations of the world.[2]

[2] Although the United States is the second largest producer of wool, it is not self-sufficient. Relatively mild climate makes the United States' wool fine-fibered, usable for apparel, draperies, and upholstery. Yet in the apparel class alone, the United States produces only 70 per cent of her consumption; Australia and New Zealand send to this country 50 million pounds annually. The United States has been de-

Until 1813 wool rags were used only for making fertilizer. Then an Englishman conceived the idea that used wool had further manufacturing value. The economic importance of reclaimed wool (shoddy and mungo) is now great, here and abroad. It probably amounts to at least two-fifths of all wool processed. The effect is to keep the price of virgin wool down somewhat. It also tends to make the manufacture of woolens more important; this is owing to the ability of the woolen industry to use shorter fibers.

APPAREL INDUSTRY

The early apparel industry of New England was in a sense a reluctant tenant of factory buildings. In this respect it was similar to shoes and certain grades of cotton cloth. Apparel and shoes kept home craftsmen occupied in villages and towns for many years after factory production of their respective products had been established.

New England's early export trade made markets in the southeastern part of the United States and the West Indian Islands accessible to its factories. Work shoes, work clothing, and uniforms for seamen were important factors in the development of these New England factories. The 1849 gold rush and the Civil War likewise caused a substantial market for both the apparel and shoe industries.

The apparel industry has been scattered in the New England states, with half or more of the plants being located in or near Boston, Fall River, New Bedford, Lowell, Lawrence, Worcester, in Massachusetts; Boston dominates with approximately one-third of all apparel employment. The 80,000 wage earners have never been among those who are very well paid; the industry is seasonal and highly competitive.

LEATHER MANUFACTURES

Tanning Industry. Historically, the leather industry and the manufacture of boots and shoes have been important in New England's manufacturing. Although both of these industries remain important in these states, their relative importance has declined. As compared with tanneries in Pennsylvania, the leading state, New England units are smaller. Waning supplies of tanbark have caused this industry to develop farther south and west in the Appalachian states with their oak and chestnut forests. Chemically-

---

pendent upon Argentina and China, principally, for carpet wool. World War II cut off supplies from China, and the United States turned to Uruguay and increased imports from Argentina.

tanned leather had surpassed bark-tanned long before the blight had killed most chestnut trees.

Despite the importance of the livestock industry, the United States has long relied upon imported hides and skins for some of its needs. Imports account for some 12 per cent of the cattle hides, 24 per cent of the calf- and pigskins, 59 per cent of the sheep- and lambskins, and nearly all of the goat- and kidskins consumed in the United States. This fact has tended to prolong New England's tanning industry.

Shoe Manufacturing. From the days when the shoemaker was limited to his own locality for raw materials, labor, and market, to the rise of the large modern shoe factories, this industry has been intimately related not only to other industries but also to New England's crafts. The shoe industry in New England has had little to do with water-power sites. The more accessible power sites had been occupied by the textile industries before the wide-spread application of power-driven machines to shoe manufacture.

It has been stated that the shoe industry was given its first great stimulus by the export of shoes to the laboring classes of our South, of Mexico, and of the West Indian Islands. The rapidly-growing carrying trade of New England offered not only this outlet for shoes, but also brought in hides from pastoral countries. Such markets do not seem important, but it must be remembered that most Americans of the time wore locally crafted boots or shoes.

Production Centers. Lynn, near Boston, dominated all other towns in shoe making during the early days. Here was inaugurated the subdivision of labor in shoe making. By 1800 Lynn, Gloucester, Beverly, Salem, and Marblehead were turning out some 300,000 pairs of shoes annually.

Because of the long continuance of shoemaking in the home and the small workshop, the larger shoe factories which eventually developed were found, for the most part, in towns where textile manufacturing had not absorbed all of the available labor. Shoe manufacturing south of Boston amounted to little prior to the Civil War and at first no town dominated the shoe industry; it was important in a dozen. While the Boston area remained most important, shoe factories were established at Nashua and Manchester in southern New Hampshire, Auburn in southern Maine and at Windsor, Vermont (*Fig.* 7-4).

Shoe manufacturing has become one of the most mobile of industries. This is largely because of its labor orientation. Contributing factors have been the leasing system on the part of the shoe-machine manufacturers and the fact that the buildings are often rented.

FIGURE 7-4: Goodyear Rubber Plant, Windsor, Vermont

The rubber-products industry is exceedingly varied and geographically widespread. Labor supply and proximity to market have enabled the manufacture of footwear to prosper in this community. (Goodyear Rubber Co.)

PAPER INDUSTRY

Distribution. The manufacture of paper is carried on in three principal areas in New England: the Thames Valley and the Connecticut Valley, both in southern New England, and Maine, New Hampshire, and Vermont (*Fig. 7-5*). The region's greatest concentration of wood-pulp mills is in the north, at Millinocket, Orono, Old Town, and Brewer in Maine, and Berlin in New Hampshire. The second ranking district is centered about Holyoke in the Connecticut Valley. This is the greatest rag-paper center of all. Nearby is the paper district of the Thames Valley.

Important factors in locating the paper mills in New England have been (1) supply of raw materials; (2) abundant power; and (3) large quantities of water suitable for processing the pulp. The size and the varied nature of New England's market for paper products have, in large measure, determined the distribution and the nature of the primary paper manufacturing there. The need for paper boxes and containers of many sorts has profoundly influenced the type of output of the Connecticut mills particularly, where the New York market is so near.

Depletion of Materials. Depletion of local sources of pulpwood has promoted imports from Canada and Europe. Some of the large paper companies have transferred a considerable portion of their activities to the Canadian forests. Approximately half of the pulpwood consumed by New England mills is now imported from Canada and northern Europe. The northern mills are largely dependent upon local pulp, but the southern mills which manufacture a greater variety of paper, rely on imported pulp and upon rags. Besides these larger mills, there are scores of others making paper products of various sorts, nearly always from purchased pulp or other paper-making materials.

METAL-PROCESSING INDUSTRY

Early Development. New England made iron from local ore and charcoal in the seventeenth century. What may have been the oldest commercial-iron venture in the colonies has been restored at Saugus, near Boston. The distance from Great Britain gave the colonial iron masters the equivalent of an estimated 25 per cent protective tariff. Within the colonies the diffi-

FIGURE 7-5: Paper Mill, Bangor

This is one of the manufacturers of high-grade paper which have kept New England in the lead. The machine in the foreground shows the headbox, the Fourdrinier wire with the press section, and the driers beyond. (Eastern Corp.)

culties in transportation kept iron manufacturing a local industry. The principal exception to this was Massachusetts where the shipping industry provided a considerable outlet for iron goods. A farmer in his home and about his farm could get along with little in the way of iron products, but in shipbuilding and subsequent operation of the vessel, iron was a vital necessity, including the making of chain and anchors. Up to the middle of the eighteenth century Massachusets led the colonies in iron making, with the greatest works about the Narragansett Basin and the Boston Lowland. Local bog iron, oyster shells for flux, and charcoal sufficed for this infant industry; these materials cannot be used economically today in making iron.

Every step toward the subjugation of the physical environment tended to enhance the importance of iron manufacture. The westward movement of colonists from the seaboard of the Middle Atlantic and New England sections into the nearby Appalachian valleys, created new markets for the manufactured necessities of pioneer life, limited though the farm market was at the time. It was not long before the iron furnaces in some of the more recently-settled areas were able to sell to the older New England market. As soon as the size of the furnace increased beyond the ability of New England bogs to supply the iron, the interior furnaces with their more abundant ores had an advantage.

Iron and Steel. Today New England is a deficit steel-making region, producing in 1952 some 550,000 tons, with the only large blast furnaces at Everett, Massachusetts. Steel mills are located at Worcester, Massachusetts, Bridgeport, Connecticut, and Philipsdale, Rhode Island. New England is the largest industrialized region in the United States without adequate primary steel facilities.

There is in all New England no example of the heavy industry landscape as it has developed farther west. The technological changes which have taken place in the manufacture of iron and steel during the past half century have weakened the bonds which tied the industry to its former localities. During and since the last war, the facilities for making steel in the United States have nearly doubled, and the geographical distribution has changed significantly. Neither of these fundamental changes has altered the New England picture. Even the relatively small and independently-located electric furnace, producing special high carbon and alloy steels so much in demand in Massachusetts and Connecticut, has made little gain in these states, although New England is a regular exporter of almost a million tons of scrap steel each year.

Nonferrous Metals. Of the 69,000 employed in the manufacture of basic metals, about one-third are engaged in rolling, drawing, and alloying non-ferrous metals. This phase of the metals industry has few things in common with iron and steel. The types and number of industries attracted to the source of nonferrous metals are probably greater than in the case of steel. The Connecticut cities of Meriden, Ansonia, Torrington, and Waterbury specialize in copper and brass goods. Taunton and Stratford are primarily silver manufacturers. Aluminum fabrication is important only at Waterbury.

METAL-FABRICATING INDUSTRY

The goal of all manufacturing regions similar to New England is the manufacture of commodities in which there is the maximum of skilled labor. Certain types of the metal industries best fit this regional objective. Machine tools, electrical equipment, a wide variety of textile and other machinery, machine shops and foundries are the phases of metals manufacture which dominate the New England scene. The wages paid in this group are somewhat higher than the average for New England, although within the group there is wide variation.

Most of the buyers of special steels in New England are the largest manufacturers in these six states. Among them is Connecticut's ball- and roller-bearing industry in the Hartford-New Britain-Bristol area. Another is the machine-tool industry in more than a score of cities in Massachusetts and Connecticut. So also are the aircraft-engine and-parts industry in the same states, textile machinery concerns in Rhode Island and Massachusetts and the valve and fitting makers in Connecticut and Massachusetts (*Fig.* 7-6).

Textile Machinery. Most of this type of machinery made in the United States comes from the New England states; four-fifths come from Massachusetts and Rhode Island alone. As would be expected, the location and fortunes of firms engaged in this manufacture are dependent upon the cotton and woolen textile mills.

Electrical Equipment. Although this industry is important in the region, New England's share of the nation's output of electrical equipment is much less than in the case of textile machinery. For the most part, this phase of metals manufacture is carried on in large units centered primarily in cities along the north shore of Long Island Sound, Bridgeport, New Haven, and the cities of the Narragansett-Blackstone lowland. Products include equipment for the generation, transmission, and utilization of electric power.

FIGURE 7-6: *Pratt and Whitney Aircraft Plant, East Hartford*
The manufacture of aircraft engines is an example of an industry which came to New England after World War I partly because of the availability of the kinds of workers needed and at a relatively lower wage than would have to be paid in other highly industrialized regions. This huge plant has repeatedly expanded its facilities. (Pratt and Whitney Aircraft)

The long-time importance of these cities in the manufacture of copper and brass is antecedent to this modern industrial specialty.

Machine Tools. The machine-tool industry is the best example of the so-called "New England" type of product. Although machine tools may be enormous, most of them are not. They represent the maximum of skilled labor in their construction and thus have the dominant quality of what is often referred to as the New England-type product.

The machine-tool industry is sometimes referred to as the parent of all manufacturing since the basic machines drill, bore, mill, grind, and broach metal parts which, when assembled, become the machines which make the machines of industry. They are precision-made and their builders are artists among metal workers. With no more than sixty machine-tool plants prior to World War II, New England manufactured about one-fourth of the nation's total product.

The building of machine tools did not emerge as a distinct industry until after the Civil War, although every blacksmith in a limited way partook of this function. The distribution of the factories today is as widespread as the market centers. The "feast or famine" nature of machine-tool building as an industry tends to keep the capacity at peacetime level. The emergency of 1941-1945 enormously increased the market; so-called "bottlenecks" developed in production. In an attempt to relieve this, some subcontracting was practiced, even in such a craft-type industry.

Instruments. The manufacture of scientific and professional instruments would seem to be an industry suited to New England. Raw material and shipping costs are relatively low, and the industry is dependent upon technically trained persons as well as skilled labor. Despite this, the industry is one of the smallest in New England, representing but 2.5 per cent of the value added by manufacturing in this Census division, and but 5.5 per cent of the nation's total for this industry.

There is difficulty in distinguishing between instruments and some electronic devices. The complexity of this group is increasing; Connecticut now produces the major share of the New England total. This electronics manufacture is one of the reasons for the relative vigor of Connecticut's industry.

Timepieces and Silverware. Silverware, jewelry, watches and clocks have long been important industries in New England. World War II with its demand for precision workers in metal for the array of new weapons and missiles made inroads upon the labor supply for timepieces, particularly. The post exchanges were stocking Swiss watches in all parts of the world where United States armed forced were stationed. By 1955 the New England (and United States) watch industry was successful in gaining further tariff protection. Opinion is divided as to the net gain of this measure.

Foundry and Machine Shops. The apparent wide distribution of foundry and machine shops is due largely to the indefiniteness of the classification. In the three southern states of New England the shops are found in nearly every town of industrial importance. The northern states have shops localized for the most part in southeastern Maine, southern New Hampshire, and the Vermont lowland. Wherever machinery is made or repaired, the machine shop will be found.

Shipbuilding. Shipbuilding, historically one of New England's important industries, is today carried on principally at Bath and South Portland, Maine; Portsmouth, New Hampshire; Boston and Quincy, Massachusetts;

and Groton, Connecticut. New England never has regained the shipbuilding importance achieved in the days of wooden ships. Although during World War II there were wooden ships built in these yards, it was indicative of no permanent change.

CHEMICAL INDUSTRIES

In a number of sections in the United States the establishment of chemical industries has ushered in a revival of industrial activity. New England appears to have a very modest future in the manufacture of chemicals. Companies making chemical products employ only 2 per cent of New England's wage earners. Six lines of products constitute the bulk of the industry: soap and glycerin, pharmaceuticals, plastics, cleaning and polishing compounds, glue and gelatine, and toilet products. About a third of the production is sold to New England industry.

Although eastern Massachusetts is the principal producer of chemicals in New England, there is no chemical center as such. There is but one oil refinery in these six states with a capacity of some 40,000 barrels per day, at Everett, Massachusetts. Nearly all of the refined petroleum products are imported from the Gulf Coast; only a minor portion is from the New Jersey refining area.

MANUFACTURING DISTRICTS

Reference to the map of manufacturing activity will orient the New England states within the Manufacturing Belt of the United States. About 85 per cent of New England's manufacturing takes place in the three southern states, slightly more than half of it in Massachusetts alone. This distribution corresponds closely to that of population, but the relative importance of wage earners differs markedly in the various states.

Reference has been made several times to the "small landscapes" of New England; probably in no other aspect of its economic life is this concept more appropriate than in manufacturing. In New England manufacturing frequently is associated with river valleys. With the exception of the Connecticut River Valley, all of these are relatively short, and no other serves as an important interregional trade route.

These valleys have had long-standing specialization in manufacturing and to them have recently come new industries seeking the same type of labor that was developed there earlier. This specialization hindered the conversion to war goods in 1942. More recently local manufacturers have sought to diversify their lines by making new products. What a variety of

FIGURE 7-7: Bristol Brass Company, Bristol, Connecticut
The nonferrous industry ranks high in New England. (Bristol Brass Co.)

goods are produced! Although the individual valleys are often identified with certain products, the specialization is by city rather than by valley.

The localized areas of maximum manufacturing activity are readily identifiable: Boston Basin, Narragansett Basin, Blackstone Valley, Connecticut Valley, Merrimack Valley, and the Naugatuck Valley. Minor areas include the Champlain lowland, the eastern plains of Massachusetts, and the southeastern coast of Maine.

Boston Basin. The concentration of population around Boston is the largest in all New England, approximately a fourth of the region's population. Only one city in this agglomeration, Everett, failed to gain in population during the past twenty years.[3] Boston completely dominates the city group in its economic life. The industrial interrelationships among some of these cities perhaps are not surpassed by any other district in the nation.

The Boston district is the most diversified of all New England manufac-

---

[3] The Census of 1950 gives the population for *Boston* (790,863); *Cambridge* (120,-676); *Somerville* (102,254); *Lynn* (99,521); *Newton* (80,996); *Quincy* (83,190); *Medford* (66,109); *Malden* (59,779); *Brookline* (56,952); *Salem* (41,840); *Everett* (45,789); *Weymouth* (32,695); *Beverly* (28,855); *Gloucester* (25,548); *Waltham* (47,187); and *Brockton* (62,860).

turing districts. Although in the commerce in raw wool and in the manufacture of woolens and worsteds it remains first in the nation, metal manufactures predominate.

Port of Boston. The economic base of this urban district has been the activities of the port of Boston. The excellence of the harbor and the accessibility to New England cities have in no sense deteriorated, but the port has declined from second to eighth in the United States during the past 150 years. This decline is in large part owing to the failure of New England producers to retain their national ranking and to the decline of commerce from the interior through this port. Primarily a coastwise trader today, its import tonnage is nearly ten times that of its exports. New England must import all of its coal and oil and most of its industrial raw materials. Despite the greater congestion of the port of New York, the average turn-around time for a freighter is reportedly less than at Boston.

Blackstone Valley and Narragansett Basin. Southwest of Boston is an attenuated city group in the Blackstone Valley between Worcester and Providence. Several of these cities have declined in population since 1930.[4] Perhaps the best-known metal industry in the Narragansett Basin is the manufacture of low-and medium-priced jewelry. More jewelry and related items are produced in the Providence metropolitan area than in any other single area in the United States. Oddly, this industry is not based upon a body of skilled labor; mass production techniques are employed. Providence and Woonsocket are important centers for the manufacture of wool textiles.

Connecticut Valley. Although the Connecticut River rises in northern New Hampshire some 400 miles north of Long Island Sound, it is only the lower section, 160 miles in length in Massachusetts and Connecticut, which is known as Connecticut River Country. It is narrow as valleys go, but in New England it is the largest valley and the most important localization of agricultural and industrial production.[5] Hartford's present industrial fame rests upon the production of aircraft engines, machine tools, electrical machinery, and a variety of foundry and machine-shop products. Springfield, Chicopee, and Hartford share in the manufacture of most of the nation's firearms. New Britain, between the Connecticut and Housatonic valleys, is the nation's greatest manufacturer of hardware.

[4] *Providence* (248,674); *Pawtucket* (81,436); *Worcester* (203,486); *Fall River* (111,963); *Woonsocket* (50,211); *Fitchburg* (42,691); *Cranston* (55,060); *Bristol* (35,961); and *Warwick* (43,028). (1950).

[5] *Hartford* (177,397); *Holyoke* (54,661); *Springfield* (162,399); *Chicopee* (49,-211); *Middletown* (29,711); *Northampton* (29,063). (1950).

Merrimack Valley. Few valleys are better known for a manufacturing specialty than the Merrimack Valley. The widespread closing of small woolen mills in most sections of New England (and the United States) during the first half of the present century has helped concentrate wool manufacture, particularly in Lawrence, Lowell, and Nashua. Lawrence still depends upon direct water power from a series of falls in the Merrimack River. Despite the widespread failure of textile mills in New England since World War I, no city in this valley declined in population during the past ten years.[6]

Naugatuck Valley. The small Naugatuck tributary valley in western Connecticut has the long-time specialty of brass-goods manufacture. More recently the manufacture of rubber products and of bearings have become important in the valley. The only city to have lost population is Ansonia, one of the specialists in brass manufacture.[7]

Housatonic Valley. The Housatonic Valley in western Massachusetts and Connecticut bears less relation to Boston and New England than to New York. It is the least industrial of all southern New England valleys. The principal city is *Pittsfield* (53,348) where the Boston and Albany Railroad crosses the principal north-south corridor in the mountain country of western Massachusetts. Its major industry is the manufacture of electrical equipment.

Other Areas. *Bridgeport* (158,709) and *New Haven* (164,443), on the north shore of Long Island Sound, have undergone industrial transformation since the days of whaling. At one time manufactures were related to the outfitting of fishing and whaling vessels and with the whalebone and other products of a maritime economy. Today Bridgeport manufactures electrical equipment, hardware and firearms. New Haven has foundries, machine shops, hardware and firearms manufacture.

NEW ENGLAND'S PROSPECT

For 300 years there has been industrial selection among New England's manufactures. For almost as long there has been competition with the factory products of districts outside of New England. There are few better illustrations in this country of the "timeless creative experiment."

[6] *Lowell* (97,249); *Manchester* (82,732); *Lawrence* (80,536); *Haverhill* (47,280); *Nashau* (34,669) and *Concord* (27,988). (1950).
[7] *Ansonia* (18,706); *Waterbury* (104,477); *Naugatuck* (17,455); *Torrington* (27,-820). (1950).

FIGURE 7-8: *Small Arms Plant, Hartford*

The manufacture of firearms is in the tradition of precision manufacturing, a characteristic of the "New England type" of factory product. (Colt Patent Firearms Manufacturing Co.)

Partly as a consequence of its age, it may well be that no other region in the United States is quite so aware of its advantages and disadvantages. This is not discounting the self-examination that has been the experience of many other areas, particularly the South.

New industrial centers such as Harborside Industrial Park, near Providence, Rhode Island, and Thompson's Point in Maine are but two of some 15 similar undertakings which seek to establish new manufacturing centers on the site of some war-built plant or other attractive facility. Where such attempts were developed around abandoned factories, the success has not been great; often the location and the building both were discouraging. The growing power of labor to attract a manufacturing plant may be of some future value to New England, but thus far it has been of modest importance.

Just what difference the power and navigation aspects of the St. Lawrence-Great Lakes Seaway will make to New England's industry, remains to be seen. Opponents of the Seaway have contended that the port of Boston will suffer from a diversion of freight.

Alexander Hamilton's plea for more governmental control over manufacturing in order to promote the general welfare still has its spokesmen.

A United States senator from Massachusetts in 1954 advocated some form of federal subsidy for power developments available to New England manufacturers.

In 1954 the New England Council published 19 separate studies of the principal New England industries, including fishing, forestry, commerce and manufacturing. These impressive studies should be examined by all who would know New England's prospect.[8]

BIBLIOGRAPHY

ACKERMAN, Edward A., *New England's Fishing Industry* (Chicago, Univ. of Chicago Press, 1941).

BLACK, John D., *Rural Economy of New England* (New York, McGraw-Hill Book Co., Inc., 1951).

BRIGHT, J., *The Economic State of New England* (New Haven, Yale Univ. Press, 1954).

The Changing Fertility of New England Soils, Agricultural Information Bulletin No. 133 (U.S. Dept. of Agriculture, Washington, 1954).

HARRIS, S. E., "New England's Decline in the American Economy," *Harvard Business Review,* Vol. 25 (1947).

HIGBEE, Edward C., "The Three Earths of New England," *Geographical Review,* Vol. 42 (1952), pp. 425-438.

ISARD, Walter, and J. H. CUMBERLAND, "New England as a Possible Location for an Integrated Iron and Steel Industry," *Economic Geography,* Vol. 26, No. 4 (Oct., 1950), pp. 245-259.

KLIMM, Lester E., "Empty Areas of the Northeastern United States," *Geographical Review,* Vol. 44, No. 3 (July, 1954), pp. 325-345.

SMITH, Thomas R., *The Cotton Textile Industry of Fall River, Massachusetts* (New York, Kings Press, 1944).

[8] J. Bright, *The Economic State of New England* (New Haven, Yale University Press, 1954).

CHAPTER 8

MIDDLE ATLANTIC LITTORAL

REGIONAL IDENTITY

LYING BETWEEN the Blue Ridge Mountains and the Atlantic Ocean, from New York City to the Virginia capes, is the embayed section of the Atlantic Coastal Plain and most of the northern Piedmont which together constitute the Middle Atlantic Littoral (*Fig.* 8-1). The heart of this plains area is the lowland nested within the four prongs of the middle Older Appalachians. The Reading and Manhattan prongs of the northern Blue Ridge and Piedmont, respectively, and the Carlisle and Trenton prongs of the southern portion of the same provinces, together frame the fertile Triassic Lowland of southeastern Pennsylvania and northwestern New Jersey. This oasis of good soils is largely the result of a crustal depression with subsequent deposition in Triassic times of limestone and sandstone, which yield richer soils than the underlying crystalline rocks.

Situation. Whether one enters this famed lowland by way of the Pennsylvania Turnpike from the west, the Susquehanna Trail from the north, or the New Jersey Turnpike from the northeast, there is no mistaking its identity. Its agricultural productiveness and its accessibility to major continental thoroughfares as well as to the Atlantic Ocean, have combined to make it one of the most important regions in America.

Although the Middle Atlantic Coastal Plain and Piedmont are essentially plains areas, there is enough physiographic diversity to influence the patterns and characteristics of occupance. Long Island comprises the northern portion of the Middle Atlantic Coastal Plain. Here the usual coastal

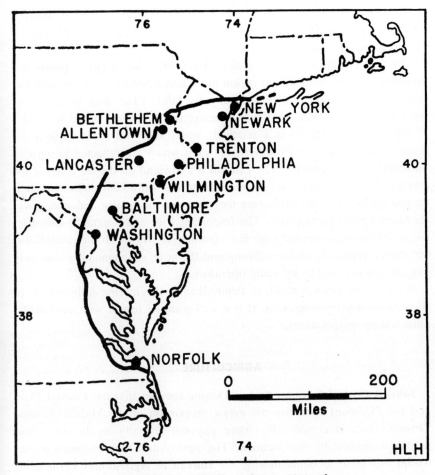

FIGURE 8-1: *Middle Atlantic Littoral*

plain features have been modified by glacial deposition, the only part of the Atlantic Coastal Plain to be thus affected. Two east-west moraines with an extensive outwash plain along southern Long Island constitute the dominant physical features of the island. Its situation with respect to the New York urban nucleus has been its strongest developmental factor. The distribution and character of its agriculture, the distribution of its population, both urban and rural, and its share of New York's manufacturing are in large part consequences of this location.

The peninsular coastal plain embraces most of the remainder of the eastern Littoral. Much of New Jersey, all of Delaware, and eastern Maryland are peninsular; in the latter two areas this feature has probably been in effect the "backdoor" to the Littoral, for their principal economic horizon has been to the west where great bays have enticed an important part of the world's commerce.

The lower sections of the major rivers of these Atlantic plains are drowned, making parts of the region more accessible to coastwise and for- eign trade, but less accessible locally by land. (The first bridges over the lower Delaware River and over Chesapeake Bay were opened in 1952.)

Although the Littoral is a relatively small area and its latitudinal ex- panse is not great, climatic differences exist which are reflected in agricul- tural and resort industries. The Littoral is a lowland on the lee coast of the continent, a fact which tends to accentuate the latitudinal difference. It is an embayed land, thus increasing the extent of the marine influence, over the coastal plain particularly. The important fruit and vegetable industries are nevertheless concerned with the frost danger. Although the rainfall dis- tribution is relatively uniform throughout the year, supplementary overhead irrigation is resorted to by many operators.

West of the coastal plain in Pennsylvania, the marine influence is of slight economic consideration. It is a well-watered region with continental influence on temperatures.

AGRICULTURE

Soils: A Critical Location Factor. Despite the fact that the Coastal Plain and the Piedmont comprise the major proportion of the Middle Atlantic Littoral, there is considerably more physical diversity to the area than might be implied by this location. The agricultural regions encompassed within this area, as delineated by the Bureau of Agricultural Economics, suggest something of this diversity.[1] As one progresses toward the interior from the shore of New Jersey or Delaware, the soils generally improve and also exhibit a more complex pattern. All of the Atlantic margin of New Jersey and portions of that of Delaware and Maryland are sandy plain lying between sea level and 400-feet elevation. From quartz sands and gravels have been developed generally light gray and gray-brown sandy soils which for the most part have as low agricultural carrying power as any in the United States. Peat and dark-colored sandy soils and large areas of peaty tidal marshland are interspersed among the predominant soil types.

[1] New Jersey Piedmont, Southern New Jersey Pine Barrens, Delaware River Sandy Coastal Plain, Northern Piedmont Plateau, Sassafras Loam Coastal Plain, Eastern Shore White Oak Lands, and Chesapeake Rolling Coastal Plain.

In some of the marsh lands where the clay subsoil permits it, cranberries have become an important crop. This soil belt comprises almost half of New Jersey, lying south of New York harbor.

From New York harbor to lower Chesapeake Bay on the east side of the Delaware River there is a broad soils belt which is generally favorable for crop agriculture. Owing to its sandy nature and its underlying gravel there are relatively few areas of poor drainage under normal conditions.

Middle Atlantic Trucking Region. This trucking region is more or less continuous from the Connecticut Valley to the Carolinas. Nowhere is it more than fifty miles in width, and in the deeply embayed northern portion it is quite narrow. Not all of the region is cultivated; more than half of the area is still in scrub forest or brush. About 40 per cent is in farms, and perhaps 15 per cent in crops of all kinds. Despite the inclusion of districts which are very highly specialized, the cropped region as a whole is best described as mixed farming, about one-fifth the cropped acreage and half the value of all crops consisting of vegetables, including potatoes, and fruit. In no other major agricultural region of eastern United States does the same high proportion of truck and fruit obtain; in only three major regions is there as small a proportion of cultivated fields to total land.

Camden District. Lying on the narrow inner lowland of central New Jersey, across the Delaware River from the Piedmont dairy region, is the famed Camden District, largest truck-producing section of the North Atlantic Coastal Plain. For a distance of fifty miles this narrow clay and marl lowland is given over to the production of vegetables and small fruits. It is more uniformly cropped than similar districts to the south in Delaware and in eastern Maryland. The smooth expanse of the Coastal Plain north and south from Camden is as intensively farmed as any area in the nation. Scientific fertilizing, hand labor, machinery and advanced marketing practices are characteristic of these farms.

General farming and dairying preceded truck growing on this clay and marl belt, but of these former types there are relatively few remnants left. The rise of population centers suburban to Philadelphia has also enabled truck specialization to displace dairying as the principal source of income. For certain crops, the embayed nature of the Littoral is especially favorable because of its tendency to hold back the budding in the spring and the frost in the autumn; in the northern portion this is particularly important. It is often the critical climatic factor.

The sandy soils warm up earlier in the spring than the heavier clay soils

FIGURE 8-2: *Vegetable Freezing Plant, New Jersey*

Freezing of fresh vegetables is by no means confined to producing areas distant from market. This modern freezing and processing plant is on a large truck farm in southern New Jersey within easy trucking distance of eastern urban markets. (Seabrook Farms)

on the Piedmont. Rainfall is adequate for plant growth at all seasons. The attenuated nature of this region has resulted in an all-year sequence of growing seasons, beginning with the southern end and progressing northward at a rate of about 15 miles a day. This results in a series of exporting centers, each depending upon its earlier harvest for good prices in the markets of the large cities farther north.

Canning and freezing plants have been established in Camden and other south-central Jersey towns to care for the surplus vegetables and fruit from these specialists (*Fig.* 8-2). Cranberry bogs are situated to the east of the intensively farmed acres, in the otherwise useless pine belt.

Tristate District. Delaware, eastern Maryland, and Virginia share the Coastal Plain farther south and share also the fruit and vegetable industry (*Fig.* 8-3). Both sweet potatoes and white potatoes are grown to a greater extent than on the inner lowland of New Jersey. These so-called "Eastern Shore" counties are not able to dispose of such a large proportion of their crops to urban markets as their northern neighbors, consequently more of their products must be canned or frozen. Baltimore canning plants rank first in the nation for this type of food product. The embayed character of the

FIGURE 8-3: *Pea Viner, Maryland*

Even with the use of such machines as this, migratory labor must be used on many farms on Maryland's Eastern Shore. (Scott Viner Co.)

Eastern Shore country has kept boat transportation dominant. Several counties have no railroad.

The so-called Delmarva Peninsula is the country's pre-eminent broiler land; nine shore counties in Delaware, Maryland, and Virginia produce most of these broilers. For about a generation, this industry has been an important source of farm income. The mild climate permits year-round foraging; the sandy loam soil dries quickly; and the twelve-week-old fowls have a ready urban market to the north. In 1950 broilers accounted for 60 per cent of the income of Delaware farmers.

Southern Maryland. Immediately south of Baltimore there are five counties which specialize in growing tobacco. The crop is important in no other part of Maryland. Other crops also are grown here, including potatoes and corn.[2] Over the years these Maryland tobacco counties have developed marked homogeneity, including a partial dependence upon fresh and salt-water for fishing.

Future of Agricultural Economy. The larger part of the Atlantic Coastal Plain is not cropped. Similar soils and climate have accommodated the

[2] "Southern Maryland, A Tobacco Economy," *Studies in Business and Economics* (University of Maryland, March, 1954, Vol. 7, No. 4).

dairy industry of the Low Countries in Europe. However, before such a transformation is possible on the Middle Atlantic Coastal Plain, the pressure of population upon the land resources of this extensive region must be much greater than is now believed likely. The trends in agriculture in this country since World War II appear to be especially significant of the future of agriculture on the North Atlantic plain. Under federal guidance, the national production of vegetables for canning has increased 30 per cent, the number of milk cows 25 per cent, and peanuts 300 per cent.

Even broilers may have competition in store; between 1946 and 1950, broiler output increased 30 per cent in Delaware, but 130 per cent in Arkansas. Georgia, California and Texas each gained over 100 per cent. Maine increased its flocks by 1,000 per cent. Along the main Delaware highways are fields of lima beans, soybeans, corn, wheat, rye, and an occasional peach orchard. They may be prophetic of a change from broiler raising to other types of land use.

Wasteland and noncommercial agriculture exist within a few miles of the most highly commercial farmlands in the nation, within sight of railroads bringing from midcontinent farms the raw materials for these great urban markets. The second-densest rural population in the United States may be found in the southeastern counties of Pennsylvania, yet the term "factories in the field" is aptly used to denote dependence upon nonresident farm labor in the Camden trucking district just across the Delaware River.

The Dairying Piedmont. Immediately west of the inner Coastal Plain is the Piedmont. As with the two eastern soils belts, those of the Piedmont widen toward the south. Most of the area is in farms and many of the farms are good. Derived from limestone and occasionally from shale, these silt loams and clay loams produce good crops of wheat, corn, hay, oats, potatoes, and tobacco. The hilly portions support pasture for the large numbers of beef cattle which are fattened here. Southward in Maryland the quality of the soils declines and with it the excellence of the agriculture.

For all of this dairying region, whether on good or on poor land, there is a stability born of the tendency to form the so-called milk "sheds." These milk-producing districts become fixed by the practices of their city market and by the limitations upon the economical shipments of fresh milk. Although some of these milk sheds overlap (that is to say, neighboring farmers may ship to different markets regularly), it appears that the fortunes of individual dairy farmers are determined by the conditions of employment and purchasing power in their particular city market.

By and large the dairy farmers have, by organization, so stabilized their market as to set them apart from the farmers producing farm crops exclusively. Although milk sheds are common to most parts of the United States, these in the Middle Atlantic area are more complex, particularly in the areas tributary to New York, Philadelphia, Baltimore, and Washington.

Other Districts. Despite the prevalence of dairying on the farms of the Piedmont, there are districts characterized by certain other agricultural specialties, among them are Chester, Lancaster, and York valleys, long noted for good farms and good farmers. These southeastern Pennsylvania counties must be regarded as areas of diversified agriculture with hay, corn, wheat, oats, apples, tobacco, and an accompanying livestock industry. Sometimes this includes fattening western beef cattle for market, as in the Chester Valley, but more often it is dairying. Tobacco is particularly important in Lancaster County.

Lancaster County. Since 1720 a quarter of Pennsylvania's 10,000 Pennsylvania Dutch farmers have lived in and near Lancaster County, in such communities as Bird-in-Hand, Smoketown, and Blue Ball. The farms are characterized by crop diversity and by large barns and other farm buildings indicative of a livestock economy. These farmers have built up in two hundred years an impregnable farm economy based on the simplest formula: feed the family, feed the stock, and sell the rest. The effect of such a program is evidenced both in the prosperity of the people and in the carefully-farmed land.

Chester Valley. The Chester Valley offers a somewhat more specialized agriculture. The scrupulous attention the Quaker farmers gave to their farming practices is still evident in the Chester Valley. Chester County produces half of the nation's mushrooms and an important part of its roses, carnations, orchids, gardenias and other varieties of flowers that are grown under glass. The town of *Kennett Square* (3,699) is often referred to as the mushroom capital of the United States, although milk yields more revenue than mushrooms by about 30 per cent.

Of the approximately 350 producers within a radius of 25 miles of Kennett Square, most operate mushroom plants in conjunction with dairy farming, cattle feeding, or general farming; the largest may do nothing else but grow mushrooms. The plants are nearly all family-owned and operated, with Quaker or Italian ownership predominating. From Kennett Square through Avondale, West Grove, and Oxford, mushroom growing is a major activity. Manurepiles, mushroom sheds, and canning plants are common sights along Route 1 which serves these towns.[3] Increasing industrialization on the Delaware is of greater concern to the dairymen.

York Valley. The York Valley is another productive agricultural district, with emphasis upon potatoes and nursery stock. One aspect of its economy is shared with the so-called mountain land of the Carlisle prong of the Blue Ridge, where a large part of the state's apple crop is grown. York Imperial, Staymen, Delicious, Jonathan and Rome Beauty apples go from these foothill orchards to the processing plants in nearby Aspers, Biglerville, Gardeners, and Orrtanna.

FISHING

Fishing remains an important source of livelihood along the Middle Atlantic Littoral. From Long Island Sound southward the drowned rivers and innumerable embayments offer commercial and recreational fishing. Much of the socalled "deep-sea" recreational fishing is done in these waters. Commercial inshore fishing has declined, but recreational fishing has increased. New York leads commercially with $14,364,000, followed by New Jersey, $9,744,000, and Pennsylvania with a minor catch.

Where the Maurice River empties into Delaware Bay are extensive oyster beds, both natural and planted. The oyster farms vary in size from eight acres to several hundred. The farm units are marked off by stakes set in the bottom. Dredging is not permitted in the shallow waters; the oysters must be harvested by tongs. Three to five million oysters are harvested in this Maurice River cove each day during the season for nearby urban markets. This is not a livelihood in which it is easy for new operators to begin. It is extremely expensive to establish an oyster farm. A 200-acre oyster farm may require $300,000. Land costs $400 per acre, plus $1.50 yearly rental to the state of New Jersey. The boat license is $3 per ton.

There is much need for labor. Oysters are transplanted in these oyster farms or gardens in June, and care is taken to maintain the markers and equipment. Pollution of the water by industrial wastes and sewage creates a serious problem for all of these fishing grounds. The oyster catch is declin-

[3] *Estimated Growing Space Available for Mushrooms,* 1951

STATE	1000 OF FEET
Pennsylvania	19,025
New York	3,148
Illinois	1,505
Ohio	1,375
Delaware	850

SOURCE: Philadelphia Federal Reserve Bank, *Business Review*, April, 1953.

ing for all of the states of this area. Shad fishing is another specialty, particularly in the Delaware River and Delaware Bay.

SITUATION

The fact that the Hudson, Delaware, Susquehanna, and Potomac rivers pursue courses which afford corridors through the eastern Appalachian barrier has meant that the trade of New York, Philadelphia, and Baltimore has been with areas west of the Appalachian Highland as well as within it.

After the initial impetus supplied by agriculture on these relatively inviting plains and by the coastwise trade of an early day, all three cities became the focus of trans-Appalachian routes to the interior of the continent. Their trade with the Middle West has always greatly exceeded that with nearby Appalachian counties. Like Dutch Governor Wouter Van Twiller of New Amsterdam, whose plump cheeks seemed to have taken toll of all that entered his mouth, these cities have literally taken toll of the heavy flow of commodities and people which has crossed the Appalachians during the two centuries of occupance.

New York has access to the interior of the United States by way of the corridor of the Lake Erie plain and the Mohawk and Hudson valleys. It has shared with Philadelphia the corridor through central Pennsylvania. Philadelphia also shares with New York the Delaware and the upper Susquehanna valleys. Baltimore has been served by the Potomac and Roanoke gaps through the eastern Appalachians. South of the Roanoke River there is no important trans-Appalachian corridor. The favorable aspects of the drainage of the Appalachians are outstanding in the development of all three Middle Atlantic port cities and their urban clusters. They were utilized by the pioneers who went west; they are used by their descendants today.

The Erie Canal, and the railroads which followed it, enabled New York to outstrip Philadelphia and Boston in population. The New York Central Railroad follows the valleys of the Hudson and Mohawk rivers westward to the Lake Plain. This corridor soon became the prime trade route of the continent. A little later the Pennsylvania Railroad was constructed, following in turn the Susquehanna, Juniata and upper Ohio valleys through the Appalachian Highlands. The Baltimore and Ohio Railroad follows the Harpers Ferry gap and much of the Potomac River valley through the Blue Ridge and the Newer or Folded Appalachians. The Chesapeake and Ohio Railroad follows the valleys of the James, New, and Kanawha rivers through the Appalachians. The Norfolk and Western Railroad, most southerly of these trans-Appalachian lines, follows the Roanoke and Big Sandy gaps through the same highlands. All of these roads focused upon the Middle Atlantic port cities in the east and the upper Ohio River in the west. Without this kind of accessibility, no Atlantic port city has grown to major proportions. As more remote hinterlands were made accessible, the relative importance of these port cities increased. Railroads made possible the export of midwestern agricultural products and, with the later settlement of the Canadian Prairie Provinces, south central Canada exported important tonnages through the Middle Atlantic ports. After the Panama Canal was opened in 1914, the trade territory of these port cities extended farther inland. The "zone of indifference" as to which direction to ship midwestern commodities varies by geographic section and by commodities, but in general it may be defined as lying just east of the Mississippi River. Although based upon commerce, these port cities have become important manufacturing centers. They dominate the economy of the plains of the Middle Atlantic Littoral. Their daytime population has long been partly drained off to the countryside at night; the extent and pattern of this commuting is determined by several factors, only one of which is distance.

The Middle Atlantic Littoral has retained its regional identity throughout the development of the United States. As the keystone of the tidewater colonies, these plains acquired characteristics that were determined by situation. Local trade was bounded by the Blue Ridge and by the Folded Appalachians. Maritime trade with New England, the southeastern states, and the West Indies laid the foundation for the far-flung commerce of the nineteenth century, the trade with China, the Pacific Coast, and western Europe.

The Middle Atlantic Littoral and New England had 150 years of growth before white settlement began in the trans-Appalachian country. Recognition of the significance of the new West to the seaboard communities was implicit in the construction of the Erie Canal, opened in 1825. The states of the lower Great Lakes basin soon became an important factor in the development of the Middle Atlantic port cities. The effect of the Erie Canal upon the peopling of the old Northwest Territory was likewise important. Ohio, for instance, grew slowly from 1789 until 1829, but by 1845 it had nearly two million people.

NEW YORK DISTRICT

New York City's Location. It is something of a paradox that where man-made landscapes are the most conspicuous, the nature of land use is often difficult to discern. The largest cities usually exhibit the maximum in geographical specialization, yet the regionalism of an urban landscape is not widely known. Reference points, intra- and interregional relationships, and the most densely utilized trade routes are relatively unknown to out-landers. Many of the observable features in the economic complex of a great city are foreign even to most of its residents. Vertical growth of cities con-tributes to this inchoate quality.

To some New Yorkers the East River has personality and the North River merits its name. The satellite cities assume a meaningful pattern and there is regionalism to the circulatory system of urban routes.

The Middle Atlantic Littoral is a comparatively small region containing three of the nation's largest cities; there is no other area on the continent with a comparable third dimension. The overwhelming size of the dominant cities of the Littoral has fostered an intercity bond equaled, probably, by no other region of North America. In the Middle Atlantic Littoral the term "satellite" or "sister" city has a connotation not often encountered in the urban geography of North American cities.

New York, Philadelphia, and Baltimore, together with their associated urban clusters are therefore less susceptible of regional differentiation and analysis than most other sections of the United States or Canada. The urban dominance gives rise to a concentrated economic pattern. Three islands, Manhattan, Long, and Staten, together with the adjacent portions of the Coastal Plain and Piedmont, have localized about 10 million people com-prising the city group known as Greater New York. The Hackensack and Passaic rivers contribute to the insularity of the site by means of the long peninsulas formed by their respective courses. Much of the land west of the Hudson River in New Jersey is swampland and tidal meadows; reclama-tion of this uninviting area has permitted the urbanization of its more accessible portions (*Fig. 8-4*).

From Bayonne north to Englewood, urbanization of the peninsula is almost complete, with Jersey City, Hoboken, and Union City constitut-ing the major urban centers. Beyond the Hackensack River, the Passaic Valley has localized Paterson, Passaic, Rutherford, Harrison, and Newark, culminating in Elizabeth on Newark Bay. Still farther west are Madison, Summit, Plainfield, Rahway, Metuchen, and New Brunswick which com-prise the outer ring of north Jersey cities.

East of Manhattan Island is the East River which connects Long Island Sound with New York Bay. The embayed character of the northern and southern shores of western Long Island, determines the pattern of urbanization, rather than river valleys as in New Jersey. The largest city is Brooklyn, east and southeast of Manhattan Island.

Population. Within the corporate limits of *New York City* there are 7,891,957 (1950) persons, an increase of about 400,000 since 1940. Several cities in northern New Jersey, and identified with metropolitan New York, declined in population between 1940 and 1950. Bayonne, Jersey City, Paterson, and Passaic declined. Other north Jersey cities gained in population during this period, including Newark and Montclair. Most of New York's growth took place in Nassau County and in Long Island counties, the former increasing by 65 and the latter by 40 per cent; this represents about half of the increase for New York.

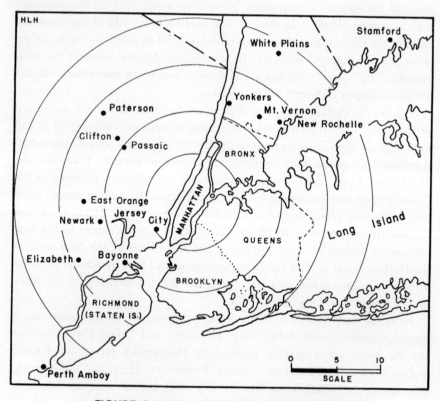

FIGURE 8-4: New York City, Urban Cluster

Concentric circles are at 5-mile intervals.

This great population represents a conglomeration of races and tongues, since 73 per cent are foreign-born or the children of foreign-born. Two hundred foreign-language newspapers are published for these minority groups. First to come were the Irish, then the Germans, Russians, and Italians, to list only the largest groups. Probably the largest group of recent arrivals are Puerto Ricans. From our southeastern states have come nearly half a million Negroes. Half of the Jews in the United States and an eighth of those in the world live in New York, the largest proportion being in Brooklyn. Foreign elements are not assimilated as readily as was once believed, and the prospect for this in the future is not bright.

Manhattan reached the peak of its population in 1920 with a total of three million; Brooklyn appears to have reached a stationary figure. New York's most rapid growth followed the opening of the Erie Canal and the later influx of immigrants, 75 per cent of whom landed in New York and many of whom remained there. Metropolitan New York has grown somewhat faster than the nation as a whole.[4]

Port of New York. Unlike any other port on the eastern seaboard, New York has not less than six distinct harbors: Lower and Upper bays, Newark Bay, Jamaica Bay, Flushing Bay, and Raritan Bay. Each one is a large harbor. All are connected by a series of sheltered waterways which possess a total of 900 miles of shoreline.

The rivers and swamplands which have restricted the uniformity of urban growth, have been expensively overcome by the construction of 56 vehicular and nine railroad bridges, 42 tunnels under the Harlem, East, and North rivers, and by 24 ferry routes over these streams. The island of Manhattan as the most accessible by water, has the major share of port functions; competition from the cities across the bay came after Manhattan was well established.

Yet Manhattan does not have a single steamship pier with direct trunk-line railroad connection. There is one railroad freight classification yard on the island. Railroad freight must be delivered to the ship by lighter or by cars on railroad floats (*Fig.* 8-5). Three hundred common carrier motor truck lines and many private carriers accounted for 40 per cent of all pierside loadings in 1950.

But the port is more than statistics; it is people at work. The physical conditions under which the several thousand employees perform port functions can appropriately be recorded here, but the social and economic con-

---

[4] In 1840 New York had 2.29 per cent of the total population; in 1890 the proportion was 3.98 per cent; in 1930 it was 5.64 per cent, and in 1950 it was 5.60 per cent.

FIGURE 8-5: New York City
(Nyspix-Commerce)

ditions under which they must labor are for the most part beyond the scope of this book. The piers are narrow and so are the slips; only 44 of New York's 140 city-owned piers are 100 feet or more in width. The width of the slip is often insufficient for berthing the larger vessels and for loading lighters along side. This obviously contributes to high transfer costs, serious congestion in and near the port, and delays in loading and unloading. Delivery of a carload from a New Jersey terminal to the port of New York is about as costly as from Albany, 100 miles up the Hudson.

Many of the piers cannot accommodate the 40-foot trucks now in use, so that the freight must be loaded and unloaded in the marginal streets outside the piers. Trucking companies charge for waiting time; in 1950 this amounted to $2 million. Shore labor charges, once a relatively minor cost, are now greater in many instances than the combined costs of vessel operation, insurance, crew wages, maintenance, and fuel oil. But these costs have been accepted and racketeering tolerated because of certain port advantages and public apathy.

As with other monopolies or near monopolies, the numbers employed are as great as "the market will bear." The work year for the average stevedore and longshoreman is about 100 days. During 1954 a strike at this port diverted all traffic to other ports, particularly Philadelphia and Baltimore. This work stoppage highlighted the weaknesses of New York's port functional organization.

The marked increase in port traffic on the lower Chesapeake ports and those on the Gulf and Pacific coasts may augur much for the future termination of such conditions in the port of New York. Thus far New York has lost primacy in shipping commodities of great bulk and relatively low value. In the shipment of grain from the ports of the Great Lakes for export, New York dropped from 76 per cent of the total tonnage in 1930 to 17 per cent in 1952. During the same period, the port of Baltimore rose from 8 per cent to 46 per cent in this commodity. New York's share of general cargo tonnage declined from 33 per cent to 20 per cent for imports in the pre-Korean War trade, and from 46 per cent to 38 per cent for exports during the same period.

The fact remains that New York is still the greatest port city in North America; ten thousand vessels clear its 600 piers every year, carrying $5 billion of cargo. An estimated 700,000 persons make their living in some branch of New York's foreign trade. On the whole, its import functions are relatively greater than export; an important part of the exports are termed "invisible," that is to say, they are the services of men, money, and ships.

The two major exports of the United States which have suffered most in recent decades by the dislocation of foreign markets are wheat and cotton, but for neither commodity was New York the principal exporter. Foods, particularly meats, have kept their high rank as exports; manufactured goods have steadily increased. New York, as the chief port for the Manufacturing Belt, has secured the lion's share of manufactured exports. The effect of the St. Lawrence Seaway upon this port can now only be surmised, but it seems probable that there will be competition. The rise of the Pacific area in the foreign trade of the United States may advance the proportional share of our Pacific Coast ports at the expense of New York. This seems likely in view of the post-World War II industrialization of the Pacific coastal cities, but New York still has superior access to money, available cargo space, and the greatest markets.

New York City's Free Port. In 1934 Congress permitted certain port cities in the United States to establish free zones where goods may temporarily come to rest without the payment of duties. In 1937 New York created a free zone on municipally-owned waterfront properties at Stapleton on Staten Island. These facilities were constructed originally for the needs of World War I. They include some 90 acres of land, four large, double-decked piers, and something in excess of a million square feet of storage space. Most cargoes come to this zone by water, but it is also served by three bridges, several highways and trucking lines, and eight railroads.

There are numerous reasons for the utilization of free zones. Commodities which have a tendency to shrink considerably may advantageously be stored there by the importer. When commodities come in under the quota system, it often helps to store some part of them until the next quota period. Processing and packaging frequently are reasons for storage in free zones, since some exporting countries have inadequate facilities for processing certain of their commodities. World War II added at least one advantage to this free zone when the disruption of normal trade in Sumatra leaf tobacco gave this zone an opportunity to become a leading Frascati or Sumatra leaf tobacco market. Among the commodities which have become important in the use of this free zone in New York are: Argentine beef, Brazilian nuts and coffee, Indian spices, Scottish woolens, Chilean copper, Canadian asbestos, Spanish olive oil, Chinese and Peruvian peas, Bolivian antimony, and Swiss watch movements.

Although re-exports have not been a major part of our foreign trade, New York's free zone accounted for approximately 5 per cent of the New York customs district's merchandise imports in 1950, and gave employment to some eight hundred persons.

Industrial New York. New York City and the cities near it in New Jersey and New York account for about 20 per cent of the nation's manufacturing concerns by number, 12 per cent of the total value-added-by-manufacturing, and 10 per cent of the factory workers.

Of the 18 major employment categories listed in the Census of Manufactures, New York ranks first in foods, textiles, apparel, chemicals, and electrical machinery. It ranks second in transportation equipment, nonelectrical machinery, metal fabrication, and in stone, clay, and glass products. It is third in rubber, coal, and petroleum products. It is seventh in primary metals. And in 1952 New York was growing industrially about as fast as the national average.

Of the approximately one million (September, 1952) industrial wage earners, Manhattan had 60 per cent, Brooklyn 24 per cent, Queens 10 per cent, and the remainder in Bronx and Richmond.[5] Manhattan has clothing as the dominant industry (35.1 per cent of the wage earners in manufacturing), printing and publishing (12 per cent), food (7.7 per cent), fabri-

[5] *New York State Commerce Review,* published by the state of New York, November, 1952.

FIGURE 8-6: *Garment District, New York City*

This area located in the heart of mid-Manhattan is one of extreme traffic congestion; large trucks such as the one in the foreground which is loaded with dresses for Pacific coast cities are obliged to deliver and pick up loads from the curbs of these narrow streets. The small hand-truck is used for the transportation of cloth or finished clothing between manufacturers, distributors, and retail stores within the garment district. (International Harvester Co.)

cated metals (4.6 per cent), and miscellaneous (7.8 per cent). Despite this industrial importance, only one person in four in the working population is in manufacturing, in contrast to an upstate ratio of one in three. The main reason for this is the dominance of commerce. While the New York metropolitan area has many large, nationally-known manufacturing concerns, the distinguishing characteristic is the array of small plants, many of them in the nondurable goods manufacture.

Another characteristic of Manhattan's industry is reflected in the fact that of every five persons engaged in the "miscellaneous industries" group in the city, three work in Manhattan and one in Brooklyn. Specialized types of manufacturing are concentrated here because substantial markets exist in the metropolis for articles with only scattered demand elsewhere. Three-quarters of the city's apparel employment is in Manhattan (*Fig.* 8-6). Most of the city's printing and publishing is also in Manhattan. Food processing is not so concentrated in its distribution; Brooklyn and Manhattan together have about two-thirds of the total employment.

Brooklyn is the top borough in the manufacture of fabricated metals. Brooklyn traditionally has been a chemical center and now leads the five boroughs. The list includes pharmaceuticals, paints, soap, inks, shoe polish, cosmetics, dyes, waxes, and industrial chemicals. Machinery manufacture is about equally divided between electrical and nonelectrical; much of the former group is concerned with communications. Much of the latter group is composed of precision and calculating machines.

Refining industries of several types are conducted on a tremendous scale, in part because of the local urban market and in part owing to the ready accessibility to other large markets, domestic and foreign, and access by way of water to raw materials. These port-type industries include petroleum, copper, and sugar refining, vegetable oil and other food processing, drugs, fur and leather, and a number of chemical industries. The value added by the manufacturing process is generally low in these industries.

The prestige of the city often is an important factor in localizing some of the industries; listed as prestige items are cosmetics, pharmaceuticals, apparel, toys, and novelties.

Brick and tile manufacture has become very important in the Hudson Valley north of New York. The Jersey shore has much of the oil storage and refining for the metropolitan district. Where the product is extraordinarily heavy and the market rather spotty, New York usually makes it; in this category are linotype machines, ships, and several types of refining machinery.

Long Island has a long agricultural history. Recreation and residential uses of the island are important. Consequently, this portion of greater New York was slow to industrialize. In 1950 only 14 per cent of the locally employed workers were engaged in manufacturing. Most spectacular growth took place in the 1940's when aircraft manufacture and precision instruments became large industries. In 1950 transportation equipment manufacture employed 36 per cent, and instrument manufacture 20 per cent of western Long Island's factory workers. Growth in factory employment since 1945 has been very great. The Atomic Energy Commission operates the Brookhaven National Laboratory in Suffolk County. Garden City has one of the world's largest book printing plants.

Yonkers is the center of an important industrial area at the junction of the Nepperham and Hudson rivers. Leading types of manufacture are apparel, textiles, chemicals, electrical machinery, and food.

Suburban Cities. Although politically not a part of New York, the several cities of north Jersey across the bay and river from Manhattan constitute, to a high degree, parts of the economic city. The inter- and intracity bonds are intimate and strong. Probably no other urban group in America manifests equally strong ties. It is logical to expect a high degree of specialization, with a certain rigidity of economy as a consequence. Because bodies of water surround most of New York, many industrial concerns dependent upon immediate rail facilities have located in the north Jersey cities adjacent to New York harbor. This has necessitated the transshipment of goods and people on a very large scale. Here, too, are industries which require a great deal of ground space. These cities, although economic spillovers from Manhattan Island, have become major cities in their own right and as such have offered markets large enough to attract manufacturing industries. Where congestion is so great, it operates as a centrifugal force to dispel certain industries. Those remaining must absorb high ground costs, varied handling costs, and in some instances, a labor shortage. Urban planning is more than providing for parks and playgrounds.

Despite the density of urban population at both ends of New Jersey's inner lowland, only two of her cities approach a half million, *Jersey City* with 299,017 and *Newark* with 438,776; only Newark increased in population since 1940.

Jersey City manufactures are important and highly diversified, and they also exhibit the characteristics of those of a port city. Prominent among these factory products are steel, steel barrels, coke, electrical appliances, carpet, tobacco, soap, chemicals, and cereals.

While not one of the port cities, Newark has been the principal city in New Jersey since the canal to Phillipsburg was completed in 1837. Antecedents of present plastic and electrical machine industries date from local inventions by Hyatt and Edison respectively, about half a century ago. Jewelry, leather, brewing, shoes, and meat packing likewise are rooted in the past century. Other ranking industries are chemicals, paints, pigments, electrical and other machinery, and baked goods. More recent arrivals include aircraft, motor parts, nonferrous metals, and furniture. Newark's increases in population, in number of factories, number of wage earners, and in value added, have been equaled by no other city in New Jersey since 1940.

Bayonne is another port city. It is located on a small peninsula between Newark and New York bays. The docking facilities are excellent. It is near the important motor traffic routes between New York and Philadelphia; by bridge it is accessible to Staten Island. It has long been known as an oil refining center and it remains one, but important new industries have been established which give present-day Bayonne some industrial diversity.

These include the manufacture of railroad tank cars, steam heating equipment, steel cable and barrels, brass, electrochemicals, and a dry dock and naval base. Further growth of this city of 77,203 is not likely in view of the peninsular restriction of available space and the loss of some refining facilities.

Paterson (139,336) is an interior city of northern New Jersey. In some respects its earlier industries were more widely known than its present products. Early in the nineteenth century Paterson was manufacturing textiles of cotton, wool, linen, hemp, and jute. Silk came a little later, along with firearms, locomotives, cutlery, and tools. Silk manufacture has been declining for half a century, but the textile dyeing and finishing industries have increased. More recent industries included aircraft engines, aluminum, foundry products, chemicals and dyes, apparel, rubber, and electrical appliances.

Elizabeth, with a population of 112,817, is the southernmost of the industrialized old cities of New Jersey which lie west of the New York harbor group. Leather, ship building, brewing, and the manufacture of food products are very old industries. Sewing machines, primary metals, chemicals, apparel, transportation equipment, and machinery products are among the variety of manufactured products that have recently come to diversify local industries.

Hoboken, with steel, ships, paper, and pencils, is the only city with more than 50,000 population in this group of north Jersey cities. *Perth Amboy* (41,330) refines oil, and *New Brunswick* (38,811) makes pharmaceuticals.

Impact of World War II. The amount of industrial facilities built in the New York district [6] by the government during World War II was about $940 million, ranking it next after Chicago and Detroit. The cities of northern New Jersey received some $167 million in increased facilities.[7] The breakdown of this increased industrial capacity shows its diversified nature (*Table* 8-1).

Only in explosives did northern New Jersey surpass, and only in chemicals did these cities approach, the increase of facilities in the New York district. New York led the nation in ordnance, machinery, and foods; it was tied for first place in shipbuilding facilities increase.

---

[6] N. Y., Kings, Bronx, Queens, Richmond, Nassau, Suffolk, Westchester and Rockland counties in New York, and Bergen, Hudson, Essex, and Union counties in New Jersey.

[7] Passaic, Morris, Somerset, Middlesex, and Monmouth counties in New Jersey.

TABLE 8-1: *Industrial Facilities Expansion, 1940-44*
($1,000)

	AIRCRAFT	SHIPS	ORDNANCE	EXPLOSIVES	IRON-STEEL	NON-FERROUS	MACHINERY	CHEMICALS	FOOD
N. Y. Dist.	222,299	296,080	121,166	53	30,567	45,782	95,689	50,591	79,813
No. N. J.	90,991	2,289	7,597	15,434	3,385	4,032	11,158	22,498	10,163

SOURCE: *Geographic Distribution of Manufacturing Facilities Expansion, July 1940-May 1944* (War Production Board, Washington, June 1, 1945), p. 23.

DELAWARE VALLEY

This is the second of the trans-Appalachian valleys to be considered in the Middle Atlantic Littoral. Unlike the Hudson Valley, the entire lower third of the Delaware River Valley is properly a part of this geographic region, while the upper portion is important to the region because it is a part of the natural corridor between New York and Buffalo. The roughly "S" shaped course of the Delaware River across parts of two physiographic provinces, however, has made it expedient to treat it in the chapter on the Appalachian Highlands.

The portion of the Delaware which is in the Middle Atlantic Littoral reaches from the Delaware Water Gap to Delaware Bay. It flows quietly along the Pennsylvania-New Jersey boundary for much of its middle distance, coinciding below Trenton with the western margin of the inner lowland of New Jersey's coastal plain (*Fig. 8-7*). Here the valley plain is much more extensive and supports a more uniformly prosperous agriculture than farther north. The inner lowland is part of the direct route between New York and Philadelphia, commerce is much more important in this lower third of the Delaware Valley than in the upper two-thirds.

The role of the Delaware River in the early trade of the tidewater colonies was such as to give it the leading position in coastwise and in foreign trade. The chief inland port was and remains Philadelphia. A canal between the Raritan and the Delaware rivers gave water access between New York and Philadelphia. The Schuylkill River was canalized at an early date to bring anthracite coal to Philadelphia.

A third canal was constructed many years later to connect Chesapeake and Delaware bays. The Delaware and Raritan Canal and the Chesapeake and Delaware Canal are links in the ambitious undertaking to provide an intracoastal waterway from Massachusetts to Miami, Florida, and across the Gulf coastal margin to the bayous of western Texas.

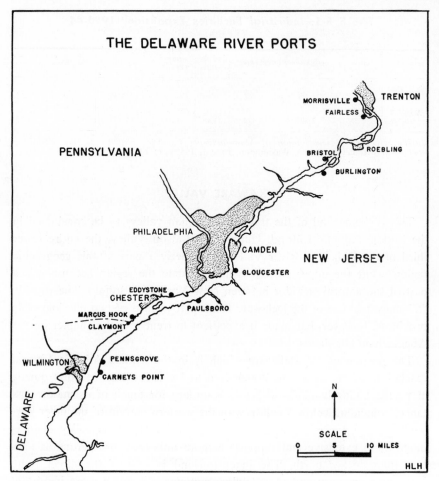

FIGURE 8-7

The middle and lower Delaware River has localized a number of cities on both sides which combine important manufacturing and commercial activities.

Population. So long as the immediately accessible hinterland largely determined the size of the cities, Philadelphia was the dominant city of the Middle Atlantic Littoral. The North Atlantic Coastal Plain farmers looked inland to their two great bays, Delaware and Chesapeake, for access to market. Ultimately this tidewater region was to grow less rapidly, but its initial impetus to commerce and manufactures arose from these agricultural beginnings and from the natural routes of trade afforded by the embayed Coastal Plain. Primarily for these reasons, Philadelphia led New York in growth for several decades.

TABLE 8-2: *Population of Philadelphia, New York, and Baltimore*
(× 1,000)

City	1890	1900	1910	1920	1930	1940	1950
PHILADELPHIA	1,046	1,293	1,549	1,823	1,950	1,931	2,071
NEW YORK	2,507	3,437	4,776	5,620	6,930	7,454	7,891
BALTIMORE	434	508	558	733	804	859	949

SOURCE: Bureau of the Census.

Early settlers in these southeastern counties of Pennsylvania and the New Jersey counties across the Delaware included English Quakers, Swedes, Dutch, Germans, Scotch, Irish, and Welsh. The Quakers were inclined to finance and commerce. The Germans, Swedes, and the Dutch came from countries where spinning, weaving, printing, paper-making and iron making were important industries; many of their descendants have followed similar trades. More recently many Italians and other south Europeans have come to work on the fruit, truck and poultry farms across the Delaware River in New Jersey; their Old World experience fitted them for this work.

Upstream from Philadelphia, both sides of the Delaware River are dominated by rural activities. *Trenton* (128,009) and *Camden* (124,555) are the only two cities of consequence on the Jersey side between the New York agglomeration and Delaware Bay. Although there are but two large cities south of Philadelphia, *Chester,* Pennsylvania (66,039) and *Wilmington,* Delaware (110,356), there are many more small ones with commuting populations.

Since 1940 Philadelphia's population has increased, reversing its trend during the previous decade. The seven counties comprising the metropolitan Philadelphia area have experienced greater relative growth than any of the major cities of the valley.

The City Planning Commission delineates metropolitan Philadelphia as extending on the north as far as Newtown, Souderstown, and Schwenksville; on the east as far as the Jersey towns of Moorestown, Marlton, and Swedesboro; on the south to the Delaware state line; and on the west beyond Phoenixville, almost to West Chester.

The most startling growth in population has been in the eastern river townships of Bucks County where the new Fairless Works of the United States Steel Corporation is the nucleus for urban growth on both sides of the Delaware River (*Fig.* 8-8). The population of New Jersey declines rapidly from the river counties eastward to the seashore. Running generally northwest-southeast through central New Jersey is a Coastal Plain waste-

FIGURE 8-8: *U.S. Steel Corporation's Fairless Works, Morrisville, Pennsylvania*

In the foreground is the water-filled slip where ocean-going carriers bring in ore from foreign mines. Back of the slip, center, are unloading docks, ore storage yard, ore bridge and blast furnaces. To the right of this area is the power house. Reading from upper left to right are the coke and by-products area, maintenance and storage facilities, open-hearth furnaces, and the sheet and tin mill area. (United States Steel Corp.)

land known as the "Pine Barrens" in which isolation stems mainly from poor drainage and poor soils.

The population of Delaware is dense on the inner or Delaware Bay margin. Maryland is primarily an Appalachian Highlands state, but its eastern Coastal Plain section is embraced within the Middle Atlantic Littoral.

Delaware Ports. The Delaware River is navigable the year 'round for ocean freighters to a point just south of Trenton, about 135 miles from Over Falls Lightship anchored just beyond the capes.

The Delaware River Port region is composed of compound ports; Camden-Gloucester-Paulsboro; Trenton-Morrisville-Roebling-Bristol-Burlington; Chester-Marcus Hook-Pennsgrove-Wilmington, and the dominant port of Philadelphia. As will be observed later, these four groups of ports have more in common than mere geographical propinquity.

FIGURE 8-9: *Port of Philadelphia*

Industrial and commercial growth of the Delaware River Valley, both north and south of Philadelphia, has made this city's harbor the nucleus of a dozen or more functionally related ports. Cork piers are in the lower foreground of the photograph. (Delaware River Port Authority)

At Philadelphia the river is about 1,000 feet wide, with a 35-foot channel to the Atlantic Ocean. Here the Delaware is fringed by about 200 piers, and the usual mechanical aids and storage facilities associated with ocean commerce. Some of the piers are specialized, for instance, petroleum at Point Breeze and grain at Port Richmond and Girard Point (*Fig. 8-9*).

Philadelphia offers relatively better rail and highway connections with the seaboard and interior cities than does New York. A belt-line railroad connects the extremities of the port with the four trunk-line railroads which tie this city with the Great Lakes basin and points between: The Reading, Baltimore and Ohio, Erie, and Pennsylvania railroads.

The nature of Philadelphia's commerce is quite unlike that of New York's port. Although the second-ranking Atlantic Ocean port, Philadelphia's tonnage in 1950 was 69 million, of this 37 per cent or 25 million tons was foreign trade, including 1.2 million tons of iron ore, mostly from Venezuela. This foreign commerce was 94 per cent imports, and three-fourths of this was petroleum. Of the 63 per cent of Philadelphia's commerce which was domestic, 44 per cent was coastwise traffic.

Ships plying the Chesapeake and Delaware Canal carry bituminous coal, primarily for the Delaware port industries; returning they carry coal tar, gasoline, and fuel oil. Local commerce among these Delaware ports is composed mainly of anthracite and bituminous coal, crude oil and its products, gravel and sand.[8]

Antecedents of Manufacturing. The antecedents of Philadelphia's manufacturing have been suggested in the section concerned with commerce. The early accumulations of capital from the profits of shipping served to promote manufacturing industries. The settlers from western Europe brought interest and skills in manufacturing as well as in commerce. The first paper mill in America was built on Wissahickon Creek near Philadelphia by an early German settler. As a consequence of a series of changes in the technique of paper making, this industry has spread to other regions; there remains in Philadelphia an important high-grade magazine and book paper industry. The great magazine-publishing concerns in Philadelphia cause the name to be a household word over most of the United States. The key position with respect to commerce along the Atlantic coast has served to promote the manufacture of those articles that have a ready market in the areas served by Philadelphia traders.

The manufacture of wool and cotton textiles, leather, ships, paper, machinery, and food products was important in early Philadelphia; several are still significant. Many a silver spoon treasured by families today in the country west of the Appalachians bears the "Phila" imprint on the handle, testimony to the dominance of Philadelphia in the production of luxuries as well as staples for the early Ohio Country trade. Some of the old stone factory buildings remain in use, many of them housing wool textile manufacturing.

For many years after the establishment of the Commonwealth, the Quaker influence was strong in political and economic fields; their conservative principles encouraged the foundation of insurance companies, and discouraged the establishment of certain industries, particularly those based upon the employment of cheap, imported labor; they also suppressed the manufacture of intoxicants. The Quaker influence has declined politically, but in the retailing, insurance, and manufacturing fields, and in the colleges and schools inaugurated under the auspices of this Society, there has been no decline in the Philadelphia region (*Fig.* 8-10).

[8] Federal Reserve Bank of Philadelphia, *The Business Review,* March, May 1952, August, December, 1951, makes a detailed port study from which much has been drawn.

FIGURE 8-10: *George School, near Philadelphia*
Schools and colleges are manifestations of the population density characterizing the undulating northern Piedmont counties which are suburban to New York, Philadelphia, Baltimore, and Washington. This is a preparatory school operated by the Society of Friends, first settlers of the Philadelphia region. (George School)

Philadelphia's Manufactures. Unlike some cities in the Middle West and in New England, Philadelphia is not known for one or two specialized factory products. Furthermore, it is definitely a manufacturing city despite its commercial importance; 45 per cent of its wage earners are engaged in factory work, as compared with a national urban average of 23 per cent. Some 6,000 industrial establishments in Philadelphia employ 350,000; within the seven counties which comprise the metropolitan area there are 8,000 factories employing half a million persons.

Pennsylvania is the second ranking carpet-making state, and the Philadelphia district is the greatest single producing region. This is the only major division in the state's textile industry in which employment has increased since 1939.

Philadelphia and the nearby cities are so much smaller than New York and its principal satellites that the uprooting forces which have developed within the latter region are, for the most part, less important in accounting for changes in the nature or location of Philadelphia's manufacturing.

In 1952, before the Fairless Steel Works began operations, primary metals industries accounted for but 7 per cent of the total; this category includes representatives of iron, copper, brass, and aluminum manufacturing. Philadelphia has been the port of entry for iron and ferroalloys for the local steel makers and for the Bethlehem district on the north and Coatesville on the west. With the recent impetus given iron and steel manufacture not only at the Fairless Works but also at other primary steel centers in the Delaware Valley, the commerce in these materials must of necessity greatly increase.

In general, Philadelphia's industrial districts border the two rivers which form the southern and southeastern margin and the north-south axis of Philadelphia, the Delaware and the Schuylkill, respectively. The belt along the Delaware River includes such bulk industries as shipyards, sugar and petroleum refineries, and plants manufacturing chemicals, ordnance, linoleum, and utilities.

The Schuylkill Valley has a high percentage of heavy industries, including the manufacture of electric storage batteries, auto bodies, railroad rolling stock, roller bearings, steel, saws and tools, transmission machinery, and laboratory glass. The urban core also has some manufacturing; aside from the loft types of manufacturing, there are publishing and the manufacture of apparel, instruments, and a variety of light metal goods.

Trenton is significantly situated at the great bend in the Delaware River which marks the important junction of two interregional trade routes: (1) the upper Delaware Valley with its access to the industrial cities in the vicinity of the Reading prong (Allentown, Bethlehem) and ultimately the Delaware Water Gap route to Phillipsburg, Stroudsburg, and the Pocono Mountains, and (2) the principal New York-Philadelphia-trans-Appalachian route to the Great Lakes basin. A glance at a Pennsylvania-New Jersey map will reveal this relationship.

Trenton's older industries include the clay industry, food products, pharmaceuticals, worsted goods, steel wire and structurals; among the more recently established industries are fabricators of rubber products, radios, auto parts, aircraft, turbines, jet engines, and electrical goods. The impact upon this old manufacturing city of the new steel plant at Fairless is just beginning, and it is decidedly disconcerting to the established ways of a commuting population to have property values soar.

Suburban Centers. Between Trenton and Philadelphia there are several small river cities each with some industry. Immediately south and west of Trenton there are no important manufacturing centers until Philadelphia's northern suburbs are reached. The countryside has been dotted with a dense rural population and numerous towns with a commuting population. Small truck farms are interspersed among the prevailing dairy farms and country homes of the city's commuters.

West of Philadelphia are the so called "mainline" cities. Most of them are residential, but auto trucks, publishing, food products, and textiles are well established and some new industries are coming in. Some New Jersey cities across the river are likewise suburban to Philadelphia. *Camden* dominates the group with its large payrolls in ship building and repair, radio and electronics, food products, and chemicals. As was noted earlier, these river counties of central Jersey have had significant population increases since World War II.

The sand plains of central and southern New Jersey supply the labor pool upon which Philadelphia industries have drawn for generally lower wage jobs. We will note similar situations elsewhere among American cities; it is an industrial location factor of increasing importance.

Down-River Cities. Down river from Philadelphia, the Delaware River has localized an important part of the industry of the Littoral. Chester exhibits the characteristic appearance of a heavy-industry center with its large shipyards, oil refineries, paper mills, chemical plants, automobile assembly plants, electrical establishments, and helicopter factories. Nearby is Eddystone with locomotive manufacture. Marcus Hook manufactures linoleum and refines petroleum. On the Jersey side is Paulsboro with two large refineries; there is also the possibility of a primary iron and steel plant being erected here. A little farther south is Pennsgrove, location of the first large American dye-manufacturing plant.

Today Wilmington is known as a chemical research center and is in close proximity to chemical plants on both sides of the Delaware River. Its manufactures include some paper-making machinery, auto parts, and textiles. Smaller places in the Wilmington area carry on the vast and varied activities of the du Pont chemical empire.

West of Philadelphia, good agricultural lands of the Piedmont and Triassic plains, there are three small cities of some industrial importance: Coatesville with primary iron and steel manufacture, Lancaster with the manufacture of watches and linoleum and processing of meat products, and York with the manufacture of electrical refrigeration.

Glass-Manufacturing Cities. In the generally rural area of South Jersey there are four small cities which have been making glass since the Ameri-

FIGURE 8-11: *Glass Manufacturing Plant, New Jersey*

This modern plant in the southern part of the state is one of several descendants from the oldest successful glass-making industry in America. This unit manufactures medical and technical glassware and glass tubing. (Kimble Glass Co. and Fairchild Aerial Surveys, Inc.)

can Revolution, when a German named Stang founded the industry at Glassboro. The neighboring cities of *Bridgeton* (18,378), *Millville* (16,041), and *Vineland* (8,155), have since developed as major glass-manufacturing centers (*Fig.* 8-11). Glassboro, the first glass-company town in America, has discontinued glass production and has converted its facilities to the manufacture of metal and plastic closures for glass containers produced in large volume in Bridgeton and Millville.

The glass-container plants move heavy tonnages of sand, soda ash, lime and other raw materials through large-capacity melting furnaces, accounting for relatively high material cost in this highly mechanized part of the glass industry. Glass tubing and medical and technical glassware made from tubing, the principal products produced in the Vineland area, make up an industry characterized by high labor and relatively low material cost. In all glass industries fuel is an important part of the cost of production. An abundant supply of excellent glass sand may be had locally. Over the years the fuel has changed from charcoal to producer gas and oil, and more recently to natural gas piped into the South Jersey area from southern fields.

Despite its proximity to Philadelphia, this district has had relative isolation, a common characteristic of much of the embayed Coastal Plain. These small cities are an exception to the generally peripheral location of Coastal Plain industrial centers. Until recently the labor pool of the Coastal Plain communities has never been completely absorbed into the larger industries along the lower Delaware River. The Germans and Swedes who first settled the lower Delaware have provided the core of management for many plants both on and off the river.

Delaware Valley Since World War II. The impact of World War II upon the Delaware Valley was important but not spectacular. Ship building was the principal industry affected. The most significant industrial changes have been made since the war.

Prior to 1950, the largest steel capacity of the Delaware Valley had been located farther up its course in the Appalachians, an integrated industry at Bethlehem on the Lehigh River. Farther downstream were several smaller steel mills, only one of them integrated. The war accentuated the shortage of light-steel capacity in the valley. Students of the area had anticipated that new primary steel-making plants would be built somewhere along the Atlantic seaboard. New England sought such a plant. Wartime expansion took place in California, Utah, and Texas; in 1951 the integrated Fairless Works of the United States Steel Corporation was built on the banks of the Delaware River northeast of Philadelphia.

This event has sparked an industrial rejuvenation in this section of the valley. Steel-fabricating industries have come to the source of steel. Ore docks to handle iron ore from Venezuela have been built. The problem of securing water for these plants and the thousands of new homes for the employees is reportedly solved. Pollution of the Delaware water by plant waste has been avoided by the largest concerns.

CHESAPEAKE BAY CITIES

Baltimore (949,708) lies on the margin of the Coastal Plain and the Piedmont, about 150 miles from the capes which mark the entrance to the Chesapeake Bay. Like New York and Philadelphia, Baltimore is situated east of an important trans-Appalachian corridor, Harper's Ferry and the valley of the Potomac River. It has no cluster of satellite cities about it; it stands virtually alone, with no urbanized railroad route between it and the cities of the lower Delaware Valley.

Historically, Baltimore has been primarily an import port with a large coastwise trade. In its water-borne foreign trade Baltimore's exports are slightly greater than imports and it ranks fourth among United States' ports. Imported raw materials constitute an impressive list, including iron ore from Chile, Venezuela, Liberia and Cuba; nitrates from Chile; phosphates from Florida; cork from Spain; wheat from the upper Mississippi Valley; coal from the Appalachian plateau; and lumber from the Pacific Northwest. Exports include sugar, steel, refined petroleum products, food, fertilizer, aircraft. The increase in the tonnage of this port in recent decades is due in no small measure to the acquisition of large iron-, steel- and machinery-manufacturing industries, but recent port development at New Orleans is of concern to Baltimore. New Orleans in 1951 ranked second in foreign water-borne commerce, with a value nearly twice that of Baltimore. Both ports have had an important export trade of products grown on the farms of the interior.

Manufactures. Despite the age and accessibility of Baltimore, its manufacturing industries are neither as diversified nor as important as those of Philadelphia. The dominant industry in Baltimore is iron and steel manufacture. It is relatively a newcomer, developed as one of the specialized units of two eastern and a midwestern steel companies.[9] The mills located on suburban Sparrows Point are well situated to receive their ore from the Tofo iron mines in Chile and new mines in Venezuela and Liberia. In 1953 Baltimore was the leading iron-ore importing saltwater port in the nation, with receipts of 7.6 million tons.

In addition to primary metals (including nonferrous), other important industries in Baltimore include the manufacture of transportation equipment for sea, land, and air; foods; apparel; machinery including electrical; chemicals; porcelain steel products; and a variety of fabricated metal products. Despite the importance of primary metals, aircraft, and chemicals, the manufactures of Baltimore are relatively balanced. During World War II, the dominant industries were aircraft manufacture and the building of ships; postwar years saw shipbuilding virtually cease.

The most numerous industrial plants are the processors of food products: seafood, fruit both domestic and imported, meat, cane sugar, vegetables, and tobacco.

Impact of World War II. The city and county of Baltimore received significant increases in their industrial facilities as a result of government

---

[9] Prior to 1952, Baltimore steel mills were the only integrated producers on the Atlantic Coast. Shipyards at Quincy, Mass., Staten Island, Baltimore, Portsmouth, N. H., Philadelphia, Chester, Wilmington, New Orleans, Hampton Roads and Norfolk have been markets for some of Baltimore's steel.

FIGURE 8-12: *Port of Norfolk*

A combination of naval and commercial coal exports has given the sister ports on Hampton Roads the greatest foreign export tonnage in the United States. (Norfolk Port Authority and PHOTO CRAFTSMEN, INC.)

spending for new industrial capacity during World War II. For them it was in effect "more of the same" rather than the establishment of new industrial types. The city gained new capacity primarily in nonferrous metals, shipbuilding, ordnance, and chemicals. The county gained primarily in aircraft and iron and steel. None of these industries was new to the district. The high level of factory production since the war has kept Baltimore's manufacturing at its maximum. Shipbuilding has not fared well, but aircraft, chemicals, machinery and petroleum products have increased.

Both the so-called "Chessie Corridor" of the Chesapeake and Ohio Railroad and the route of the Baltimore and Ohio ("Horn of Plenty") have sought and gained new industrial payrolls at some cities along their rights-of-way during the postwar years. This, together with increased industrialization in the southeastern states, has contributed to Baltimore's commerce. Among the consequences of American economic aid to western Europe has been the export of coal to Norway from Chesapeake Bay ports.

Norfolk (213,513) and *Portsmouth* (80,039) are twin cities on the south side of Hampton Roads, separated by the Elizabeth River. On the north side of Hampton Roads are *Newport News* (42,358) and *Hampton* (5,966). The fame of this urban cluster rests upon the excellent harbor and the use made of it by the United States Navy and by coal-hauling railroads (*Fig.* 8-12).

Great piers and handling machinery characterize these ports. Tobacco, oysters, oils, wheat, and peanuts are important exports. Manufactures are relatively unimportant, and include cement, fertilizers, textiles, and vegetable oils.

Washington. This planned federal capital was once near the geographical center of the United States. Without industry and without commercial advantage, *Washington* (802,178) has passed Boston and ranks next after Baltimore as the fourth largest city in the Atlantic states. Its suburban growth, greater than Baltimore, has recently been extraordinary, overflowing the District of Columbia into Virginia and Maryland.

Situated on the Potomac River, it has access to the trans-Appalachian West by way of the same corridor that gave early Baltimore its dominance in trade with the Ohio country. The founding function has persisted; beyond the utilities, printing, and food processing of a large city, industry does not exist in Washington.

The natural opportunities for a prosperous agriculture near the city have been limited by the Coastal Plain and Piedmont soils; commercial agriculture is primarily the consequence of an increasing urban market for dairying and vegetables. The recent large-scale invasion of the rolling Piedmont rural areas by home builders must have established something of a speed record. The pattern of such suburban growth bears little relation to the railroad; personal transportation afforded by the automobile has permitted a more diffuse form of urbanization than is common to large cities in the United States. Although Washington has no factory districts or industrial population, it is not free from blighted districts, even within a short distance of the White House.

The commerce of Washington is predominantly that generated by the office-holding population, but both railroad and airline traffic is very heavy by virtue of seasonal movement and administration. Other Chesapeake Bay ports perform many of the normal functions lacking in the port of Washington.

BIBLIOGRAPHY

BROWN, Ralph H., *Historical Geography of the United States* (New York, Harcourt, Brace and Co., 1948), Ch. 10.

Business Review, Federal Reserve Bank of Philadelphia, especially for 1951, 1952, 1953, and 1954.

LEE, Alvin T. M., *Land Utilization in New Jersey: A Land Development Scheme for the Pine Area* (New Jersey Agricultural Experiment Station, 1939), Bulletin 665.

MURPHY, Raymond E. and Marion MURPHY, *Geography of Pennsylvania* (Harrisburg, Keystone Press, 1932).

WOLMAN, Abel, "Utilization of Surface, Underground, and Sea Water," *United Nations Scientific Conference on the Conservation and Utilization of Resources,* Vol. 4 (1951), pp. 98-102.

CHAPTER 9

APPALACHIAN HIGHLANDS

PHYSICAL CIRCUMSTANCES AND SETTLEMENT

THE APPALACHIAN HIGHLANDS form the major part of the great hill-and-mountain province extending southwestward from the St. Lawrence Valley to Alabama, and west from the Atlantic Littoral to the Central Lowlands (*Fig.* 9-1).

The Appalachian Highlands south of the Adirondack Mountains consist of the Newer or Folded Appalachian, the Older Appalachian, and the Appalachian Plateau provinces. These provinces may be subdivided into sections as is indicated in *Figure* 1-2. In setting up the geographic region, Appalachian Highlands, it seems proper to exclude the Piedmont section of the Older Appalachians. The northern portion was included in the last chapter on the Middle Atlantic Littoral and the remainder will be included in the geographic region, the South.

Adirondacks. The Adirondack section is a highland of from 1,000 to 5,000 feet in elevation, with the greater proportion under 2,000 feet; only in the mountainous eastern front are there peaks which reach 5,000 feet. The descent to the Champlain-Hudson lowland on the east is abrupt; but toward the St. Lawrence lowland on the northwest and the Mohawk lowland on the south the decline is more gentle.

Many lakes and the remnants of lakes dot the hilly surface of this glaciated upland. Population is sparse, perhaps five persons per square mile. The fact that this "island" of rugged terrain and many lakes is accessible to large urban centers has made it possible for the cut-over timberland to experience a seasonal rejuvenation in population by the sale of its climate and scenery to tourists.

194

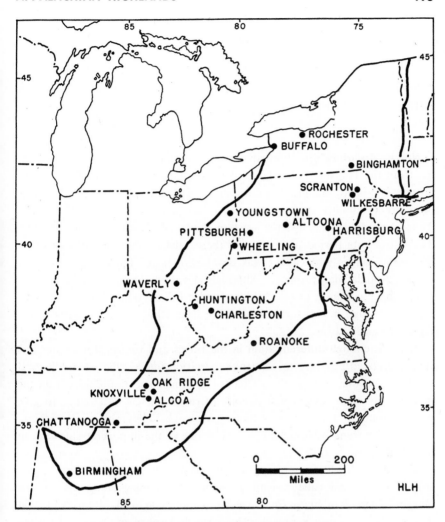

FIGURE 9-1: *Appalachian Highlands*

Blue Ridge. The Blue Ridge section is a mountain belt lying between the Newer Appalachians and the Piedmont. In southeastern Pennsylvania, the Blue Ridge is approximately 20 miles in width; in central Virginia where the gap of the Roanoke River separates it from the main block of the province, it is 70 miles wide. North of the Roanoke, the term Blue Ridge is very suggestive of its physical appearance, but south of the river only the eastern portion of the province bears the name and appearance of Blue Ridge. Immediately west lie higher and more rugged mountain groups:

the Great Smokies and the Unakas. The mountains terminate in northern Georgia, beyond which the Piedmont borders the eastern margin of the Newer Appalachian province for a distance of 200 miles. In eastern Pennsylvania, the Reading Prong, an extension of the New England upland, fails to meet the northern end of the Blue Ridge and thus leaves open a wide gateway to the Newer Appalachian province from the Atlantic seaboard.

Newer Appalachians. Immediately west of the Blue Ridge, and extending from the Hudson Valley to central Alabama, is the Newer or Folded province. It is not one great physiographic region in the sense that all parts of it are essentially uniform. It was developed upon sedimentary rocks which were folded against the western flanks of the Older Appalachians. Through a long period of erosion of these folded strata the present series of parallel ridges and valleys was developed, hence the name, Newer or Folded Appalachian province. Although elevations are nowhere great, the steep slopes common to most ridges render this section a barrier to commerce, although not so forbidding as the Blue Ridge or many parts of the Appalachian Plateaus.

There is enough differentiation in the ridges and valleys throughout this very attenuated province to warrant subdivision into northern, middle, and southern sections. The north or Champlain-Hudson section differs from the others in its minor extent and paucity of ridges. It has no streams to give it accessibility to the east. The tributary Mohawk Valley, the most northerly of the major trans-Appalachian routes, is one of the important gateways to the west.

The middle or Pennsylvania-Virginia section has fairly uniform cigar-shaped ridges and valleys, with a much larger valley along the eastern margin. There is a hiatus in the eastern mountain wall of this valley in Pennsylvania where it is breached by a nearly level plain between Reading and Harrisburg. This section has much greater accessibility to the Atlantic seaboard than the portions to the north and to the south. Appalachian drainage focuses upon this portion of the Newer Appalachian province virtually all of the commerce between the Middle Atlantic port cities and the Middle West.

The southern and largest subdivision of this province has smaller valleys, a larger proportion of the surface in ridges, and a large eastern valley interrupted with numerous ridges. It is less accessible from the east and west than the other two sections farther north.

The eastern portion of this province, from the Hudson Valley to central

Alabama, is a series of connected valleys, from ten to twenty miles wide and over a thousand miles in length, known collectively as the Great Appalachian Valley. It was long the principal corridor between the northeastern and southeastern states. Thousands of people came into Kentucky and Tennessee by way of the valley and the Cumberland Gap near the Kentucky-Tennessee border. There are no other important gaps through the western Appalachians between this gap and Wills Creek in Maryland; there is none south of it. Many portions of the Great Valley are best known by names taken from streams which follow the valley for part of their courses, such as the Shenandoah, the Roanoke, and the Coosa.

Appalachian Plateaus. West of the Newer Appalachians lie the extensive Appalachian Plateaus. Bounded on the north by the Mohawk Valley and the Ontario Lake Plain, on the west by the Central Lowland and the Interior Low Plateaus, this region offers much diversity within its expanse of hill country. The extensive northern portion was glaciated, and, as a consequence, the hills and valleys are more broadly sweeping than they are farther south. Isolation here is not so general as farther south; the relatively sparse rural population maintains a fairly prosperous agriculture.

The central and southern portions were not glaciated. Streams have carved an intricate pattern of narrow, steep-sided valleys in the plateaus. On these slope lands and the limited areas of flat land an agriculture has been developed that is little above the subsistence level. No part of the Appalachians is more isolated than a section known as the Cumberland Plateau.

Major Drainage Features. The rivers of the northern Appalachians rise in the Adirondacks and the Appalachian Plateau and flow eastward across the Newer Appalachian province to the middle Atlantic seaboard. In the central section of the Highlands the streams rise at or near the Allegheny Front, the eastern margin of the Appalachian Plateau, and flow westward to the Ohio. South of the Roanoke, the major stream is the Tennessee which has its source in the Blue Ridge and flows westward across the Folded Appalachians and the Cumberland Plateau and eventually also discharges into the Ohio. This arrangement of the major drainage lines in relation to the physiographic provinces was at the time of settlement a very important factor in facilitating the movement of the pioneers along the water courses and the fertile valleys. The trans-Appalachian migration was in its early stages a movement southwestward along the Great Valley and across the western ridges and the Cumberland Plateau to the fertile lowlands of

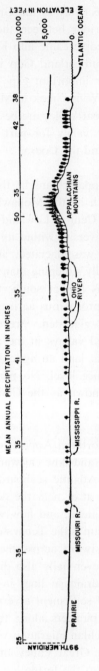

FIGURE 9-2a: *Profile Showing Atlantic Forest*

(U.S. Dept. of Agriculture)

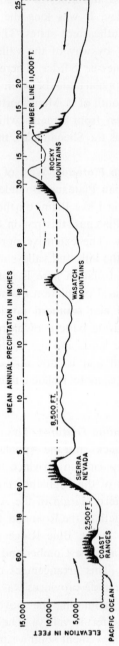

FIGURE 9-2b: *Profile Showing Pacific Forest*

(U.S. Dept. of Agriculture)

Tennessee and Kentucky. Along the main routes of travel isolation was largely dispelled, but the more inaccessible sections of the highland have become the repository of cultural and economic customs dating from an early day.

FOREST INDUSTRIES

Northern Forest. The Northern Appalachians and the Adirondacks have been intimately related to the forest industries of the northeastern part of the United States. This section shared with New England the spruce, balsam, fir, and white pine forest. The dividing line between northern and southern types of Appalachian forest is in Pennsylvania; north of this boundary grow birch, beech, maple, and hemlock, generally at medium elevations and on better-drained soils. Although the forest economy of the Adirondacks and northern Appalachian Plateau is largely a thing of the past, about half of the land is classed as woodland. The proportion is slowly increasing at the expense of submarginal farm land (*Fig.* 9-2a and b).

The only considerable forest area that remains is in northern Pennsylvania, where state forests occupy about half of the most rugged of all parts of the northern plateau. Extensions of this large forest area cross the Newer Appalachians into Maryland. There is virtually no permanent occupancy of these forests. Fishing in the spring and summer, and hunting in the autumn have enticed many tourists into the area; Pennsylvania issues almost as many hunting licenses as Michigan. Isolation precludes the possibility of developing the profitable part-time agriculture characteristic of the New England woodlands.

Although commercial lumbering in the Adirondacks and the northern Appalachians closely followed that of New England in terms of time, the character of the industry and the role it played in the development of the region are in contrast. Large-scale commercial lumbering began just before the middle of the nineteenth century, but instead of the industry following the excellent stand of trees southward along the Appalachians, it moved from Pennsylvania to the Lake states in the search for white pine. The lumberman followed the westward-moving rails and the center of population rather than the continuous stand of good saw timber to the south. However, by the end of the century, the southward advance along the Appalachians had begun.

The first clearings in the northern forest were for agriculture in eastern Pennsylvania and central and southern New York. Last to go were the forests of the Adirondacks, Catskills, and less accessible slopes of western Pennsylvania.

Although lumbering was generally a prelude to farming in the Appalachians, there were exceptions. In some places farming was impossible. In early times charcoal for iron furnaces drew heavily on local wood, particularly in eastern Pennsylvania. Later prop timbers for the expanding coal-mining industry made demands upon these forests. By 1870 the commercial cutting of white pine in New York and Pennsylvania was at its height; a little later spruce reached its peak. Last development was the pulpwood industry of the Adirondacks. Abandoned lumber towns, abandoned power sites with their mills, and an atmosphere of desolation today characterize many districts of the western Adirondacks and the plateau to the west.

Nevertheless, in some districts the wood-products industry remains the important source of livelihood. Making of charcoal, cutting of timbers for coal mines and for the state highway department, and the manufacture of containers and of toys are forms of the industry in the upper Susquehanna Valley and the Adirondacks.

Southern Forest. The Appalachian Highlands are in effect a peninsula of northern climate and mixed forest extending deep into the South. Although most of the region has been cut over, much timberland remains dispersed over the area. Several timber and pulp companies have sought to replenish the timber in their extensive holdings in the southern Appalachians.

In every state of the Appalachians, there are thousands of acres of state or national forest. More is being added each year. The programs for flood and erosion control, and public recreation have advanced the conservation of timberland. The deplorable conditions following the strip-mining of coal in the Plateau counties have aroused some public indignation which has brought about some reforestation by operators and public sponsorship.

As isolation was dispelled by the improvement of the highway system, public recreation promoted the conservation of woodland at many places in the southern Appalachians. This also brightened the economic prospects of many of the agricultural lands. Agricultural communities have developed in small mountain valleys of the southern section of the Blue Ridge. These valleys or "coves" are more or less self-sufficing farming communities, with small wood-working industries in a number of places.

In nearly all parts of the Appalachian Highlands, except the industrialized valleys of western Pennsylvania and eastern Ohio, and the numerous arable valleys throughout the Newer Appalachian and Plateau provinces, the cash income from wood products has always been relatively important.

MINERAL INDUSTRIES

Coal Mining. The Appalachian Highlands are the greatest storehouse of high-grade coal in the United States; they contain probably 85 per cent of the good coal in the nation. The Appalachians embrace the anthracite fields of northeastern Pennsylvania and the bituminous fields extending along the plateaus from northern Pennsylvania to central Alabama. Coal mining is not one of the industrial "first families" of the United States; there was no commercial mining of coal during Colonial times. It was not until after the turn of the nineteenth century that domestic and industrial needs gave rise to coal mining of even local importance. Today the coal industry is represented by hundreds of bituminous and dozens of anthracite mines in the Appalachian Highlands.

Two main factors retarded the early development of coal mining in eastern United States: the coal mining districts everywhere lie two hundred miles or more from tidewater, and the terrain is such as to make the shipment and export of the coal expensive. Again, eastern United States offered a great stand of timber and an abundance of water-power sites. Together, these substitutes for coal served to retard commercial coal mining. The physical presence of coal did not then, and does not now, determine its use by man in that vicinity.

Labor has never been cheap in the United States. Most economic activities therefore have been scrutinized to the end that a machine or a method may be devised to lower the cost of production, whether in the field, mine, or the factory. The use of machines in bringing the American continent into production promoted coal as the chief fuel for the manufacture of labor-saving machines, and subsequently it became, until recently, the principal source of power for their motivation. Lately, the use of petroleum and natural gas have increased at a more rapid rate than coal.

The coal-mining industry in the Appalachian Highlands has undergone three main periods of development: (1) the rise and decline of the anthracite fields in the Newer Appalachians of eastern Pennsylvania, (2) the rise of the northern bituminous fields, and (3) the rise of the southern bituminous fields. The bituminous fields are in the Appalachian Plateaus.

Anthracite. Owing to the location of the anthracite fields, it was the first major industrial fuel in the United States. These anthracite fields were near the center of iron manufacturing. The canalized Schuylkill River was used to bring the coal to the factories and homes of the lower Delaware Valley. Despite its limited areal extent, anthracite was the dominant industrial fuel until after the Civil War. Since then, and particularly since 1910, its use in manufacturing and in homes has declined greatly. By 1954, even the anthracite-owning railroads were turning to diesels. Anthracite deposits are worked at four major fields in Lackawanna, Luzerne, Carbon, Schuylkill, and Northumberland counties in northeastern Pennsylvania. If all four mining districts were brought together, the combined area would be about four hundred square miles, as against thousands of square miles of bituminous deposits farther west.

Anthracite deposits average much deeper underground than bituminous, and the preparation of the coal for market is considerably more exacting and expensive. The greater amount of capital needed to bring these deposits under production has always curtailed widespread ownership; probably 75 per cent of the coal rests in the hands of not more than ten companies.

The limited extent of the anthracite fields was conducive to early unionization of the miners, with the result that for 50 years the buying public was critical of the interrupted supply and quality of the coal. Today there is the anomaly of the anthracite regions lying inactive in many parts, in spite of the high favor this solid fuel has always enjoyed. Because it is a partial monopoly, and because its unionized labor has insisted on maintaining high wage rates, anthracite coal has not manifested one of the characteristics of a declining industry—that is, prices have not declined materially.

From what has been said, it will not appear strange that, although the bituminous tonnage mined is eleven times that of anthracite, the consumption of the former by industrial plants is perhaps twenty times that of the anthracite. Only in the industrial periphery of the mining districts and along certain of the anthracite railroads are there industries consuming anthracite coal.

In spite of a century of activity and an estimated second century of productivity ahead, the anthracite-mining districts appear to have only a fairly bright future. This is due, in part, to the diminishing returns from mining and to the nature of the geologic setting of the industry. World War II could not revive this industry.

The depth of mining operations has greatly increased; less accessible coal has been worked. Coal supports for the roof of the mine (pillars) have been removed and columns of steel or wood substituted. Despite some mechanical aids in mining, the use of substitute fuels has been ruinous to the livelihood of many mining towns. Further attention will be given to this region later in this chapter.

But what of the anthracite landscape itself? What changes are apparent in the folded mountain country in which the anthracite is mined? It has been described as an abandoned countryside by one student of the conditions there.

> Years ago someone with imagination surveyed the wild and gloomy region of Pennsylvania's anthracite district and said that if one stood on the crest of the Alleghenies and looked eastward, he might not see hills and valleys, but long rolling breakers of stony surf, petrified waves a thousand feet high. In the trough of one of these waves lies the coal-mining town of Shenandoah—a town that reflects the rise, power, and decline of a great industry.
>
> The traveler looking down from Bear Ridge can see a large hummock thrown up on the valley floor; Shenandoah is on the hummock. The houses are huddled and crowded together, the roofs close, sloping gradually to a rounded peak at the top of the hummock, with only the Latin crosses and the bulbous Greek domes rising above the town.
>
> A blackened colliery can be seen, shut down. On the right is another great colliery, also closed down, with a thousand window lights smashed, the dark mountains of culm behind it; it is a wild ruin. There isn't a light or puff of smoke. The great stacks are rusted, the engine room is shut up. On the railroad spur which runs to the breaker are empty cars, the rails are rusted.
>
> From the north end of the town, where the mountain rises abruptly once more, the picture is complete. There is the town on its hummock; away overhead is the road which climbs Bear Ridge and winds through the little coal towns, over the hills, to the county seat, Pottsville. Below on every hand are the collieries and toward the southeast, the huge St. Nicholas breaker. In and out, crisscross, all over the Valley, thread the railroad tracks, Lehigh Valley, Reading, and Pennsylvania.[1]

Statistically, the situation in the anthracite mining industry as compared to bituminous is as follows: since 1910, the anthracite tonnage has declined from 84,485,000 short tons to 44,077,000; the number of men employed dropped from 169,497 to 72,624; and the number of days worked dropped from 229 per year to 211. The number of tons of coal mined per miner per year during this 40-year period increased from 498 to 597.

Bituminous Fields. In many ways the bituminous fields and the bituminous coal-mining industry are in contrast with the anthracite fields and the anthracite-mining industry. Bituminous fields employ six times as many men, mine eleven times as much coal, and each miner produces almost three times as much coal per year. These figures are for all of the nation's bituminous fields, but the contrast is valid for the Appalachians as well.

Unlike anthracite, bituminous coal is an important raw material for industrial uses; the products made from coal number in the hundreds. Bituminous coal is mined in the Appalachian Plateaus from northern Penn-

[1] Reprinted with permission from George Leighton, *Five Cities* (New York, Harper and Bros., 1920).

sylvania to central Alabama. It is mined under every conceivable condition: large mines and small mines, mechanized and manual, private and corporation-owned, union and nonunion, shaft mines and strip mines.

The flat-lying strata of the Plateaus have been deeply and intricately dissected by streams over a very long period of time. While such erosion has carried away great quantities of coal, it has at the same time rendered the coal seams more accessible to the miner. Railroads follow the more important of these winding valleys through the Plateaus; it will be recalled that the Highlands lie athwart the principal east-west trade routes between the Atlantic coastal cities and the heart of the continent.

Unlike the coal-mining landscapes of the anthracite districts, the coal economy of the bituminous fields is not everywhere apparent. The mines are tucked away in obscure valleys at points where coal is accessible and its removal facilitated by the system of valleys.

The northern Appalachian (Allegheny) field in western Pennsylvania, eastern Ohio, and northern West Virginia has seams which average 7 feet of mineable coal and are generally thicker in the east and south. The quantity, quality, and accessibility of this bituminous coal have had incalculable effect upon the economic development of the United States. The Ohio River with its north-flowing tributaries have dissected parts of the upland so completely as to make these coal seams accessible to the miner and to offer a relatively easy route to the markets.

Southeast of Pittsburgh, in the vicinity of Connellsville, the coking quality of a particular seam gave it more than local importance during the days of bee-hive ovens for coke making. During the past twenty-five years, the amount of bituminous coal marketed and the number of miners employed have declined.

Meanwhile there has been an attempt on the part of certain large coal companies to lower the delivered price of bituminous coal by using coal-mining machines which greatly reduce the number of miners underground (*Fig.* 9-3). One type is the auger which is adapted to the terrain of the Appalachian Plateau. Another is the remote-controlled mining machine known as "colmol" and the "colveyor." One mining company in eastern Ohio is constructing a pipeline about one hundred miles long which will move powdered coal and water from its mines to Cleveland power plants. In strip mining of coal, larger shovels are being introduced to lower costs per ton of coal. Coal cleaning has advanced (*Fig.* 9-4).

The outstanding development of this coal field has been its industrialization. Manufacturing cities are strung along the railroads which cross the Plateau. Between Lake Erie and Pittsburgh, the manufacture of steel has become especially important. Industrial landscapes which have developed here are overwhelmingly those of heavy industry. Prominent among these industries based upon heat and power are primary iron and steel, coke, clay, glass, oil refining, aluminum manufacture, and industrial chemicals. The great number of urban centers has promoted the manufacture of many kinds of commodities which are attracted by markets or concentrated labor. Heat and power industries invariably attract other industries which utilize their byproducts and process their semimanufactures.

South of the Northern Appalachian field lies the second important bituminous coal mining area of the Plateau, the Middle Appalachian field of southern West Virginia and eastern Kentucky. On the eastern side of this coal mining area lie the New River and Pocahontas fields, famous for smokeless coals of high heating value. To the west lie the Kanawha, Tug, and Logan fields which produce coal of high quality.

Since industrial development in this region is not comparable to that in the Pittsburgh area, most of the coal mined is exported to other states. The great coal routes from this field cross Ohio to cities on Lake Erie which forward the coal to Canada and the states of the Great Lakes basin (*Table 9-1*).

TABLE 9-1: Coal Shipped From Great Lakes Ports, 1953
(bituminous net tons)

Port	Cargo To		
	Canada	*United States*	*Total*
LAKE MICHIGAN			
Chicago	578,839	173,551	752,390
LAKE ERIE			
Toledo	4,284,595	19,483,718	23,768,313
Sandusky	1,584,190	6,819,410	8,403,600
Ashtabula	2,190,593	587,980	2,778,573
Fairport	665,008	395,038	1,060,046
Lorain	1,374,080	1,259,435	2,633,515
Erie	899,327	1,111,482	2,010,809
Conneaut	410,496	566,941	977,437
Buffalo	528,154	149,509	677,663
Huron	5,021	1,267,409	1,272,430
Cleveland	2,994	125,885	128,879
LAKE ONTARIO			
Rochester	849,663	22,991	872,654
Gr. Sodus Bay	1,626,389	396,007	2,022,396
Oswego	563,885	5,285	569,170
Totals	15,563,234	32,364,641	47,927,875

SOURCE: *Annual Report,* Lake Carriers' Association, 1953, p. 86.

FIGURE 9-3: *Coal Cutting Machine, Kanawha Section of the Appalachian Plateau*

As wages have risen in the coal-mining industry, mechanization of operations has proceeded from the face of the seam to loading on gondola cars. This machine is the product of one of the two major manufacturers of such mining machinery. (Jeffrey Manufacturing Co.)

Important shifts in mining have occurred in these two fields. In Pennsylvania during recent decades, there has been an increase in the amount of coal mined in the Allegheny Valley, and a decline in the Monongahela Valley to the south. A more important change has centered around the production of coal for export to the cities of the Great Lakes region. This has involved about thirty million tons of coal each year, shipped northwest and west to Michigan, Wisconsin, Minnesota, and the Dakotas. Coal consumption has been declining, but there are signs of a reviving demand.

The southern portion of the Plateau has bituminous mines in Tennessee and Alabama. In several respects these fields have supported a different type of coal-mining industry. The factors which account for these differences are predominantly economic.

Whereas many of the larger Pennsylvania, Ohio, and West Virginia mines are captive, that is, they are owned by large steel, utility, and chemical companies of the United States and Canada, there is very little of this in the southern Appalachian coal fields. The coal industry refers to these southern

FIGURE 9-4: Coal Preparation Plant, Kanawha Section of the Appalachian Plateau

Competition with oil and natural gas has forced upon the bituminous industry handling and cleaning processes suggestive of a manufacturing plant. Not far from this plant is the first pipeline to move powdered coal on a commercial scale. (United States Steel Corp.)

mines as "commercial" or independent mines. The southern mines are generally the first to suffer in an industrial recession.

The Warrior coal fields in Alabama have a steel-manufacturing center at Birmingham for an industrial market. The export of coal southward by rail and water has been a profitable and growing part of the market. The growth of industry in the southeastern states has aided the southern Appalachian coal fields, but has not yet given this coal an important industrial market elsewhere.

Settlement throughout most of the Appalachian fields is on a very different pattern from that in the anthracite country with its parallel valleys and ridges. The bituminous mines are generally smaller and very much more numerous. The coal is much more accessible to the miner, due in part to the absence of folding and of faulting so characteristic of the anthracite region. Historically, the bituminous industry has necessitated fewer structures above ground than the anthracite industry. This is changing as mechanization of grading and cleaning progresses.

Petroleum and Gas. The Appalachian Plateaus have a long history in the oil and gas industry. Beginning with the Drake discovery in northwestern Pennsylvania, this region has produced a very high-grade oil and in quantities great enough to have given to "Pennsylvania grade" the equivalent of "sterling" to silver. Thirty years ago the oil industry of western Pennsylvania, eastern Ohio, and northern West Virginia was thought to be on its way out. This has proved to be the case in most of these fields, producing from 25 barrels to 45 barrels per day. The greatest revival in production recently has been in the Bradford district north of Pittsburgh, in the Alleghany Valley. Water under a pressure-flooding system increases production about 50 per cent.

Iron Mining. The same Lyon Mountain district in the Adirondacks which supplied iron for the cannon of the United States' fleet in its first war with England is still producing iron ore. These ore bodies, so hopefully opened in the late eighteenth century, failed to support a flourishing industry, primarily for lack of cheap transportation, the necessity for sintering the ore before use in a furnace, and the comparatively small extent of the deposits.

In 1950 between three and four thousand miners living in the small communities of Lyon Mountain, Port Henry, Clifton, Benson, and Tahawus produced about 4 million tons. Although the rejuvenation of the mines is recent, it was not a part of the World War II revival of marginal-mining communities. Awareness of the limited future of the high-grade iron deposits in the Lake Superior district and an expansion in the iron- and steel-making capacity of the eastern district were probably the most important factors in the increased mining activity in Adirondack fields.

The ore is crushed and mixed with powdered anthracite coal, then fused into sinter resembling black, metallic clinkers. The sintered ore is then sent to Bethlehem, Pittsburgh, and Cleveland blast furnaces. A cut-over forested region, after a long period of hardscrabble farming, experienced rejuvenation 150 years after settlement.

An iron mine has been opened near Morgantown, Pennsylvania, some 30 miles from the old, still productive Cornwall mines. The magnetic ore from this latter mine has been used for more than a century. The new 3,000-foot Grace Mine yields ore with 44 per cent metal content.

Zinc Mining. In the Appalachian section of northern New Jersey the principal zinc mines in eastern United States are located. The future of this mining district is uncertain. Although iron is also mined in northern New Jersey, it has never become important.

Brine. The basis for a relatively new and very important chemical industry (alkalis) is the brine pumped from deep beneath the surface at several places in the plateaus. Among them are the Kanawha Valley in West Virginia, some river counties in eastern and southeastern Ohio, and part of the panhandle of West Virginia.

AGRICULTURE

The agriculture of the Appalachian Highlands is not susceptible to precise regionalization to the extent that Great Plains areas are. The intricacies of terrain are too great to permit the development of broad zones of agricultural similarity. Yet in a general way there are three regions discernible: the northern Appalachian area, a portion of the Hay and Dairy Region; a central Appalachian zone, where urbanization has intensified the agriculture; and finally, an extensive, rugged region of the southern Appalachians where farming is self-sufficing.

Northern Appalachians. There are two physiographic provinces represented in this great region: the Appalachian Plateaus and the Newer Appalachian province. The former is the more extensive but the latter contains most of the superior farm lands. The several sections of the northern Appalachian Plateau of New York, Pennsylvania, and Ohio are all a part of the Hay and Dairy Region. Large parts of the Adirondack Mountain area, the Catskills, and the Pocono portions of the Plateau are largely forested or classed as woodland. Where dairying has developed, it has been in conjunction with mixed farming in an attempt to utilize the poor thin soils in cutover regions. Tourists, both summer and winter, have fostered the development of dairying.

Over the larger part of southern New York, where much of the land is fit for pasture but unfitted for plow crops, dairying has developed upon a rather poor mixed farming economy. Accessibility to eastern markets has enabled most of the region to dispose of fluid milk. Although grain farming is relatively unimportant, buckwheat is grown for its grain and during the blossoming period the bees reap a harvest of nectar which they convert into buckwheat honey. The cool climate favors the growing of oats. Corn is grown for ensilage and supplies a very suitable feed for the dairy cattle during the winter.

Where the farms are not readily served by transportation to city markets, the manufacture of butter and cheese has persisted (*Fig.* 9-5). Farther south in the northern tier of counties in Pennsylvania, the slopes are steeper and the land less productive. Milk condenseries have come in to replace cheese plants and creameries. Without minerals or urban development to increase the carrying power of this land, these portions of the northern Appalachian Plateau have little prospect for a change in livelihood (*Figs.* 9-6, 9-7).

In the Catskill Mountains, the Poconos, and the Finger Lakes districts, tourists have increased as a source of income. In certain of the northern Pennsylvania counties just west of the Susquehanna River, it is reported that the income from hunting and fishing licenses is the most important source of public income, in an area which is primarily woodland.

Although not a part of the Appalachians, the fruit districts between the Appalachian Plateau and Lake Ontario and Lake Erie are included here. They are an important exception to the prevailing dairy economy of the Plateau. On this lake plain of western New York is the nation's second greatest apple-growing area and one of the major grape districts. This narrow fruit belt continues along the south shore of Lake Erie. The principal advantage rests in the moderating effect of the lake breezes, not only preventing early opening of the buds and forestalling early frosts, but also somewhat lengthening the growing season. The Cleveland district, for in-

FIGURE 9-5: Cheese Factory, Allegheny Section of the Appalachian Plateau

Dairying is the dominant phase of commercial agriculture in many parts of the Plateau in New York, Pennsylvania, and Ohio. This is the storage room in a factory located in an area inhabited by many of Swiss and German ancestry. (Ohio State Agricultural Extension Division)

stance, has on the average a growing season twelve days longer than the district a hundred miles south.

The lake silt soils likewise promote the growing of vegetables for market. They mark the location of a former glacial lake or swamp; when drained and cleared many areas became suitable for such crops as celery, onions, potatoes, tomatoes, and cabbage. The nearby large cities of the lower Lakes have stimulated this type of farming not only because of markets but also because of the abundance of cheap hand labor, much of it foreign-born, so necessary in market gardening. The same factors have promoted the erection of large areas of greenhouse, particularly along the Lake Erie plain.

Immediately south and east of the Plateau counties lie the ridges and valleys of the Newer Appalachians. Dairying is important, but chiefly in the northern tiers of counties. The soils are best in the limestone valleys. Soils on the ridges are invariably thin and poor; in the areas where agriculture is attempted it is in sharp contrast with that of the generally prosperous lands of the valleys.

Central Appalachians. In nearly all of the central valleys of the Newer Appalachians, there is evident the careful farming practices noted in the famed Lancaster and Chester, Pennsylvania counties of the Middle Atlantic Littoral. To one traveling through the rural areas the land use pattern shows up distinctly, owing to the canoe-shaped valleys; dairying, small grains, and stock-feeding are common to nearly all. But the substantial homes, big barns, silos, and ordered appearance of the farms are common only to the more accessible valleys of the central Folded Appalachian province.

In eastern West Virginia and Virginia many of the ridges are given over to apple orchards, but throughout the entire region the farming system is based on corn and livestock. There are many departures from this system where markets enable the farmers to specialize in some other crop or crops. Thus in Pennsylvania the corridors through this province enable farmers to engage in dairying for the great markets of the Middle Atlantic port cities. There are small-scale representatives of this dairy landscape in such interior limestone valleys as Bedford, Nittany, and Kishacoquillas in central Pennsylvania, and Greenbrier in central West Virginia.

In southeastern Pennsylvania where the Blue Ridge Mountains are breached by a lowland (See the Middle Atlantic Littoral), the resulting prongs of this upland are named after their respective terminal cities, Reading for the northern and Carlisle for the southern. On the so-called mountain farms of these two prongs about half the apple crop is grown.

Although not more than a fourth of the land in farms is devoted to

FIGURE 9-6: Second Frontier Day, near the West Virginia-Ohio Border
State, county, and local agencies co-operated in redesigning, fencing, plowing, and
seeding a farm in a public demonstration of rehabilitation of a hill country farm in
the Appalachian Plateau. (Ohio Implement and Tractor Co.)

apples, outside labor must be brought in for the harvest, some of it Puerto
Rican. Despite the proximity to large Middle Atlantic and New England
cities, a large part of the apple crop must be canned. Orchardists of the
Reading Prong district can about half their crop; Carlisle Prong growers
must can about 90 per cent. Exports to western Europe have not revived
since the World War II decline.

The broad stretches of the Plateaus in western Pennsylvania, eastern
Ohio and northern West Virginia are characterized by more narrow-floored
and tortuously winding valleys than the ridge and valley country. There are
no extensive valley plains with productive soils, although many of the
valleys are relatively wide and definitely productive.

Owing to the fact that several of these valleys in the Plateaus provide
access partly through the Highland barrier, parts of these valleys are urbanized and the agriculture is modified accordingly. The greatest number of
these urban centers are in the valleys of the Pittsburgh region.

Southern Appalachians. Agriculture in the southern Appalachian Plateaus is in marked contrast with the north and center, despite the apparent

FIGURE 9-7: Water Conservation

Such farm ponds as this are becoming fairly common on the hill farms of the Appalachian Plateau and the Central Highlands. This conservation project is in the Kanawha section of the Appalachian Plateau. (Ohio State Agricultural Extension Division)

similarity in topography. Isolation is the principal factor in accounting for this contrast; climate differences are also important. Where dissection is more advanced and has exposed the underlying limestone, the valleys may be wider and more productive than farther north, yet isolation remains. The over-all cropping system is classed as Corn and Winter Wheat, but the regional variations are so great as to make this quite indefinite.

Everywhere south of central West Virginia similar conditions prevail. Here agriculture is made self-sufficing only by lowering the standard of living. Farming has been supplemented by coal mining which is declining in importance.

Except for certain areas and during certain periods, these hills have always been "The Land of Do Without." Timber exploitation went first, then the decline of large sections of the mining industry has accentuated the poverty of the region.[2] Yet it is in this part of the Appalachians that

[2] Statistics compiled from a questionnaire sent to the parents of the 400 pupils in the High School in Berea, Kentucky, indicate that: 82 per cent live in the country, with an average distance of ten miles from town; 76 per cent get no daily, 63 per cent get no weekly paper; 68 per cent are farmers, yet 53 per cent do not own a team of

rural population increase is the highest in the United States. In some counties the birth rate is so high that population would be doubled in thirty years were it not for emigration. Population density reaches 100 per square mile on some of the bottom lands, while ridge tops are sparsely populated.

The Southern Appalachians constitute the greatest surplus labor pool in the United States. They supply the industrial North with white labor. In some years this margin amounts to 40 per cent of the cityward shift. These southern counties must export labor or clear more slopes to move more people on as tenants.[3]

The economy of the region has to all intents and purposes "left man out." The cultural and physical endowments of today's population in many of these counties are relatively inferior to those of their forbears in the same regions. Mining of the land continues unabated; so does mining of the people. Professor Odum of North Carolina has suggested that nothing short of a complete reconstruction of the agriculture, together with adequate support of the tools and institutions of science and learning, will solve the economic problems of this large region.

Although improvements are being made, there is a very great difference in the conditions under which agriculture is carried on in these hill counties and in the Corn Belt. This was illustrated by a program set up during World War II. The scarcity of labor on Corn Belt farms during the war years was critical. An attempt was made to bring in workers from the Kentucky and West Virginia hill counties But the differences in farming techniques was so great in the two regions that certain midwestern colleges and universities with departments of agriculture undertook to train groups of white farmers from south of the Ohio River in the ways of Corn Belt farms. After a training period of six weeks, these young farmers were deemed sufficiently familiar with Corn Belt procedures to perform their part on these northern farms.

MANUFACTURES IN THE NORTH AND CENTRAL APPALACHIANS

Steel Industry. From its first establishment during Colonial times, the iron and steel industry has been intimately related to the Appalachians.

---

horses or mules; 83 per cent own no automobile; 65 per cent of the houses have never been painted; the average distance of the water supply from the house is 172 feet; the average number of children is six. From *Annual Report,* President of Berea College, 1939. The situation has not changed much today.

[3] See especially: F. J. Marschner, *Rural Population Density in the Southern Appalachians.* Miscellaneous Publication, No. 367 (U.S. Dept. of Agriculture, Washington, March, 1940).

The accessibility afforded by several of the major valleys both directed and accelerated the westward movement of settlers. The fertile valleys and the mineral resources of these Highlands slowed this movement by inviting permanent settlement and establishment of industries. The longest-lived and most important of these is the manufacture of iron and steel. Many parts of the Highlands have become closely linked to the steel industry because of their raw materials, the experience in making steel and availability of labor and of market. As a force in the development of the several Appalachian provinces, nothing has equaled the iron and steel industry.

In the Folded Appalachians, between New York and central Alabama, beds of hematite and other ores occur. These deposits generally are relatively low-grade ores but some have the advantage of being nearly self-fluxing; iron has been made at scores of communities in the province and its manufacture persists today in a dozen or more centers. The ironmaster was in many instances the blacksmith. The mine was simply a local ore deposit and fuel was charcoal from the neighboring forest. With relatively widespread raw materials, the industry spread with advancing population to many parts of the Highlands, but especially it was centered in the parts which, by virtue of accessibility, were most densely settled. The advent of the railroad marked the period of greatest growth of these early furnaces which reached their peak late in the nineteenth century.[4]

The first coal field developed for the iron industry was the anthracite field of the upper Schuylkill Valley, and it was in this and neighboring valleys of eastern Pennsylvania that the rising iron industry received its second impetus. The anthracite iron industry surpassed the charcoal-iron industry rather promptly, and, when the railroad had opened up the coking coal

---

[4] Mount Joy, better known as Valley Forge, was one of dozens of "iron plantations" that existed in the valleys of the Schuylkill, Susquehanna, and Juniata rivers in Pennsylvania during the eighteenth and early nineteenth centuries. Others were Pine Forge in Berks County, Windsor Forge, Martec Forge, Hopewell Village, and Elizabeth Furnace in Lancaster County. Some of these plantations covered 10,000 acres; clustered about the "mansion house" were houses for the thousand workers, as well as the necessary work buildings, vegetable gardens and orchards essential to their self-sufficiency.

The iron plantation had virgin forests of oak, hickory, ash, chestnut, and pine. From these trees was made the charcoal used in smelting the local iron; on a plantation of this size, 15,000 cords of wood were made each year into charcoal; wood-cutters and charcoal burners greatly outnumbered the miners.

At about the same period charcoal iron was made in the hills of the western margin of the Plateau in Ohio, West Virginia, and Kentucky by methods essentially the same as those just described. In the Ohio Valley, however there was no known plantation system; instead, the economic and perhaps social life of the people working in the woods, iron pits, and furnaces crystallized into villages, some of them persisting today, many with the suffix "furnace" to the town name.

(Information from Dr. Wilber Stout, formerly of the Ohio Geological Survey).

of the lower Pittsburgh district by 1875, coke-made iron had surpassed the tonnage of anthracite-made iron. But still the ores of Pennsylvania, Ohio, and West Virginia were adequate for the manufacture of iron and steel. When in 1884 the iron ores of the upper Lakes began to supplant the ores of the Appalachians, the iron-and-steel-making centers were able to take in their stride the changed source of ore.

Iron manufacturing has not remained concentrated in the same places, but its importance has continued. Local ores of the Cornwall district near Harrisburg, northern New Jersey, and the Adirondacks still supply part of the requirements of mills at Bethlehem. The contribution of these iron and steel regions to the freight of American railroads is very great. Single cities along the Lake Erie shore handle a greater tonnage of these heavy materials from the upper Lakes than the total tonnage of the United States wheat crop for a year.

In 1899 there were in the United States a total of 575 furnaces for the production of pig iron and ferro-alloys. Although by 1938 the number of furnaces had decreased to 236, their total capacity was about 51 million tons, or four times as great.

TABLE 9-2: Growth of Steel Capacity in the United States, 1939-1954

State	1939 capacity	1954 capacity	Tons gained
PENNSYLVANIA	26,250,322	34,037,460	7,787,338
OHIO	17,543,008	24,388,060	7,245,052
INDIANA	10,196,677	14,968,500	4,771,823
ILLINOIS	6,893,820	10,800,200	3,906,380
NEW YORK	3,984,960	6,349,530	2,364,570
MICHIGAN .	3,496,226	6,550,780	3,054,554
MARYLAND	3,371,200	5,884,000	2,512,800
ALABAMA	2,611,840	4,721,520	2,109,680
CALIFORNIA	848,131	3,158,470	2,310,339
WEST VIRGINIA	2,032,800	2,668,000	635,200

SOURCE: *Steel Facts,* No. 124, 1954.

These changes in number and location of plants were made possible by a long series of improvements in the manufacture of steel. Just after the Civil War, a new process known as the basic open hearth was introduced in the United States. This eventually proved to be one of the principal factors contributing to the development of the United States' steel industry, since it made possible mass production of high-grade steel from relatively impure raw materials. It also permitted the use of scrap iron and scrap steel. Approximately nine-tenths of the steel is still made by the open-hearth process today.

Another change in production which enabled the steel industry to move to new districts was the use, and subsequent dominance, of by-product coke. This freed the coke makers from the Connellsville coking coal south of Pittsburgh. Yet another and more recent change in steel making is the use of the electric furnace. This process enables the manufacturer to make steel in smaller quantities and with closer quality control, both factors contributing to the recentralization of steel manufacture. The huge costs of an integrated steel plant are avoidable with an electric furnace. The net effect of these and other improvements in steel making may be inferred by a study of *Table* 9-3.

TABLE 9-3: *Steel Capacity by Furnace Type in the United States*
(1,000 net tons)

Year	Open-hearth	Bessemer	Electric
1940	73,722	6,010	1,887
1950	86,985	5,537	6,871
1953	102,678	4,637	10,232

SOURCE: American Iron and Steel Institute.

In view of the great losses in weight of the materials from which steel is made, the changing sources of iron ore become significant in the localization of the nation's steel industry, particularly for the Appalachian Highlands. *Table* 9-4 lists these sources from the upper Great Lakes districts of the United States and Canada.

TABLE 9-4: *Sources of Iron Ore*

Range	Year Opened	Total production to 1947
MARQUETTE	1854	234,710,595
MENOMINEE	1877	212,328,816
GOGEBIC	1877	249,491,922
VERMILION	1884	77,198,587
MESABI	1892	1,436,330,392
MAYVILLE	1892	2,379,865
CUYUNA	1911	55,579,932
CANADIAN MINES	1904	3,935,450
MICHIPOCOTEN	1939	2,868,964
STEEP ROCK LAKE	1944	2,531,927 (1950)

SOURCE: Lake Carriers' Association, 1950.

The Benson and Harmony iron mines of the Adirondacks, Cornwall mines in Pennsylvania, Red Mountain in Alabama, and the scores of mines supplying the charcoal furnaces in the Appalachians are producing iron ore. Appalachian furnaces began using Cuban ore in 1884, Chilean ore in 1911, and are now securing ore from Venezuela and Liberia also.

The Great Lakes have been the private ocean for the steel industry and the Appalachians have kept pace with developments. *Table* 9-5 indicates what students of the steel industry believe will be the sources of iron ore for the 1955-1965 period.

TABLE 9-5: Projected Sources of Iron Ore for the United States, 1955-1965

(annual supply in thousands of long tons)

Ore source	Central District	Eastern	Western	South	Gulf	Total
LAKE SUPERIOR direct and concentrated ores	60,000	5,000	——	——	——	65,000
LAKE SUPERIOR taconite & concentrates	15,000	——	——	——	——	15,000
SOUTHERN	——	——	——	10,000	——	10,000
ADIRONDACK	5,000	——	——	——	——	5,000
E. APPLS. AND N. J.	——	5,000	——	——	——	5,000
WESTERN	——	——	5,000	——	——	5,000
LABRADOR	10,000	10,000	——	——	——	20,000
VENEZUELA	5,000	5,000	5,000	5,000	5,000	25,000
OTHER SOUTH AMER.	——	5,000	——	——	——	5,000
OTHER FOREIGN	5,000	5,000	1,000	2,000	1,000	14,000

SOURCE: *Resources for Freedom, A Report to the President* (The President's Materials Policy Committee, Washington, June, 1952).

The steel industry of the Appalachian Highlands enters the second half of the twentieth century about as well situated with respect to raw materials and market as ever, despite the growing dependence upon foreign sources of ore. Even with the expansion of the nation's Manufacturing Belt, these Highlands remain a major part of it (*Fig.* 9-8).

The manufacture of iron and steel is not the only important industry in the Appalachian Highlands. It will be the only one treated in such detail, because of its importance and the limitation of space. We turn next to a consideration of manufacturing districts in the Appalachians.

Mohawk-Lake Plain Lowland. Although neither the Ontario Lake Plain nor the Mohawk Valley is part of the Appalachian Highlands, their inclusion in this chapter seems proper in view of their geographic associations. Between the Adirondacks, the Tug Hill Plateau, and Lake Ontario on the north, and the northern escarpment edge of the Appalachian Plateau, lies an east-west corridor which breaches the Appalachian Highland. Here the New York State Barge Canal joins Lake Erie and the Hudson River. Railroads follow this "water-level" route to the Middle West.

This highly industrialized lowland has developed a great variety of manufactures characteristic of the maturing economy of many older industrial districts.

Buffalo, at the eastern end of Lake Erie enjoys a strategic commercial position. Traffic for eastern cities leaves the Lakes at this point, because of Niagara Falls and because of the pattern of the Lakes themselves. Buffalo

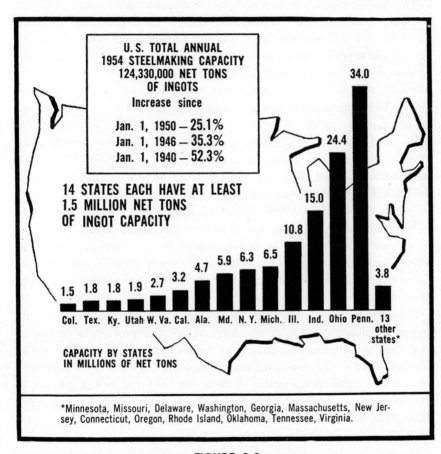

FIGURE 9-8

(*Steel Facts,* August, 1955)

also lies at the western end of a natural corridor across central New York through which virtually all of the trade must pass that is destined for the great Atlantic ports of Boston and New York. It also lies at the northwestern end of the principal passes through the northern Appalachian Plateau. A narrow plain borders Lake Erie and provides an easy detour around the Appalachian Plateau of Pennsylvania and New York; Buffalo lies on this plain.

From the point of view of situation, *Buffalo* would appear destined to be one of the nation's largest cities. The same factors which gave it early importance still do so. That it numbers only 577,395 persons appears to be due to the presence of *Rochester* (332,488), and *Syracuse* (220,583), near enough to share many of the advantages of Buffalo's situation.

The leading industry is iron and steel. Suburban *Lackawanna* (27,658) assembles iron ore, coal, and limestone nearly as cheaply as Detroit, cheapest of Great Lakes steel districts today. Lackawanna coal costs less than it does at Gary, yet its ore costs no more. By barge to New York City, steel costs less than from any other steel mill, prior to the Fairless Works' establishment. As one of the largest plants of the nation's number two steel maker, Lackawanna steel products supply the northeastern states market, the automobile factories of Detroit, Toledo, and Cleveland, and the eastern railroads. The Buffalo steel district complements rather than competes with other Bethlehem plants at Baltimore and at Bethlehem. Growth in Buffalo's steel industry waited, therefore, upon a more or less specialized market; the Lackawanna works were originally at Scranton. During the past twenty years the steel capacity of this district increased about 2 million tons.

The manufacture of flour has likewise been related to the decline of small flour mills in the interior of the country, cheaper costs of Lake-borne wheat, and the large market of the northeastern states. Today Buffalo ranks second to Kansas City but ahead of the long-time leader in milling, Minneapolis.

Buffalo's second-ranking industry is the electrothermal and electrolytic groups of industries in both of which this district ranks first or second in the nation. Although Niagara Falls' hydroelectric development supplies only one-third of the power requirements, it has been the most important single factor in the development of these two industrial groups. Market is the other main location factor. Every ferro-alloy is manufactured here, chlor-alkali products from the extensive salt beds of New York's Appalachian Plateau, and abrasives from the electric furnace.

Other Cities. Rochester is another of the large group of American cities which began as a commercial center of, and manufacturer for, an important

FIGURE 9-9: Schenectady Works of the General Electric Co.

That this Mohawk Valley location has been appraised repeatedly over the years as desirable, is apparent from an inspection of the types of factory buildings in the photograph. (General Electric Co.)

agricultural area. The falls of the Genessee River provided power for an important milling industry. Subsequently the rise of the enormous precision-metals manufacture has transformed Rochester. Photographic, optical, and electrical industries now dominate. In the manufacture of men's clothing it ranks among the first four in the nation.

Syracuse is another of the important cities located on the famed corridor traversed by the Barge Canal and the railroads. Its industries are of a heavier type than Rochester. Foundries, clay and salt products, steel, and shoes are among the leading employers.

Farther east in the Mohawk Valley are a score of smaller cities which have become specialists in manufacturing. *Albany* (134,995), *Schenectady* (91,785), and *Troy* (72,311) are the largest. This triumvirate of industrial cities lie on or near the junction of the Mohawk and Hudson rivers. Their manufactures include a wide range of electrical equipment and machinery, some heavy machinery including locomotives, textiles, and chemical products (*Fig. 9-9*). In the score of cities in the lowland, nearly every conceivable commodity is manufactured; certain specialties are well known: collars and shirts, knit goods, gloves, copper and brass goods, and electrical equipment. They have two things in common: raw materials are imported, and their markets are nationwide.

Farther south, in the Susquehanna Valley of the Appalachian Plateau in southern New York, there are a few smaller industrial centers, chief among them being Binghamton with its great shoe plants, Elmira with tools and machinery, and Corning with its immense glass works.

Anthracite Region. An older iron-making district but by no means so important as the Pittsburgh area is the eastern portion of the Newer or Folded Appalachians where the mining of anthracite coal has been dominant for so long. Although the steel industry persists in *Bethlehem* (66,340), the increases in the national capacity of this industry have not taken place in this area. Bethlehem began its iron industry with local ore and charcoal and changed to nearby anthracite before many years; most of the raw materials today are brought great distances. The main factor in Bethlehem's success lies in its accessibility to the steel-deficient Atlantic Littoral, together with its ability to import the raw materials at relatively low cost. Buffalo and Baltimore plants of this company complement the production at Bethlehem. *Allentown* (106,756) is the twin city of Bethlehem astride the Lehigh River. It is not a steel city; nineteen large cement plants, storage battery, auto truck, cotton and silk textile plants comprise the major industrial groups.

Farther north are several small cities which once were prosperous anthracite mining towns. *Scranton* (125,536) is the largest city in the entire anthracite area. Its economy reflects the general decline in mining; between 1940-1950 the population declined by some 20,000. The number of jobless miners is increasing, in part due to mechanization and strip mining, but fundamentally because of a declining market for the fine, solid fuel, anthracite coal. The demands of World War II could not restore the fortunes of anthracite coal mining. Even the railroads which used (and owned) this hard coal as fuel have turned to diesels. With a decline in coal tonnage, railroad employment drops; there is little else to haul.

Despite attempts on the part of Scranton, only limited industrialization has taken place. Silk once was important; work clothing continues as an industry; shoe manufacturing, metal stamping, and metal products have come in since World War II.

Hazleton (35,491), *Carbondale* (16,296), *Nanticoke* (20,160), *Wilkes-Barre* (76,826), *Shamokin* (16,879), and several smaller cities are in the same straits as Scranton. All have declined in population for two decades. In recent years there have been vigorous attempts at self-help; a variety of industrial projects have been undertaken with community backing; some have paid off. The Lackawanna Industrial Fund Enterprises, the Wyoming Valley Industrial Development Fund, and Panther Valley Industrial Association have been active in this "operation bootstrap." Hazleton was the envy of the region when it succeeded in attracting a large branch plant of Electric Auto Lite Company of Toledo. At the other extreme, Shamokin returned the funds collected after vainly trying to secure an industrial prospect.

Local attempts at self-sufficing economy are not promising owing to the meager agricultural opportunities afforded by these stony ridges and narrow valleys. The miners are most reluctant to venture into the bituminous fields of western Pennsylvania; some have gone to industrial jobs in the Delaware Valley and other eastern districts.

Industrialized Valleys of the Plateaus. The greatest concentration of early steel-making capacity developed on the Allegheny Plateau between Pittsburgh and Lake Erie. Since the process of iron and steel making in this upper Ohio Valley was the same as that employed in the older iron districts in eastern Pennsylvania, the comparative youth (by a century or more) of the former region does not preclude a comparison of the factors of location and development.

The industrialized valleys of western Pennsylvania may be thought of as a center of a larger industrialized area embracing the eastern Ohio and northern West Virginia sections of the Allegheny-Kanawha plateaus. The names of such valleys as Conemaugh, Allegheny, Monongahela, Ohio, Mahoning, and Beaver are synonymous with the making of iron and steel. The most conspicuous feature of the landscape is the steep hills, with 400 to 500 feet relief. From these hills and valleys the steel-making cities of this portion of the Plateaus take their attenuated shape and series of occupance levels. Such a terrain is the principal reason for the great number of smaller cities and towns which form the suburban agglomerations.

Pittsburgh District. Pittsburgh is the center of the largest steel tonnage manufacture in the United States with most of this tonnage coming from the lower Monongahela Valley to the south of the city. Blast furnaces, rolling mills, tin-plate mills, and steel fabricators combine with coke, chemical, glass, clay products, and oil-refining plants to make up this heat-and-power-landscape (*Figs.* 9-10, 9-11).

The Allegheny Valley north of Pittsburgh has developed somewhat differently; it has added to its somewhat lighter steel products the manufacture of glass, aluminum, and chemicals. Pittsburgh itself, at the junction of

FIGURE 9-10: *Pittsburgh Works, Jones and Laughlin Steel Corp.*

This is an aerial view down the Monongahela River toward the junction with the Allegheny. The new open-hearth shops have replaced slum properties since World War II, left center. (Fairchild Aerial Surveys, Inc.)

the Allegheny and Monongahela rivers, is more of a steel fabricator than the producer of raw steel or iron. The market for steel is self-generating to an important extent. The machines used in mining, loading, and transporting ore and coal, the machines used to make the steel in the mill, and those which fabricate the basic steel into hundreds of steel products, constitute the core of Pittsburgh's industry. With the postwar increases in railroad freight rates, there has been a tendency for steel-using fabricators to come to the Pittsburgh district. This reverses an earlier trend when concern was felt for Pittsburgh's industrial future. Even the casual traveler notices the change in the new look to the "Triangle" and the improved routes through the city.

A number of the suburban cities in the Pittsburgh region have declined in population since 1940.[5] The increase in industrial production has not been reflected in population growth.

[5] Among them are: *McKeesport* (51,502), *Duquesne* (17,620), *Ambridge* (16,429), *Braddock* (16,488), *Aliquippa* (26,132), *McKees Rocks* (16,241), *Homestead* (10,-046) and *Carnegie* (12,105). Other small cities in the region which have increased somewhat in population include: *Clairton* (19,652), *Munhall* (16,437), *Swissvale* (16,488), and *New Kensington* (25,146).

FIGURE 9-11: Ohio River at Aliquippa, Pennsylvania

The steel industry continues northwestward from Pittsburgh along the Ohio River. This view is of the Jones and Laughlin steel plant. (Fairchild Aerial Surveys, Inc.)

The site for heavy industry within the Pittsburgh region has changed only with difficulty. Topography dictated a riparian location for the railroads. The rivers supplied water for the mills and much of the bituminous coal came down the Monongahela by barge. Congestion and land values have kept all but two of the primary steel mills out of Pittsburgh proper. As the manufacture of finished metal products has grown until it surpasses primary steel in employment, the location of industry was increasingly freed from the congestion of the river valleys. The aluminum, zinc, and chemical industries likewise tended to break up this congestion. The supplanting of beehive-oven by by-product coke likewise enabled the manufacture of coke to follow its market.

Although glass manufacture is a part of this heat-and-power landscape, its manufacture is largely in the Allegheny Valley north of Pittsburgh. Glass sand in the region attracted this industry at the turn of the nineteenth century. The industry was subsequently stimulated when coal replaced charcoal as a fuel, and again when natural gas replaced coal. Oil is becoming increasingly important as fuel, with no discernible effect upon the localization of the industry. Part of the glass sand is still produced in

FIGURE 9-12: *Belle, West Virginia*

This plant is an example of the relatively recent industrialization of the middle and lower Kanawha River Valley in which petrochemicals, carbochemicals, and ferro-alloys play an important part. (DuPont Photo Library)

Allegheny County, but sandstone for good glass is quarried near the central part of the state. Other than the Plateau counties, there is but one important glass center in Pennsylvania, and that is at Philadelphia, where laboratory and technical glass products are manufactured.

The food-products industry has long been an important industry in Pittsburgh. Originally the available cheap female labor was an important reason for its being there. Essentially this same situation persists, with access to market increasingly important.

The postwar growth of manufacturing at several places along the Ohio River downstream from Pittsburgh has given new importance to river transportation and, indirectly, to Pittsburgh itself. In the maturing of the city's industries the growth of finished metal products assumes a larger role. In this transition, the accessibility of the city's raw materials and fuel will be less important than the extent of markets and the skill of the labor pool upon which the district's industries draw.

East of Pittsburgh on the Conemaugh River is Johnstown, a small-scale Pittsburgh. Although it is in an active coal-mining region, half of the wage earners in manufacturing work in steel. On the Plateau between Pittsburgh

FIGURE 9-13: *Clay Products Plant, Eastern Ohio*

Clay bank, fuel, kilns, railroad siding, and homes of the workers all show in this photograph of a clay-products operation in the Kanawha section of the Appalachian Plateau. This is a "tonnage" or "miscellaneous" clay-products manufacturer, one of many which enable Ohio to lead the nation in this greatest of clay categories. (Ohio Development Commission)

and Johnstown are several large towns with economies based on coal, iron, glass, clay, and gas.

Upper Ohio Valley. West of Pittsburgh is the first section of a great commercial and industrial route to the cities of the Middle West. Although not so highly industrialized as the immediate Pittsburgh region, manufacturing cities follow the Beaver, Mahoning, and Shenango valleys. This natural corridor for trade has long served to move upper Lakes iron ore to the Pittsburgh area furnaces, and coal to the lakeshore cities. In the direction of Youngstown and Cleveland, the corridor is more industrial. The manufacture of iron and steel products predominates in the cities of the Beaver-Shenango valleys, but clay, glass, and cement manufacturing, in that order, are also important in the area.

Youngstown, Niles, and Warren form a group of cities in which the manufacture of basic iron and steel products dominates the economy to a degree surpassed by no other major steel district in the United States. With nearly 90 per cent of its wage earners engaged in steel, Youngstown's specialization is considerably greater than Pittsburgh's. There is no other industrial landscape in North America quite like the industrialized valleys of eastern Ohio's and western Pennsylvania's Appalachian Plateau. The flow of coal northward to the Lake ports, the flow of iron ore to the interior furnaces of western Pennsylvania and eastern Ohio steel cities, and the flow of clay and steel products from this heavy industry region give rise to an enormous tonnage on the railroads which serve this corridor. With the manufacture of coke and of clay products as the only exceptions to the steel economy, these cities are particularly vulnerable to the fluctuations in the steel industry.

The demand for a canal connecting Lake Erie and the Ohio River by way of Youngstown has been persistent for many years. For a time after a continuous strip mill was erected in Youngstown during the early 1930's, the canal was not mentioned because costs went down and orders went up; but the erection of huge new steel plants in other midwestern steel centers, in the South, and on the Pacific Coast has again brought to the fore the desirability of the canal. A giant series of moving belts between the Ohio River and Lake Erie has been proposed; thus far the Ohio legislature refuses permission to build them.

Not far to the west are smaller steel centers, *Massillon* (29,594) and *Canton* (116,912), specializing in stainless steel, roller bearings, electric sweepers, springs, and stampings. This is sometimes known as the Central Alloy District. In view of the large increase in steel-making capacity as a result of wartime needs, the future of several of these smaller steel cities of eastern Ohio, western Pennsylvania and northern West Virginia seems anything but promising.

On the Ohio River are other Plateau cities in which some form of steel manufacture takes place. *Wheeling* (58,891), *East Liverpool* (24,217), *Steubenville* (35,872), *Weirton* (24,005), *Huntington* (86,353), *Portsmouth* (36,798), *Charleston* (73,501) on the Kanawha River, and *Ashland* (31,131). Fastest growing industrially is the lower Kanawha Valley with its glass, rubber, chemical, and ferro-alloy manufacture (*Fig.* 9-12). An Atomic Energy Commission installation near Portsmouth has made necessary the erection of large electric power plants near Marietta.

A combination of physical resources and market have functioned to make these cities part of the nation's greatest clay-products center (*Fig.* 9-13). The region has abundant and excellent buff-burning clay and natural gas. The farmland of the Middle West offers the greatest market for drain tile, the midwestern steel industry needs refractory materials, and the growth of cities has constituted a market for the brick and hollow tile.

FIGURE 9-14: Birmingham, Alabama

Birmingham terms itself "youngest of the great cities." This photograph from the top of Red Mountain suggests reasons for the claim. (Birmingham Chamber of Commerce, Photo by WATSON MCALEXANDER)

On both sides of the Ohio River, clay products and steel dominate the industrial landscape.

Associated with steel and clay manufacturing are other representatives of the heat and power industries. Most important are the manufacture of glass, industrial chemicals, explosives, and oil refining. Accessibility by rail to both eastern and midwestern consumers, cheap labor, abundant bituminous coal and gas have brought these industries to the Ohio Valley.

MANUFACTURING IN THE SOUTHERN APPALACHIANS

The Southern Appalachians comprise a large area of more rugged terrain and higher elevations than most of the Highlands thus far considered. The Cumberland and part of the Kanawha sections of the Appalachian Plateaus have more rugged terrain and are thus less accessible. *Birmingham* (326,037) is the largest city (*Fig. 9-14*), with *Chattanooga* (131,041) and *Knoxville* (124,769) next in order. All of them are in the eastern portion of the Folded Appalachians. Birmingham is unique among American steel cities in that all of its major raw materials are found within a few miles of the plant. In Red Mountain on the eastern slope of Jones Valley, where ore and limestone lie one above the other, are the Wenonah, Muscoda, and Iskabooda mines. From the Warrior coal field in the Cumberland Plateau just to the west of the city come the vast tonnages of fuel and limestone needed in the making of iron.

Suburban Bessemer, Ensley, and Fairfield make the steel which is fabricated in Birmingham's mills. Chief products have been pipe for the South's oil, gas, sulphur, and water needs; ship plates for the Gulf's shipyards; and a wide range of ship fittings. World War II and the postwar years have brought about a substantial increase in steel-making capacity at the Birmingham steel center. The deplorable slowness with which the southeastern market developed seems to have experienced a definite change since 1940.

Chattanooga and Knoxville are the largest cities in the Folded Appalachians between Birmingham and Harrisburg. Cement, brick, wood products, knit goods, and machine-shop products are important in the economy of both cities. Alcoa is a small city with a big aluminum industry, using power from the tributaries of the Tennessee River. Oak Ridge near Knoxville is the location of a huge plant of the Atomic Energy Commission.

BIBLIOGRAPHY

DAUGHERTY, C. F., M. G. DE CHAZEAU, and S. S. STRATTON, *Economics of the Iron and Steel Industry,* 2 vols. (Pittsburgh, Univ. of Pittsburgh Press, 1937).

DURAND, Loyal, Jr., and Elsie T. BIRD, "The Burley Tobacco Region of the Mountain South," *Economic Geography,* Vol. 26, No. 3, (July, 1950), pp. 247-300.

HOOVER, Edgar M., *The Location of Economic Activity* (New York, McGraw-Hill Book Company, 1948), Chap. 11.

McINTYRE, Wallace, "Niagara Falls Power Redevelopment," *Economic Geography,* Vol. 28, No. 3 (July, 1952), pp. 261-273.

MILLER, E. Willard, "The Industrial Development of the Allegheny Valley of Western Pennsylvania," *Economic Geography,* Vol. 19 (1943), pp. 388-404.

MURPHY, Raymond E. and Hugh E. SPITTAL, "Movements of the Center of Coal Mining in the Appalachian Plateaus," *Geographical Review,* Vol. 35 (1945), pp. 624-633.

MURPHY, Raymond E. and Marian MURPHY, *Geography of Pennsylvania* (Harrisburg, Keystone Press, 1932).

ZIMMERMANN, Erich W., *World Resources and Industries* (New York, Harper and Brothers, 1951), Chaps. 26, 27, 28, 38, 39, 40, 41, 42.

CHAPTER 10

CENTRAL HIGHLANDS

PHYSICAL DIVERSITY

IN THE COMMONLY accepted ways of delineating a geographic region, the Central Highlands hardly deserve regional identity. Two major provinces comprise the Highlands: the Interior Low Plateaus east of the Mississippi River and south of the Ohio River, and the Ozark-Ouachita Uplands west of the Mississippi and south of the Missouri River (see *Fig.* 1-2). As was noted in an earlier chapter, the Appalachian Highlands have a degree of unity due to their great extent and to the over-all uniformity of each of the major provinces comprising them; no such unity obtains in the Central Highlands (*Fig.* 10-1).

Nowhere in these Highlands are elevations so great as in the Appalachians; nearly all of the summit areas of the Interior Plateaus are less than 1,000 feet in elevation; nearly all of the Ozark-Ouachita Uplands rise above 1,000 feet. The Highlands are predominantly hill country, but the nature of the hills varies greatly. Throughout most of the Interior Plateaus and Ozarks, the hills are relatively low and broad; the Ouachitas consist of parallel ridges similar to the Folded Appalachian province. Within each of the two major areas there are likewise important differences in relief.

Transition Zone. There is one characteristic which most parts of the Central Highlands have in common, the transitional nature of the climate, the terrain, and the economy. The north and the south share in the character of these Highlands. Here southern people may be raising northern crops under conditions which partake of both north and south. If the hills were not dominant, northern aspects of the economy would probably be uppermost. No matter which of the several regional maps of climates in

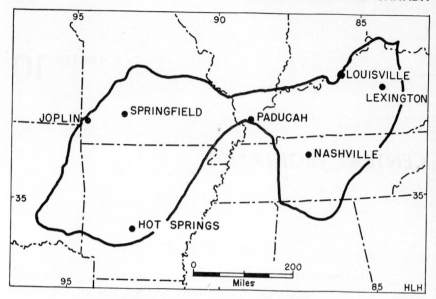

FIGURE 10-1: *Central Highlands*

the United States is used, the Central Highlands are classified as the equivalent of Humid Continental, long summer phase. Although much of the area
is hilly, elevations are generally too low to have pronounced effect upon
temperatures or rainfall. Yet within a given section there are local differences which are appreciable and often lead to economic advantage, such
as the resort and agricultural industries.

Lowlands and highlands alike have a slight summer maximum of rainfall; this is more Tennessee than Ohio in character, being earlier and more
abundant than the latter. The usefulness of the rainfall is conditioned by
the greater runoff and the higher rate of evaporation than in the Corn Belt
to the north.

To northern industrialists, the abundance of satisfactory labor in these
hills has long been recognized and utilized. Newspaper comment in the
Deep or Gulf South has more than once pointed out that the Upper South
looks to the Middle West and the Middle Atlantic areas for its industrial
and commercial ties. Certain types of manufactures have been moving into
some of these hill areas in recent years.

In a political sense, too, the Central Highlands have regarded issues
being debated on the floors of Congress more as northern than southern
states. The routes followed by the westward-moving settlers brought eastern people into Tennessee and Kentucky. Most of southern Ohio and

Indiana were settled by the same stock. The westward movement in the Deep South was a somewhat different phenomenon; it was domestic and was wholly southern in its scope. It was actuated by the need for more cotton lands to replace the worn-out acres in the seaboard South. Manufacturing was not an accompaniment of the westward movement in the South.

Interior Low Plateaus. Possibly the Interior Low Plateaus display this transitional character more conspicuously than the Ozark-Ouachita area west of the Mississippi River. By some, this eastern region is known as the Lower Ohio Valley; its streams flow toward the Ohio. Others have classed it as part of the interior plains of agricultural fame. Its boundaries are roughly set by the Ohio River on the north, the Tennessee River on the west and south, and the Cumberland Plateau on the east. In southern Indiana and southern Illinois a section of this province crosses the Ohio into the Middle West.

The surface of this province has hill rather than plateau characteristics. The most rugged portions are near some of the stream courses. Within the hill country are two famed basins of rolling land and fertile soil derived from the underlying limestone: the Blue Grass of Kentucky and the Nashville Basin of central Tennessee. No part of the province has experienced the smoothing effect of the ice sheet. The best soils are found in the two limestone basins noted and along certain parts of the Ohio, Cumberland, Green, and Tennessee rivers. On the whole, soils are more like those of the Middle West than those of the Deep South. The characteristic red and yellow soils of the Gulf states have given way to grey-brown podzolic soils.

Despite these gross similarities to the plains of the Middle West, the Low Plateaus are distinct from them in the other physical and economic characteristics. Rainfall and steep slopes have promoted serious erosion. The long-continued attempt on the part of the relatively dense population to make a living from the soil has hastened the depletion of the soils of entire townships. Although most of the same crops appear in this region as in the Middle West, neither their areal distribution nor the conditions under which they are produced and marketed are similar to the north. Arable land is much less extensive and attempts at self-sufficiency in agriculture are widespread. The climatic factor is the main reason for the transitional nature of agriculture in the area. It lies near the northern margin of the humid subtropical type of climate, and elevations generally are lower than most of the southern Appalachians farther east.

Ozark-Ouachita Uplands. West of the alluvial plains of the Mississippi Valley, the Central Highlands continue as the Ozark-Ouachita Uplands. There are three main subdivisions of this Upland, the northern or Ozark Plateau, the southern or Ouachita Mountains, and the intervening lowlands of the Arkansas Valley. Despite the variety of landscapes within this Upland, the boundaries are everywhere more distinct than in the Interior Low Plateaus farther east.

The Ozark Plateau is for the most part a region of broad rolling hills with the rugged St. Francis Mountains in the northeast and the Boston Mountains in the south. The proportion of cleared land in the Ozarks is much greater than in the narrow valleys and ridge-like mountains of the Ouachita Mountain province in the south. In general, the Ouachita Mountains are similar to the Newer or Folded Appalachians, which extend from the St. Lawrence Valley to central Alabama.

Settlement in both parts of the Upland preceded that in the plains on the north and west. This is not strange in view of the attraction these secluded fertile valleys must have had for the pioneers. The temperate climate must have encouraged them to linger. Many parts of the area remain secluded and pleasant today. In some the seclusion has become isolation, an isolation so complete that it has not yet been dispelled from many parts of the Upland.

ECONOMY OF THE INTERIOR LOW PLATEAUS

Self-sufficient and Specialty Agriculture. This is a province of marked contrasts in agriculture. Self-sufficing farming prevails over most of the area, yet there are many districts where crop specialties have resulted in a prosperous countryside. These more prosperous regions are the fertile basins and valleys nestled in the hills which comprise most of the province: Blue Grass, Nashville Basin, and parts of the alluvial plains of western Kentucky and Tennessee. Elevations in this hill country are not great enough to affect the climate of the province, except to retard the northward advance of spring. The slope of the land does lead men to do strange things with a mule and a plow, however. Although local self-sufficiency has disappeared slowly from some counties of this region, in others it is still dominant. This type of farming has lowered living standards to a point where the fairly dense rural population ekes out a living based solely on the crops grown.

Corn occupies by far the largest proportion of cropped land; its production is localized in no one region. Although the yield per acre is nearly twice that of the Coastal Plains, it, and corn yield per farm, are low in comparison with the Corn Belt.[1]

Very little of the corn leaves the farm on which it is grown, either as grain or livestock fed upon it. Practically every condition under which it is grown offers a contrast with the Corn Belt on the north.[2] The field pattern of these hill farms is such as to make impossible the economic use of labor-saving machinery. The methods employed in many districts are more those of mining the soil than farming it.

Wheat has been declining in acreage in this area since the middle of the nineteenth century. Open winters during which there is repeated freezing and thawing are hard on young wheat plants. The U.S. Department of Agriculture classes every state in the Central Highlands as "wheat deficient."

Tobacco is strongly entrenched, both physically and economically. Climate and soils favor it. Its heavy and exacting labor demands fit in well with this labor-surfeited hill country, but its depletion of soils is serious. At every stage of its growth, from seedbed to cutting, curing, and packing, tobacco calls for much hand labor. Women and children have done so much of it that machines have only recently been used in the tobacco fields. Tobacco sells readily for cash but it may be stored awaiting higher price. A relatively few acres will keep a family.

The kinds of tobacco grown and the methods of harvesting and curing vary with the locality. Paralleling the Ohio River from West Virginia to western Tennessee is the largest tobacco acreage in the southern states (*Fig.* 10-2). Most of it is either Burley air-cured or dark air-cured. The western portion of this belt has dark fire-cured tobacco; the heavy soils of these counties give darker, more aromatic, small leaf tobacco. This is more like the tobacco grown across the Ohio River in southwestern Ohio. This tobacco is used for cigar and chewing purposes. Tobacco barns likewise vary, from the large, two-storied structures with alternate strips of siding hinged to permit opening for air-curing, to the decrepit structures used in fire-curing.

The bedrock of the surrounding plateau is predominantly sandstone and shale, while in the basin of the Blue Grass it is limestone, differing in places

[1] Yield per farm in Illinois is 1,450 bushels, in Tennessee 284 bushels, and in Alabama 176 bushels, thus discouraging stock feeding in the South.

[2] For instance, the average weight of cattle and swine when slaughtered is:

Cattle	State	Swine	Cattle	State	Swine
932	Iowa	237	850	Kentucky	190
547	Louisiana	170	690	Carolina	200
437	Florida	131	450	Georgia	150
815	Tennessee	186			

in its age and composition. The basin limestone is generally free from impurities; lime and cement are manufactured from it at several places. Entering the Lexington Plain, heart of the Blue Grass, from the hills of the outer basin and the surrounding plateau is an experience not soon forgotten. The change in land use and general prosperity of the countryside is unmistakable. The Blue Grass on the north and northwest grows tobacco as a specialty; [3] for the Blue Grass as a whole, general farming prevails with emphasis upon livestock, although the total number of cattle in this basin will not exceed that of two counties in the Iowa Corn Belt. The cities of Kentucky are in and along the northern margin of the basin; dairying is increasingly important, but the best known, and in the Lexington Plain the most important, phase of livestock is blooded horses.

The Nashville Basin in central Tennessee is similar to the Blue Grass in the proportion of its land in hay and in the excellence of its general farming. Blue grass is not so well adapted to the Nashville Basin and the emphasis upon blooded horses does not obtain. Like its northern counterpart, however, it is the agricultural heart of Tennessee. Although there are no other districts of similar agricultural excellence and advanced living

[3] Although tobacco is known as a crop fitted for hilly areas, there are within this tobacco region differences between the hill lands and basins which are important examples of the economic costs of relief. For instance, the tobacco yield of the Blue Grass and Nashville Basin is 30 per cent greater than that of the surrounding hill counties. Even with tobacco, the costs of farming small scattered fields is greater, to say nothing of the losses due to greater runoff and erosion.

FIGURE 10-2: Tobacco Warehouse, Ripley, Ohio

On good land, tobacco is a specialty crop grown in various crop combinations throughout the General Farming Region. Labor costs are too high for the yields on poor land to enter commerce. This is a scene in an important tobacco-growing region. (Ohio Development Commission)

conditions in all the Highlands, there are many limestone valleys in the Highland Rim of Kentucky and Tennessee which support a prosperous agriculture. For the greater majority of the rural districts, farming is distinctly noncommercial, and in that fact there is not a little security for the hill farmers. Standards of living have declined to the level necessary to support the relatively dense rural population in these hills.

Urban markets have made possible the commercial production of strawberries, apples, and other fruit, poultry, dairying, and truck crops. Locally, agricultural specialties have invaded areas traditionally devoted to corn, wheat, and forage crops.

TVA Transition. The program of the Tennessee Valley Authority is not confined to the Central Highlands, in fact many of the dams have been built in the Southern Appalachians. But since the Tennessee River bounds the Low Plateaus on the west and south, and the benefits from this major undertaking in reclamation accrue in large measure to the people of the Plateaus, a brief résumé of this venture in regional planning is included in this chapter (*Fig.* 10-3).

This improvement in the Ohio's southern tributary, the Tennessee, is a major environmental fact of the Low Plateaus. The area involved is about the size of Ohio, with a population approximately one-third that of Ohio's 8 million. The Authority does more than develop power and attract industry to these power sites. Soil erosion, flood control, navigation, reforestation of cut-over hill country, and the improvement of farming in the valley are all embraced in the program. Something new has been added by TVA in the form of industrial location and plant expansion in the interior of the country

World War II saw the project well along in construction but by no means complete. Twenty-seven dams have been built. During World War II, the acute shortage of power won many converts to the government's plan for developing hydroelectric energy. Power from TVA has been transported as far as Cincinnati, St. Louis, the Piedmont cities, and to some Gulf coastal plain cities.

Manufacturing. The Interior Low Plateaus are not part of the American Manufacturing Belt. The area north of the Ohio River has witnessed a rapid urbanization and industrialization; south of the Ohio these processes have lagged, but a certain degree of industrialization has taken place.

On paper, the accounting of resources for manufacturing found within the Low Plateaus is rather impressive. Commercial quantities of iron ore,

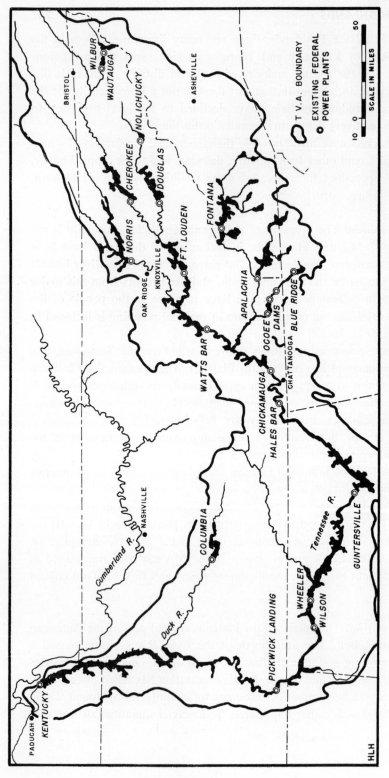

FIGURE 10-3: TVA Dams and Power Plants

At mid-century the TVA region has 34 major dams, 12 steam-generating plants, 10,000 miles of powerlines, 8 million kw. capacity, and 1,300,000 retail customers. The per capita income in the region, as a percent of the national average, in 1929 was 44 per cent; in 1952 it was 62 per cent. In 1933 only 3 per cent of the farms in the region had electricity; in 1954 it was 93 per cent. (*New York Times*, June 19, 1955)

bituminous coal, petroleum, natural gas, phosphate, brine, clay, limestone, and timber are found. Nowhere, in the United States, probably, is there more abundant labor; the rural population density is equalled by only two regions in the United States.

But there are also factors which discourage manufacturing. A glance at a railroad map will show that most of the Central Highlands lies well south of the prevailing east-west trade routes. Railroads cross the area from east to west only along its northern margin. Although two main railroads cross the heart of this region from north to south, this interregional bond has not greatly stimulated manufacturing. Not until recent years, when national industries were experiencing some recentralization, were plants established here.

These resources for manufacturing have awaited the change in the nation's industrialization which gives value to these environmental factors. There have been four manifestations of this timing which are contributing to the growth of a manufacturing economy in parts of this area. First is the manufacturing based upon local surpluses of farm and forest. Meat packing, flour milling, distilling, the manufacture of tobacco, wood, and leather products are examples. Some combination of them is found in most of the Plateau cities. Second is the rise of iron and steel, petroleum refining, railroad equipment, firebrick, coke, and farm implement industries. The western Kentucky coal fields provide a location factor common to all of these industries.

Third is the manufacture of commodities attracted to the plentiful labor from the hills, among them are cotton, wool, and synthetic textiles, shoes, furniture, pottery, and some chemicals. Streams for waste disposal are of value to the chemical manufactures. Fourth is the impact of the so-called chemical revolution which began during World War I. Representatives of rayon, cellophane, synthetic rubber, and alkali manufacture and a number of less well-known products have come to the area. Power from TVA, brine, coal, and labor have been attractive to these industries. The large Atomic Energy Commission installation at Oak Ridge has thus far attracted no industry to it.

Cities of the Plateaus. *Louisville* (369,129), at the Falls of the Ohio River, occupies a position which has appreciated in importance with changes in transportation. It is the largest city in the Central Highlands and is developing as the nucleus for a group of smaller industrial cities along the Ohio. While its industry is somewhat diversified, the bulk of its industrial importance has rested upon furniture, distilled products, and large tobacco plants. Other industries have come to widen the range, but these older ones still dominate.

World War II gave Louisville some new types of manufacturing: aircraft parts; auto-assembly parts; butadiene for synthetic rubber; aluminum sheet, rod, and extruded products; and explosives. Since the war, the growth of electrical-appliance manufacturing has been outstanding. With the development of the electrochemical industry just west of Louisville, the future of this section of the lower Ohio Valley seems bright.

In the past, *Paducah* (32,828) industries were limited to the manufacture of clay products, whiskey, dark tobacco products, and veneer and other lumber products. Recently the electrochemical industry has built large plants here; this industry may well become the greatest phase of local manufacturing and reverse the downward trend of population in Paducah.

Covington (64,452) is situated across the Ohio River from Cincinnati and shares in its employment opportunities. Its own factory products include X-ray machines, tobacco, cotton textiles, and meat.

Evansville (128,636) is on the Indiana side of the Ohio River, but its economy relates it to the Kentucky cities. Long known for its furniture, it has taken on metal stampings and home-appliance manufacture.

Nashville (174,307) has the most diversified industrial development of any city in the Low Plateaus. Located in a splendid agricultural region, it early became an important trading town. The commercial importance of its situation on a route between north and south has never declined.

The district's industries represent both the old and the new order in the Highlands. Tobacco, cotton, flour, furniture, and shoes are common to several of these cities, but the manufacture of fertilizer, rayon, cellophane, railroad equipment, and the construction of the largest titanium plant in the United States, suggests that the foundations of its industrial economy are by no means static or dated. The chemical industry is one whose products connote very little to the layman; a recitation of the firms engaged in various aspects of this industry probably would be more suggestive than a detailed listing of products.

ECONOMY OF THE OZARK-OUACHITA UPLAND

Agricultural Contrasts. Like the Interior Low Plateaus farther east, the Ozark-Ouachita Upland exhibits the same regional transition between the Corn Belt and the Cotton Belt. Within the Upland there are marked contrasts among its principal subdivisions. Two areas stand out in their agricultural excellence, the Springfield-Salem portion of the northern Ozark

Plateau, and the alluvial plains of the Arkansas Valley. Elsewhere the agriculture is more or less of the self-sufficing type common to many parts of the Interior Low Plateaus.

The larger of the two areas of commercial farming is in the northern Ozarks. It resembles the Corn Belt north of the Missouri River. Erosion has dissected the eastern limestone area; its farms and farmers are not very prosperous. The rolling uplands generally support a balanced agriculture which contributes to a pleasing countryside and a profitable economy. Dairying has slowly advanced into the districts easily accessible to the cities to the northeast and northwest. Fruit has become of major importance in some districts; grapes, apples, peaches, and strawberries have developed as rapidly as the midwestern markets have permitted. As in many districts of the eastern Corn Belt, tomatoes have become increasingly important. There are several specialized districts. Around Bentonville there is fruit, berries, and broilers. Tontitown has grapes. Fayetteville is the center of an apple, strawberry, and grape district. Clarksville is in an important peach-growing area.

The Arkansas Valley is to all intents and purposes a part of the Cotton Belt. Its fertile soils have supported cotton farms, with their attendant problems, for a long time. Tenancy, resettlement projects, and an ostensibly profitable but uneconomic cotton system have prevailed here as in the Cotton Belt. Corn occupies an important acreage, but in common with the other three alluvial basins of the Mississippi, cotton continues to be the chief source of farm income.

Elsewhere, the rugged terrain has fostered self-sufficiency in agriculture. The proportion of cleared land is less than half that of the Low Plateaus and much less than in the Springfield-Salem Upland farther north. In some of the most rugged portions of the area, mineral springs, higher elevations, and dense forests have accounted for the location of well-known resorts. In summer the Upland rises as an island of more equable temperatures above the hot plains which surround it on all sides. Although the area is a conspicuous blank space on railroad maps, many parts are accessible by automobile. The proximity of large urban centers within a day's drive appears to augur an increase in the development of recreation in the Upland.

Minerals. Lead and zinc have been mined in the Ozark Plateau for many decades, and their respective districts are among the most important on the continent. The older district, some 60 miles south of St. Louis, has been producing lead for more than a century. It has no superior in the

FIGURE 10-4: *St. Joseph Lead Co.*

This view of a refining operation is a part of a famed lead mining district in Missouri. (Missouri Division of Resources and Development, Massie Photo)

United States. The mines are deep shafts and the surface is dotted with waste brought up from the cavernous workings (*Fig.* 10-4). The only industry attracted to this district is ore-processing before shipping to the lead refineries. The second important mineral district is also a lead producer, although its principal ore is zinc. It is known as the Tri-State District and embraces adjacent parts of Missouri, Kansas, and Oklahoma. For many years it was the most important zinc producer in the United States, accounting for half or more of the domestic supply, but within recent years its premier position has declined. The landscape is even more like a strip-mining operation than that in the lead district; 600 square miles are pocked with small shafts and their waste accompaniments.

The only other important mineral industry in the Upland is bauxite mining on the eastern border of the Ouachitas in central Arkansas (*Fig.* 10-5). Nearly 98 per cent of the domestic supply comes from this district, about equally divided between open-pit and shaft mines. Seven miles east of Benton, Arkansas, are vast open-pit bauxite mines, the most important in the United States. World War II vastly increased the demand for aluminum with the result that much government money went into Arkansas aluminum

242

FIGURE 10-5: Bauxite Mine, Arkansas

This bauxite mine is in the most important producing district in the nation. In the surface mining of bauxite, the ore is loaded by power shovels into huge 22-ton trucks and taken to the crusher. It is then dried and sent to an alumina plant, generally not far distant. The alumina is shipped to a source of cheap power for conversion into aluminum, often involving a transcontinental haul by rail. (Aluminum Co. of America)

facilities. These are the only fully integrated aluminum producers depending upon domestic ore. Ore processing takes place locally and shipments are made to the large reduction center at East St. Louis. There are minor deposits of manganese near Batesville, Arkansas, barite in the St. Francis Mountains, and glass sand in the northeastern Ozarks. World War II spurred activity in the mining of these and other minor mineral resources but the activity lapsed even before the cessation of hostilities. In general, stockpiling tends to retard mineral exploration in this country.

Manufacturing. In the Ozark-Ouachita Uplands the trend to manufacturing is more recent and more narrowly specialized than in the Low Plateaus. Lacking important government-sponsored power projects, the hydroelectric development has proceeded more slowly. As with the Low Plateaus, the backbone of industry has been the manufacture of wood products, processing of lead, clay, zinc, and bauxite (*Fig.* 10-6). Rayon and nylon plants have come more recently (*Fig.* 10-7).

243

FIGURE 10-6: *Brick Manufacturing Plant, Ozarks*

Although the lower Hudson Valley and Cook County, Illinois, lead the nation in the manufacture of brick, the industry is found in many other places. This modern plant caters to the St. Louis-Kansas City markets. Abundant fuel, clay, and labor are available. (Missouri Division of Resources and Development, MASSIE Photo)

Little Rock (102,213) lies on the eastern periphery of the Ouachitas. Its principal industries are bauxite ore-crushing, wood and cotton products manufacture. *Springfield* (66,731) is the largest commercial and resort center in the Ozarks. Its proximity to the better farmland of the Springfield-Salem Plateau is reflected in its high rank in butter manufacture; the livestock industry is its mainstay. Flour milling and railroad shops add a little diversity to its economy.

Fort Smith (53,037) is the chief distributing center for the central portion of the Upland. It is virtually surrounded by semianthracite coal mines, natural gas wells, and clay deposits. Its relatively minor manufactures are based upon these resources. *Joplin* (38,711) is the economic center for the famed Tri-State lead and zinc fields (*Fig.* 3-5). Its limited manufactures include cigar, leather, machinery, and wood treatment plants.

Resort Industry and Conservation. Surrounded upon all sides by the plains of the Central Lowland and the Coastal Plain, the hill-and-mountain terrain of the Ozark-Ouachitas offers tempting recreational retreats for the

244

FIGURE 10-7: *Nylon Knitting Mill, Farmington, Missouri*

The manufacture of nylon fiber is localized in the Appalachian Highlands, for the most part. The weaving of the fabric is in the cotton- and silk-textile districts. This modern mill is in the Ozarks. (Missouri Division of Resources and Development, MASSIE Photo)

urban population of adjoining states. There is even a choice in terrain; the contrasts in this particular area are probably greater than in most parts of the Appalachian Highlands. This Upland is abundantly supplied with hot and mineral springs (*Fig.* 10-8). The attraction of this resource is great. Prominent among these resorts are *Hot Springs* (29,307), *Fayetteville* (17,071), *Mena, Bentonville, Excelsior,* and *Eureka Springs.* Although the immediate Upland is isolated, the general area is bordered by major transportation routes in all cardinal directions.

Agriculture must pay the way for most improvements, particularly in Arkansas. Within the past twenty years the United States Soil Conservation Service has established a number of large land-planning projects, ranging from 15,000 to 100,000 acres in extent. The need for such projects is obvious. The Lake of the Ozarks is one of the conservation projects which has attracted an important tourist industry. The number and size of state and national forests and parks is disproportionately large for the area of the combined Uplands. The Ozark National Forest and the Ouachita National Forest, each a million and a half acres, are the largest.

FIGURE 10-8: *Resort Hotel, Excelsior Springs, Missouri*

Wooded slopes and mineral spring water baths have been the basis for an important resort industry in the Ozarks. (Missouri Division of Resources and Development, Massie Photo)

BIBLIOGRAPHY

COLLIER, James F., *Geography of the Northern Ozark Border Region,* Univ. of Missouri Studies, Vol. 26, No. 1 (Columbia, 1953).

DURAND, Loyal, Jr., and Elsie Taylor BIRD, "The Burley Tobacco Region of the Mountain South," *Economic Geography,* Vol. 26, No. 4 (Oct., 1950), pp. 274-300.

Generalized Types of Farming in the United States, Agricultural Information Bulletin No. 3 (U.S. Dept. of Agriculture, Washington, 1950).

HEWES, Leslie, "Tontitown: Ozark Vineyard Center," *Economic Geography,* Vol. 29, No. 2 (April, 1953), pp. 125-143.

CHAPTER 11

THE SOUTH

INTRODUCTION

NO OTHER SECTION of the United States has had the cultural unity of the South. Here under the humid subtropical climate so favorable to the cultivation of cotton, has evolved an economic and political region unlike any other part of America. In spite of topographic and soils differences, the climate has been a unifying factor. Economic and political bonds have given to the South a traditional separation now largely obliterated by problems which threaten the whole nation. A transformation of the South is in progress and the older agrarian economy is yielding to the industrialism which is destined to change the fundamental character of the region.

The South is largely a plains province or at least a land of low relief. Most of the Atlantic and all of the Gulf Coastal Plain, together with the Piedmont south of Chesapeake Bay and a small portion of the Central Lowlands make up this distinctive geographical region. The boundary between the South and the provinces to the north are sharply drawn on the map but actually the South and the Appalachian Highland become intermingled at several places (*Fig.* 11-1).

This great region stretches from Chesapeake Bay to the Rio Grande River, and from the mouth of the Ohio to the Florida Everglades. Owing to its great extent there are a number of important differences in its physical character. It is, however, a world apart from the hill-and-mountain country which borders it on the north and west.

The vast region is overwhelmingly rural. For a long time it has been a problem area. The spirit of some of its hillier portions may be expressed by the "dogtrot" house, porch chair, and yard swept clean each Saturday.

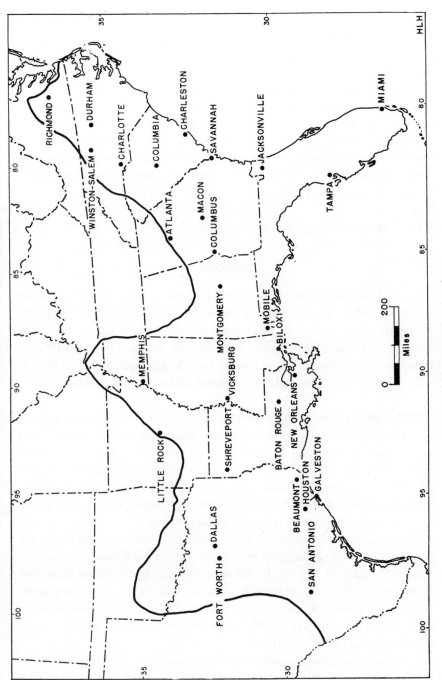

FIGURE 11-1: The South

The cotton fields stop at the cabin doorstep. Although the creature comforts of more than half the white and most of the Negro farmers are governed entirely by the price of cotton, this crop does not dominate the use of land for agriculture. Probably half of the cropped land is corn, varying of course with the district. In 1948 the commodity sales in all southern states for cotton and cottonseed products constituted 27.2 per cent of the farm income; livestock and its products accounted for 38 per cent.

Physical isolation and the cotton economy have yielded slowly to the changes in cropping which result from urbanism and industrialization. Not only in the South, but for the nation, cotton has ranked first as an export for more than a century. World War II caused great changes in the southern economy, both rural and urban. In 1948 the South supplied 13 per cent of all United States exports; in 1925 it was 30 per cent.

REGIONS

Most of the South consists of the Coastal Plain; much of the remainder is the Piedmont, the easternmost division of the Appalachian Highland. There are in general three main subdivisions of the Coastal Plain: the Atlantic from Florida to Virginia; the Gulf from the Rio Grande to Florida, including the Mississippi alluvial plain; and Florida itself. In Texas there is a fourth plains area, the southern extremity of the Central Lowlands.

Piedmont. In contrast with the Coastal Plain to the east, the Piedmont has been seriously eroded by the many streams which cross it. Its soils were formed under an original forest of longleaf pine, oaks, and some walnut, hickory, and gum in the southern portion; in the northern part the vegetation was dominantly hardwood: oaks, hickory, poplar, dogwood, and shortleaf pine. Although its soils are in general gray sandy or red clay loams, there are many districts with more productive soils.

As the scene of the eastern South's principal agricultural economy, the crops grown on these naturally productive soils of the Piedmont have seriously depleted their fertility. In the north tobacco has been the main cash crop; with corn, wheat, clover, and timothy hay as the supporting crops (*Fig.* 11-2). Livestock has been of minor importance. Farther south cotton is the dominant cash crop, with sweet potatoes, melons, peaches, truck crops, and peanuts as specialties.

In some parts of the southern Piedmont erosion has been dramatic in its destruction and the wasted acres are beyond the redemption of individual

FIGURE 11-2: *Tobacco Field, North Carolina*

Tobacco is one of the last crops to undergo mechanization. This field on the Carolina Piedmont is being mechanically sprayed. (North Carolina Dept. of Conservation and Development)

farmers. Soil exhaustion is critical in many counties and farming has impoverished man; soil mining yields a meager living.

The margin of the Piedmont and the inner Coastal Plain is known as the Fall Line or Fall Zone. Here the rivers leave the hard rocks of the Piedmont for the less resistant sands and silts of the Coastal Plain. Falls have invited the growth of cities all along this Fall Line; many of the oldest and best-known of the southeastern cities are located at the coastal margin or on the Fall Line. Nearly all of the water-power developments in the South are located on the southern Piedmont, where the number and character of the streams which flow from the interior are generally favorable for power development. The mountains receive from 50 to 70 inches of rainfall, fairly uniformly distributed, but with a minimum in late summer.

Before the federal program began in the Tennessee Valley, many or most of these power sites were already developed. On the Catawba, Saluda, and the Tallulah-Tugaloo are important power developments. The sites on the Catawba River system in the Carolinas have been almost completely developed. At the southern extremity of the Piedmont, the Coosa and

Alabama rivers have important installations. These power developments are possible because of the relatively high head rather than the large size of the streams. The proximity of the southern plains to the important power developments on the Tennessee system and the smaller projects in the Ozark Highlands has served to compensate for the dearth of power sites in the greater portion of the province itself.

Atlantic Coastal Plain. The Atlantic Coastal Plain, once the bed of the ocean, is a relatively featureless plain. An occasional cuesta or inland-facing escarpment is its most conspicuous feature. On the basis of elevation, soils and drainage this plain may be subdivided into three sections, all paralleling the coast. The outermost section is level to undulating, interspersed with numerous swamps, bays, low sand ridges, and indented by many estuarine embayments. The greater part of the area is poorly drained, the highest portion being under 60 feet above sea level. The original vegetation was longleaf and shortleaf pine, oak, hickory, holly, and sweet gum on the better-drained portions, with gums, cyprus, and some hardwoods prevailing in the swamps. Soils are generally light-colored except for the alluvial plains. Most of this outer province is unused for agriculture, although truck crops, peanuts, some cotton, tobacco, and corn are produced in the oases of arable land which dot the margin.

Bordering the flatwoods on the west is a broader and higher belt of undulating to gently rolling sandy plains. Soils here were formed under much the same type of forest as in the eastern flatwoods section. Neither the sandy character of the soil nor the pine-forest cover has favored the accumulation of organic matter, so the prevailing color is light or yellowish gray. Soil differences rather than relief give rise to regional differences. These plains are by no means of monotonous uniformity.

Although these soils are deficient in plant foods, their productivity has been relatively high with the application of commercial fertilizers. Cotton, tobacco, and peanuts are the principal money crops, with fairly important acreage in truck crops and fruit. This is the most important belt of the south Atlantic Coastal Plain.

Just west of it is an agriculturally unimportant sand-hill strip which lies along the front of the Piedmont from North Carolina to Alabama. Most of this forest belt is covered with scattered longleaf pine and several varieties of scrub oak which have grown up since the original heavy longleaf pine forest was lumbered. These sand hills make up a narrow strip of country which is somewhat higher than the Coastal Plain to the east or the Piedmont to the west.

Gulf Coastal Plain. The Gulf Coastal Plain is much larger than the South Atlantic. It extends from the Gulf to the mouth of the Ohio River and from the Rio Grande to Florida. The belted characteristics are much more pronounced than in the case of its Atlantic neighbor. Its alluvial plains are more numerous and of very much greater extent.

The same sequence of terrain, forest, and soil mark the nearly concentric belts inland from the Gulf coastal margin that were noted along the South Atlantic, although the individual belts differ from the Gulf margin of the Mississippi delta, and westward toward Texas is a coastal marshland of considerable extent. Drainage conditions are somewhat inferior to the South Atlantic margin and a smaller proportion of the new land is used for farming purposes. Parts of the Louisiana section of these coastal prairies are locally known as *prairie tremblant.* It is a strange country of land and water. West of the lower Mississippi River there are several rivers which flow across the plains of Texas and Oklahoma, among them are the Brazos, Colorado, Trinity, Sabine, and Rio Grande.

Along the coast subsidence has produced estuarine embayments giving great irregularity to the inner coastal margin. Seaward a series of long narrow islands, tied to the mainland at a number of places, gives to the Gulf Coast a high degree of regularity in contrast to the inner coastal margin. The lagoons between the offshore beaches and the mainland are irregular and discontinuous. The Intracoastal Waterway connects the estuarine and river ports of the coastal area with the Mississippi. Deep-water ports have been created at Orange, Sabine, Port Neches, Port Arthur, and Beaumont, all on a 32-foot canal. Galveston, Houston, Texas City, and Port Bolivar are grouped on Galveston Bay and adjacent bayous. Freeport, Port Isabel, and Brownsville are also on deep-water harbors. All of these Texas port cities will ultimately be served by the Intracoastal Waterway.

Mississippi Alluvial Plain. The St. Francis, Yazoo, Tensas, and Atchafalaya basins of the Mississippi River flood plain comprise the greatest single diversity in the surface of the Gulf Coastal Plain. From the mouth of the Ohio River to the Gulf these flood plains of tributary rivers comprise a great province of fertile soils and flat terrain extending for more than 600 miles along both sides of the Mississippi. The peculiarities of drainage and the hazard of flood have combined to keep portions of this great region from being usable. The principal cities are located on the bluffs where the Mississippi flows toward the eastern margin of its flood plain. On the west side, the cities are well back from the active flood plain on principal tributaries. Smaller towns are scattered over most parts of the plain.

The alluvial soils which have been deposited by the Mississippi and its tributaries once supported a river bottom forest of cypress, tupelo, and red gum. The principal farm income is from cotton, with rice, sugar cane, and truck corps as important specialties. On the newest land south of New Orleans where dry land is at a premium, the slightly higher lands which slope away from the bayous toward the interstream areas have localized most of the people and some unusual means of making a living.

High up on the bluffs south of Vicksburg, at the confluence of the Yazoo with the Mississippi, the United States Waterways Experiment Station has duplicated in small scale a model of the lower Mississippi River system, complete to the last cut-off. Here for twenty years engineering experiments have been conducted which later will save time, money, property, and lives on the southeastern plains. This station symbolizes the most important feature in the landscape of the Mississippi alluvial plains, the river itself. The problems connected with the control of the river during flood times have occupied the attention of government engineers ever since the territory has been a part of the United States. The great volume of water carried, the meandering course of the stream, and the economic importance of the lands periodically inundated and left covered with the silt, combine to make Mississippi floods a national disaster. The system of levees, spillways, and overflow basins has left its mark on the countryside of the lower Mississippi.

Fundamentally, the floods of the lower Mississippi are related to the rivers of western Pennsylvania's Appalachian Plateau, the till plains of the lower Lakes states, the Highlands of Kentucky, Tennessee, Arkansas, and Missouri, and the melting snow of the Rockies and the Great Plains. Water control along the tributaries in the head-stream area must precede flood control on the lower Mississippi. But such work is very expensive; thus far only the Miami Conservancy District (1918), Tennessee Valley Authority (1935), Muskingum Watershed Conservancy District (1946) have been established and begun to function. The Missouri River program is under way. This leaves the greater number of the offending streams without adequate control measures. So long as agricultural interests were the ones mainly affected by floods, the minimum improvement was done. When urban and industrial destruction become great, control measures will be adopted.

World War II focused attention upon water-borne commerce and upon the shortage of industrial power; consequently the conservation of productive lands and the causes of floods in the Mississippi system are receiving more attention. The most important agricultural lands of the lower

Mississippi Valley states are included in these alluvial plains, parts of which are periodically flooded. Included also are urban centers and the major part of the commercial activity of these states. Less obvious, and therefore more insidious, is the destruction by runoff before the water reaches the permanent stream courses.

More than any other part of the United States, the southeastern plains abound in rivers. There are many kinds; their characteristics are known far beyond their locality. Dominating the entire region is the Mississippi, the system with the greatest length and the greatest volume on the continent. But its enormity is not its only unusual feature. Throughout the ages its waters have built up a delta from the mouth of the Ohio to a point well out into the Gulf. Upon this alluvial plain the river follows a tortuous course southward, cutting off portions of its course by straightening, and building new land along its main distributaries in the Gulf. Through the years the level of the river bed has been raised; tributary streams have difficulty in gaining access to the main stream. For 70 miles south of New Orleans the usual drainage pattern is reversed: the best-drained land is the river bank; interstreams areas are first to be flooded.

Several of the streams of Louisiana are in fact bayous, which in times past were, and in times of high water may still be, distributaries of the Mississippi and the Red rivers. These quiet streams have localized most of the villages and the individual homes in the Deep Delta country. Among the larger and more populous bayous are Teche, LaFourche, and Barataria west and south of New Orleans. These bayous are often congested with the dense growth of water hyacinth which renders navigation difficult for the boats which ply them.

Florida Section. Peninsular Florida differs from the Gulf and the South Atlantic coastal plains chiefly because of its 300-mile extension into the Atlantic and its lake-dotted central limestone plain. The northern or mainland section of Florida is similar to its eastern and western neighbors, but the peninsula has poorer drainage, poorer soils for the most part, and originally was less densely forested. The rivers of peninsular Florida are unlike those of the rest of the Coastal Plain. Solution of underlying limestone has given rise to underground drainage and to a series of sinkholes extending through central Florida. The Florida ship canal project, now abandoned, was to divert the headwaters of the St. Johns River westward to the Gulf of Mexico.

CLIMATE

One of the world's most productive climates for agriculture is humid sub-tropical. This type of climate supports a large part of the world's rural population. Summers are long and hot; winters are short and cold or cool, depending upon the latitude. Despite its southerly latitude and its situation well below the prevailing paths of cyclonic and anticyclonic storms, the climate of the South is characterized by occasional severe "cold waves," with temperatures near zero persisting for a few days. Many winters have freezing temperatures as far south as middle peninsular Florida. It is defi-nitely a continental-type climate, although modified by its southerly lati-tude. While rainfall is heavy, Parkins, a close student of the South for many years, has said that in his opinion "dry spells (mostly less than 30 days duration) are the most widespread and destructive of all weather phenomena to agricultural operators in the South." [1] Despite this hazard, the cost of creature comforts necessary to support life in this climate is probably less than for any other region in the United States. When these extremes in temperature and in precipitation are anticipated in establishing farming practices, less damage results. But where they are infrequently ex-perienced and no precautions taken, the damage is serious, as in Florida and along the Gulf coastal margin.

Climatic conditions are more appropriately regarded as relatively favor-able rather than optimum for cotton and corn, two of the principal crops. Daytime temperatures on the Gulf Coastal Plain are too high for too long a period to make a good corn crop. Autumn rains make cotton unprofitable along the Gulf Coast; crops are damaged and harvesting is difficult. The eastern South is so humid that cotton bolls do not ripen so quickly as in the drier plains of Texas. Humidity also is conducive to insect pests of cotton and other crops.

Visher estimates that the Deep South receives more than one-third of its annual 55 inches of rainfall as downpours. No other section of the United States has so many thunderstorms; no other has them commonly at all seasons; no other has such a high average precipitation for thunder-storms.[2] Along the south Atlantic coast and to a lesser extent along the Gulf coast the tropical hurricanes of late summer and early autumn in-crease the total precipitation and may produce a seasonal maximum at this

---

[1] A. E. Parkins, *The South* (New York, John Wiley and Son, Inc., 1938), pp. 44-45.
[2] S. S. Visher, "Torrential Rains in the South," *Geographical Review*, Vol. 31, (1941), pp. 44-52; see also "Regionalization of the United States on a Precipitation Basis," *Annals Assn. of American Geographers*, Vol. 32, (1942), pp. 355-370.

time of year. The growing season varies from 180 days along the southern border of the hill country of the Central Highlands to 220 days along the Gulf margin. Only on the Pacific continental margin is the dependability of a frost-free season greater than here.

West of the Mississippi River the direction of climatic change is east-west as well as north-south. This is true for the amount of precipitation and its seasonal variability, as well as for the temperature.

Because the southeastern plains are on the lee coast of the continent, the region enjoys certain relative climatic advantages. No other coast has a steeper thermal gradient from north to south than eastern United States. This puts the southeastern plains with their subtropical climate at an advantage with respect to the great urban markets of the Middle Atlantic Littoral. Spring advances toward the northeast, thus enabling the production of early fruits and vegetables to move northeastward in profitable stages.

Northern urban centers are but a two-days' automobile ride from the winter resorts of the South Atlantic and the Gulf coasts. This location is a permanent natural resource, one that increases in importance as the northeastern and the middle western states increase in population and purchasing power. Its enjoyment is by no means confined to the money classes; many well-paid northern factory workers live in trailer camps and in tourist cottages during the slack season for their particular industry. The carrying power of the South is materially enhanced by this relative climatic advantage.

Where once summer climate was popularly supposed to militate against factory work, the trend during the past generation has not supported this contention. During and since World War II the rise of new manufacturing industries in the South has been a striking feature of the growth in plant capacity. Air-conditioning units were installed in the gigantic synthetic rubber plants of Texas and Louisiana.

LUMBERING

The history of commercial lumbering in the South reflects something of the same type of migration noted in the North, yet there were several distinguishing features. First, the movement was slower; there was no frenzied period in the lumbering industry. Lacking the phenomenal increase in rural and urban population of the North, southern commercial lumbering was dependent upon exports to lumber-deficient districts as they developed in the North. Second, destruction was not so complete in the wake of the westward-moving southern lumber industry. Third, forest reproduction was more rapid in the South than elsewhere in the United States. Not only do pines grow more rapidly in the South, a stand maturing in forty years, but they grow on a greater variety of soil types than do hardwoods in the North. And, finally, land abandonment began very early in the South's history; it was more widespread and progressed more rapidly than in the North. With these facts aiding in the natural reforestation of the South, commercial lumbering played a more persistent role than in the North.

The only states producing more than a billion board feet a year each are the Gulf coastal states, and with the exception of Arkansas, the lumbering is mostly in the pine forests. Mississippi, Louisiana, and Alabama have consistently led in southern lumbering. Less than half as important have been Texas, Arkansas, Georgia, the Carolinas, and Florida. The remaining states, all in the upper South, have never been important. Essentially the same relative grouping is preserved with respect to the area of their forest reserves.

Although most of the southern lumber cut is pine, the hardwoods once were its equal. Today the hardwoods are the basis for an important wood-products industry only in the Upper South. Seventy per cent of the nation's pulpwood is now produced south of the Mason-Dixon Line.

The lumber industry of the South still has many of the characteristics of a colonial industry. Approximately three-fourths of the lumber cut is exported as lumber; only one-fourth becomes raw material for southern wood mills. The role of wood in the economy of farmers is an important one. The ubiquitous woodpile is a necessary part of every farm home and cabin. Charcoal is a necessity for the urban Negroes; no other source of fuel is available to many of them, even with bituminous coal so near. As has been observed, an estimated two-thirds of the nation's farm population lives on land classed as "fair" and "poor," much of it being in the South. For them, products of the commercial forests and of the turpentine orchards, saw logs from small wood lots, cut-over lands and swamplands, and cutting mine and highway-construction timber, and even burning charcoal, combine to make wood one of the main crops in many districts on the southeastern plains. A commercial newcomer in the South is the tung tree. The fruit or "nut" of this tree yields a quick-drying oil which formerly was imported from China. It is a tree that requires a long growing season and hot weather. Tung does best where both the days and nights are warm and there is a minimum of 45 inches of rainfall evenly distributed throughout the year. Low-priced land and labor are essential. The tung belt borders the Gulf from Gainesville, Florida, to Hattiesburg, Mississippi. From a nut tonnage of 1,160 in 1939, this industry grew to 120,200 tons in 1952.

AGRICULTURE

Cotton Economy. The part played in American history by the exports of raw cotton to western Europe has been important. The purchasing power it created for the struggling republic was so timed as to enable the economic structure to withstand the strain of costly war, the Westward Movement, and supply capital for the rise of manufacturing. Cotton was the raw material which gave British manufacturing its first important factory industry. For the South itself, it enabled the purchase of the staples and luxuries of life which a society of that type demanded.

Long before World War II the planters felt the pangs of the rise of nationalism in Europe, the Orient, and South America. The British Empire Cotton-growers Association was a symbol of the empire's desire to foster the production of cotton in India, Egypt, Nigeria, and a few other districts. Brazil has increased its cotton acreage on old coffee lands. Japan was encouraging the growing of more cotton on Mindanao and in China.[3] Partial liquidation of the Empire has retarded but not ended this program.

Under one set of conditions or another, cotton is grown from the Atlantic to the High Plains of Texas; indeed if the irrigated districts of the Rio Grande, Imperial Valley, and California be considered, it is grown from coast to coast. For so long a time so many people of the South have been dependent upon the cultivation and harvesting of cotton that this region generally is known as the Cotton Belt.[4]

The Cotton Belt in the United States has the 77 degree isotherm (summer) as the northern border. Along this margin the average date of the last killing frosts in the spring is April 10 and the first frosts of autumn come about October 25, so the frost-free season is approximately 200 days. Along the western margin the elevation of the Great Plains shortens this period to 180 days. Most of the cotton-growing region has from 20 to 50 inches of rainfall, most of it falling during the summer and less of it during the autumn than any other season. Improvements in seed have pushed the production of cotton into dry, not wet, regions.

---

[3] The six major areas of cotton production in 1948 were: United States, 42.8 per cent; Pakistan and India, 15.5 per cent; China, 9.7 per cent; Brazil 6 per cent; and Egypt, 6.2 per cent of the world's crop.

[4] In reality there are seven individual districts: Georgia-Carolina inner Coastal Plain; Georgia-Carolina Piedmont; Northern Alabama Section, Tennessee Valley; Mississippi River Plains; Northern Black Waxy, Texas; South Texas Coastal Plain; and High Plains of Texas and Oklahoma.

Cotton is grown on practically all well-drained types of soil in the Cotton Belt. Generally the maturing is more rapid on the sandy loams of the southeast than on the heavier clay soils. Early planting and rapidly growing varieties have been important in restricting the damage by the boll weevil.

The Sea Island section of Georgia once was noted for a long-fiber cotton bearing that name. After a third of a century, the crop is returning to Georgia as a result of weevil controls. Within the past twenty years cotton growing has moved into the hot valleys of New Mexico, Arizona, and southern California. In these irrigated cotton districts the yield per acre is high, thus compensating for an acreage decline in the old eastern Cotton Belt.

Eastern Cotton Belt. The eastern Cotton Belt comprises the oldest cotton- and tobacco-growing region in the United States, the South Atlantic Plain and the Southern Piedmont, with some of Georgia's and Alabama's Gulf Plain (*Fig.* 1-2).

Continued cropping is possible in most of this large area only with liberal applications of commercial fertilizers; approximately one-fourth of the gross income is spent for fertilizer; no other section of the United States approaches this figure. Cash outlay for seed, fertilizer, and the necessities of life have given rise to a system in which a very large proportion of the farmers are tenants of one sort or another, some of them on plantations, and many of them Negroes.

The ready credit accorded these cotton farmers has been their undoing. Cotton has a ready cash value. It can be stored. It provides an acceptable basis for a bank or store loan, a factor which is often the deciding element in the situation. After a century and a half of this sort of farming, it is very difficult for the farmer to change his farming practice. Every community agency and way of life has been patterned after the crop requirements of cotton. Even the ravages of the boll weevil could not entirely uproot it.[5]

During the past quarter century, due to a combination of circumstances, fundamental changes have taken place in the agricultural economy of the eastern Cotton Belt. In 1930 there were 10.7 million acres in cotton in this area; in 1954 there were only 3.5 million acres.

[5] In the past, a country town and the adjacent farms could in effect become the monopoly of one enterprising family. For instance in Pelham, Mitchel County, on the inner coastal plain of Georgia, these conditions obtained in 1910. The Hand Trading Company bought all of the cotton in the surrounding countryside; the Hand Gin cleaned and baled it; the Hand mill crushed the seed. Another Hand mill spun the fiber. In October when the picking season opened, the Hand Trading Company began to pay off; the Pelham Bank was swamped with deposits; by February it was all gone.

In the eastern Cotton Belt corn has a brighter future, perhaps, than any other field crop, but it is definitely no panacea for all agricultural ills. In many southern Piedmont counties of the eastern Cotton Belt, corn has become an important crop, particularly in Georgia where nearly 40 per cent of the Piedmont's cropped land is in corn. In some counties 60 per cent is in corn. Neither the soil nor the temperature and rainfall are optimum; the yield per acre is low, 14 bushels in Georgia (Illinois yields an average of 40 bushels); the cost of producing a bushel is higher than in the Corn Belt; and the yield per acre and per farm is lower than in any section except New England and the Far West. Despite the higher price per bushel of corn in the Georgia Piedmont, the Department of Agriculture estimates a loss of from $1 to $3 per acre. How else can these farmers get a return for their labor? The answer may be the practice on the 315-acre farm of W. B. Hammett, near Inman, Spartanburg County on the South Carolina Piedmont, who fed the following in 1940: 6 head of horses and mules, 4 dairy cows, 2 young cattle, 150 chickens, 15 hogs. Fifty-five acres were in cotton; 35 in corn; 25 in lespedeza; 8 in oats; 8 in cowpeas; and 21 in fallow.

Life Magazine (1940) reported that a bright red metal tomato, not an iron general on a prancing horse, decorates the railroad station at the same Pelham, Georgia, noted earlier in this chapter. The Wingate farm in this community raised 200 acres of corn, 100 of Kudzu vine or other legume, 45 of tomatoes, 1 of sugar cane; the remainder of the farm, 600 acres, was in pasture and wood swampland. The 40-bushel average yield of corn for this farm was three times the average for the country.[6] World War II accelerated the trend to this noncotton farming.

Cotton was once king in the Alabama Black Belt, and as elsewhere, cotton's imperious demands on top of poor farming methods, wore out the soil. Today a regeneration has given wealth to the Black Belt, wealth based on cattle, milk, and sweet potatoes. Local beef has been improved and marketed as feeder calves. The marbled steaks that make top-quality beef call for corn-fattening. Corn does not do well in the state, so after grazing a year, the calves are sold to feeders in the north or packers of veal or baby beef. Cotton still grows here but it no longer dominates.

Middle Cotton Belt. The middle Cotton Belt includes all or parts of the alluvial plains of the major tributaries of the Mississippi River: St. Francis, Yazoo, Tensas, Red, Arkansas, Ouachita and Atchafalaya. Here the physical appearance of the cotton-growing region differs sharply from the eastern area. It is predominantly flat land, has larger fields, and is nearly all in

[6] Prof. Calvin B. Hoover goes into this matter in detail in his *Economic Resources and Policies of the South* (New York, Macmillan Co., 1951).

cotton. More than 60 per cent of the rural population is Negro, and the ratio of tenant farming (90 per cent) is higher than for any other district in the United States. Although the soil is fertile and the climate at the optimum, the yield of cotton is not a great deal higher than in the poorer eastern fertilized section. In the use of hand labor and the growing importance of livestock, these bottom lands are similar to the older eastern area.

One planter from this region was articulate. Mr. W. A. Percy, in his Lanterns on the Levee, suggests that sharecropping as a system of employment was the best solution for the type of labor in the cotton economy in many parts of the eastern and central South.[7]

This region has not been subject to the forces for change to the same degree they affect the eastern Cotton Belt. In 1954 cotton acreage showed an increase over 1944. Less manufacturing has come; the local markets for dairy and other food products have not grown so rapidly.

Western Cotton Belt. The western Cotton Belt is the newest of the large cotton-growing regions in the South. Negroes never have constituted an important part of the population. The plantation system never obtained the widespread dominance it once did in the eastern and middle South. These relatively level black prairies have good soils and a climate that permits cotton and discourages the boll weevil. Farms are larger, tenancy is lower (60 per cent in Texas), and more of the farm work is mechanized. In Texas the size of the farm is not determined by the ability of a man with a mule to plow and cultivate, and with some help to pick 25 to 30 acres of cotton. On these relatively level western lands the introduction of machinery has resulted in larger farms. For nearly twenty years the cotton stripper has been used to pick cotton on the subhumid plains of Oklahoma and Texas. With this implement a Texas farmer can pick as much as eight hand pickers. With the cotton picker, four men can pick an acre an hour; the work of a hundred men picking by hand (Fig. 11-3). Prospects for some machines are bright in the sense that the field of operation is not confined to the west margin of the Cotton Belt. On the other hand the introduction of such a machine in the more densely populated middle and eastern cotton-growing regions must inevitably have as an accompaniment widespread disemployment of cotton hands. Despite the mechanization of cotton growing in Texas and Oklahoma, the decline in acreage noted in the eastern Cotton Belt is the present trend here. In 1930 Texas and Oklahoma had 20.1 million acres in cotton; in 1950 there were only 8.3 million. This seems to be in part the result of the extraordinary growth of industry, particularly in Texas, with its attendant changes in the extent and nature of the market for food

[7] W. A. Percy, Lanterns on the Levee (New York, Alfred A. Knopf, Inc., 1934).

FIGURE 11-3: *Cotton Picker in East Texas*

One of the factors in the increase in cotton acreage in the Southwest has been the mechanical cotton picker. This machine weighs only 950 pounds and harvests about 1.25 acres per hour. (Ford Motor Co.)

products. Alternative employment opportunities are greater than ever before.

The improvements in the cotton plant and the methods of production have enabled cotton to cross the Texas prairies into the High Plains, the Open Basin country, and California's Central Valley.

Subtropic Coast Agriculture. The largest part of this "left-over" region of the South, frequently called "flatwoods," is put to no productive purpose. In this term are implied the vast stretches of sandy outer coastal plain, most of it in forest with clearings intricately dispersed, many of them occupied by bodies of water, some by cropped land, some by both. The drainage is poor, the soils generally very poor, and the autumn rainfall too heavy for inclusion in the Cotton Belt. West of the Mississippi delta country the flatwoods give way to coastal prairies with few trees. The growing season of the subtropic coast is longer, two to ten days, than for any other part of the United States except peninsular Florida. Where man has reclaimed parts of this coastal margin for agricultural purposes, the land use has become highly specialized, in keeping with the subtropic climate, the soils, and the distance from large markets.

Florida Citrus Districts. The largest of these arable "islands" along the coastal margin are the citrus-growing districts of east central Florida. The peninsula reaches about three hundred miles into the warm waters of the Gulf of Mexico and the Atlantic. Despite the fact that the soils are among the poorest in use anywhere in the nation and that irrigation must sometimes be used to supplement rainfall, the climate has made citrus fruit the best-known of Florida's crops.[8]

There are three principal producing districts on the peninsula: the central belt of limestone sinks and low hills which parallels the coast, the district around Tampa Bay on the west, and the attenuated coastal strip on the east coast bounded by Indian River. Both oranges and grapefruit appear to do best in the central district where the low hills and many lakes offer some protection from frosts. Orange and grapefruit trees are grown in comparable numbers; most orchards grow both. Limes are found only in the far south, below Miami and on some of the rocky keys. Lemons are so sensitive to winter temperatures that their production is of slight importance.

---

[8] Of the national total of 46,580,000 boxes of grapefruit, 1950, Florida grew 33,200,000; Texas 7,500,000; Arizona 3,150,000; and California 2,730,000. Of the 116,910,000 boxes of oranges grown, Florida accounted for 67,300,000; California 45,210,000; Texas 2,700,000; Arizona, 1,400,000; and Louisiana 300,000. SOURCE: *Agricultural Statistics, 1951,* (U.S. Dept. of Agriculture, Washington), p. 210.

There are several score varieties of oranges grown in the state; many of them never attain the characteristic orange color, or they lose it after ripening on the tree. Many have a rusty appearance. To gain the necessary sales-provoking color, about half the orange crop is stamped "color added" after exposure to ethylene gas. Such a procedure is not peculiar to Florida oranges alone.

The ease of reaching Florida citrus centers by truck from the north has led to marketing procedures not common to California or Texas citrus districts. In Florida, citrus growing constitutes a way of life. There is less "industrialization" and the holdings are smaller than the other two areas. Florida had to secure markets after California had become well established as a producer and shipper. Although there are co-operatives in Florida, they are not so large and powerful as in California. As late as 1935 Florida officially undertook to reduce the number of varieties, to make rigid the enforcement of standards of the fruit, and to control the marketing and shipping aspects of citrus production. Since the imposition of strict regulations, a certain amount of "bootlegging" of fruit has taken place by free-lance truck drivers anxious to take back a cheaper load. The largest producing and shipping center is Orlando, Orange County. One-seventh of the grapefruit crop is canned locally. Very little of the orange crop is canned but the proportion which is frozen has increased greatly.

Florida Vegetable and Small Fruit Districts. Even in the heart of the orange and grapefruit country of central Florida, the production of vegetables and small fruits for northern markets is generally an accompaniment of agriculture. Capitalizing upon the situation of this subtropical region with respect to large, luxury urban markets of the North, hundreds of communities grow the staple vegetables. Deland, Volusia County, may be taken as a representative general farming district of the peninsula. It is located east and north of the principal citrus areas, although oranges are grown. Grapes, strawberries, celery, string beans, tomatoes, cabbage, carrots, beets, potatoes, white and sweet, eggplant, peppers, okra, cucumbers, and watermelon are grown for export. Corn is the only cereal crop; commonly the melons are grown with the corn. Recent specialties have been Easter lilies and ferns. Dairying and poultry are making some headway in Florida agriculture, but the state still imports three-fourths of all poultry consumed, and 450,000 dozens of eggs. By alternating the vegetables with the root crops, the farmers spread their risk over a three-crop season.

Sanford, Seminole County, ships 2 million crates of celery grown on the 5,000 acres devoted to this crop; subirrigation is practiced. As in all other parts of Florida except the south, fertilizer is an important factor in production. By staggering the planting for several weeks after July first and transplanting in September, cutting proceeds after the New Year for a period of seven months. Another specialized region is the Hastings potato district, near Palatka.

One of the newer vegetable-growing districts is around the shores of Lake Okeechobee in the south where Clewiston and six smaller towns grow vegetables for northern markets. In this reclaimed portion of the fresh-water Lake Okeechobee, 40,000 acres of black muck soil are worked by Negro labor. Beans, tomatoes, peas, lima beans, celery, cabbage, peppers, potatoes, oranges, and avocados are grown. This is one of the few districts in Florida which have something of the "factories in the field" atmosphere to be noted in the agriculture of several districts in California.

Another specialty is the sugar cane grown on land reclaimed from the Everglades. Fourteen hundred acres of cane are grown at costs reputedly lower than any other part of the United States. There is no refining done here; the raw sugar is shipped to Savannah for refining.

Delta Sugar Parishes. Another district of specialized agriculture in this subtropic coastal region is the cane sugar-growing parishes of southern and central Louisiana. Despite the populous and apparently prosperous landscape, they constitute an exotic and uneconomic feature in southern agriculture.[9] There is no rotation of crops and there are few supporting crops grown in these cane lands. Like the other specialized farming districts of the Gulf, these are arable "islands" in a region predominantly forested.

Cane sugar as produced here calls for heavy capital investment in drainage, transportation, and mill equipment, heavy labor costs, and annual planting due to its northern latitude. Production is maintained by a tariff, at the behest of this cane region and the more widespread northern and western sugar-beet growers. Nearby Cuba, one of the world's most economical and the only unprotected sugar producer, has had to accept quotas of import imposed by the principal buying nation in order to protect U.S. growers.

Much of the land in the sugar parishes is too poorly drained for cropping purposes, but cane fields occupy most of the cropped land west and northwest from New Orleans. The river-bottom soils have no more profitable crop than sugar cane (*Fig.* 11-4). Two districts centering around Bayou La Fourche and Bayou Teche have localized a great deal of the

---

[9] Approximately 5 per cent of our sugar consumption comes from these Louisiana sugar parishes. The bulk of it (40 per cent) comes from American possessions, chiefly Hawaii; Cuba supplies 30 per cent and the remainder (about 25 per cent) is from domestic beet sources.

FIGURE 11-4: Sugar-Cane Harvester, Louisiana
Mechanization has come to the cane fields of Louisiana's sugar parishes. (Louisiana Dept. of Commerce and Industry)

sugar-cane acreage. It is an unusual landscape for the United States; the flat fields are large but irregular in pattern. Dominating the landscape are the large gray refinery buildings, each refinery surrounded by the iron-roofed cottages of the Negro and the French-speaking employees. In the fields are the familiar loading devices and the narrow-gauge tracks. Associated with some of the refineries is the plant which manufactures wallboard from the bagasse or dry stalks of the cane. Another by-product is molasses, increasingly important as a source of certain chemical products.

Rice Prairies. Another unusual landscape is found farther west in Louisiana and Texas where are located the major rice-growing districts of the flat coastal grassland. This coastal prairie has two sources of agricultural income; rice and beef cattle.

As with sugar cane, the cultivation of rice calls for large capital outlay. Unlike cane, rice has no tariff protection; mechanization has enabled these rice growers to meet the world price set by cheap labor areas of the Orient. The Texas-Louisiana rice production is almost two-thirds of the nation's total, and approximately one per cent of the world's figure (*Fig.* 11-5). Local natural gas is used to power the pumps that flood the fields.

FIGURE 11-5: *Rice Harvester, Louisiana*

This harvester in action in the fertile rice belt helps to gather in the crop worth about $53 million yearly to Louisiana farmers. With well over 500,000 acres under cultivation in the state, Louisiana is the second largest rice grower in the nation. (Louisiana Dept. of Commerce and Industry)

One of the big rice-growing centers in this area is the Crowley community in Louisiana's Acadia Parish, where rice has been grown since 1886. Flooded, diked rice fields are sown by ordinary grain drills and sometimes by airplane. Planting is from February to June; harvest is from August to November, after the fields are drained for combining as with wheat. Bayou water must be constantly checked for salt; generally it is fresh, but upon occasion saltwater has invaded some of the Texas rice fields. Rotation with clover or other forage crops is practiced, thus supporting a cattle business. The rice economy is complete with co-operatives, a Rice Experiment Station, and the International Rice Festival held at Crowley each October.[10]

The beef-cattle industry has had an important relationship with rice

[10] But there may be a "return of the native" in South Carolina where a revival of rice growing is in prospect. Growers from Texas are raising rice on a 30,000-acre venture in old rice country, abandoned years ago. In South Carolina there will be no dry seasons, no need for crop rotation, and no saltwater problem. Rice left here because the soils could not take the heavy rice-harvesting machinery which would make the cost competitive. Improved machinery may make this a successful venture.

growing. The rice farmers introduced the superior bloodlines of Brahman stock.

Other "islands" of productivity are in the prevailing wasteland of the coastal prairies and the irrigated valley of the lower Rio Grande. On the Texas side of the river lies an agricultural community extending some 60 miles upstream from Brownsville. The small cities of Laredo, Harlingen, San Benito, and McAllen are centers of the irrigated citrus districts where 9,000 citrus growers and a few hundred vegetable growers are completing the first 50 years of occupancy.

Rio Grande Valley. In 1904 the railroad came to this cattle country. When the land boom began in 1912, the Brownsville area had very little land for sale. Speculation moved upstream. Today land changes hand normally and without emotion. The 3 million boxes of oranges, 5 million boxes of grapefruit and lemons, and the cars of vegetables exported from these communities are but a small fraction of the nation's production. But some of the conditions under which they are grown and marketed are unusual. Two-thirds of the growers are nonresidents; they come in each year from farther north to grow and market the crop. Owing to a fruit-fly infestation, the state sets a date when all grapefruit must be off the trees. The packing company which buys the fruit does all harvesting. Local canneries take most of the grapefruit. These communities face the competition from California's more highly organized and controlled citrus association. There are perhaps twenty-five other irrigated communities along the lower Rio Grande Valley producing winter vegetables, cotton, sorghum, and sugar cane. Beef is as yet only a minor source of farm income, which is derived mainly from poultry and dairying.

Livestock and Dairying. The earliest use of Florida lands was for grazing of cattle and hogs, generally of an inferior type. Pasture was scanty and the cattle tick was a serious problem. The size and quality of the beef animal was improved by tick eradication, improved bloodlines, and better feeding. Today stock raising dominates the farm economy of southern Florida, in the Lake Okeechobee area, where a savanna-like sandy plain was the last stand of the pioneer-type of open-range grazing. There are today more beef cattle in Florida than in Wyoming. Prominent among the new types is the Santa Gertrudis breed in which the resistant strain from Indian humped cattle has been successfully bred in the South.

Florida is by no means a natural pasture area and its population is widely fluctuating as the tourist seasons determine. Despite this, the number of dairy cattle has increased 13 per cent since 1910, and the quantity of milk produced has trebled. Today Florida has approximately the number of dairy cows as New Jersey with nearly double its population.

The Florida swine industry is minor, there being fewer than one-third as many as in Georgia and half as many as in Alabama. Very little corn is grown. The fluid milk market dominates, leaving little for the milk products industry and its skimmed milk for feeding value. Only Rhode Island, among all other states, raises fewer sheep than Florida. The state is near the bottom of the list of poultry producers; neighboring Georgia raises seven times as many.

Along the coast plains westward from Florida, the beef industry continues on about the same scale as in Florida. Dairy cattle and swine increase in numbers westward along the Gulf Coastal Plain.

Louisiana, with approximately the same population as Florida, has more than twice as many dairy cows. New Orleans with 500,000 population and year-round market, together with the abundance of pasture, makes the difference. North and west of New Orleans nearly a million head of beef cattle graze in the valleys of the Red and Ouachita rivers. Between the Louisiana delta and the southern margin of the Appalachian Highlands is found the only major development of milk condenseries, cheese plants, and meat packing. It is probably the only region where silos are fairly common to the farmsteads. The West Gulf Coastal Plain, of course, has the largest livestock industry in all of the South. Texas alone has six times as many beef cattle and more than twice as many dairy cattle as any other Gulf state. It also has a greater variety of livestock. It has almost as many swine as Wisconsin; more sheep than all of the West North Central States, more goats than any other state, but in poultry it lags behind a dozen states. The almost spectacular increase in urban population in Texas means that an increasing proportion of its farm food crops and livestock remains in the state.

FISHING INDUSTRY

Role in the Economy. The fishing industry of the South has never occupied such an important role in the economy as in New England or the Middle Atlantic Littoral. A smaller proportion of people have had to turn to the sea in order to eke out a livelihood. There are fewer good harbors; there has been no local carrying trade to open up markets for the seafood. Most of the important food fish of the northern Atlantic and Pacific coasts are lacking in these warm waters, but there is a fishing industry of some importance, largely inshore.

Three states stand out in the South for the size of their catch: Louisiana,

Florida, and North Carolina; Louisiana, the most important, has an annual catch less than half as great as Massachusetts. The remaining southern states have relatively minor production, but the combined catch of the South Atlantic and Gulf States is about the equal of New England, both in amount and in value. On one basis, however, these southern states lead all other regions of the United States: they have more fishermen and more fishing boats.

Florida. Out of an estimated 17,000 commercial fishermen utilizing perhaps 11,000 fishing boats, Florida has 5,000 men engaged in this industry. In commercial and recreational fishing Florida ranks next after Massachusetts. The most important fish is the shrimp which is sold both fresh and canned on a large scale. This state accounts for about one-third of the nation's catch of shrimp, with the industry operating out of St. Augustine principally.

Florida has almost a monopoly in sponge fishing now concentrated near Tarpon Springs; financial control of this industry is held largely by the American branch of the Greek Orthodox Church. Sponges grow in shallow water (6 to 15 feet) offshore as far south as Key West. Very long hooks are used to bring them to the surface. Where the water is deeper, divers go to the bottom for them. Processing sponges for markets consists largely of cleaning away the animal matter and drying them.

The largest part of the deep-sea catch is menhaden, a fish sought for manufacture into oil and fertilizer. Mullet, blue fish, grouper, red snapper and a few other edible fish are caught off the Gulf Coast. Florida's west coast catch is not quite half as important as that of its east coast.

Gulf Coast Fisheries. A quarter of the nation's oysters and much of the shrimp are caught along the Gulf Coast from Apalachicola westward to New Orleans. A large part of the oyster catch is canned before marketing, but the canneries are not so large as those for other seafood in the northeastern states.

Shrimper's cabins and the shrimp-drying platforms are rather common sights along the Gulf Coast from Florida to western Louisiana. They are especially numerous along the streams of the lower delta country south of New Orleans. The long stretches of quiet water between the offshore bars and the mainland attract many hundreds of fishermen operating in small boats. The Intracoastal Waterway provides easy access to saltwater from scores of coastal communities.

The third-ranking area is the North Carolina coast. This fishing industry lacks the unique aspects noted in Florida and Louisiana, but it exemplifies the predominance of small fishing boats (rather than vessels), and the minimum of mechanical equipment. Small farmers along the relatively poor agricultural coastal margin are attracted to fishing as they once were in New England.

TRAPPING INDUSTRY

The trapping of fur along the Gulf Coast is an important industry, particularly for the people who dwell along the marginal lands of Louisiana. For those who live on the long narrow strips of land which border the bayous and distributaries of the Mississippi River, the seasonal trek to the leased muskrat-trapping grounds is a diversion and often the source of the major part of the year's cash income. The value of Louisiana's annual fur catch is somewhat greater than that for Canada.

Many nationalities are found in this half-water, half-land territory, but the French stock is most numerous. Most of the people are descendents of Acadians from Canada who migrated to this land of many flags; the isolation of the region has aided them in preserving many of the customs of their forebears.

MINERAL INDUSTRIES

Although the mineral resources of the South are varied, petroleum has single-handedly raised this province to a position of national importance in the mineral industries. The other mineral resources of commercial importance include sulphur, phosphate, salt, bauxite, natural gas, and kaolin. These are not the kind of minerals which exert a strong pull on industrial location. An exception is the attraction of certain industries to the sources of hydroelectric power, natural gas, and the by-products of refining industries. Only sulphur and helium are confined to the South; in the production of all others, the South must compete with northern or western sources.

Petroleum. There is only one major petroleum-producing district in the South, the Gulf Coast field, and it shares in one other, the midcontinent. Texas alone produced a billion barrels (about half the total of the United States), Louisiana 232 million, and Mississippi 37 million barrels.[11]

These southern oil and gas fields have been more spectacular in their development than the Older Appalachian fields. This is in part due to the

[11] United States' production of crude oil in 1950 was 51.2 per cent of the world's 4.47 billion barrels. In that year the countries of the western hemisphere produced 71.4 per cent of the world total.

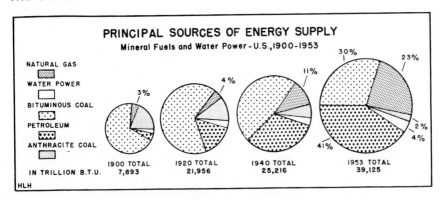

FIGURE 11-6

In this chart observe that the increase in the use of gas and oil is at the expense of coal. Water power's share remains relatively stable. (*Chemical and Engineering News*)

timing of their exploitation, and in part to the vastly increased use of powered machines. No other factor has accounted for such spectacular changes in southern economy since the rise of cotton. No other section has witnessed such an increase in exports, most of this development occurring within the past 25 years.

The yellow flame, burning the waste gas off the oil, blazes day and night from the oil fields of west Texas where dull gray derricks push up through the hard, brown earth of the cattleman's vast ranch lands. It burns in the swampland oil fields of the coastal prairies and the Mississippi swamps above and below New Orleans. It burns in the wheat-country oil fields of northwestern Texas and in the corn-and-cotton country oil fields of central and eastern Texas. It may burn in Florida. Tremendous quantities of natural gas are piped to the largest southern and some northern cities (*Fig.* 5-12). There is also an increasing use made of the products from gas, such as lampblack made in Louisiana.

Chronic overproduction has characterized the oil industry ever since the east Texas field opened in 1926. Delirious heights in land speculation, dislocation of land use over considerable areas, the rise of skyscrapers in the oil cities, and the vastly increased population consequent to the increased carrying power of the land, all of these, some believe, are ephemeral features of the regional economy.

Oil has given rise to three related types of areal phenomena: (1) it has fostered rapid urban growth in and near the fields themselves: Fort Worth, Dallas, Amarillo, Shreveport, San Antonio, and Baton Rouge; (2) even more startling has been the expansion of commercial cities through which the oil and its products move to market: Beaumont, Houston, Galveston, Port Arthur, and New Orleans; (3) the third type of phenomenon is the refining center, of which there are 83 in Texas alone, 45 in Oklahoma, 14 in Louisiana, and 10 in Arkansas. Enormous affairs even by modern standards, these refineries are still expanding in the South.

The oil industry has four characteristics not common to other mineral industries, and from these characteristics a great deal of the frenzied nature of the midcontinent and Gulf Coast economy appears to stem. These four are: (1) the original source of the oil is unknown; (2) the extent of the supply is unknown, (3) the supply is migratory in the sense that gas and oil do not necessarily remain fixed, and (4) the industry has its own transportation system.

It will be recalled that anthracite coal presented a seeming anomaly in that its price remained fixed despite a diminishing market; the effect of this on the landscape of the anthracite country was described as abandonment. Oil presents another seeming anomaly in that low prices have but slight effect upon the number of wells drilled and the volume of production. Unless the price of crude oil drops to a few cents a barrel, the owner of a gusher very likely will produce at a profit and is therefore uninterested in limiting his volume for the sake of conservation. Again, the market for oil and its products has been increasing. The effect upon the land use of the region embraced by these southern oil fields is apparent. Petroleum in the South, particularly in the midcontinent and Gulf Coast fields, has been an impelling factor in population movement and in industrial and commercial growth. Will the factors which determine the carrying power of this land for farming purposes, the commerce of port cities, and the relatively few industries which have come to oil and gas for fuel or raw material, alter the trend of growth?

To get most of this oil to market, the industry has built a system of pipelines connecting the several producing districts with the lower Lake cities. The first pipeline directly from Texas to New York, "Big Inch," was opened in 1943; it is now used for natural-gas transport. Pipelines also run to the Gulf ports which ship crude and refined oil to the Atlantic states (half the domestic market), and abroad. A great oil tonnage moves by the economical ocean tanker. The vulnerability of the tanker system of transport was demonstrated during World War II when the diversion of tankers plus the destruction by German submarines off the south Atlantic Coast caused an oil and gasoline shortage in the northeastern states. The completion of the Intracoastal Waterway in 1942 enabled barge-tows of oil to creep from Corpus Christi and Houston to the Mississippi, thence upstream

FIGURE 11-7: *Oil-Drilling Rig, Louisiana Gulf Coast*

This rig is at work 25 miles off the Louisiana coast, where drilling costs are from three to five times as high as on land. Although the Submerged Lands Act was passed in 1953, at least one state claimed ownership seaward some three leagues or 10.3 miles. Leases sold by the state or the federal government have run as high as $1,500 per acre and a royalty of one-sixth of all the gas and oil produced. Some authorities believe that the federal government owns up to 80 per cent of all potential oil land on the continental shelf and that this may well be the nation's greatest oil supply. (Louisiana Dept. of Conservation and Industry)

to the Ohio, Cumberland, Monongahela, and Allegheny to head-stream terminals, thence by tank cars to the eastern cities. The principal limit to this type of oil commerce was the availability of barges and towboats.

Something reminiscent of the days when boom times accompanied the discovery of new wells is currently being experienced off the Texas and Louisiana coasts in the quest for petroleum from underwater wells (*Fig. 11-7*). In 1955 the most distant off-shore claims are being made by Louisiana, 35 miles out in the Gulf! Dozens of successful operations take place from man-made steel platforms or "islands" with piers sunk into the shallow Gulf bottom. This activity stems from the recognition of the state's rights to offshore oil.

Phosphate. Phosphate rock from the Tampa district in Florida comprises nearly four-fifths of the nation's total production. It is strip-mined in a district about one hundred miles in extent. Although most of the current phosphate comes from Florida, most of the known reserve is in the mountain states of the West.[12]

Sulphur. Texas produces 80 per cent and Louisiana 20 per cent of the native sulphur output of the United States. Huge quantities (3.5 million tons) are heaped upon the flat coastal prairie to solidify after extraction in molten form. Hot water (300° F.) is forced down a large pipe to melt the sulphur which is then drawn up through another pipe. For forty-five years, Texas and Louisiana have enabled the United States to supply domestic needs and export some. Galveston and Freeport exported more sulphur than the entire world consumed just prior to World War I.

Salt. West and south of New Orleans in Louisiana and Texas are salt mines producing nearly half a million tons of rock salt annually, with the tonnage from Texas twice that of Louisiana. Texas also produces twice as much salt by evaporation as by quarrying. The several curious domes, which rise a hundred feet above the flat coastal prairie and may extend for a mile or so, are salt domes (locally called islands). One of them, Jefferson Island, produced most of Louisiana's tonnage. The leading salt-producing state, New York, mines somewhat more than these two Gulf States.

Other Minerals. China clay or kaolin is the only commercial clay of importance in the South. Georgia and South Carolina together produce 92 per cent of the total. Its principal market is the paper industry, with the manufacturers of rubber, refractories, and pottery taking most of the remainder.

In the production of granite, Georgia leads the nation, producing a fifth more than Vermont, second-ranking state. In marble, Georgia and North Carolina together produce half again as much as all other states in the United States combined. Limestone is quarried in Texas, third-ranking state in the country.

BIBLIOGRAPHY

See bibliography at end of Chapter 12.

[12] Phosphate production, 1950: Florida, 8,085,870 long tons; Tennessee, 1,384,493; Idaho and Wyoming, 573,044; and Montana, 210,165.

MANUFACTURING IN THE SOUTH

EVOLUTION OF THE SOUTH'S INDUSTRIES

Antecedents. Despite an early start, manufacturing in the South did not successfully compete with agriculture until the twentieth century. The markets for raw cotton, after the cotton gin was invented which lowered the price of the fiber, were so large as to make cotton growing more attractive to southern planters. Although the South possessed coal, iron, wood, water for power, and some copper, the attitude of most southerners was inimical to the introduction of and dependence upon a manufacturing economy.

Paucity of alternative opportunity, the accumulation of capital from commerce, and an early start placed the northeastern states at an industrial advantage. The accessibility of the Northeast to markets was an added factor. It may well be that two of the strongest factors in industrialization are the desire and intention to manufacture, granted access to the needed materials. These were not discernible factors in the South until late in the nineteenth century. By this time the expansion of the nation's domestic market had leveled off appreciably as a result of the end of cheap farmland, imposition of immigration restrictions, and a lowered birthrate. Railroads had been built, skyscrapers and homes constructed, farms equipped, and settlement virtually completed. Thus the South would have to compete for a market for factory goods.

Characteristics. Today manufactures of the South are much less free from northern competition than are the farmers. There are few industries found entirely within the South. In such items as tin smelting, naval stores, cotton-seed products, kraft paper, one type of synthetic rubber, and oils from the

·tung and peanut, the South has virtually a monopoly. Her most important industries are those with northern competition: refining of oil, sugar, iron, sulphur, and aluminum, cotton spinning and weaving, shipbuilding, processing tobacco and leather, and manufacturing furniture and flooring. The overwhelming proportion of the manufacturing of the South is termed simple manufacturing. The value added by the manufacturing process is low; interplant dependence and the development of diversified industrial landscapes are rare. The South is still essentially an agricultural region. The proportion of her people engaged in manufacturing varies from 29 per cent in North Carolina to 8 per cent in Mississippi, but the transition is under way.

Impact of World War II. The impact of government spending for new industrial facilities in the South was both important and easily observed. These new plants were rarely additions to old ones, and they were not hidden in congested industrial areas. The expansion of manufacturing was largely financed by the government. The War Production Board reported in 1945 that of the 26 manufacturing districts in war production solely because of new plant construction, 13 were in the South. Texas was the only one of these states which was awarded at least $1 billion in industrial facilities. Three states (Alabama, Virginia, and Louisiana) were in the second category ($250-999 million). Four others (North and South Carolina, Florida, and Mississippi) were in the third or "less-than-$100-million" group.

The largest categories of new facilities were for aircraft assembly, synthetic rubber, chemicals, aviation gasoline, ships, and nonferrous metals. The end of the war promptly closed the shipyards, some of the aluminum, magnesium, aircraft, chemical, and all ordnance and explosives plants. The postwar years resulted in very little retrenchment on the part of the others, owing in part to the Korean conflict and to increased southern markets. The major effect of the war on many communities was to draw off much of the surplus labor; relatively a small proportion of these workers returned to their former homes if wartime employment had taken them entirely out of the South.

On the basis of the number of persons employed, the 10 leading industry groups in the South (1950) were textiles, lumber products, food, machinery except electrical, apparel, chemicals, furniture, metal products, paper and its products, and tobacco products. If the 10 leading industries based on the value-added-by the manufacturing process are listed, 6 of them will be common to the foregoing listing.

There is implicit in this comparison something of the change in the types of manufacturing industries in the South; this is reflected in the rise of industries in which the net value is proportionally higher. Statistically the shift in industry and population during the first half of the present century is shown in the table below.

TABLE 12-1: Regional Shifts in Industry and Population, 1899-1949

U. S.	NO. E. STATES	MIDDLE ATLANTIC	E. AND W. N. CENTRAL	SOUTH-EAST	SOUTH-WEST	NORTH-WEST	FAR WEST
Population *% of total*							
1900-100	7.4	23.8	30.4	23.8	5.5	6.	3.2
1947-100	6.3	23.7	26.7	20.5	7.5	5.2	10.2
Manufacturing *% of U. S. fac-* *tory wage earners*							
1899-100	18.1	37.3	27.4	11.8	1.0	1.9	2.6
1947-100	10.5	30.1	34.3	14.6	2.5	1.7	6.3

SOURCE: *Economic Almanac, 1951-1952* (New York, *National Industrial Conference Board,* 1951), p. 257.

During the past fifty years the federal program for water development has strengthened the natural competitive advantage of the South. For instance in 1952 the electric bill for a factory using 100,000 kwh per month in Boston was $26,500, while in Chattanooga it was only $11,000 because of TVA. There must be some relation between this utility rate and the fact that the South secured, on the average, one multimillion-dollar factory per day in 1951.[1]

Distribution of manufacturing. Although geographically detached from the Manufacturing Belt of the eastern United States, the growing importance of manufacturing in the southeastern states suggests that the use of the term "belt" should be qualified. On the basis of wage earners employed in factories, this is especially true; on the basis of net value the need is not so apparent. The correlation of manufacturing with physiographic sections in the South is so natural that this approach is used in the present chapter.

INDUSTRIES OF THE PIEDMONT

The term industrial "crescent" has been used to describe the distribution of industrial centers on the inner Piedmont, southward from Virginia to

[1] John F. Kennedy, "New England and the South," *Atlantic Monthly,* Vol. 193, No. 1 (Jan., 1955), p. 134.

FIGURE 12-1: *Furniture Factory, North Carolina*

The manufacture of furniture was an established industry on the Piedmont before the cotton textile industry went south. The factory buildings reflect this difference in timing. (North Carolina Dept. of Conservation and Development)

central Georgia. Even here there are no cities of half a million population. Most of them have but one or two large industries; and functional relationships among the plants, so characteristic of the North, is of minor importance.

Cotton Textiles. This inner Piedmont crescent of industry is predominantly cotton-textile manufacturing. In North Carolina, however, tobacco and furniture manufacturing are also important industries. One is seldom out of sight of one of these cotton mills on the Piedmont. Furniture and tobacco factories are generally multiple-story, brick buildings set in an urban location (*Fig.* 12-1). Many cotton and a few woolen mills are one-story and of more recent construction (*Fig.* 12-2). Their setting is often rural or suburban. More often than not, the textile payroll is the only important one in the town. Textiles of man-made fibers are a recent and growing source of employment on the Piedmont.[2]

[2] Of South Carolina's manufactures, 67 per cent, North Carolina's 57.4 per cent, and Alabama's 26.9 per cent, in 1950, were in textiles. The increase in wool manufacture in these states is suggestive of a trend, although New England retains nearly two-thirds of the wool industry.

FIGURE 12-2: *Hatch Textile Mill, Raleigh, North Carolina*

The changing economy of the South is apparent in such photographs as this one. Rural setting, air-conditioning, single story, and modern machines have enabled these southern mills to manufacture more than 80 per cent of the nation's cotton textiles, despite rising wages. Agricultural landscapes lag behind the advancing industrialization; nevertheless fundamental advances have been made. (North Carolina Dept. of Conservation and Development)

Although water-power development preceded industrialization on the Piedmont, many recently built mills are near water-power sites "just in case," as one plant executive phrased it. Dependence is placed upon carboelectricity. Owing to its three specialties (cotton, tobacco, furniture manufacturing), each of which has a dominant position in the nation, the Piedmont is one of the best-known industrial areas in the United States.

The shift of looms to the South has also followed the general pattern set by spindles. The South in 1948 had over 80 per cent of all cotton cloth production in the United States and the proportion is increasing since the region is getting considerably more than 80 per cent of the expenditures for new plant and equipment.[3]

Whereas New England's cotton industry has been localized in a few cities in three relatively small districts, southern mills are widely scattered. Every

[3] Calvin B. Hoover and B. U. Ratchford, *Economic Resources and Policies of the South* (New York, 1951), pp. 142-145.

southern state manufactures cotton to some extent. In recent years, Texas has experienced the most rapid rate of increase.

Piedmont mills supply much cotton yarn for New England weavers; it is in spinning that southern mills have had their greatest advantage. Knitting is increasing more rapidly than any other branch of textiles; most of the increase is outside of the Piedmont but in North Carolina, Tennessee, Virginia, and Georgia. Finishing and dyeing are also being undertaken by the southern manufacturers, whereas the goods "in the gray" were formerly shipped to northern processors. This manufacturing trend is increasing among southern industries and contributes to the stability of and wages in southern industry. The Carolinas, Georgia, and Virginia are increasing their manufacture of woolens and worsteds; to some extent cotton spindles are used in this wool manufacture. In view of its growth compared with the same industry in New England, the South seems to have a future in this hitherto New England industry.

Relatively few Negroes are employed in cotton and woolen mills in the South. In fact, relatively few persons, white or black, are employed in the mills with modern textile machines. The competitive advantage of southern labor cost rests principally on the combination of more modern textile machines and somewhat cheaper labor and power than in the New England states.

In the manufacture of women's full-fashioned hosiery, so-called "nylons," the South has achieved another industrial advantage over the northeastern states. In 1937 the South manufactured 30 per cent of all United States' nylons; in 1953 the proportion rose to 62 per cent, most of the rest were made in the 10 northeastern states, Pennsylvania first. North Carolina leads the South in the manufacture of nylons, but there are nylon mills in every southern state. The nylon industry began in Pennsylvania and the state led for several years; despite the decline, this state still has more mills than any other state, north or south. In 1937, northern mills produced 70 per cent of the nation's output; the growth of southern at the expense of northern nylon mills is attributable to more modern knitting machines, somewhat cheaper labor, lower cost power, and taxes (*Fig.* 12-3).

Tobacco. Sharing in the economy of the Piedmont, and dominating it in North Carolina, is the manufacture of tobacco. Nearly all of the large tobacco factories are in the cities of the North Carolina Piedmont: Winston-Salem, Durham, and Reidsville, all within a radius of 75 miles. These large modern mills concentrate on cigarette manufacture. In North Carolina the value of tobacco grown is five times that of cotton or corn, and its manufac-

FIGURE 12-3: *Nylon Plant, near Pensacola, Florida*

The "new look" in northern Florida is reflected in this wholly-integrated plant. The 30 different structures shown in the photograph afford employment for 3,000 persons. (Chemstrand Corp.)

ture is about twice the value of cotton and its products, the second-ranking industry. Furniture, knit goods, and fertilizer, the state's next most important industries, are together less than half as important as tobacco, on the basis of value added by the manufacturing process. Localization of the factories in North Carolina illustrates the influence of market as well as raw material.

Furniture. A third important industry in the South, and especially in the Piedmont cities, is furniture manufacture. Although its value is about half that in the state of Michigan, this industry makes period as well as cheap furniture. Wood and cheap labor are the major factors in its localization here.

Wood Pulp and Paper. Wood pulp and paper are manufactured at many places in the southern Pine Belt. The manufacture of kraft paper for bagging and wrapping purposes has taken place in the South for years. Insulation and building board have recently become important in the use of wood waste and bagasse. With the perfection of processes begun by the late Dr. Charles Herty, it is possible to make newsprint paper from ordinary slash pine.

The manufacture of newsprint appears to have a bright future in the South. With the decline of available pulpwood in the North, the difficulties involved in importing it from Europe, and current dominance of Canadian pulp, the recent successes in the use of southern woods border on the spectacular. Estimated reserves of wood, the rate of reproduction and growth, and their accessibility, place the South in the front rank of potential newsprint makers.[4] The heavy power requirements are likewise readily met in the southern Piedmont.

The ability to produce trees for pulpwood in 25 years instead of the 60 or more in the northern forest areas, has acted as a stimulant for southern pulp manufactures. Building board, insulation, kraft paper and newsprint paper are manufactured from materials formerly burned as waste. This recovery of wood product has become a major industry in the forested areas in the South. The extent and variety of these new wood products is increasing, but the net effect upon the southern lumber industry is not far-reaching as yet.

The actual rise of the industry, however, is conditioned by a number of factors not within the power of the South to control. For one, the price of Canadian pulpwood can well be lowered, which would reduce the apparent advantage of the South. Again, most of the paper plants are in the Lake states and the interior of the Middle Atlantic states, thus placing southern pulp mills at a disadvantage. So far, most of the southern pine used has been in the manufacture of kraft paper, a tough brown wrapping paper.

Naval Stores Industry. One of the oldest export industries in all the South is the manufacture of naval stores. The source of the raw material, the methods of production, and the nature and extent of the market have all undergone a quiet revolution since colonial days.

This industry began in North Carolina, moved into South Carolina, Georgia, and Florida as the older areas declined. Driving along the highways of southern Georgia and northern Florida one sees mile after mile of the tall trunks of loblolly pines with small earthern cups fastened at their most recent (lowest) scar. Occasionally the traveler sees an open-roofed building in a clearing in which the sap is distilled to secure turpentine and rosin, but 90 per cent of all naval stores are produced by large corporations in large modern plants.

---

[4] For instance, near Savannah two paper mills employ 7,000 people, have a reforestation program on a million acres of land owned, or on long lease in Georgia, Florida, and South Carolina (*New York Times,* June 28, 1947).

The size of the individual company's orcharding operation may reach 50,000 acres of pine forest, involving approximately 8 million cups. Such a unit will keep in operation a still large enough to ship tank cars of turpentine and flat cars of rosin barrels to Jacksonville and Savannah for a year.

Atomic Energy. The largest single industrial venture in the south Atlantic plains area is the production of atomic energy near Aiken, South Carolina. The impact of this enormous installation has thus far been confined to the construction demands for housing, utilities, food, and creature comforts. Its effect upon industry remains to be seen. The payroll for its operation will be the brightest fact in the economy for most people in the region.

Piedmont Cities. Although the Piedmont cities are among the oldest in the South, they are not the largest nor do their industries exhibit the newer types which have come to the South. A group of cities marks the Fall Line water-power sites from Baltimore to Columbus, Georgia. Originally these cities were commercial; basically, they remain commercial, but have achieved some industrial importance.

The largest city in this group is *Richmond* (230,310) on the James River. Its principal manufactures are tobacco and paper products; the only iron and steel industry of the Fall Line cities is in Richmond. *Columbia* (86,914), on the Congaree River, is basically a political, commercial, and educational center. Its principal industry is the manufacture of cotton textiles. *Augusta* (71,508), on the Savannah River, is a winter resort, cotton-fiber market, and textile manufacturer. *Macon* (70,252) is one of the many cities making cotton work clothing in the South. *Columbus* (79,611) manufactures textiles.

The largest city on the Piedmont is *Atlanta* (331,314); it also has the greatest railroad commerce and most diversified manufactures. For many years it was a great wholesaling and warehouse city; these functions have declined as Gulf Plain cities have surpassed Atlanta in population. Its principal manufactures include cotton textiles, cottonseed products, furniture, machinery of several types, auto assembly, auto parts, foods, and fertilizer.

Charlotte (134,042) is the only Piedmont city to have increased its population by a third during the past ten years. No other city surpasses it in the degree of forward integration taken by its textile manufacturers. Cotton textiles, the machinery for making them, and the chemicals for finishing and dyeing them are important industries in this district. Charlotte's history of producing relatively high-grade furniture is a prestige factor in locating such plants in or near the city.

FIGURE 12-4: *Dacron Plant, Kinston, North Carolina*

Man-made textile fibers have also come to the southern Piedmont. This plant is representative of these facilities. (North Carolina Dept. of Conservation and Development)

Roanoke (91,921) is in the gap of the Roanoke River through the Blue Ridge Mountains. The Norfolk and Western Railroad maintains large repair shops and manufactures steam locomotives and rolling stock in this city. The South's largest rayon plant is located here. Roanoke has a bond with other Piedmont cities in its furniture and textile manufacture.

Winston-Salem (87,811) is one of the largest bright-leaf tobacco markets. Its manufactures include tobacco products, furniture, textiles and hosiery. *Gastonia* (23,069) makes most of the fine combed cotton yarn in the United States. It also makes warp and dyeing machinery for cotton textiles. Production of rubber tires has introduced almost a foreign note to this representative Piedmont industrial city.

INDUSTRIES OF THE ATLANTIC COASTAL PLAIN

The best-known cities in the South are those on the Atlantic plain. They are among the oldest and largest in the southeast. They seem to show a certain detachment both from other southern cities and from the northeastern cities.

Industry, in a sense, is older in the coastal plain, but factory industry

FIGURE 12-5: *Miami Beach*

This resort is an extraordinarily successful purveyor of subtropical climate, ocean bathing, and creature comforts to northern well-to-do. This is a part of "hotel row" looking north from Pancoast Lake. (Miami Beach News Bureau)

is older on the Piedmont, due to the migration of New England's textile mills to the latter area. Population growth was most active in the Florida cities, where the resort industry has spurred the growth in urban population (*Fig.* 12-5). The decline in cotton exports through these south Atlantic ports has not yet been compensated for with other commodities; the likely one appears to be wood products.

Reference has been made to the virtual economic immunity these cities have had to one another in the past. There are several port cities south of Baltimore which have become manufacturers in their own right, as well as resort centers. Largest of these is *Jacksonville* (204,517), on the St. Johns River in northeastern Florida. It is the only city along these hundreds of miles of coastline with a definite air of industry about it. It is the largest lumber market and the second largest naval-stores and coffee market on the coast. Its manufactures are varied, including fertilizers, naval stores, cotton products, foods, and wood products.

Not far up the coast is *Savannah,* Georgia (119,638), once noted as a great cotton port, now exporting lumber and no cotton. Its manufactures include cottonseed products, refined sugar, fertilizer, and naval stores.

Camden, South Carolina, has a new orlon plant employing 3,000 wage earners. Brunswick, Georgia, has a big seafood canning industry. Gainesville, Florida, freezes much poultry.

Charleston, South Carolina (70,174), is the only phosphate producer-exporter on this coast. It has declined in population since 1940. The last of the port cities is *Wilmington,* North Carolina (45,043). Its manufactures include bromine, lumber products, textiles, foods, and foundry products. Tampa, Jacksonville, Savannah, Charleston, and Wilmington are south Atlantic cities (save Tampa on the Gulf) which combine commerce with fishing and the resort industry for a livelihood.

The cities and towns of the Atlantic coastal plain have long been identified with a variety of food-processing industries, agricultural and seafood. Most towns have representatives of this industrial group, particularly those concerned with vegetables, fruit, vegetable oils, and poultry. Citrus fruit, tobacco, pecans, seafood, meat packing and dairy products are more specialized in their distribution.

INDUSTRIES OF THE GULF COASTAL PLAINS

Food. The production of food and related products makes up the most widespread industry group in the Gulf Coastal Plain. Aside from the ubiquitous bakery, creamery, and ice-cream plants, there are several specialized aspects of this industry some of which are peculiar to the South.

The canning industry is important along the Gulf coast and Florida. Shrimp, oysters, citrus fruit, cane syrup, cottonseed and peanut oil, pecans, and some vegetables are nationally dominant (*Fig.* 12-6). Sugar refining in and near New Orleans accounts for about 1 per cent of the domestic supply of cane sugar. At Chalmette, Louisiana, one refinery produces 1,000 barrels daily. Dairy products have not developed rapidly, due in part to lack of refrigeration facilities for distribution and consumption, the predominantly rural character of the population with low purchasing power, and a lack of pasture.

Meat packing is rather widely distributed over the South, but its main centers are north of the coastal plain in Texas, Oklahoma, Tennessee, and Alabama. The two-score rice-processing mills, handling some 20 million bushels of grain yearly, are located in Texas, Louisiana, and Arkansas.

Oil Refining. More refineries and a larger proportion of refining capacity are located in the states of Louisiana, Texas, and Oklahoma than in any other section of the United States or Canada. This refining industry is

FIGURE 12-6: *Shrimp Cannery, Golden Meadows, Louisiana*
The greatest concentration of shrimp canneries in the nation is along the middle Gulf
Coast. (Louisiana Dept. of Resources)

identified with the leading position of these states in petroleum production.

During the fifty-year period since the first refineries were built at Beaumont and Port Arthur, the industry has grown to 107 refineries with a crude capacity of between 3 and 4 billion barrels per day or about 40 per cent of the nation's capacity.[5] Within Texas and Louisiana, refining capacity is concentrated on the Gulf coast, where nearly one-third of the nation's refining is located. The major centers are: New Orleans, Baton Rouge, Lake Charles, Beaumont-Port Arthur, Houston-Baytown-Texas City, and Corpus Christi (*Fig. 12-7*).

Three factors largely account for this concentration: (1) access to water transportation, which is at present the cheapest form of transportation; (2) nearness to a very large and relatively stable supply of crude oil; and (3) nearby large quantities of natural gas which supply the refineries with a relatively cheap fuel.

Farther north and west of the coastal concentration are other refineries, most of them in central Oklahoma, and with a belt extending from El Paso eastward across northern Texas to northern Louisiana. Oklahoma has some

[5] "The Oil Refining Industry in the Southwest," *Monthly Business Review,* Federal Reserve Bank of Dallas, Vol. 39, No. 10 (October 1, 1954), pp. 141-149.

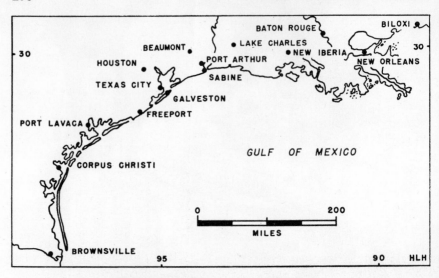

FIGURE 12-7: *Gulf Coastal Cities*

12 per cent of the refining capacity of these three states. These interior refineries are more dependent upon local markets; some of them do not have pipeline connections to the Gulf coast. Most of them have access to the transcontinental pipeline system to the Great Lakes basin and Atlantic coast. The largest refineries in the South, and in the nation, are in coastal Louisiana and Texas; interior refineries are all relatively small.

The markets for coastal refineries, mostly reached by ocean tanker, absorb a greater variety of petroleum products than the interior markets of Oklahoma, Texas, and Louisiana. Within recent years the shallow offshore waters of the Gulf of Mexico have been yielding quantities of petroleum. The man-made islands or drilling platforms are at various distances from the coast; some of them are fifty miles out. Tankers bring this crude oil to mainland refineries (*Fig.* 11-7).

Chemicals. The Texas Gulf Coast has become the greatest chemical manufacturing area on earth and is still growing. The rise of petrochemical products manufacture constitutes a near revolution in industry (*Fig.* 12-8). Reportedly, two of every five new plants are built here.

From such a large refining center as the one near Baton Rouge come carbon black (from natural gas) and synthetic rubber (Buna S). Three-fourths of the nation's carbon black comes from these Deep South refineries. From the youthful, but very large (30 acres) copolymer plant

FIGURE 12-8: *Monsanto Chemical Plant, Texas*

The Gulf coast of Texas has become one of the three major concentrations of the chemical industries in the nation. This large manufacturer of styrene monomer is representative of the size and type of plant. (Monsanto Chemical Co.)

nested in the hundreds of acres of the oil refinery at Baton Rouge, comes a large part of the Buna S rubber from petroleum production. (In 1943 more than half of Buna S rubber came from alcohol; this type of rubber plant is located farther north in West Virginia, near the source of alcohol.) At Baton Rouge, Buna S rubber is made from butadiene, a product of the oil refinery, and styrene a product of coal tar and of petroleum refining. The butadiene is piped directly from a Baton Rouge oil refinery; the styrene comes in tank cars from Texas City. There is another kind of synthetic rubber made at Baton Rouge. It is the butyl rubber and its present manufacture is a unit in the midst of the great oil-refining center itself. Its constituents, butylene (a refinery gas) and isoprene (from turpentine) are of local origin.

The enormous capital outlay for such types of rubber plants is apparent from the physical appearance of the structures: steel towers rising 170 feet, enormous globular tanks, and miles of pipes of various colors. The importance of the manufacture of synthetic rubbers in the economy of the South may be appraised, in part, by the number and size of the participating centers of production. So far as number of factories is concerned, there were nine cities and towns in Texas, and three in Louisiana engaged in making the rubber or some of its constituents.

These synthetic rubber plants employ relatively few people; they rely upon skilled personnel. But it is an important addition to the payrolls sought by this area. Although virtually all of these were government-owned plants, the process of selling or leasing them to private companies is almost completed.

Iron and Steel. Although there were charcoal iron furnaces in Alabama and Georgia by 1810, and in Texas by 1840, the manufacture of iron and steel in the South may be regarded as a new industry brought there by the demands of World War II. New plants have been constructed at Houston, Fort Worth, and Galveston. The principal market for their product was the hundred-odd new shipways that were built along the Gulf margin after the lend-lease program started, just before World War II. The Korean War kept many factories in operation, but not the shipyards. The rapid industrialization of the west Gulf coastal margin since 1941 has provided an adequate market for this capacity. Prior to the recent war, the most widespread of southern iron and steel markets were the small foundry and machine shops found in every state but Mississippi. Birmingham supplied pipe and much of the iron and steel for southern manufacture.

Aluminum, Tin, and Other Metals. Despite the presence of bauxite in Arkansas and the relative abundance of water and coal for the production of electricity, there was no aluminum industry in the South prior to World War II. The emergency brought government financial support. Prior to 1950 there was no aluminum produced on the expanse of plains west of New Orleans. In 1955 Texas became the second largest producer of primary aluminum in the United States, with a capacity of 225,000 short tons (*Fig.* 12-10). These integrated facilities are near Corpus Christi. They use bauxite imported from Surinam and Jamaica; the fuel is natural gas and lignite. Aluminum production is on an ore-to-ingot basis at one general location.

Another recent aluminum installation is at Chalmette, just below New Orleans. These two states, when combined with Arkansas, give the southern states ranking with the Northwest in primary aluminum. At the close of World War II, several northern government-owned aluminum plants were closed; the increase in capacity took place in the South and West.

The only North American tin smelter is at Texas City, using ores from Bolivia. It is government-owned and operated; its future is dependent upon government support. Lead is shipped from Guatemala for refining at Houston. Magnesium is extracted from seawater at Freeport. Several southern cities manufacture commercial fertilizers, using potash from New Mexico, nitrate from Tennessee and Alabama, and phosphate from Florida.

Wood Products. There are numerous manufacturers of wood products in the South. Most of the mills using hardwoods are near the Ozark-Ouachita and the southern Appalachian sources of hardwood timber. At Laurel, Mississippi, one of the largest of southern mills turns out several types of board made of wood fibers. Wood containers for fruit and other commodities are made at a number of places. Hercules Powder Company is one of the largest wood distillers in the South. Bulldozers root out the old dry stumps from about a million acres a year. They are trucked to Hattiesburg, Mississippi, or to Brunswick, Georgia, for distilling. The Glidden Company operates a large installation at Valdosta, Georgia. This state now produces nearly three-fourths of all naval stores in the South.

A new bond has developed between this industry and one of the most recent arrivals. Rosin derivatives are used in the manufacture of synthetic rubber in Louisiana and Texas. They are also used in the manufacture of such dissimilar commodities as paper and cement. These bonds illustrate the growing trend among manufacturing industries in this and other parts of the South. Thus far, such bonds have not been an important location factor for southern industry.

Cotton By-Products. Although cotton textiles are manufactured in the Gulf coastal plain, this industry was discussed in an earlier section on Piedmont industries. Cotton by-products include cottonseed oil, cake meal, and linters. Southern mills manufacture 97 per cent of all cottonseed oil made in the United States.[6] The middle and western cotton-growing sections localize by far the largest number of mills. More common than grain elevators in the North, are cotton gins and compressors in the South; they are usually small affairs employing but a few men; taken as a group they constitute an important industry of the Gulf section of the South. The season of activity is short, generally from October to the first of the year.

Cities of the Gulf Plains. On the basis of recent population growth, the cities of the east and west Gulf coastal plains and the Mississippi alluvial plains are regionalized distinctly, primarily on the rate of growth. The west

[6] See George F. Deasy, "Geography of the United States' Cottonseed Oil Industry," *Economic Geography*, Vol. 17(1941), pp. 345-352.

Gulf ports have grown rapidly, in a manner reminiscent of the cities of the lower Great Lakes margin nearly a generation ago.

West Gulf Plain Cities. In much the same growth category are New Orleans, Baton Rouge, and Memphis. All have grown impressively as ports, but the extraordinary development has been in manufacturing. In their economy are most of the familiar industries of the South, but they have grown because of petroleum, petrochemical, and gas-based industries. There are exceptions even in the oil cities and, of course, in the largest cities, New Orleans and Houston.

TABLE 12-2: *Urban Population, 1940-1950*

West Gulf Cities	1940	1950
BEAUMONT	59,061	94,014
CORPUS CHRISTI	57,301	108,287
HOUSTON	384,514	596,163
GALVESTON	60,862	66,568
LAKE CHARLES	21,207	41,272
TEXAS CITY	5,748	16,620
Mississippi Plains Cities	*1940*	*1950*
NEW ORLEANS	494,537	570,445
BATON ROGUE	34,719	125,629
NATCHEZ	15,296	22,740
VICKSBURG	24,460	27,948
MEMPHIS	292,942	396,000
SHREVEPORT	98,167	127,206
East Gulf Cities	*1940*	*1950*
MOBILE	78,720	129,009
TAMPA	108,391	124,681
ST. PETERSBURG	60,812	96,738
MERIDIAN	35,481	41,893
MONTGOMERY	78,084	106,525
TUSCALOOSA	27,493	46,396

SOURCE: Bureau of the Census.

Although the immediate site of New Orleans is not a prepossessing one, the situation has enabled it to become the first city of the Mississippi alluvial plains with a population of half a million. The river meanders over this low plain at an elevation somewhat higher than the city streets. Periodic floods have contributed to the general inaccessibility of New Orleans, yet the facts of situation have been enough to overcome the disadvantages of the immediate site. Nine railroads, seventy steamship lines, and a barge line using the 9-foot channel to Pittsburgh, Chicago, and St. Paul serve New Orleans and delineate the pattern of its hinterland. Postwar statistics of the growth of the port at New Orleans have confounded some students of our ports. From a tonnage ranking of sixteenth in 1939, it has risen to third in the nation in 1953. A five-story International Trade Mart has been erected and the facilities leased to South American and European shippers. An Inner Harbor Navigation Canal links the city with the Intracoastal Waterway.

Here at New Orleans, for five miles on both sides of the Mississippi, are modern quay-type docks, warehouses, loading and unloading devices of a great seaport. The docks are classified by type of commodity, including facilities for handling bananas, bauxite, sulphur, coffee, oil, refined sugar, cotton, and lumber. New Orleans is primarily an exporter. During World War II her imports increased somewhat as Middle Atlantic ports had some of their trade diverted to the Gulf Coast. Cuban sugar, South American oil and bauxite were important items in this diversion. A free-zone was established in 1946.

New Orleans' manufactures are specialized and factory employment is secondary to commerce. The industrial sites are along the river, extending in an open pattern as far as Baton Rouge, nearly 80 miles upstream. Except for the city's margin, there is very little manufacturing to the south. The most important factory products include refined sugar and sugar products, refined oil and aluminum, synthetic rubber, ships, steel, cement, lumber, cotton textiles, foods, and clothing. Since the War, several industries have come to New Orleans, among them are makers of anhydrous ammonia, nitrogen, and tanks. In view of the rise of Houston particularly, of Dallas and Forth Worth, and the recent growth of Mobile's industry, the future of New Orleans as an industrial center does not appear dominant. The vacation industry of New Orleans and other Deep South cities and towns is an important source of income, not only in winter but summer as well. The plantation "open houses," the food, the French Quarter, Mardi-Gras, and, more recently, its military camps have combined to make New Orleans a principal magnet west of Florida and possibly the best known of southern cities.

Lake Charles (41,272) has doubled its population since 1940. Two hundred million dollars in new chemical plants have come during the same years, based largely on the brine from local salt domes, lime from shells, natural gas, electricity, and a deepwater port. It has a 100,000-barrel oil refinery. It manufactures liquid chlorine, butadiene rubber, ammonia, and rubber tires. And this in a logged-over cattletown! (*Fig.* 12-9).

FIGURE 12-9: *Firestone Rubber Plant, Lake Charles, Louisiana*

An important part of the chemical industry in the Gulf South is the manufacture of synthetic rubber in Louisiana and Texas. This is a petroleum-based industry. Not many years ago the Lake Charles district was a livestock-lumber community. (Firestone Tire and Rubber Co.)

Houston (596,163), largest of the cities in the South, has a record of growth for the past fifty years unequalled by any other southern city. Not many years ago it was the size of Galveston; today it is nine times as large. It is primarily as a railroad city that it has grown, although it has become the great port for half a dozen Texas cities farther inland, handling a tonnage that ranked it second among United States ports in 1950. Houston has had a series of specialties in its economy: first it was cattle with the coming of the railroads, then it was cotton and pine, finally oil and gas.

In 1914 the ship channel was built which enabled Houston to attract commerce from older established ports. For the wheat country of Kansas and Oklahoma, and the salt and sulphur districts of the coast, Houston has become the major port; it is a raw material exporter par excellence; exports have 10 times the tonnage of imports. Because of its size and access to the raw materials mentioned above, Houston began to forge ahead in manufacturing. Industry has developed beyond the refining, milling, and packing stages of the earlier days. The Second World War was responsible for the establishment at Houston of an airplane assembly-manufacturing plant, a new iron and steel plant, new shipyards, and, nearby, a tin plate mill. Older factories make machinery for the petroleum, cottonseed, rice mills, and foundry industries.

Since the war, the population of the city dramatically increased. The net value of manufactures is up 261 per cent over 1940. The reasons for this are not hard to see. Within a radius of two hundred miles, there are some 300 oil fields producing, in 1950, approximately 200 million barrels annually. The manufacture of petrochemicals from this petroleum and the use of brine have given rise to the most rapid increase in the chemical industry in the nation. Nearby are tremendous quantities of natural gas, at once a fuel and a raw material for manufacturing. And also cotton, rice, cattle, and forests are present.

Galveston (66,568) has diminished in its relative importance as a commercial port and has failed to share much of the manufacturing activity of its near neighbor on the mainland. The Houston ship canal attracted much of insular Galveston's trade to the inland city; this is especially true of exports from the common hinterland. Galveston has lost less of its import trade in sugar, bananas, and oil, principally because they are foods and not related to industrial needs, directly.

Corpus Christi (108,287), on a far western bayou of the Texas coast, virtually doubled its population between 1940-1950. The rise of the aluminum industry is the most significant industrial acquisition in a decade. The San Patricio aluminum reduction plant went into production in 1953, with an annual output of 80,000 short tons. A second plant, La Quinta, completes the first integrated facility. Bauxite from Jamaica comes to La Quinta to be turned into alumina; San Patricio converts this into aluminum. Both natural gas and lignite are used as fuel (*Fig.* 12-10).

The western Gulf ports are relative newcomers to the coastwise trade. A common sight along the flat coastal prairie margin west of New Orleans is the oil tanker which carries 90 per cent of the oil consumed on the Atlantic seaboard cities.

A specialized type of Gulf port is represented by the twin agglomerations of Beaumont and Port Arthur. They single-mindedly devote their energies to the commerce in petroleum and, more recently, its refined products. Unbelievable tonnages of oil from the East Texas fields clear through these ports each year. With Baton Rouge, these ports rank as having the largest refining units in the world.

East Gulf Plain Cities. The cities of the east Gulf margin do not display the same spectacular growth in population or industry. The economic structure remains simpler; an exception is Mobile, where shipyards, bauxite re-

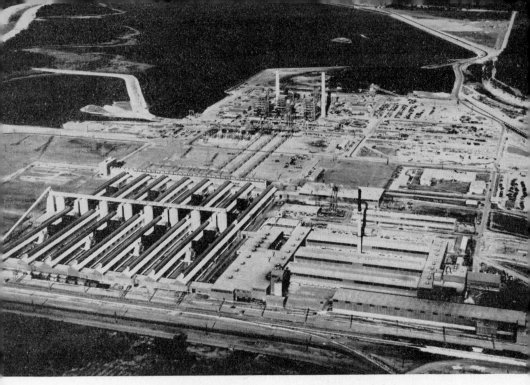

FIGURE 12-10: *Aluminum Center, Rockdale, Texas*

The opening of this integrated aluminum center made Texas second only to Washington (1956) as a producer of aluminum. Here for the first time the necessary electricity is generated by using lignite as fuel. The lake in the background is man-made. Aircraft and automobiles which consume important quantities of aluminum are also made in Texas. The automobile-making facilities of the state were doubled in 1954-55. (Aluminum Co. of America)

duction plants, paper mills, fertilizer plants, and fruit and seafood canning factories are represented. Mobile's imports include bananas, potash, phosphate, nitrate, bauxite (*Fig.* 12-11).

A third group is composed of inland cities including those on the Mississippi River plain which display none of the rapid growth of the coastal group. There is a succession of small cities about 150 miles inland and extending in almost a straight line west from Montgomery, through Meridian, Vicksburg, Monroe and Shreveport. Their prime reason for growth has been as distributing points between the port cities and the smaller collecting towns of the upper coastal plain.

Memphis, with a population of 396,000 is the principal Mississippi River city between New Orleans and St. Louis. Memphis is less of a river-trade city and more of a distributing center and branch assembly-manufacturer in its modern development. Wood products, fertilizer, tin cans, agricultural machinery, paper, tobacco, cotton and its products are its most important

FIGURE 12-11: *Port of Mobile*

Through this Gulf port come large tonnages of bauxite, iron and steel products, cotton, wood and food products. (Mobile Chamber of Commerce)

manufactures. World War II and the years since have brought much new manufacturing to the city. Among the new industries are automobile assembly plants and factories producing electric storage batteries, rubber, and chemicals.

Dallas, Houston, and Fort Worth were wartime centers for the assembly of airplanes from parts produced principally by northern auto and plane parts manufacturers (*Fig. 12-12*). Rarely are the parts or subassemblies of southern manufacture. The future of these government-built plants still appears uncertain. In some ways, Dallas is the Atlanta of the western Cotton Belt; it is on the fertile Black Prairie; it is a focus of railroad transportation, and the jobbing center for many concerns. Dallas is a vigorously growing city, largely due to the prosperous stage of its cotton agriculture and the importance of the oil industry a short distance to the west. Although Fort Worth is only 30 miles distant, it is more of an oil center and a livestock city than its rival Dallas. In most other respects Fort Worth and Dallas are similar in their commercial interests.

The post war years have witnessed a big increase in *Dallas'* population, from 294,734 in 1940 to 434,462 in 1950. What this means to a city with

FIGURE 12-12: Convair Plant, Fort Worth

This Convair plant is representative of the aircraft industry which has come to the Southwest since 1940. A certain amount of work is done out of doors. (Convair Division of General Dynamics Corp.)

the types of industry Dallas had, is of especial significance. Primary iron and steel has increased in importance; the integrated steel mill at Daingerfield has a capacity of 500,000 tons. Its iron ore (100 years' supply) is mined not far east of the city, and coking coal comes from Oklahoma. Considering its location, its devotion to the production of cast-iron pipe and oil market pipe is not surprising. The first aluminum fabricating plant in the southwest is at Rockwell, a short distance northeast of Dallas.

PROSPECTS FOR THE SOUTH

Few areas in the United States manifest more industrial change than these states of the South. Statistically the increases are extraordinarily large. But the South embraces such a large area that this rate of industrialization must proceed for years before the South is dominantly industrial. For the most part, new southern factories do not in themselves attract many other industries. Exceptions include the new primary steel plants, the great petrochemical industry, and to a lesser extent aluminum and textiles.

The rise of a market for factory goods in the South is significant; it is not

FIGURE 12-13: *Air-conditioning Equipment Plant, Decatur, Alabama*

Industrial air-conditioning is an important aspect of the South's growing market. This plant in Alabama was the first to manufacture air-conditioning equipment in the South. Its first large shipment, however, was consigned to a new factory in Illinois. (Worthington Corp.)

based primarily on government payrolls, although that continues as an important factor. (*Fig.* 12-13). The agricultural "revolution," the increase in mineral industries, and the increased commerce all are modifying the southern economy in a manner and to an extent conducive to increased manufacturing.

BIBLIOGRAPHY

"A Decade of Growth in the Southwest," *Monthly Business Review,* Federal Reserve Bank of Dallas, February, 1950.

CARSON, Rachel L., *Fish and Shellfish of the South Atlantic and Gulf Coast,* (U.S. Dept. of the Interior, Washington, 1944). Conservation Bulletin 37.

COLBY, D. S. and B. E. OPPEGARD, "Natural Gas," *Minerals Yearbook, 1951* (U.S. Dept. of the Interior, Washington), pp. 865-892.

ERICKSON, Franklin C., "Tobacco Belt of North Carolina," *Economic Geography,* Vol. 21 (1945), pp. 58-61.

Four Leading Ports of the Fifth District, Federal Reserve Bank of Richmond, March, 1949.

HOOVER, Calvin B., and B. U. RATCHFORD, *Economic Resources and Policies of the South* (New York, Macmillan Co., 1951).

JOHNSON, B. L., and G. E. TUCKER, "Phosphate Rock," *Minerals Yearbook, 1951* (U.S. Dept. of the Interior, Washington), pp. 1053-1066.

JONES, Philip E., J. E. MASON, and Joseph T. ELVOVE, *New Settlement Problems in the Northeast Louisiana Delta* (Louisiana Agricultural Experiment Station, Bulletin 335, 1942).

PARKS, M. H., "Petroleum Production from Continental Shelves," *Proceedings of the United Nations Scientific Conference on the Conservation and Utilization of Resources,* Vol. 3 (1951), pp. 21-23.

PARSONS, James J., "Recent Industrial Development in the Gulf South," *Geographical Review,* Vol. 40 (1950), pp. 67-83.

POTTER, George F. and Harley L. Crane, *"Tung Production,"* Farmers' Bulletin, No. 2031 (U.S. Dept. of Agriculture, Washington, 1951).

PRUNTY, Merle, Jr., "Recent Quantitative Changes in Cotton Regions in Southeastern United States," *Economic Geography,* Vol. 27, No. 3 (July, 1951), pp. 189-207.

RESEN, F. Lawrence, "The Gulf Coast Today: Its Billion Dollar Petro-chemical Industry," *The Oil and Gas Journal,* Vol. 51, No. 6 (1952), pp. 190-192.

RYAN, John A., *The Production and Marketing of Flax in Texas* (Austin, Texas Bureau of Business Research, University of Texas, 1951).

STRAIN, Warren, "Florida Phosphate Industry," *Journal of Geography,* Vol. 44 (1945), pp. 257-264.

WHITE, Gilbert F., *Human Adjustments to Floods: A Geographic Approach to the Flood Problem in the United States* (Chicago, Univ. of Chicago Press, 1945).

CHAPTER 13

THE MIDDLE WEST

INTRODUCTION

THE MIDDLE WEST has evolved into one of the greatest economic regions in North America. The open prairies, dense forests, and fertile soils presented a challenge to the pioneer homeseeker who wrested the land from the aborigines and transformed the wilderness into fertile farm land unsurpassed as an agricultural area.

In a century, this rich agricultural region has changed from a frontier to an agricultural and industrial area of major importance in the national economy. It has achieved a regional character which transcends the economy and involves the cultural and political attitude of the people. Midland America has become a dominant region in the nation.

Identity of the Region. The Middle West as shown on the accompanying map (*Fig.* 13-1), embraces the Central Lowlands, a small portion of the Interior Low Plateaus, the Superior Upland, the eastern or low Great Plains; a portion of the Allegheny Plateau in northeastern Ohio is treated here also. It is essentially the East and West North Central division of the Bureau of the Census. Within this major region certain overlapping specialty regions are commonly distinguished: Corn Belt, Hay and Dairy Region, the two Wheat regions, and the western half of the Manufacturing Belt.

Varied Economic Character. Despite its agricultural excellence, this section is no longer predominantly an agricultural area. Its fertile lands are crossed by an intricate pattern of railroads and highways, by pipe lines and air lines. At its northern border is a great waterway upon which plies freight tonnage greater than that of our merchant fleet of the high seas. Through its

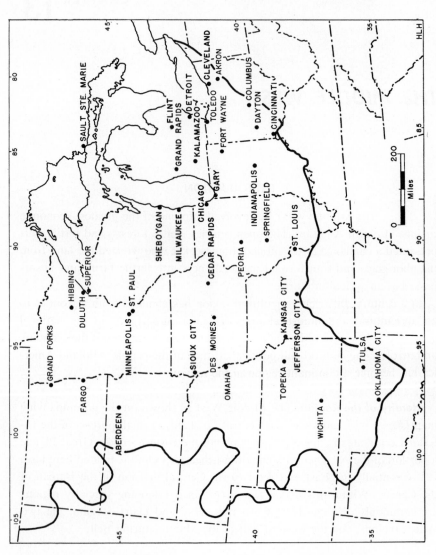

FIGURE 13-1: *The Middle West*

center and along its southern border a very large tonnage is borne by the successor to the river packet boat: the enormous barge tows that traverse the 9-foot channel from the Lakes to the Gulf, and from Pittsburgh to Kansas City. The shape of the Middle West has changed as each improvement in transportation has dispelled the isolation of some of its parts. It has become a great manufacturing region east of the Mississippi River. Two wars and an intervening depression have increased its share of the nation's manufacturing. The postwar years have witnessed further increases in its industry.

The economy of the Middle West is the most commercial of all great sections in the United States; yet if separated from the rest of the nation, it could, by a fundamental realignment of its trade, be as nearly self-contained as any section in America and probably in the world. There is no other farming region like it. The farmers are the most commercial and at the same time the most independent in the world. Its mineral wealth is both varied and abundant. The nation's centers of population, of manufacturing, and of agriculture have all moved to the lower Lake states.

During a century and a half, the Middle West has developed some specialized economic regions, but the boundaries are nowhere definite and are everywhere overlapping, retreating or advancing with the change in the market price of a dominant commodity in the farm economy.

SITUATION

Land Accessibility. Aside from the general excellence of its natural environment, the principal physical fact about the Middle West is its accessibility, among its several subdivisions, and with respect to the great port cities of the Middle Atlantic Littoral, the Gulf Coast, and Canada's most populous areas. The Middle West may be said to lie within a great funnel through which flows the greater portion of our domestic commerce. The northern margin of the funnel is the rock-and-water surface of the Laurentian Upland, a barrier that forces the flow of commerce to pass to the south. The southeastern margin of this funnel is the hill-and-mountain country of the Appalachians, stretching from the eastern Great Lakes to the seaboard, and from Maritime Canada to central Alabama.

Water Accessibility. The Great Lakes dip deeply into this directed stream of people and commodities passing between the relatively low and flat plains of the Central Lowland, heart of the continent, and its Old World margin on the Atlantic. The Middle West occupies a very large part of the Great Lakes basin, and also the watershed areas between the two great river systems, St. Lawrence and Mississippi.

The importance of the Mississippi River has varied with the times. The early relative importance of the Mississippi and its tributaries declined after the coming of the railroad. In recent decades, the relative importance of this great central river system has materially increased; it now carries more freight than at anytime in its history.

RELIEF AND SOILS

Favorable Topography. This region presents a remarkably favorable terrain for agriculture. It is for the most part the great low plains province of the Central Lowlands. The gently undulating till plain extends from Central Ohio to the Great Lakes almost to the Ohio-Missouri rivers. Diversity to this landscape is provided by the glacial moraines, outwash plains, and lacustrine plains which are features of most of the area. West of the Mississippi River dissection is somewhat greater and the landscape more rolling, due in part to loessal deposits.

Not all of the province is as uniformly attractive as the glacial plain just described. An extensive hilly belt borders the Ohio and the Missouri rivers, where the more recent ice advances failed to reach or to mask the eroded surface of an earlier till plain. Still another hilly section marks the northern limits of the Middle West; westward across the upper Lakes region the low hills and rock-and-water surface of the Superior Upland of northern Minnesota and Wisconsin, and the moderately hilly plains of the Driftless Area in southwestern Wisconsin complete the rough periphery of the Middle West.

The Great Plains of the Middle West are the transitional portion of the eastern Great Plains. Other exceptions to the prevailing uniformity of the till plain include the sandy plains of the northern portion of Michigan's lower peninsula, the swamps of northern Illinois and Indiana, southern Minnesota, Wisconsin, and Michigan. Less conspicuous are the moraines which festoon the till plain in great loops from the north.

Varied Soils. There are three main soil groups found within the Middle West. Across the upper Lakes region from western Minnesota to New England are the light-textured podzol soils, low in fertility and with a thin surface mat of partially decomposed vegetable matter. There are many areas of sandy loams whose porous nature has allowed the minerals to be leached from them into the subsoil. These soils were produced under forest cover and are, therefore, low in humus. Such farming as is found here is generally the subsistence type. Tax delinquency and poor soils loom so large in state affairs that the Michigan Land Economic Survey was established more than thirty years ago to classify, map, and plan for ultimate use the soils of the state. The current program of reforestation in so many sections of this and neighboring states is indicative of the low carrying capacity of the soils. A similar organization is trying to develop the most economic use of these soils in Wisconsin.

The second important soil group includes the gray-brown podzolic area of western Ohio, central Indiana, southern Michigan, and southern Wisconsin. These soils are transitional between the northern podzols and the old grass-land soils of Illinois and Iowa. They are moderately fertile, although some very productive but poorly drained lands are interspersed among them. Their texture is heavier than the northern podzols and they are less subject to leaching. In the Wisconsin and Michigan portions of this division, exten-sive sandy areas and some stony areas are rather common.

The third important soil group consists of the prairie soils of Illinois, Iowa, southern Minnesota, and northern Missouri. Formed under grass, these silty soils are dark colored and highly productive; their gently rolling landscapes are not only pleasing to the eye, but evince prosperity as well. No better agricultural lands are to be found. The principal disadvantage of the prairie and gray-brown podzolic soil groups is the necessity for drainage. Of all the agricultural divisions of the United States, these two soil groups are the most widely tile-drained. Represented elsewhere in these states are many soils of lesser extent and economic importance.

CLIMATE

Major Divisions. The climate of most of this region is of the humid con-tinental type with long summers; the upper Lakes area has the short summer phase. All of the qualities of a continental climate are here. It has hot sum-mers and cold winters, destructive winds, hail, and snow, occasional serious floods—and yet good crop weather. The cold winters help prevent soil leach-ing and erosion, aid in soil making, and destroy many of the plant pests. Critical droughts are rare. The heart of the Middle West is the Corn Belt, and its climate is famous. Thunderstorms on hot days bring quick rains when growing crops need them. Hot nights are essential to the growth of corn par-ticularly. Professor Ellsworth Huntington has characterized the changeable nature of this type of climate as best for producing energetic and provident men.

Critical Climatic Elements of the Lower Lakes Area. Floods and inundation have been both a curse and a blessing to several parts of the Middle West at one time or another. Where repeated inundations have left a coating of fertile silt over many years, continuous cropping of corn has resulted in no diminution in crop yield. In some sections where a large part of a farm is low enough to have benefited from inundation, the farmer may be locally known as a "bottom" farmer, not without a note of derision. Minor and major floods have occurred so often that they are an accepted part of the environment for farmers of the flood-plain portions of the Mississippi, Illinois, Wabash, and Scioto valleys, as well as along the hundreds of smaller tributaries to these rivers. Fortunately, the extent of such districts is small compared with the total farm area of the Middle West.

On the land subject to flooding, the type and pattern of fences, choice of crop, and the location and material used for farm buildings make proper allowance for the spring inundation. Occasionally a severe flood becomes a major disaster, as, for instance, the 1913 flood of the Great Miami River in southwestern Ohio, where heavy spring rains on the frozen ground caused damage to the middle and lower Miami Valley of well over $100 million. In 1937 heavy winter rains along the Ohio caused enormous property damage as the flood waters reached record heights and spread widely across the bottom lands. The Mississippi River flood plain suffers yearly. Floods are not the only critical factor. Sleet storms, summer hail, and occasional drought have also played their part in reducing crop yields in the lower Lakes portion of the Middle West.

Critical Climatic Elements of the Upper Lakes Area. This section has fewer floods. The rivers are much shorter and many of their drainage basins have great numbers of lakes and ponds to serve as reservoirs. The winters are somewhat longer and colder. The summers are generally cooler. The Great Lakes serve to stabilize temperature for fruit growing on the lee sides of Lake Michigan and Lake Erie. Some windward areas are likewise affected, for instance, the Door Peninsula.

It is for the most part a grassland region; pastures are not apt to burn out in summer. In recent years the consistent cold of winter and the considerable snowfall of the upper Lakes states have been turned to advantage for the winter sports festivals that have been established in Michigan, Wisconsin, and Minnesota.

FORESTS AND LUMBERING

Natural Vegetation. Reference to *Fig.* 2-1 reveals the extent to which the Middle West was forested. Hardwood forests closed upon the prairie peninsula which extended eastward across the Mississippi into Illinois. West of the Mississippi, the prairie grasses spread to the eastern Great Plains, northwestward into a similar province in west central Canada, and southwestward along the Central Lowlands to the High Plains of Texas. No finer hardwoods could be found than those of the upper Ohio Valley; no finer white pine than that of the upper Lakes states.

Contrasts in Lumbering. The natural contrasts between the upper and lower Lakes regions persisted as well in their forest economy. Although the Ohio Valley was the first to cut timber, it was never dominated by commercial lumbering. Here trees were cut in order to clear the land for farming; in the upper Lakes the land was a by-product of the lumbering operation and lumbering was the chief commercial enterprise.

In the hardwood forest the farm wood lot became a characteristic feature of the farmstead, supplying firewood, fence posts, and saw logs. Repeatedly these wood lots have yielded products of value on the farms of the Middle West. Unfortunately many of the wood lots were heavily pastured and as a consequence depreciated in usefulness. But an enlightened tax plan has encouraged farmers to maintain and improve their wood lots.

The timing of the Westward Movement and lumbering in the upper Lakes area was such as to fuse them into one experience. The migratory nature of lumbering is discernible in the North Central as well as in the Northeastern division. After 1820 Michigan shared leadership with Maine in the white-pine cut. Several decades before the supremacy of Michigan, lumber camps were dotting the rivers of that state; by 1850 inroads were being made in Wisconsin, and in 1875 the Lakes states surpassed the northeastern division in lumber cut. By 1890 Minnesota was a leader. For nearly a century, lumbering surpassed all other industries in the upper Lakes. The upper Lakes states had, in addition to great stands of pine, important stands of spruce, fir, hemlock, and maple. The fifty-year period immediately following the Civil War was one of "frenzied lumbering"; for the first time machinery entered the forest. By the end of the nineteenth century, from Maine to Minnesota, the first exploitation was over. During this time the domination of the upper Lakes region by the lumber industry was almost complete. With its decline, there were ghost mill towns, quiet rivers, and new farms. Because the forest economy there ran its course in such a short time, it is sometimes said that the frontier passed more rapidly through the upper Lakes region than in any comparable area in the country.

The initial harvest of the vast lumber resources of the upper Lakes was related to the settlement of the prairies of the middle Mississippi Valley. Fortunately headwaters of the Mississippi and the Wisconsin rivers reached deeply into this great forest. In the spring rafts of logs and lumber, cut and sawed during the winter, moved out of the head-stream areas with the melting snow. Downstream in the treeless prairie great quantities of lumber were needed to build the homes, stores, and other structures so necessary in a rapidly expanding area.

So long as the northern lumber was used for building homes for the rapidly growing middle Mississippi and Ohio valleys, lumber meant white pine, clear, straight, and easily worked. But with railroad construction, fenced fields, and the rise of wood-using industries, cedar, tamarack, and hardwoods were called for. Old lands were cut over again; little was left this time. The lumbermen and the forest fires which followed have made some of the upper Lakes region a virtual desert of bare rocks and sandy soil.[1]

In many areas, Minnesota for example, the state government has become the principal owner of land. Ten cents per acre was paid by the state to the counties for this land, some of it good enough for agriculture but not extensive enough to support communities.

Passing of Timber. During the lumbering period, rivers were of paramount importance in collecting the timber. The large towns were therefore on the rivers in Michigan, Wisconsin, and Minnesota. The population pattern of the upper Lakes was set by this industry which dwarfed all others, but the passing of timber withdrew support from even the larger population centers, from the trade routes which bound them, and from the countryside which nourished them. During the half-century that followed, the lumberman in many cases took up agricultural pioneering on the cut-over lands. This has proved unprofitable in the majority of instances.

FISHERIES

Although commercial fishing is very much less important in the Middle West than in the North Atlantic, the North Pacific, or the Gulf regions,

---

[1] In *Burning an Empire* (New York, Macmillan Co., 1943), Stewart Holbrook writes a very sobering history of American forest fires. In 1942 for instance there were reported by the Forest Service 208,000 forest fires, of which 26,000 were "incendiary" or deliberate. No part of the United States escaped, north, south, east or west.

recreational and commercial fishing merit some attention. Six species of fish constitutes the bulk of the catch in the Great Lakes: herring, trout, white-fish, pike, sturgeon, and blue pike. The fishing takes place near the larger centers of population on Lakes Michigan, Erie, and Huron. In winter there is some fishing through the ice, particularly along the southern shore of Lake Erie. The catch is marketed fresh to eastern and midwestern cities. This represents an income to the fishermen averaging over $5 million a year, not including this district's share of the smaller catch from the Mississippi River and its tributaries.

Recreational fishing takes place not only in the Great Lakes but in the thousands of smaller lakes in the Great Lakes basin as well. River fishing is a minor part of the fresh-water fishing industry. Recreational fishing is inextricably a part of the total recreation industry of these states. In the upper Lakes states particularly the recreation industry brings in a greater revenue than did the original forest industry. Water pollution, reforestation, and the delinquent tax lands play a related and an important part in the economy of Michigan, Wisconsin, and Minnesota.

TABLE 13-1: *Fishing Industry, Great Lakes, 1950*
(1,000 lbs.)

Lake Superior	Lake Michigan	Lake Huron	Lake Erie	Total
12,584	27,077	5,073	23,982	70,882

Lake Ontario, Lake St. Clair, Lake of the Woods, and the St. Clair and the Detroit rivers are of relatively minor importance and are given in the total figure only. SOURCE: *Statistical Abstract of the United States, 1953.*

Proximity to large midwestern cities has brought about an important recreation industry quite apart from the fishing in interior lakes and the Great Lakes. Many visit the parks and country-side just for scenery and climate. The sand dunes on the southern and eastern shores of Lake Michigan attract many visitors. The extent of lake shoreline within several states has made recreation accessible to many people. Hunting is so important in the upper Lakes states as to constitute an important source of public revenue in Michigan, Minnesota, and Wisconsin.

MINERAL RESOURCES OF THE UPPER LAKES AREA

Copper. Michigan's Keweenaw Peninsula has had one of the most spectacular careers of any mining section of the United States. For a century the Copper Range, major axis of the Peninsula, supported a copper-mining industry which for sustained employment and profit is probably equaled by no other mining district in the world.

The fabulous mining district became a part of Michigan because Ohio and Indiana had secured the valuable Erie and Michigan lake frontage at the expense of what was then the Territory of Michigan. These Laurentian rocks contained the largest deposits of pure copper metal known. Earliest mines were based on great blocks of copper metal. Later, copper in the conglomerate became the main source of the red metal. The mines were scattered along the 150-mile range and varied in size from the thousands of prehistoric shallow pits to the 6,000-foot Red Jacket shaft. The largest mines were in the vicinity of the twin cities, Houghton and Hancock.

From 1832 to 1935 the copper industry gave employment and paid dividends, with few lulls and but one major strike. Nearly ten billion pounds of copper were shipped from the lake ports of the upper Peninsula. So long as native copper was mined, no stamping mills and smelters were needed. Lake vessels carried barrels of copper down the Lakes to Middle Atlantic refiners and manufactures. When conglomerate rock was mined, stamping mills and smelters were constructed on the Peninsula. For a number of years the new mines prospered.

As the telephone, streetcar, automobile and electrical machinery came into use, Lake copper exports increased greatly. It was 1905 before Lake copper interests were aware of competition with the new mines of the Southwest. As Keweenaw mines went deeper, costs went higher. To lift the rock one mile to the surface cost so much in the face of falling copper prices, that after World War I the Keweenaw mines did not resume their former status. In their time they had broken the hold of the Welsh copper-refining interests, but in due course the copper country of Upper Michigan began to feel the competitive pinch of the new copper-producing areas in Montana, Utah, and Arizona. Decline set in and continued until after World War II. The Peninsula today is experiencing a revival in copper mining; the properties are old, but the mining techniques are new.

Iron Ore. A cartographical mistake has played an important part in the upper Lakes' greatest resource—iron ore. On the famed Dr. John Mitchell map of the Minnesota "arrowhead," the Pigeon River, rather than the St. Louis River some 90 miles farther south, was taken as the northern boundary of Minnesota. Nearly forty years before Michigan surrendered the premier position in copper, iron was discovered in this "arrowhead" of Minnesota. As with copper, this led to national dominance, but not until late in the nineteenth century.

Unlike copper, the extraction, processing and shipping of iron ore gave rise to a dozen cities and towns. *Duluth* (104,511) and *Superior* (35,325) handle most of the ore tonnage, with minor ports in Two Harbors, Minnesota, *Ashland,* Wisconsin (10,640), and *Marquette* (17,202) and *Escanaba,* Michigan (15,170). Mining towns in and around the Mesabi (world's greatest producer), Gogebic, Vermillion, Cayuna, Menominee, and Marquette ranges have localized most of the mining population of the Upper Lakes region.

The extraction of ore, its handling, and its transportation are marvels of mechanical efficiency. Manpower is relatively a minor factor in this industry. These population centers are but points of transfer, the creatures of iron ore whose work year is shortened by winter's closing of the Lakes for five months. Their relations to the surrounding countryside and with the more distant cities of Minneapolis and Winnipeg are of little importance. From these iron districts some 90 to 120 million tons of ore are exported each year. While many of the usual sordid accompaniments of mining are lacking here, the stumps left by the lumberman led the state to tax the iron ore while it could. The result has been that the iron districts display every evidence of community wealth but very little of individual prosperity.

Hibbing, a perennial boom town in the Mesabi Range, has been moved two miles from its early site in order to make way for the huge electric shovels of the open-pit Hull-Rust mine. Its schools and public buildings have been elaborately reconstructed and richly furnished. A $4-million-dollar school educates the third generation of Finns, Norwegians, Cornishmen, Poles, and Slovenes, whose grandparents came in after the Civil War. With 16,276 population, *Hibbing* spends about as much as *Duluth* (104,-511) to carry on city services and government. In 1924 Hibbing levied taxes on mineral wealth of an estimated $94 million; by 1950 it had shrunk to $60 million. From a yield of 25 million tons in 1945, this mine in 1947 yielded only 14 million. The land cannot carry this sort of cultural landscape after the iron ore goes.[2]

For scores of miles the iron ranges are pock-marked with open pits, active only during the seven warm months. Less frequent are the shaft mines, which are able to operate throughout the year.[3] In 1940 more than 80 per cent of our total iron shipments came from this Lake Superior

[2] Both Hibbing and Superior declined in population between 1940 and 1950.

[3] A little over half of the ore is mined by the open-pit method on the Mesabi Range where the ore lies near the surface. The remainder is mined by the shaft method; this is the most common method in all ranges except Mesabi. This range is virtually the sole producer of this easily mined ore, and the only high-grade field which can yield large tonnages on short notice. Grading and blending are done in the yards.

district.[4] More than half came from the Mesabi Range alone, which yields more than any other district in the world. In this range is the world's largest open-pit mine, the Hull-Rust Mine at Hibbing 350 feet deep, 2.5 miles in length, and producing 15 million tons in one season. (Germany's prewar yearly total averaged 10 millions.) In its operation, Mesabi has accounted for more than 1½ billion tons, two-thirds of our total ore production. A like amount of high-grade ore remains, and vast unknown quantities of lower grade are just beginning to be commercially developed in this re-

TABLE 13-2: Iron Ore Shipments, By Ranges, 1854-1945

Range	Year opened	Total production (gross tons) 1,000
MARQUETTE	1854	237,710
MENOMINEE	1877	212,328
GOGEBIC	1877	249,491
VERMILLION	1844	77,198
MESABI	1892	1,436,330
MAYVILLE	1892	2,379
BARABOO	1894	643
CUYUNA	1911	55,579
FILLMORE	1942	279
CANADIAN (OLD)	1904	3,935
CANADIAN, MICHIPICOTEN	1939	2,868
CANADIAN, STEEP ROCK LAKE	1944	521

SOURCE: *Annual Report,* Lake Carriers' Association, 1946.

gion and in northern Michigan. The processing of lower grade ore is relatively expensive, but the extraordinarily hard rock is being broken, the ore beneficiated in new plants in the iron country, and increasing tonnages are being shipped down the lakes to steel-making centers. More labor is required for this mining industry; new towns are being built to care for the working force (*Fig.* 13-2).

The spectacular nature of the Great Lakes' iron industry stems not only from ore mining but as well from its loading, transportation, and unloading at lower Lake ports. In about seven months of the year, a total of more than 100 million tons may be moved a thousand miles by some 300 ore boats averaging 14,000 gross tons. Unloading ports see the freighters about nine hours on an average; loading ports only about five hours. The integra-

[4] Next in importance was the Alabama district with 11 per cent of the total. Three per cent came from Pennsylvania, and the remaining 3 per cent was made up of small amounts from eleven other states.

tion of ore properties, lake vessels, ore-carrying railroads, and iron and steel manufacture has established the world's greatest iron and steel industry (*Fig.* 9-8). Along the spurs of nine railroads, cars from the ore pits and the stock piles start their downhill run to the Lake port and roll on high trestles to the loading docks which are approximately half a mile long. Each car is dumped into hoppers from which the waiting ore boats are filled. Loadings are unbelievably rapid; the record time for loading a standard ship is under seventeen minutes. Nor is this saving of labor confined to iron ore; coal is handled on the Chesapeake and Ohio docks in Toledo, the Pennsylvania docks in Cleveland and Sandusky, and the Nickel Plate at Loraine, in a manner as mechanized and as economical as is iron ore.

Limestone. Among all products of mines and quarries of the United States, limestone is normally exceeded in tonnage only by bituminous coal, and in some years by sand and gravel. Its value is relatively much less. In its production Michigan is second only to Pennsylvania, followed by Ohio, Illinois, and Indiana. The uses for this limestone are exceedingly varied; something less than half of the limestone quarried in the Middle West is used as a flux in the manufacture of iron and steel.

FIGURE 13-2: Concentrator, Mountain Iron, Minnesota

In this building the taconite rock which previously had been crushed to one-half inch size is ground in rod-and-ball mills to powder fineness in order that the iron particles may be separated magnetically from the unwanted silica. (United States Steel Corp.)

FIGURE 13-3: *Bulk Carrier on the Detroit River*

Carriers like this are part of the lifeline of the steel industry in the Middle West. These great vessels in a season of eight months or less make the equivalent of two trips around the world. The average turnaround time in a loading port is 4 hours, and in an unloading port it is 11 hours. (National Steel Co.)

Michigan's limestone consists of large, thinly-covered deposits of very pure, high calcium stone in the northern part of the state, some of it conveniently located on or near shores of the Great Lakes, within sight of the great ore boats plying from upper Lakes mines to lower Lakes mills. Stone ranks third in the tonnage of the Great Lakes, three-fourths of which is consumed outside of the state of origin. The principal exporting ports are Calcite, Port Inland, Alpena, and Rockport.

The huge freighters which carry the ores, coal, grain, and other commodities of great bulk reflect the physical conditions under which they operate and the nature of the cargo carried (*Fig.* 13-3). They are built very long (600 feet or more), and rather shallow (20 feet), and with much of the deck surface given over to hatches. These dimensions are imposed by the relatively shallow canals and rivers which provide connection between the Great Lakes, and by the depth of the harbors; the hatches enable these vessels to be loaded and unloaded mechanically in the shortest possible time. Since some of the harbors are without unloading devices on a scale commensurate with the vessels serving them, some of the large freighters are self-unloaders. Ore, coal, and wheat cargoes are seldom destined for any but the larger and well-equipped ports.

LOWER LAKES MINERALS

From the resource point of view, the upper and lower Lakes regions are complementary; between the two regions flows the greatest inland domestic tonnage on the continent. Toledo often exceeds in coal tonnage the Chesapeake Bay port of Norfolk. The commerce on the Great Lakes is mainly coal, oil, and package freight moving north, and ore, wheat, and limestone moving south.

Coal. Bituminous and anthracite coal move over the Lakes; none of the anthracite and but little of the bituminous is mined in the lower Lakes region; most of it is from Appalachian fields. But coal is also mined in Illinois, Indiana, Kansas, and Iowa.

Petroleum. Minor oil fields have been in production at many places in Ohio, Indiana, Illinois, and Michigan for half a century. Production has declined in all but the newer fields of Michigan, Indiana, and Illinois.

One of the older fields is that lying between western Lake Erie and Richmond, Indiana. Most of this area is a plain of gentle relief. Here the oil industry is superimposed upon a superior general-farming economy. This field lies athwart the oil pipelines from the midcontinent field to the lower Lakes and eastern cities. Conspicuous in this oil field are the huge metal storage tanks for through traffic as well as for local storage. Inconspicuous pumps are operated from a small central power house. In most parts of this field the ephemeral use of land by the oil industry is apparent. Agriculture everywhere encroaches upon the once-active oil industry. Smaller fields with modern equipment are found in the Vincennes region of the southern Indiana-Illinois borderland, in southwestern Illinois, and in northwestern Illinois below Rock Island.

Natural Gas. Although natural gas is frequently an accompaniment of oil in wells, there have been but few and minor gas fields in the Middle West. The most important field was in northwestern Ohio. Economical access to the natural gas of West Virginia and the great southwestern fields has enabled the Middle West to hold industries established on local gas.

Salt. The brine and salt resources of the Middle West are found both in the upper and lower Lakes regions. Eastern and western Michigan and northern Ohio are the most important producing centers. As with clay, gas and coal, the Middle West is accessible to the salt resources of the Appalachian Plateaus.

Sand and Gravel. The humble sand and gravel of glacial origin have been one of the prime mineral resources of the Middle West. On many farms, the least productive field has become a valuable gravel or sand pit, when a gate is put in the fence, and a loader installed for the trucks serving some county, state, or federal road project. In northern Ohio there is sand and sandstone of a grade satisfactory for glass making.

AGRICULTURAL REGIONS OF THE MIDDLE WEST: CORN BELT

Although the Middle West is famous for its agriculture and for the institutions which have grown from it, this area does not consist of one great homogeneous farming region. Not only does the upper and lower Lakes contrast, noted above, continue over into the field of agriculture, but within each of these two regions important distinctions in farming practices are apparent. Inspection of *Fig.* 2-5 reveals that the Corn Belt, the Spring and the Winter Wheat regions, the Minnesota-Wisconsin Dairying region, and the General Farming region of the Ohio Valley all lie partly or wholly within the Middle West.

Importance of Corn. The United States is by far the greatest producer of corn in the world. Nearly all of the corn in this country is grown in an area between the Dakotas and the Great Lakes on the north and the Gulf of Mexico on the south. More than three-fourths of the farms of the Corn Belt grow corn for grain. Despite the widespread distribution of corn in America, more than half of the nation's crop is produced in portions of eight states known as the Corn Belt.

Corn was a minor crop in the northeastern states; in much of New England it does not even appear in the farming system; only in southeastern Pennsylvania is it an important crop. In the Middle West, however, there are few places where corn is not a major crop.

In delineating a Corn Belt, 3,000 bushels per square mile may be taken as the minimum limit; in much of the Corn Belt, production reaches 5,000 bushels. Throughout most of the southern states, from the Carolinas to Texas, and north on the Plains to the Dakotas, the yield of corn per acre is much lower than in the Corn Belt. Corn is widely grown under a variety of physical and economic conditions and in many small districts on a noncommercial basis.

Boundaries of the Corn Belt. The Corn Belt lies to the north and some-what to the west of the center of the corn-growing states of the United States. In northern Illinois, eastern Iowa, and southern Minnesota, corn fol-lows the northern limit of the prairie soils which characterize so much of the Corn Belt; in northern Indiana and Ohio the poorer-drained soils of the till plain and of the lake plain, respectively, have subordinated corn to a rela-tively minor crop in some places. Soils therefore largely account for the northwest-southeast trend of the Corn Belt's northern margin, although the climatic factor also plays a part.

Farther east, a different type of land use has been modifying the Corn Belt's northern limit. From Minnesota, through southern Wisconsin and southern Michigan more corn is cut for silage than elsewhere in the nation. The Hay and Dairy Belt's demand for succulent winter cattle feed has in-creased the corn acreage beyond its temperature and soil optimum for grain. Furthermore, the growth of the large cities on the southern margin of the Great Lakes has stimulated a somewhat different specialization of agricul-ture on the lake silts and mucks of this plain. Pasture, tomatoes, sugar beets, vegetables, and fruit vie with corn for the use of land in northern Illinois, Indiana, and Ohio. Along Lake Michigan's eastern shore, peaches and cher-ries have likewise brought about specialization in land use.

In the northwest the corn-and-dairy combination has been encroaching on the wheat areas. Corn has moved west from the prairie soils onto the chernozems of wheat fame. Except for the sand hills of western Nebraska, the isohyet of eight inches summer rainfall marks the western limit of the Corn Belt. In the southwest, winter wheat and corn compete for the land where the rainfall is adequate. Both the Spring and Winter Wheat regions increased in wheat acreage when the price of wheat rose during both world wars. The eastern boundary of the Corn Belt is more transitional than either the north or west. The hill and mountain country between eastern Ohio and the Atlantic reduces corn to relatively a secondary crop, grown for the most part on the bottom lands. Yields per acre often are excellent, but hillside fields produce meager crops generally.

In the south as in the east, hill topography is one of the major limiting factors in corn acreage and yield, but protracted high summer temperatures and soils of moderate fertility also reduce the yield of corn so as to keep the isopleth of 3,000 bushels per square mile everywhere north of the Ohio Valley hills.

Divisions of the Corn Belt. There are three main subdivisions of the Corn Belt. In each of them corn is the dominant crop, yet the varying circum-

FIGURE 13-4: *Sugar-Beet Harvester and Loader,*
Lower Great Lakes Region

With such machines as this, the sugar beet is able to be maintained in the cropping system of a labor-short region. This machine is used in the production of sugar beets in such specialized districts as Michigan-Ohio, Colorado, and Idaho. (Scott Viner Co.)

stances under which corn is grown and marketed merit this subdivision. The first subdivision may be termed the heart of the Corn Belt. It lies in central Illinois, Iowa, northeastern Kansas, eastern Nebraska, and southwestern Minnesota. Here the physical factors for corn production are optimum. In the sources of cash income for these Corn Belt farmers, corn is dominant; rotations are regularly practiced and the crop combinations are subject to change. The corn-hog combination holds throughout the region, although more cattle are fattened here than elsewhere in the Corn Belt. In Illinois more corn is grown for sale to industry than in any other portion of the Corn Belt. The only place where corn does not dominate the landscape is along the hilly lands of the Mississippi and its tributary valleys, where sheep production has become of ranking importance because these lands are best fitted for pasture.

The second subdivision of the Corn Belt is sometimes known as the Little Corn Belt. It lies in western Ohio and central Indiana. Corn does well here and the region appears to be as prosperous as in the heart of the Corn Belt. While corn is the dominant crop and hogs are the chief element in

FIGURE 13-5: *Corn Picker at Work in the Heart of the Corn Belt*
Hybrid corn and the mechanical picker have been the Corn Belt's response to the high-priced labor in these states. (International Harvester Co.)

the livestock economy, the agriculture in the Little Corn Belt is quite diversi-fied. Soybeans, wheat, oats, and hay crops are important. Tomatoes are grown in many districts, particularly in the north. Tobacco is grown in the lower Miami Valley. Sheep are important in Ohio. Urbanization has created an important market for dairy products, primarily fluid milk.

The third subdivision is the wheat-corn transition zone along the entire western limits of the Corn Belt.[5] Although corn predominates nearly every-where, the livestock phase of Corn Belt economy is of secondary importance. Cash grain is more important here than in any other portion of the Corn Belt except Illinois. In the northwest a corn and dairy combination has been encroaching on wheat acreage while in the southwest, winter wheat and sorghums rank along with corn. Despite occasional failure due to low rainfall, corn has become established.

Canning Crops. The production of vegetables for canning in the Middle West is important, not only from the point of view of crops, but from that of

[5] Robert M. Basile, "Drought in Relation to Corn Yield in the Northwestern Corner of the Corn Belt," *Agronomy Journal,* Vol. 46 No. 1 (Jan. 1954), pp. 4-7.

FIGURE 13-6: *Alfalfa Dehydrator, near Payne, Ohio*

The dehydration of alfalfa as a step in the manufacture of stock feed is an important aspect of the trend to grass farming in the Corn Belt. Such roadside plants as this one on the lake plain of northwestern Ohio, are found also on the Great Plains and in the Intermontane Area. (Farm Bureau Cooperative Assn.)

the canning industry as well. The leading vegetable for canning in Indiana, Illinois, and Ohio is the tomato. No monument has been raised to the tomato in these states, as was done in Georgia, but the crop has steadily increased for twenty-five years. The major producing areas are in central Indiana and Illinois, and in northern Ohio. More than half of the tomato plants are imported from Georgia, Louisiana, Arkansas, and Mississippi.

On the silt and musk soils of northern Ohio, Indiana, and Michigan onions and celery are important. Much sweet corn also is grown, particularly in the valleys of southern Ohio and Indiana. Sugar beets are grown under refinery contract in northwestern Ohio and southern Michigan (*Fig.* 13-4).

For several of these crops mentioned above, the labor requirements are so great as to bring about migrating labor from the hill country south of the Ohio River. Some labor also comes from the cities of the lower Lakes.

Changes Since the AAA. Throughout the Middle West significant and far-reaching changes have occurred possibly as a result of the Soil Conserva-

FIGURE 13-7: *Irrigated Pasture near the Indiana-Ohio Border*

Irrigation in the humid east is by no means confined to the high acre-value crops. Although less than 1 per cent of the farmland in the Little Corn Belt is irrigated, the proportion is increasing. Approximately half of the area irrigated is pasture. (Oldfield Equipment Co.)

tion Act of 1935; it is not agreed to what extent the government program has been responsible for these changes. Many responsible farmers assert that they had already begun before this Act, and will continue regardless of Federal aid.

Agricultural Adjustment Administration reduction in corn acreage hastened the development of hybrid corn (*Fig.* 13-5). The farmers found that since they were compelled to reduce acreage, they could raise more bushels per acre. As early as 1933 there were 24 million acres of hybrid corn; this was about 40 per cent of all corn land in these states. In some counties the proportion was as high as 90 per cent. The growing and selling of hybrid seed corn has become an important business.

The soybean acreage increased from 2 to 16 million since 1926. Grain sorghums, fed from the shock and as silage, are grown from Ohio to eastern Nebraska. Grass silage is likewise coming into wide use, principally with sweet clover, alfalfa, and occasionally red clover (*Fig.* 13-6).

Corn Belt farms have been getting larger; in 1925, 232 acres; in 1934, 254 acres; in 1938, 266 acres. Various reasons are given for this. One is the fact that the need for more land to fit the capacity of farm machinery more or less coincided with the government's program to pay (in effect) farmers to grow fewer acres of corn, wheat, and other grains. This frequently meant that a farmer could collect his government payments for reduced grain acreage on the farms he owned and parts of one or two more which he rented for the purpose of using his equipment more efficiently. Actually he may have tended but a few more acres in plow crops, but the payments covered the retired grain acreage on his increased farm holdings. Such cases were frequent in Ohio and Indiana, and were especially numerous in Iowa, Nebraska, and Illinois.

The growth of hybrid corn with its 20 per cent greater yield, in effect confused the government program, particularly in Iowa where 75 per cent of the corn is hybrid. It also caused a dislocation in farm labor. One farm owner said:

> Altogether I have taken twelve small, run-down farms or parts of farms, operated by eight men, and have turned them into three units with a total of 830 acres. I operate these with the aid of four men. I shift tools from farm to farm. The manure spreader runs every day in the year. Miles of fences have been torn out to make larger fields. I work a three-year rotation and am making money. With or without Government aid, this trend will continue.[6]

Urbanization. The nearness of railroads and factory towns has had a profound effect upon Corn Belt people of all ages. Nowhere in the United States is there a comparable farming region so intimately associated with manufacturing of similar importance. The value of farm land has been determined not only by its fertility, but sometimes by its location with respect to railroad and factory.

With high land values, a high degree of mechanization of farm work, and the profit accruing from farming and the sale of farm land throughout the Corn Belt to attract the city-farm buyers, the number of tenant-operated farms has steadily risen until Ohio has 40 per cent; Illinois 30 per cent, and Iowa 25 per cent tenancy. Although many farmers work on the shares, they are not sharecroppers. The relative stability of Corn Belt farming has enabled many owners past middle age to escape the rigors of winter by going to California and to Florida. Many more are content to escape the lonely life on the farm, after the children are grown, by renting the farm and moving to a nearby town, still keeping an observant eye on the home place.

[6] Information from Professor H. R. O'Brien, The Ohio State University.

GENERAL FARMING AREAS

The names given the several agricultural regions in the United States are those adopted by the Bureau of Agricultural Economics. Once known as the Corn and Winter Wheat region, this General Farming term is somewhat more descriptive of the agricultural economy of this large area. The name places the emphasis less upon crops than upon the conditions under which they are produced. Only a part of the General Farming area lies within the Middle West.

Topography. The critical factor in the environment is hills. Were it not for the thousands of low hills, much of the Ohio Valley might well be included within the Corn Belt. Corn is still the dominant crop here, and bottom-land fields occasionally produce crops comparable with the best anywhere. The terrain, however, precludes cropping of more than one-third of the area, and thus prevents production of the 3,000 bushels or more per square mile which characterizes the Corn Belt.

The soils of the Ohio Valley in many places are too acid for alfalfa, although timothy, clover, and natural pasture occupy an increasing proportion of the area each year. The last great advance of the ice sheet did not reach the Ohio River generally, and the smoothing effects of an earlier ice advance have been erased by erosion. The landscape presents a more dissected appearance than the Corn Belt on the north. The pastured hills support many flocks of sheep. Since corn is less abundant, swine are not so numerous as either sheep or cattle.

Characteristics of the Economy. In summary, the impression one gets of a representative farm in the middle western portion of the General Farming area is its amazing diversity. While livestock remains important, the effects of hills, poorer soils, and inaccessibility to large urban centers have combined to make it self-sufficing in many areas rather than commercial. Farmwork is not highly mechanized, and rotation is practiced only on part of the cropped land. The population distribution is surprisingly dense, as dense over most of the area as in the Corn Belt. Land values are approximately only half those of its northern neighbor. The Cincinnati market has intensified the agriculture in the lower Miami Valley and adjacent parts of Kentucky. Tobacco, peaches, apples, tomatoes, melons, sweet corn, and sheep are important in a number of districts.

THE HAY AND DAIRY REGION

The Hay and Dairy region is the largest of the agricultural regions within the Lakes states. In both the eastern and western Lakes plains it lies just north of the Corn Belt. In many places the southern margin is one of vague definition, but in general it approximates the industrialized lower Lakes margin, the southern limit of sandy soils in Michigan, the Driftless Area of southwestern Wisconsin, and the sandy or stony soils in central Minnesota.

Surface features range from nearly level plains to morainic ridges and bare rock knobs. Many glacial bogs and lakes dot the landscape. A great deal of the western Lakes region and much of the eastern Lake region may be characterized as cut-over land, communities of small farms, or abandoned crop land.

Farming Precarious. As was noted in the section on Forests, the upper Lakes agriculture is mainly the by-product of lumbering. It was not settled at the same time as the lower Lakes. Westward-moving agricultural pioneers passed it by and went on to the rich lands of the Missouri Valley. The farm economy of this large area bears little resemblance to the Corn Belt south of it. Where soils are not too stony, wet, or shallow, large areas have been cleared away and used for the cultivation of clover, alfalfa, small grains, and corn for ensilage. Due to the high cost of clearing the mediocre land, the short growing season, and the relative inaccessibility, the nature of the agriculture suggests the imminence of abandonment in many places.

Increased Dairying. Wherever proximity to markets allows it, dairying is the principal source of farm income. Dairying alone, or together with potatoes and small grains or even livestock, tends to set apart the several tiers of counties bordering the Corn Belt. From the southern end of Lake Michigan northwestward to the Spring Wheat district of the Dakotas, dairying steadily increases in importance at the expense of corn and wheat.

It must be remembered that only since the beginning of the present century has the United States become such an important consumer of dairy products. The change in land utilization, therefore, dates from the rise of this market for fluid milk, butter, and several types of cheese. The growth of this fluid milk market was simultaneous with the rise of the automobile manufacturing industry in southeastern Michigan. The principal city in this industry, *Detroit,* had a population in 1900 of 285,000; in 1950 it was 1,849,568. Smaller cities experienced a comparable rate of growth.

Accessibility to Lakes Cities. Whereas Edward Tiffin, then Surveyor-General of the United States, stated of this region in 1815 that "not one acre in 10,000 will support human life," the carrying power of Michigan's lower peninsula, the southern half of Wisconsin, and Minnestota, has steadily risen and now the population of the southern Lakes margin has approached the 10 million mark.[7]

This urban population has modified the farm economy of even the upper Lakes region to an important degree. Except for New England and New York state, no other part of the United States has so many farms with at least half of the income derived from boarders, lodgers, and campers. Another feature which the Lakes states' farms share with New England and much of the Appalachian Upland is the forest-products farm, where at least half the farm income is from the sale of forest products. Despite these similarities, this region supports an agricultural economy in which a much smaller proportion of farmers are able to supplement their income by working in nearby cities than is the case with most of New England. In the northern portion of the region crop or animal specialties, aside from dairying, are rarely encountered.

Areas of Crop Specialization. There are areas, however, in which specialization has become important, most of them are in the southern portion. Among these districts must be included the peach and cherry orchards of Lake Michigan's east shore and the Door Peninsula of eastern Wisconsin. Another is the sugar-beet district of eastern and southeastern Michigan, extending into Ohio. The celery-growing districts on the Kalamazoo and other silt plains are important in Michigan and Ohio. Tomatoes occupy the zone between the Hay and Dairy and the Corn Belt. Nearby cities absorb the greenhouse produce of the Lakes margin (*Fig.* 13-9).

Southwestern Michigan has a number of important tulip growing districts, accounting for nearly half of all tulip bulbs grown in the United States. Holland, Benton Harbor, Marshall, and Plainwell share in this colorful industry. Many of those engaged in tulip growing are of Dutch origin. From southern Minnesota eastward through the Ontario peninsula of Canada, manufacturing has been increasing since World War II. It is by no means uniform, and the agriculture of the region is affected by it in only a few places. The greatest concentration is in southern Ontario, north of Lake Erie. In the upper Lakes area, two of the most recent urban influences upon agriculture are iron-mining districts, taconite mines in Minnesota and jasper in Michigan. More labor is needed in processing these ores; new towns have been built.

[7] Quoted in Ralph H. Brown, *Historical Geography of the United States* (New York, Harcourt, Brace and Co., 1948), p. 275.

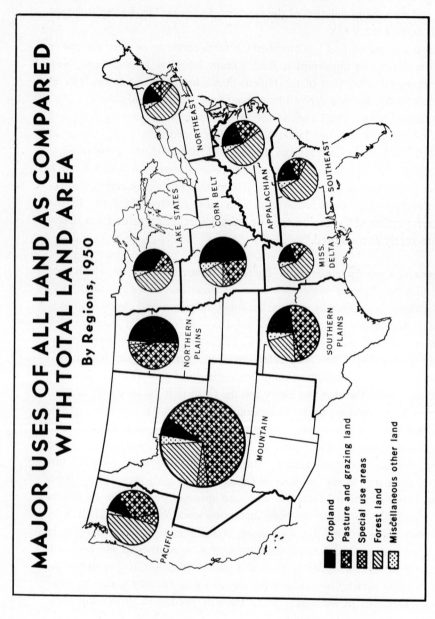

FIGURE 13-8

This chart shows comparisons with total land area. No other region has as large a proportion of its area in cropland as the Middle West. (U.S. Dept. of Agriculture)

Content inside the image:

MAJOR USES OF ALL LAND AS COMPARED WITH TOTAL LAND AREA

By Regions, 1950

NORTHEAST

LAKE STATES

CORN BELT

APPALACHIAN

SOUTHEAST

MISS. DELTA

NORTHERN PLAINS

SOUTHERN PLAINS

MOUNTAIN

PACIFIC

Cropland
Pasture and grazing land
Special use areas
Forest land
Miscellaneous other land

FIGURE 13-9: *Greenhouse on the Lake Plain*

The lake plain between Toledo and Buffalo leads the nation in acres under glass. The mulching operation shown in the photograph was taken near Toledo. (Ohio Tractor and Implement Co.)

Where conditions are most discouraging for agriculture in the Lakes area, state governments are trying to bring about a wise use of such land as has in practice proved submarginal.

THE WHEAT REGIONS

Spring Wheat. In the northwestern portion of the Central Lowlands, the production of spring-sown wheat was once so general and so persistent as to give its name to that region. In the main it is a transition zone between the rowcrops of the upper Mississippi basin and the grazing lands of the Great Plains. However, in spite of the persistent emphasis upon wheat, there have been changes in the economy of the area (*Fig.* 13-8). The southeastern border changes as the relative prices of wheat and corn mutually affect the production areas of the two crops. Dairying has become more important in both regions. This is one of the great agricultural regions in the United States which has been designated by the name of one commodity. Wheat continues to be important, but potatoes, oats, sugar beets, barley, and dairying and stock raising are also important.

329

Forming the easternmost section of North Dakota is the Red River Valley, largely an old lake plain. For many years it was the heart of the Spring Wheat-growing region; it is one of the most important agricultural areas of northern United States. Changes in its agriculture over a period of fifty years are representative of those taking place in the rest of the wheat-growing northern Great Plains-Central Lowland.

The growing season is limited, varying from 103 to 139 frost-free days. Killing frost may occur as late as June and as early as September. Corn is knee-high in Georgia when the frost line retreats to the plains of Canada, and the farmers of the Red River Valley move out on the flat fields of this old lake plain to prepare the soil for wheat. Although the period of frost-free days is not long, the percentage of possible sunshine is high and the period of sunlight is long each day. About half of the total yearly precipitation of from 17 to 22 inches falls during the summer months when crops most need it. The certainty of cold winters has precluded the possibility of crop changes which require a more temperate climate. Many of the settlers who have moved to the Matanuska Valley in Alaska were from these wheat-growing counties.

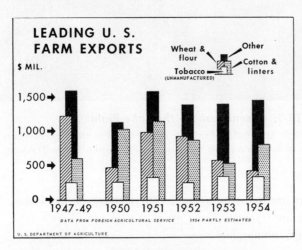

FIGURE 13-10

The Middle West's big contribution to farm exports has been wheat; its declining role is shown on this chart.

Red River Valley soils are deep, heavy, finely divided clay loams with rather poor natural drainage. As with many Great Plains soils, they are productive if adequately watered. A strip of these soils some 40 miles wide and the breadth of North Dakota constitutes the only level terrain of similar extent between the northern Rockies and Lake Superior. It has been the basis for the development of an agricultural oasis in which 80 per cent of the district is in farms and 90 per cent of the land is cultivated. Field crops have returned by far the largest part of the farm income for fifty years, but their nature is changing.

In the past quarter-century wheat acreage has declined by nearly 40 per cent; corn and oats have increased their proportion of the total cropped land. Potatoes, barley, flax (a quarter of the nation's crop), sugar beets, and alfalfa have all become important crops (*Fig.* 13-10). Since World War I, dairy products have increased in value 400 per cent; the cream sold as butterfat has increased from 7 million to 52 million pounds. It is the Red River Valley farms which put the northern plains far ahead of the southern in the proportion of farm income which comes from the sale of livestock and its products. Poultry has increased 300 per cent since World War I. There are 150 creameries, a score of small flour mills, a beet sugar refinery, and the usual service industries for a total urban population of about 100,000, more or less evenly distributed among *Fargo, Grand Forks,* and *Moorhead.* A war and postwar price supports have made the Red River Valley more prosperous than at any time in its history.

Winter Wheat. So much wheat is sown in the autumn in central and western Kansas, Oklahoma, and northern Texas that it has come to be known as the Winter Wheat region. The region does not have the optimum conditions for growing winter wheat. The western boundary of this wheat region is set by aridity, where the farmer has lost so many crops of wheat that a large proportion of his ranch is in pasture. Higher temperatures and a lighter snow cover discourage wheat and permit cotton on the south. The northern limit is a combination of poor Nebraska soils and winter-killing of the wheat plant. The eastern margin is primarily economic in nature; corn is more profitable than any kind of wheat, and where rainfall permits, corn is the dominant crop. As in the case of the Spring Wheat district, the relative price of corn and of wheat plays an important role in land use along the eastern periphery.

TABLE 13-3: *Comparison of Yields of Wheat and Corn*

WHEAT, BUSHELS PER ACRE			CORN, BUSHELS PER ACRE	
Kansas	*Illinois*	*Year*	*Kansas*	*Illinois*
1.2	17.4	1937	12.0	4.8
9.3	14.5	1935	9.0	38.5
9.1	16.4	1933	11.5	27.0
18.5	23.3	1931	18.0	37.0
12.4	14.7	1929	18.0	35.5
11.2	13.9	1927	27.0	32.0
9.2	16.0	1925	17.6	41.0
10.0	18.0	1927	23.0	37.5

SOURCE: *Monthly Review,* Federal Reserve Bank of Kansas City, April, 1954.

For half a century the farmers on these broad plains put about three-fourths of their plowed land in wheat, with the results shown in the above table. During World War I the price of wheat never fell below $2.00 per bushel; between the two World Wars it did not rise above $1.63; the average was about $1.00. World War II sent up the price of wheat; post-war price supports kept it up. Dry seasons have given rise to "dust bowls" on several occasions.

Conditions such as these have contributed to an ephemeral element in the rural population in the Winter Wheat region, particularly before World War II. Under such titles as *Adrift on the Land,* their migrations over the plains to the Pacific Coast have been told many times. Population figures for 1950 reveal that the percentage of farmers who have migrated from this region is much higher than in the Spring Wheat region.

BIBLIOGRAPHY

See bibliography at end of Chapter 14.

MANUFACTURING IN THE MIDDLE WEST

INTRODUCTION

NOTHING LIKE the rise of an industrial economy in the Middle West had ever taken place; from Indian Country it became a relatively densely occupied agricultural-industrial economy within two generations of settlement. Owing in large part to the rapidity and uniformity of settlement in a region of abundant resources, some of the industrial consequences are unique to the Middle West. Obviously not every part of this great plains region was settled at the same time, but the rapidity with which the state of the arts changed was everywhere relatively rapid.

It is no coincidence that the uniformity in many of the Middle West's physical attributes was accompanied by a relative uniformity in settlement and settlers. Part of the physical availability which induced this uniformity in occupance was related to the fact that during a century and a half of experience in Tidewater America, means had been devised of minimizing some of the handicaps imposed by distance and relatively scarce labor.

Although the Middle West was peopled with agriculturalists from the South and East, and urban people most of them from New England and the Middle Atlantic states, their respective differences were minimized in the economy developed in the Middle West. The self-sufficing period was so short-lived as to have but little effect upon patterns and habits of living. By 1810 these transplanted Easterners in the old Northwest Territory were decidedly articulate in Congress concerning their attitude toward such national issues as affected their means of livelihood, including manufacturing and commerce.

FACTORS INFLUENCING SETTLEMENT

Late Settlement. White settlement of the old Northwest Territory did not begin until the turn of the nineteenth century. Reasons for the tardy settlement are to be found in the relative inaccessibility of the region at that time, in the reluctance of both France and England to permit white settlement during the colonial period, and in the tardy formulation of a land policy for the disposition of these lands by the federal government. Once started, however, no other large section of the United States increased in population so rapidly as the middlewestern states.

Rivers and Canals. The small communities were of necessity self-sufficing; such surplus as existed had to be processed for shipment by the Ohio and Mississippi rivers to the older, eastern South. Flour was milled, whiskey was distilled from corn, brandy was made from fruit, and flax and wool textiles were made in the home for shipment by river boat to the South. The seasonal use of the rivers, the length of the journey, and the uncertainty of profits discouraged any great river-export trade. Prices for farm products were generally very low. New York's experience with the Erie Canal led some communities in Ohio, Indiana, and Illinois to plead for canal construction as a means of ending the depression. Year-round transportation is held to be the first stage in the industrial evolution of the Middle West.

The direction of trade had been mostly north-south, so the major canals planned were to connect the Great Lakes and the Ohio River. Those actually completed and used were the Ohio and Erie and the Miami and Erie canals following routes across Ohio which have continued important in trade. In Indiana there was the Wabash Canal. These canals with their respective feeders prolonged the period of river-oriented economy and helped to fix the pattern of urban population which has persisted until the present. Although canals languished and ceased operation about the time of the Civil War, the best years were those immediately after the building of the railroads which, for the most part, paralleled the canals. The influence of canals and the belief in the desirability of Great Lakes-Ohio River accessibility is manifest in the periodic advocacy of canal construction in these lower Lakes states. Most recent projects have been as parts of the water-conservation program. There is today a canal completing the 9-foot channel from Chicago to the Illinois River and thence to the Gulf.

The canals and rivers tended to raise the prices of farm products wherever the producers were within hauling distance; they thus contributed to the denser settlement of their respective corridors. They tended also to promote woolen factories, ropewalks, flour mills, distilleries, sawmills, tanyards, and blacksmith shops. Upon trade their effect was a continuation of the north-south commerce utilizing the Ohio-Mississippi system.

Railroad Influences. After the railroads came to the Middle West the ill-drained plains of the Great Lakes basin finally were settled. The railroad oriented the urban groups in these areas, as rivers and canals had done a generation earlier in the Ohio Valley. Although railroads curtailed the importance of steamboating on the Mississippi system, they by no means put an end to the trade with the eastern Cotton Belt. Cincinnati built a railroad from that city to Chattanooga shortly after the Civil War; this has been under profitable lease to a southern railroad ever since. Another railroad which testifies to the continued vitality of these gateways to the South is the Louisville and Nashville, likewise a profitable investment for an Ohio River city which, like Cincinnati, nearly bankrupted itself to pay for the project. But the new trade horizons of these states were east-west after the railroad came; southern trade was of secondary importance.

Rapid Growth in Lakes Section. For the older population centers on the Ohio River, the railroad was to mean growth, but at a declining rate; while for the urban centers on the plains of the lower Lakes margin it was to mean a phenomenally rapid growth in population. The older cities (Pittsburgh, Wheeling, Cincinnati, and Louisville) were to witness the more rapid growth of Cleveland, Chicago, and Detroit after the railroad came. The later settlement of the trans-Mississippi West experienced much the same thing.

The commercially active portions of the Middle West were largely determined by such features of interregional accessibility as the corridors through the Appalachian Highland, the Great Lakes, the Ohio River, and the Mississippi River system.

INDUSTRIAL EVOLUTION

Factory Beginnings. The antecedents of manufacturing in the Middle West differed greatly from those of the northeastern states. The latter group had a century and more of industrial experience before the Northwest Territory was established. The rise of factory industry in the East found cities acting as magnets for the new manufacturing establishments. These cities were sources of capital and of markets. The farms supplied the necessary labor. Although industrial raw materials were meager in the East, the New England merchant marine tended to offset this disadvantage. In several instances quantity production was made possible in New England factories solely because of the foreign markets reached by the Yankee ships.

In the Middle West, on the other hand, when the restrained westward movement of settlers finally did burst through the Appalachians to the plains of the upper and middle Mississippi Valley, they were numerically inadequate to the task of establishing a commercial economy in this great land. Thus every task was scrutinized with a view toward mechanization. For most parts of the Middle West, the terrain, the freedom from boulders, and the susceptibility of most crops to machine production early led to the invention and manufacture of farm implements.

When the Swedish geographer, Sten De Geer, first mapped the American Manufacturing Belt, he saw the plains of the Middle West as one of two great plains in the world which had become industrialized. The other was northern Europe. It lay north of the 40th and south of the 43rd parallels directly in the path of the westward-moving New Englanders and those from the Middle Atlantic states. These population movements were of utmost importance to the rise of manufactures in the Middle West. The selective process which was an accompaniment of this migration placed many of the best New England and Middle Atlantic stock in the older settled parts of Ohio, Indiana, Illinois, Michigan, and Wisconsin.

Factors in Manufacturing. To these people and their desire to flourish and prosper in their new homeland, a very important part in the rise of manufacturing in the Middle West must be attributed. This bond between the East and the Middle West did not languish. Whereas the Atlantic seaboard colonies have been termed the Imperial Frontier for some of the countries of western Europe, the old Northwest Territory was a frontier for the eastern states for a century or more.

The frontier Middle West discouraged manufacturing in several respects. For one thing there was only some of the surplus from farms and forest which could be called industrial raw materials. Then, too, transportation was difficult and expensive, thus limiting the extent of the market. Although many of the pioneers were of some education and means, relatively few had industrial experience. For such early factories as required special skills, artisans were imported from the east and from England. Land speculation proved to be fully as attractive as infant industries to such capital as the pioneers had. And, finally, the abundance of good land attracted men much more strongly than the factory payroll.

On the other hand, there were factors which promoted the development of manufactures. Distance and expensive transportation made the delivered price of eastern goods so high as to encourage some local industry. Again, the attraction of a southern market for farm products and a few types of simple manufactures stimulated commerce between the Middle West and the eastern Cotton Belt. This in turn led to the accumulation of capital which tempted northern enterprisers to develop the market for factory goods. Meat products, distilled grain products, flour, leather, wool goods, farm implements and wagons, paper, and rope were early exports to the South. It may well have been the best time some of the villages in the Middle West ever had. Their millers, tanners, blacksmiths (tool makers), and wood workers waited for the parade of customers to plod down the road on their way to Illinois or more distant farming frontier.

Distribution of Manufacturing. The bulk of the manufacturing in the Middle West has been localized in the East North Central states. These states are often referred to as the western half of the American Manufacturing Belt, a term which must not be taken literally, although it probably connotes a reasonably accurate phenomenon to most people. Despite the prevailing favorable terrain and the short-lived dependence upon rivers for transportation, waterways have localized manufacturing in the Middle West about as effectively as in New England. They have not localized the factories, however, except in the older sections.

Impact of World War II. Although the East North Central states received the largest proportion of public funds spent for new industrial facilities during World War II, no new industrial districts were created.[1] A number of cities got industries whose payrolls exceeded any existing industry, because of war-built plants, either publicly or privately financed. A number of smaller cities had this as their only manufacturing payroll, but no "new" industrial district was created in these states because of war plants.

Possibly the greatest result of the war effort upon the manufacturing of the Middle West is the confirmation it has given to some trends observed in the region before the war. One is that the West North Central states are not securing industries from established industries in the East North Central division; if branch plants are established they go to more distant areas. A second observation is that most new plants are going to cities with fewer than 200,000 population. Third, during the years since the outbreak of the

[1] *The Geographic Distribution of Manufacturing Facilities Expansion, July 1940– May 1944* (War Production Board Program and Statistics Bureau, Washington, 1945).

war, the East North Central division continues to grow industrially somewhat faster than the rest of the nation.

**TABLE 14-1: Number, Value and Percentage Distribution of War
Facilities Projects**

	Projects	Amount	Per cent of total for U.S.
East North Central States			
OHIO	1293	$1,677,415,000.	9.9
MICHIGAN	1145	1,549,300,000.	8.7
ILLINOIS	1067	1,490,109,000.	8.1
INDIANA	480	1,025,500,000.	3.7
WISCONSIN	435	458,200,000.	3.3
West North Central States			
MINNESOTA	217	283,000,000.	1.7
NEBRASKA	52	101,600,000.	.4
IOWA	154	174,400,000.	1.2
MISSOURI	249	513,700,000.	1.9
NORTH DAKOTA	6	1,600,000.	.0
SOUTH DAKOTA	6	1,100,010.	.0
KANSAS	104	329,700,000.	.4

SOURCE: *The Geographic Distribution of Manufacturing Facilities Expansion, July 1940-
May 1944* (War Production Board Program and Statistics Bureau, Facilities Branch, Washington, 1945).

Recent Changes. The latest developments in industrialization in the
Middle West are taking place in both old and new areas, in both large and
rather small cities; the greater proportion falls in the cities of from 100,000
to 20,000, but with rural areas and the largest cities sharing in it. Inter-
views with responsible plant officials indicate that the major forces behind
this recentralization of manufactures are centrifugal, that is they are being
pushed away from congested areas and labor troubles, generally. The tendency to integrate has meant that a growing proportion of new plant locations
have been chosen on the basis of their relation to the industrial structure
of the parent industry. The attractiveness of an individual site is therefore
increasingly based upon its accessibility and labor supply, rather than the
facts of the immediate site location.

SOME MAJOR INDUSTRIES

Iron and Steel. Reference has been made to the manufacture of charcoal
iron in a dozen Ohio River counties in Ohio (chapter on the Appalachian
Highlands). The distribution of these charcoal furnaces bears little relation to the distribution of the present steel industry in the Middle West.

Now steel production takes place in all East North Central states and Missouri, from Kansas City on the west to Youngstown on the east, and from Duluth to St. Louis. The bulk of the tonnage is produced in the Cleveland-Youngstown, Detroit, and Chicago-Gary district.

TABLE 14-2: Growth of Steel Capacity, 1939-1953
(Ingots and Steel for Castings; Annual Capacity in net tons)

State	Capacity 1953	Capacity 1939	Tons gained
ILLINOIS	9,720,600	6,893,820	2,876,780
INDIANA	13,692,000	10,196,677	3,495,323
MICHIGAN	5,805,900	3,496,226	2,309,674
MINNESOTA	918,000	336,000	582,000
MISSOURI	630,000	569,542	60,458
OHIO	22,643,260	17,543,008	5,100,252

SOURCE: *Steel Facts,* August, 1954, and Supplement.

The manufacture of steel is the most important single industry in the region, but the area's stature is enhanced by being at the same time the greatest steel-consuming region in the nation. This fact is one of the basic differences between the eastern and the western parts of the Manufacturing Belt. In the nation's consumption of steel, Michigan, Ohio, and Illinois rank first, third and fourth, respectively. In steel production Ohio, Indiana, Illinois, and Michigan rank second, third, fourth, and eighth, respectively. Indiana and Wisconsin rank fifth only in one of the twelve categories of primary steel products. Pennsylvania and Maryland are the only eastern states among the first five in steel production; in consumption Pennsylvania, New York, and Maryland are the only eastern states in the first five.

TABLE 14-3: Per Cent Increase in Steel-Making Capacity, 1946-1954.

Pennsylvania	26.75
Ohio	31.42
Indiana	34.69
Illinois	26.51
Michigan	100.00
New York	45.96
Maryland	41.10
United States	35.30

SOURCE: American Iron and Steel Institute.

It has been said that Thomas Jefferson would recognize the processes in making modern steel, there has been so little in the way of basic change. But the variety of materials used and the scale of the enterprise certainly would astound him. The Middle West has witnessed fuel changes from charcoal, beehive coke, by-product coke, natural gas, fuel oil, and electricity. Iron ore has come from eastern Ohio, Michigan's Upper Peninsula, Wisconsin, and Minnesota. Even the Adirondack Mountains, Canada, Venezuela, and Chile have shipped ore to Middle West furnaces. Also, the labor used in the steel mills involves people from distant places; among them are migrants from the hill counties south of the Ohio River, first and second generation western Europeans, Mexicans, and Puerto Ricans. The several types of steel made are dependent upon alloying minerals found in distant parts of the world; this country produces only two in reasonable quantities, vanadium and molybdenum; the latter is world dominant. The steel industry today is in the Middle West but scarcely *of* the Middle West. Its roots are in the Superior Upland and Appalachian Highlands.

And what is the steel industry in the Middle West? It is iron and coal mines; ore carriers on the Great Lakes, railroads in the upper and the lower Lakes states, limestone quarries, and of course the steel mills (*Fig.* 14-1). It even goes farther to include several aspects of its market. This constitutes integration, backward and forward.

Agricultural Implements. So much for the production of steel in this large region where virtually all conditions favor an agriculture in which the world could offer little competition. This agriculture became the source of a great market for farm implements and transportation equipment. These two manufacturing industries became the Middle West's "first families" of manufacturing.

As the first state settled in the Middle West, the implement industry rose to its first great heights in Ohio. Ohio implement centers flowered as management saw greater opportunities in a new location. Indiana, Illinois, Wisconsin and Missouri have welcomed this industry. Wherever implement manufacture passed on it left men trained in its manufacture and families committed to dependence upon a factory payroll rather than a farm income.

Automobiles. Until the automobile came early in the twentieth century, improvements in transport were simply a better rail, more powerful locomotive, a stronger wheel, continuously deeper water, or greater capacity. The principle of the automobile was as revolutionary in Boston as in Detroit, but the seed of interest fell on more receptive ground in the Middle West, thanks largely to two generations of farm-implement manufacture. To youthful readers of this book it may seem inconceivable that over 400 enterprisers have made automobiles in the United States, most of them in these middlewestern states.

FIGURE 14-1: *Continuous Strip Rolling Mill, Middletown, Ohio*

The continuous strip rolling mill has spread to all parts of the steel industry since its perfection in 1926 by this steel manufacturer. It is one reason why the pounds of steel-making capacity per person has risen from 1,186 in 1930 to 1,500 in 1954. (Armco Steel Corp.)

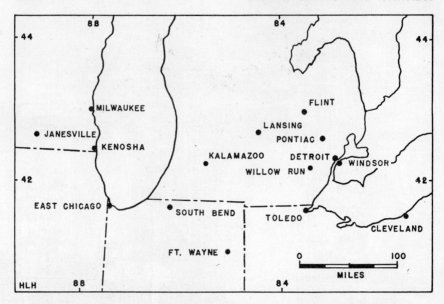

FIGURE 14-2: *Automobile Assembly Cities, United States and Canada*

Mass production of automobiles rests upon interchangeability of parts; most of the suppliers are localized in the lower Lakes states.

As this industry grew to maturity, it reached out to more cities than the 400 auto makers represented. *Fig.* 14-2 shows the distribution of factories which assemble automobiles in the lower Lakes area; many other plants are producing parts for them.

Machinery. The manufacture of machinery in the Middle West may be the most spectacular aspect of the metals industry. This quality is due to the varied types of machinery made here, to the precision nature of so much of the machinery, and finally to the importance of the manufacture of machine tools (*Fig.* 14-3). This kind of manufacturing creates a relatively high value; machine tools, for instance, have about four times as much value added by manufacturing as metal manufactures in general. The average machine tool plant takes $1,111 in materials and fuel per wage earner, and adds $2,887 or 250 per cent to it, in contrast with a 67 per cent increase by the average metals manufacturer.

The machine shop is the market for the machine tool, and the shop will be located where the machinery is to be replaced or repaired. In this manner, several of the early manufacturing districts of the Middle West began with the satisfaction of a large and growing market for agricultural ma-

FIGURE 14-3: *Warner and Swasey Machine-Tool Plant, Cleveland*

Diversification outside of the field of specialty has been difficult for the manufacturers of machine tools, the "royal family" of the machinery industry. Shown in the photograph are weaving machines coming off the production line of one of the world's largest builders of machine tools. (Warner and Swasey Co.)

chinery. This has been largely responsible for the attraction of skilled mechanics, and in turn for the coming of new concerns dependent upon skilled workmen. The average Corn Belt farm boy is something of a mechanic, upon him many kinds of city factories depend for labor.

Food-Processing Industries. In the days of self-sufficing communities every wheat-growing district had its flour mills, generally small units. Commercial bakeries were limited to the larger cities. Power and labor requirements were easily met in all but the smallest communities; the prevalence of home baking enabled many a small flour mill to operate long after its milling costs became disproportionately high. Flours ground from local wheat were not uniform in their baking qualities, and the peculiarities of their baking requirements constituted a strong tie for the small mill.

During World War I the government took over these flour mills. The change in the baking habits of the rural areas of the nation was accelerated by the wartime restrictions, so that by 1950 probably 75 per cent of the flour mills of the United States had closed. Wheat blending, improved milling machinery, the automobile and better roads, and the development of commercial bakeries serving rural routes all contributed to the decline of the small independent flour mills. For three-quarters of a century there has been a gradual reduction in the acreage of wheat in the Corn Belt states as land values rose; this and the rural-urban shift in population have further promoted the change in milling centers.[2]

Although the foregoing is specifically concerned with wheat, other grains including corn, rye, buckwheat, and oats persisted in small mills for a longer period. This is in part owing to the self-sufficing type of economy in which some of them are milled and to their less general acceptance in the diet. The largest cereal mills consuming oats are at Cedar Rapids, Iowa, and at Akron, Ohio.

Soybeans have become an important food in the United States within comparatively recent years. From northern Ohio west to Iowa, bean-processing plants have sprung up in response to acreage increases, price supports, soil conservation, war, and industrial demands for bean products.

The slaughtering industry did not involve meat packing until the middle of the 1800's, when Cincinnati became the largest center for pork products. Local butchers, many of them operating rural delivery routes, had furnished fresh beef and cured meats for most communities, large and small. Beef was not susceptible to packing methods until the development of the refrigerator car in 1875. Prior to that, beef was from locally slaughtered animals sent in from the Middle West. Chicago's packing industry, founded on pork during the second half of the nineteenth century, singlehandedly developed beef packing. Mass production methods were employed and local slaughtering declined in all areas served by rail from Chicago. In 1950 the packing industries for beef, pork, and lambs were localized primarily in Chicago, with Kansas City, East St. Louis, Omaha, Sioux City, Milwaukee, St. Joseph, and St. Paul as the other important centers. The market for corn as grain has increased for Illinois farmers with the rise of industries in and near Chicago in which corn is a raw material for the manufacture of starch, alcohol, plastics, cereals and syrup.

URBANIZATION

The Middle West is a land of many cities, but the urban distribution is by no means uniform. The lower Lakes states are much more densely

[2] Major flour-milling centers: Baltimore, 1800-1820; Richmond, Virginia, 1820-1834; Rochester, New York, 1834-1860; St. Louis, 1860-1882; Minneapolis, 1882-1930; Buffalo, 1930-1941; and Kansas City, 1941-to date. During the half century of Minneapolis supremacy, flour milling underwent revolutionary changes.

populated than the upper Lakes region; industrialization is one of the principal reasons for this. Major contrasts in the urban distribution are also observed between the states east and west of the Mississippi River, with the former much more densely populated. Within each of these major divisions there are differences in the distribution of cities; the largest cities are located on the plain between the Great Lakes and the Ohio and Missouri rivers.

Mere propinquity of these urban districts is not enough to suggest an economy common to the cities comprising the group. The appearance and the growth of these cities varied with the regional economy in which each is rooted. All cities were initially commercial; most of them achieved manufacturing importance later. The functions of these cities in the Middle West vary widely, more so, probably, than the cities of any other large division of the United States.

CLEVELAND INDUSTRIAL DISTRICT

Between the upper Ohio River and Lake Erie there is, in effect, a natural corridor of river valleys. It widens in the Mahoning Valley, and the railroads branch out to the principal ore-importing ports on Lake Erie. In this commercial funnel pours the iron ore from the Lake Superior mines, and the limestone of Michigan and Lake Erie's south shore, destined for the iron furnaces of the cities of this industrialized corridor and beyond. As the manufacture of steel expanded beyond the limits of Pittsburgh and the adjacent valleys of western Pennsylvania, the railroad towns of these eastern Ohio valleys shared in the growth of iron and steel manufacture. Like many other populous areas, the Mahoning Valley had a few charcoal-iron furnaces in operation long before the spill-over from Pittsburgh gave Youngstown the foundation of its present high rank as a steel producer. The Allegheny Plateau cities of Ohio are treated in detail in the chapter on the Appalachian Highlands.

Cleveland. The only city of a million people in the entire region between the Ohio River and Lake Erie is Cleveland. By virtue of its situation on the narrow lake plain at the mouth of the Cuyahoga River, Cleveland is directly in the path of two important trade routes: (1) the western extension of the Hudson-Mohawk Valley route from the Middle Atlantic seaboard to the Central Lowlands, and (2) the water-rail route for iron and coal between the Great Lakes and the bituminous coal fields of the Appalachian Plateaus.

FIGURE 14-4: *Port of Cleveland*

The banks of the serpentine Cuyahoga River and the Lake Erie shore give Cleveland 18 miles of dock and contribute to its prime position as a Great Lakes port. Completion of the St. Lawrence Seaway will add to Cleveland's foreign trade. Pictured here is a part of the river and the steel, oil, and chemical industries which line its banks. Only by seeing a 600-foot freighter maneuver this channel would one believe it possible. (Cleveland Electric Illuminating Co.)

Manufacturing. Cleveland's manufactures, although rooted in the flow of iron ore and of coal, have never been characterized by its blast furnaces and rolling mills; they remain an important part of the city's industries however. Cleveland is in part a heavy industry center specializing in steel products for both the upper and lower Lakes mineral empire market, including machinery for mining, handling, transporting, and processing ores. It builds many of the ships to carry Great Lakes commerce (*Fig.* 14-4).

It is a great railroad center and builds diesel and electric locomotives, rolling stock, and an array of cast and machined parts for the railroad's equipment industry. Highway and air transportation markets have given rise to the manufacture of motor trucks, auto bodies, aircraft, batteries, parts, and assembly.

Cleveland remains one of the great agricultural industrial centers, making implements, tractors, trucks, processing machinery, and welding equipment. Its early activity in petroleum refining continues. Clay industries are almost as old as the city; the line is exceedingly varied from electrical equipment to china. Cleveland leads the nation in the manufacture of machine tools. When the Second World War promoted the use of lighter metals, the city was ready with aluminum and soon was processing magnesium. The War Production Board classed Cleveland as "multiple-diversified" and awarded war contracts on that basis. Electrometallurgical and electrochemical products have been recent additions of importance.

Role in the Economy of the Upper Lakes. Clevelanders have, in effect, managed to occupy two regions: the immediate northeastern Ohio region and the mineral empire of the upper Lakes region. The commercial and financial functions of Cleveland have gone far beyond the handling and manufacturing of these mineral raw materials. Cleveland interests have virtually dominated the iron-mining and iron-transportation industries. It has been Cleveland rather than Chicago, Detroit, or Buffalo which has had the dominant role in the development of the minerals of the Great Lakes basin, in southwestern Labrador iron mining, and in the taconite plants in the Mesabi iron region that process the lower-grade iron of taconite which is abundant in these ranges.

Commerce. For the first half of Ohio's history, it was Cincinnati and the Miami Valley, rather than the Lake Shore, which dominated the states's economy. With the coming of the railroad and the changed source of iron ore which occurred in the 1870's, Cleveland began a growth which soon surpassed Cincinnati.

Cleveland's commerce is more closely related to the Great Lakes than is that of Chicago or any other large Lakes city. Cleveland today is at work making its commercial ties with the Great Lakes more important than ever. The Cuyahoga River has been straightened somewhat to secure more vessels for winter berthing as well as to ease congestion. With one eye on the Ontario Peninsula across Lake Erie and the tremendous strides our northern neighbor is making in industry and commerce, and the other on the St. Lawrence Seaway, there is a frontier in the future not only for Cleveland but for the other cities which are located on the Canadian and American shores of the Great Lakes.

Lake Shore Cities. Fairport, Ashtabula, and Conneaut are primarily commercial cities. Here are docks black with giant Hulett ore unloaders and ore bridges, and the scarcely smaller coal unloaders (*Fig.* 5-8). The harbors must be dredged to accommodate modern bulk carriers. Railroads tie these facilities with the inland steel furnaces. On the Lake shore and farther inland great chemical plants are using salt, dolomite, clay, and lake water to make a variety of commodities. Between Fairport and Ashtabula the lake margin is sometimes known as the "chemical shore" (*Fig.* 14-5). In its power consumption by the electrochemical and electrometallurgical industries, it is surpassed only by the Niagara Falls district. The

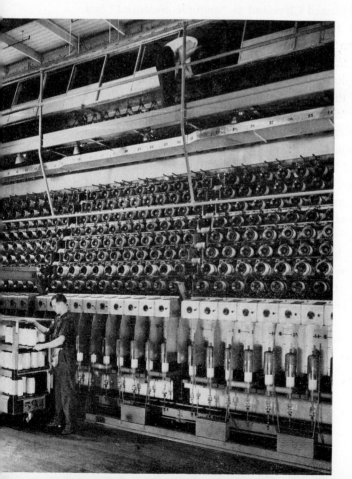

FIGURE 14-5: Industrial Rayon Plant, Cleveland

This concern makes viscose rayon. Behind the glass enclosures at the upper level, the viscose is forced through tiny holes of a spinnaret into a chemical bath and is solidified into filaments of yarn which are drawn up to the first of a series of thread-advancing reels. The yarn advances from the back to the forward end of the reel, then drops off to the processing or middle level. As the yarn travels down the bank of reels, various processing solutions are uniformly applied at each stage. On the lower level, the yarn is dried in individual strands as it passes over heated aluminum reels behind the circular windows. (Industrial Rayon Corp.)

rapidity of growth and the industrial linkage among these plants constitute one of the significant industrial developments in the history of the Lake Erie shoreline.

Akron. During its early years *Akron* (274,605) did not display the kind of population and industrial increases associated with many cities of northeastern Ohio. Its development as the world's greatest tire manufacturer is representative of the kind of industrial experience several cities of the Middle West have undergone. Canals, roads, and railroads each made some important change in the economy of Akron. The Ohio and Erie Canal made Akron an exporter of flour and cereals. The manufacture of clay tile grew as the wetlands of the lower Lakes plains were brought under the plow. Farm-implement manufacture came to Akron before canal traffic ceased, reaching a peak in the 1880's. From hard rubber tires for buggies and carriages, through pneumatic tires for bicycles and automobiles, to tires for aircraft and farm implements, Akron came to dominate rubber-tire manufacture.

Integration went backward to rubber plantations and forward to retail outlets. The manufacture of flour and clay products, and some agricultural implements with which early Akron was identified, continues. In addition to tires there is a host of relatively new products being made for the automotive market, toys, and aluminum extrusions for the construction and showcase industries. Synthetic rubber is manufactured by some of the tire companies in Akron; others produce it nearer the source of petroleum. The impact of World War II did nothing to change rubber in Akron but it stimulated the manufacture of metal products. Akron is still the largest rubber-tire producer, but much growth has taken place on the Pacific Coast, in the South, and even in the Middle Atlantic and New England states.

THE MIAMI VALLEY AND CINCINNATI

The Miami Valley. The oldest industrial region in the Middle West is the Miami Valley in southwestern Ohio. For a century and a half the Valley cities have taken in stride the changes in transportation, in the sources and nature of raw materials for industry, changes in markets, and the sequence of industrial specialties which have characterized the Manufacturing Belt in general and the Middle West in particular. Every city continues to increase in population and in manufacturing. In this evolution, the valley has developed bonds among its cities and a regionalism which is representative of several other middlewestern cities.

Cincinnati (503,998), *Norwood* (35,001), *Hamilton* (57,951), *Middletown* (33,695), *Dayton* (243,872) and *Springfield* (78,508) form the centers of the Miami Valley industrial region. The dependence upon river, canal, and railroad, was a sequence so rapid in its evolution as to keep the Valley one of the accessible regions in the Middle West.

Taking the Valley as a whole, there have been four distinct, though overlapping, periods in its industrial evolution. First was the processing of flour, meat, leather, spirits, and some iron for markets down the Ohio and Mississippi rivers. The second period was more concerned with the local market: farm implements and the necessities of daily life: this was the early railroad era. The third period brought larger industries such as automobiles, rubber, precision machinery, primary iron and steel, machine tools, calculating machines, and airplanes. The fourth period continues most of the previous industries and adds chemical products, jet propulsion, and atomic energy. The over-all qualities of Miami Valley manufacturing include a higher value added by manufacturing than any comparable area in the Middle West, due in part to automobile, automatic and calculating machines, and machine tools.

Cincinnati. Oldest and largest of Miami Valley cities is Cincinnati near the junction of the Big Miami and Ohio rivers. Across from the city is the valley of Kentucky's Licking River which offered a corridor toward the eastern South during the period of settlement. Cincinnati dominated the Ohio Valley; for many years it was larger than Pittsburgh, and Louisville never has rivaled it.

During its middle period Cincinnati turned to the rapidly developing railroad trade with the East, West, and South. Again its situation enabled it to participate in the new trade horizons. Its largest industries were established in manufacturing. Now Cincinnati shares in a rejuvenation of commerce on the Ohio River, with tonnage far surpassing that of the steamboat era. It also is benefitting from the recentralization of manufacturing which is putting some huge plants along both sides of the Ohio River, some of them in hitherto nonindustrial districts. Chemical industries and atomic energy are two of the largest of these newcomers.

Except for machine tools and one or two other items, there is something of an anonymity which derives from the diversity of the city's manufactures; it is not so specialized as other Miami Valley cities. It is not surprising, in view of Cincinnati's commercial importance, that only 30 per cent of the population are wage earners in industry; Dayton has 46 per cent, Hamilton 49 per cent, and Middletown 52 per cent. Nowhere in the Valley are textile

FIGURE 14-6: *Cincinnati Milling Machine in Use*

The manufacture of machine tools has made Cincinnati known to workers in metal the world over. This milling machine is working on four revolver barrels simultaneously. Note the newer or western half of the Manufacturing Belt in the distribution of machine tool plants: Ohio *62,* Michigan *27,* Illinois *26,* Massachusetts *16,* Wisconsin *14,* Connecticut *13,* New York *12,* Pennsylvania *10,* Indiana *7,* New Jersey *5,* Vermont *4,* and Rhode Island *4.* (Massachusetts Dept. of Commerce)

and shoe manufacture nationally important, yet in Cincinnati they employ more than any other factory enterprise. The second largest group in Cincinnati is the metals workers, yet this group is lowest for any Valley city.

On the basis of employment, Cincinnati's first ten industries are clothing and shoes, machine tools, paper and its products, beverages, soap, electrical and automotive equipment, foundries, heating equipment, communications, and vehicles. Postwar industries may well be prophetic; they include jet engines, plastics, chemicals and expansions of the 37 machine-tool plants (*Fig.* 14-6).

Dayton. Dayton was the trading center for a very fertile and prosperous agricultural region, with the usual utilities and service industries. Its role since canal days has been much more important than any other city north of Cincinnati. Steel manufactures made their start with farm implements, sewing machines, streetcars, automobiles, bicycles, cash registers, fare registers, scales, and pumps.

After 1900, there were several inventions and improvements which gave Dayton an early start in the airplane, electric self-starter, ignition, home-lighting units, and electric refrigeration. Although Dayton was founded in 1801 and grew to be the second-largest city in the Miami Valley, it has been within the lifetime of people now resident there that it has become a great manufacturing city, specializing in precision goods, with a national and international market.

The skilled labor pool which attracted General Motors, Chrysler Corporation, and other large concerns was the result of the manufacture of the machinery noted above. Dayton lost automobile and airplane manufacture, but more people are now employed in the parts for planes and cars than were ever employed in the finished product. Farm implements have gone; machine tools have greatly increased. The manufacture of refrigeration machinery is exceeded by no other city; aeronautical research has developed. Even before World War II, Dayton industries depended in part upon the unskilled white labor pool south of the Ohio River to care for the large increases in factory employment.

Dayton illustrates very well the way that manufacturing has tended to rationalize its location by throwing out roots of ingenuity, skill, and specialization which enable the industry more firmly to establish itself in a given location. Its manufactures are predominantly of the high-net-value type. To an important degree, the markets for its products are based upon the plants which make machinery. When postal zoning was established, Dayton and Springfield were in a position to undertake a big increase in printing and publishing, by virtue of central location.

Other Cities. *Indianapolis* (427,173) and *Columbus* (375,901) stand out among the score of cities located between the Great Lakes and the Ohio River. Both cities achieved commercial importance early; manufacturing came later. Indianapolis began its transformation after World War I; Columbus experienced its greatest industrialization during and after World War II [3] (*Fig.* 4-5).

A comparable situation with respect to the coal fields on the south and the iron mines of the upper Lakes has enabled both cities to make some steel, and buy more, for the production of a relatively wide range of steel products for the automobile, aircraft, railroad, materials-handling, and agricultural-machinery markets which virtually surround them.

[3] Henry L. Hunker, *The Industrial Evolution of Columbus, Ohio* (Bureau of Business Research, The Ohio State University, Columbus, 1956).

DETROIT INDUSTRIAL DISTRICT

Detroit. The dynamic nature of economic regionalism is well illustrated in the automobile-manufacturing district which radiates from Detroit to include most of the cities in southeastern Michigan, several in northern Indiana, and a few in northwestern Ohio. Detroit, together with a dozen cities integrated with the economy of Detroit, have undergone an industrial revolution since the beginning of the twentieth century. The events of the last war have added another chapter to the narrative of the home of mass production. Despite the highly specialized nature of its industry, America's entry into World War II brought about a great change in Detroit's manufacturing; to mass production of automobiles must be added subcontracting and the conversion of craft airplane manufacture to mass production. All three techniques have affected dozens of other manufacturing districts.

Situation. A glance at a map will reveal *Detroit* (1,849,568) as a gateway to the United States for much of the relatively densely populated and industrialized Ontario peninsula of Canada. It is served alike by railroads passing both north and south of Lake Erie.

Industrial Detroit is the water front. The heavy industries associated with the manufacture of automobiles have been the nucleus for the growth of other heavy industries: steel, glass, oil refining, rubber, industrial chemicals, machinery, shipyards, sulphur, aluminum, brass, paper and wood pulp, and gypsum. At the wharves of the Detroit and Rouge rivers are vessels from many parts of the world bringing raw materials to the home of mass production and carrying its products to far corners of the globe. From the center of old French Detroit southward along the Detroit River to Zug Island at the confluence of River Rouge, through Ecorse and Wyandotte to Monroe, and as far west as Dearborn, the heavy-industry section of Detroit spreads its grimy plants. Thus far the Canadian side of the Detroit River is marked by relatively few large factories.

Industrial Development. Three main periods may be observed in the industrial development of Detroit. In present-day Detroit one must search to see evidence of the industrial economy of pre-automobile days. As the economic capital of a state in which the copper and the lumber industries were waning, and where agriculture was restricted to the southern half of the state, Detroit was a medium-sized city. Stoves, farm implements, tools for the lumbering industry (machines entered lumbering for the first time as the industry was sweeping across Michigan), and a few boats for the Lake trade occupied most of its wage earners. Detroit was little influenced by the pros-

FIGURE 14-7: *Ford Plant, Dearborn, Michigan*

This plant is the world's largest example of an integrated automobile manufacturer. Ford ore boats bring iron from company mines to these blast furnaces, rolling mills, and ultimately the automobile assembly line. Ford was a pioneer in the second industry to revolutionize Midwestern manufacturing; farm implements were the first. (Ford Motor Co.)

perous Corn Belt on the south or the commercial cities of Chicago and Cleveland.

The second period has spread its effects over all of the city and dates from the centripetal forces set in motion by Ford's perfection of the assembly line method of production. There is a third period, less spectacular than the second, in which some centrifugal movement is discernible in the manufacture of automobiles, and nonautomotive products became important.

Of the 400 makes of cars manufactured in the United States at one time or another, fewer than 25 remain, most of them in the Detroit district. Yet there has been little real geographical change in the manufacture of the automobile; the change has been primarily in the assembly of the finished car. Subcontracting of parts in the United States was first practiced on a large scale by the Detroit automakers. The areal extent of the redistribution of automobile manufacture merits an examination. In peacetime, 7 of a total of 17 makes of passenger cars and 4 of a total of 50 trucks and buses were assembled within the limits of greater Detroit, including Dearborn, Hamtramck, and Highland Park (*Fig.* 14-7). The automotive industry in peace-

FIGURE 14-8: *Glass Manufacturing Plant, near Toledo*

Market, fuel, and glass sand (in that order) have brought an old, eastern seaboard industry to the Middle West. This modern plant is one of the largest of its kind. Note the suburban location so common to new factories in the United States. (Libby-Owens-Ford Co.)

time has consisted of 986 plants, large and small, scattered through 31 of the 48 states. The great bulk of the industry is in the Lakes states. These plants involve virtually every type of subcontracting (*Fig.* 14-2).

World War II Expansion. At no time since the rise of the automobile industry has there been a stimulus for increased industrial production comparable to World War II. The invention of mass production in Detroit was an accident; its subsequent pattern of redistribution resulting from forty years of industrial selection was no accident. It is instructive to observe the effects of the Second World War upon the birthplace of mass production.

Detroit and the lower Lakes region generally were profoundly affected by the flood of orders for machinery of all kinds, ordnance, chemicals, ships, textiles, all sorts of food products, and refining of many crude materials. Greatest of all was the demand for automotive equipment for use on the land, and sea, and in the air.[4]

These auto makers found they could not convert an important part of

[4] Frigates, submarines, tankers, landing craft, and marine equipment were built 1,500 miles from the Gulf, where nearly all of them were put in service.

their machine tools to airplane or tank-building purposes. Unlike English auto makers, these huge plants were in effect gigantic single-purpose machine

TABLE 14-4: *Automobile Parts Manufactures, 1947*

MICHIGAN	279	CALIFORNIA	35
OHIO	145	NEW JERSEY	31
ILLINOIS	100	MISSOURI	25
NEW YORK	92	CONNECTICUT	24
INDIANA	75	MASSACHUSETTS	18
PENNSYLVANIA	53	MINNESOTA	8
WISCONSIN	48	TEXAS	5

WASHINGTON, OREGON, COLORADO, NEBRASKA, VIRGINIA, RHODE ISLAND, NORTH CAROLINA, GEORGIA and MARYLAND each 3.

tools designed to produce their special product; this was true of individual machine tools, plant layout, organization, and labor skills. Most of the United States' planes and tanks for the war effort came from factories built and equipped for the purpose. This includes completely new plants and re-designed and retooled established plants. Detroit, the oldest and largest industrial subcontractor, was unable to handle as large a proportion of the industry's war work as it did of peacetime work, due to the scarcity of workers available in the area. Thus many of the new plants were erected elsewhere; three of the largest were in Indiana; three others were in the Chicago area; Detroit had three, and Wisconsin, New York, and Ohio had one each of this size. Detroit auto makers furnished parts for large govern-ment-built airplane assembly plants at Nashville, Fort Worth, Dallas, Hous-ton, Tulsa, Omaha, and Kansas City.

In a sense this industrial change in Detroit brought the return of a native to the Lower Lakes states, for the only relatively large-scale produc-tion of airplanes during World War I had been in Ohio; Ford made multi-engined metal transport planes in Detroit only until 1934.

Chiefly due to the large amount of automobile manufacturing within its boundaries, Detroit has become an important steel district, using the large amounts of scrap from the auto factories and selling a large proportion of their product to these plants. Additional steel imports from Buffalo, Cleve-land, and certain interior districts are necessary for the satisfaction of auto-mobile engine and body demand. Under similar auspices the manufacture of machine tools, glass, air-conditioning equipment, refrigeration, stokers, and electrical machinery have developed. Rubber tires and rubber-body mountings are manufactured by the Detroit member of the "Big Three" tire makers. The manufacture of trailers, buses, bodies, tractors, accessories, and stainless-steel railroad cars have stemmed from the manufacture of automobiles. Pharmaceuticals, chemicals, paper, ships, calculating machines, stoves and furnaces, farm implements, and toys are important industries which nearly complete the picture.

Toledo. Another city specialist of the lower Lakes margin is *Toledo* (303,616) at the western end of Lake Erie. From Toledo to Buffalo, the curving shore of Lake Erie is interrupted by long docks running out from the iron ports and steel cities: Sandusky, Lorain, Cleveland, Ashtabula, Conneaut, Erie, and Buffalo. Iron ore, coal, wheat, or oil produced along this shore or its immediate hinterland, stimulates mile for mile more commerce in these commodities than anywhere else on the Great Lakes. The featureless Lake plain is strung with railroads, and the docks have the gigantic specialized loading and unloading machines by which these cities have achieved their low handling costs. Toledo has become one of the four principal railroad centers in the nation. Upon this city, at the west end of Lake Erie, converge railroads from every direction. Toledo's manufactures initially were concerned primarily with the processing of agricultural products from the excellent farmlands which surround it on the west and south. The Maumee Valley oil and gas fields lured a Massachusetts glass manufacturer to this cheap fuel and nearby glass sand, thus starting a series of events that have made the nation's greatest inland port one of the great glass cities (*Fig.* 14-8).

Toledo is unique among the Lakes cities in that the primary iron industry has never become important. Oil refining has greatly expanded until the city is a major refinery center. The relationships of Toledo industries with the Michigan auto makers have tended to make this Ohio city an important, though perhaps somewhat anonymous, parts manufacturer. Toledo automobile manufacture has not been as stable as in Detroit.

Other Cities. Other cities in the Michigan-Indiana-Ohio manufacturing agglomeration depart from the automobile specialty, although most contribute to it (*Fig.* 14-9). *Fort Wayne* (133,607) manufactures rubber products, gasoline pumps, farm implements, and several types of machinery. *Kalamazoo* (57,704) makes paper, furniture, pharmaceuticals, and heating equipment. *Battle Creek* (48,666) is noted for cereals. *Lansing* (92,129) produces automobiles, trucks, and power mowers. *Monroe* (21,467) is a great paper center; it also produces auto parts and machinery. *Ann Arbor* (48,251) manufactures bearings, auto parts, and cameras. *South Bend* (115,911) makes automobiles and agricultural machinery. *Elkhart* (35,-

FIGURE 14-9: *New Departure Bearing Company Plant, Sandusky, Ohio*

This plant is an example of the recentralization of bearing manufacture in the United States. The parent company is in Hartford, Connecticut. This new location is about midway between the source of alloy steel and the automotive market in the Michigan-Indiana-Ohio area. (New Departure Bearing Co.)

646) makes band instruments. Midland, Michigan, is a pioneer manufacturer of industrial chemicals from the brine pumped from underground. In this brine the magnesium chloride is so concentrated that electrolytic treatment gives chlorine and pure molten magnesium. The difficulty encountered in finding markets for magnesium caused the Dow Company to fabricate products from it in order to create a market. World War II greatly increased the demand for this light metal; many of these gains, however, were temporary. *Muskegon* (48,429) is distant from these other industrial cities, but it is important for bearings, engine, and salt manufacture.

CHICAGO INDUSTRIAL DISTRICT

The location of towns and cities on the level expanse of the Central Lowland was governed by factors some of which were not shared by the hilly eastern states where urban centers developed. Situation rather than site values governed the choice of location of many of the midwestern cities (*Fig.* 14-10).

Chicago. The plain at the southern end of Lake Michigan is a low-lying, lacustrine plain with few qualities to commend it as an urban site. But its situation with respect to the prevailing paths of continental commerce has caused the growth of a great city. *Chicago* (3,620,962) is primarily the creature of railroad transportation, not of the Great Lakes. Lake Michigan thrusts its 300 miles of water southward into the Central Lowlands, thus deflecting all east-west commerce between the northern Great Plains, Central Lowland, and the Northeast. Commerce with the South has yet to equal this trade, but with continual improvement in the Mississippi River waterway, and the recent industrial growth along the Mississippi and the Intracoastal Waterway in Texas, the importance of north-south trade is growing. For many years the railroad connections between Chicago and the Gulf Coast have been vital and growing. Chicago marks the culmination of grassland settlement in this country.

FIGURE 14-10: *Chicago Urban Cluster*

This map of the Chicago area indicates how the situation of Chicago and its satellites on a relatively featureless plain has given rise to the greatest industrial-commercial complex in interior America. Concentric circles are at 10-mile intervals.

These facts of strategic situation, which accounted for Chicago's growth from a village in 1830 to a city of about three million in a hundred years, have also kept other urban centers from rivaling it on the western lake plains. *Milwaukee* (637,392), *Gary* (133,911), *Peoria* (111,856), and

South Bend (115,911) are the only cities within a hundred miles of Chicago which approach large size. Only in the instance of Chicago are there important satellite cities: *Hammond* (87,594) and *East Chicago* (54,263) on the southeast, and *Elgin* (44,223), *Aurora* (50,576), and *Chicago Heights* (24,-551) on the west. North along the lakeshore are *Kenosha* (54,368), *Racine* (71,193), and Milwaukee. *Peoria* (111,856) stands alone on the south; *Rockford* (105,438) and *Joliet* (51,601) are on the west.

While its situation has been superior, the site of Chicago has presented definite handicaps to be expensively overcome. There are 83 bridges over the Chicago River and its tributaries whose water flows past the skyscrapers down the South Branch where the barges are unloaded. A hundred years ago the flow of the Chicago River was reversed so that it empties into the Illinois River system. The Sanitary and Ship Canal was completed in 1900; it provides the deep-water transportation to the head of navigation on the Illinois River at Lockport, 36 miles distant. Army engineers maintain this, now known as the Illinois Waterway. In addition to large sewage disposal plants which border this canal, much raw sewage passes through to the river. The completion of the Great Lakes-St. Lawrence Seaway, it is believed, will add to Chicago's waterborne trade.

Commerce. Historically, Chicago has been commercial in function. The pattern of urban land use bears witness to this. As one of the major receiving cities for western grain, Chicago transships by rail the greater portion of its grain receipts. By pipe line, river barge, and rail, Chicago receives oil from the Gulf; most of the refining is done in Hammond and Whiting. Iron ore comes in by Lake freighter to the furnaces of East Chicago, Indiana Harbor, and Gary. Coal comes by Lake freighter from West Virginia mines, and by rail and barge from southern Illinois mines. Livestock from the northern Plains and the western Corn Belt come in by rail to the southern part of Chicago. Sulphur, sugar, fiber, and chemicals come by way of the Mississippi-Illinois rivers.

Chicago differs from other Lake cities in several respects. None has a comparable agricultural hinterland upon which to draw and to which to sell. The Missouri River Basin Development Program, when completed, should increase appreciably the purchasing power of the vast area embraced, a part of the Chicago hinterland.

Manufacturing. A large amount of manufacturing results from the processing of the commodities noted above which comprise such a large part of Chicago's commerce. With a population of some 3.5 millions, together with the populous suburban cities, the market for factory goods is one of the three greatest on the continent. There is scarcely any limit to the variety of the Chicago district's manufactures, although the dominant groups include iron and steel, machinery, chemicals, food products, and leather. Their manufacture is so closely related to converging rail- and Lake-borne materials that Chicago and adjacent satellites are perforce the region of greatest concentration. The principal exception to this localization is the manufacture of machinery, which is common to virtually every industrial city in the western half of the Manufacturing Belt.

For the first half of Chicago's growth, there was no important local manufacture of iron and steel. Chicago had to wait until midwestern markets made imperative further expansion of iron and steel manufacture. Finally, the changes took place within the steel industry which permitted its expansion to Chicago, provided markets were large enough to make such a move desirable. These markets, together with the open-hearth furnace, by-product coke, and the iron ore in the Lake Superior district combined to give Gary, Indiana, its first great steel mill in 1906. Thus, the beginning of the twentieth century marked, for Chicago, a new phase in its industrial history. Since that time, the manufacture of primary iron and steel and the products fabricated from them has become the biggest industry in the Chicago district.

Iron ore moves a thousand miles by water, and coal comes from as far as West Virginia, to make iron and steel in this district. Water transportation is cheap, but this is not the only factor in accounting for the low assembly cost of this steel district. Some furnaces today are oil- or gas-fired, and Chicago has access to the midcontinent oil fields. Scrap iron and scrap steel play an increasingly important role in both iron and steel manufacture; Chicago and its suburban cities make so much machinery that the district is an important source of scrap. And finally, the dense population abruptly ceases at the dry boundary for humid-agriculture which lies 400 miles west of Chicago. This means that the westward-moving market for steel in all its forms comes to a halt there. It is a big jump to the Pacific Coast market.

Another factor in growth has been the westward movement of some types of industry. The Chicago district has established certain steel-using manufacturing industries which were for a long time centralized in the eastern cities. In the emergency of World War II, despite an expressed intention on the part of the Government to make the distribution of manufacturing more uniform throughout the Manufacturing Belt, the Chicago district got a lion's share, like other primary concentrations of industry. Chicago never has had so important a share of labor-oriented industry as New England. It is this type which has shown the greatest tendency to recentralize in the United States.

But Chicago's industry is not all steel and a great variety of machinery. Oil refining in South Chicago and Whiting is exceeded only by two other districts. Aside from the packing of meat and flour milling, Chicago has developed the manufacture of foods far beyond the demands of the 5 million people in the metropolitan area. It is the most important corn-products manufacturer in the nation. Cheese and dairy products, beverages, canned soups, vegetables, preserves, and spices are all important.

World War II and Since. As a machine-making district, Chicago's industry was profoundly affected by the entry of the United States into the Second World War. The largest plants for automobile manufacture built outside of the Detroit area were in Chicago. This city received the greatest single city allotment of funds for industrial facilities expansion.[5] Of this the largest sum was for iron and steel and their product facilities; aircraft was second; ordnance was third; explosives were fourth; and machinery fifth. Every category listed by the government was a part of the industrial facilities granted to Chicago.

This impact of World War II upon Chicago's manufacturing seems to have been prophetic of the postwar years. Chicago, and every suburban city, has increased in population and in net value of its manufacturing. It is estimated that 40 per cent of the wage earners in industry in Iowa, Illinois, Indiana, and Wisconsin are employed in the Chicago industrial region, hub of their respective industrial areas.

Other Cities. *Milwaukee* (637,392) repeats a number of Chicago's industrial and commercial patterns on a smaller scale. Brewing, farm implement manufacture, meat packing, knitting, glass making, and the manufacture of many types of industrial and materials-moving machinery are Milwaukee's principal industries. This industrial district is still growing. *Racine* (71,193) and *Kenosha* (54,368) are manufacturers of electrical machinery and automobiles, respectively. The cities in the Rock River Valley in Illinois and Wisconsin: *Rockford* (105,438), *Beloit* (29,590), *Janesville* (24,899), and *Madison* (96,056) manufacture a variety of metal goods, textiles, and machine tools. Local initiative and proximity to the Chicago market have been the prime factors of location.

[5] *The Geographic Distribution of Manufacturing Facilities Expansion, July 1940-May 1944* (War Production Board, Washington, June 1, 1945), p. 23.

MINNEAPOLIS-ST. PAUL

In all the rather sparsely populated northern plains west from the Great Lakes to the Northern Rockies, there is but one urban center of half a million population, *Minneapolis* (521,718), and *St. Paul* (311,349), so-called Twin Cities on the upper Mississippi River. The erection of Fort Snelling at the little fur-trading post at the Falls of St. Anthony singled out the one settlement destined to grow. It is the dominant trading center for the densely populated farming area southward into Iowa. As middle-western cities go, the Twin Cities are relatively youthful, and their economy shows this characteristic. With the combination of furs, water power, and a crossing of trade routes, the early start afforded by the Army post was enough to outdistance rival towns. During the period of so-called "frenzied" lumbering in the upper Lakes region, the Twin Cities became important sawmill towns, two of the very few that survived and have grown from this half century of forest exploitation.

Eventually Minneapolis and St. Paul became the principal commercial and financial centers for wheat and cattle ranching on the Northern Plains. The present Federal Reserve Bank district for Minneapolis delineates much this same region: Minnesota, the Dakotas, and Montana. Decline in Minnesota's lumbering and in spring wheat crop affected the economy of the Twin Cities; co-operative organizations for consumers and producers have grown rapidly in numbers and in influence. Although top rank in flour-milling was surrendered, the "bread-and-butter" aspect of the local economy remains important.

The manufacture of electrical machinery, agricultural implements, glass, a variety of plastic products, and heating equipment have diversified the factory economy. There is somewhat less specialization than one might expect of two large cities so closely located.

These two financial and commercial centers will unquestionably profit from the increased mining activity in the Mesabi Ranges where taconite mining and preparation are causing new towns to rise. Although a derelict zone of cut-over, submarginal farming country lies between the iron ranges and Duluth-Superior on the north and these central Minnesota cities, the bonds of commerce are maintained. Alberta's oil is coming to Superior by pipe line. With inadequate storage and refining facilities in the Lake Erie area, Superior has a rather promising oil-storage industry.

The hundreds of lakes within a short distance of the Twin Cities have fostered a very important tourist industry. The entire upper Lakes region has embarked upon a reforestation and recreation program designed to increase the carrying power of the cut-over lands.

OTHER INDUSTRIAL CENTERS

St. Louis. As a trading post on the middle Mississippi between the mouths of its two greatest tributaries, the Missouri and the Ohio, as the greatest river town north of New Orleans, as an outfitting and forwarding center for the westward-moving settlers before and after the Civil War, and as the second greatest railroad center in the Middle West, St. Louis has had a varied history. It is still a river port, but its commerce now rests primarily upon the railroads. It is still a commercial city, but manufacturing has become as important.

Site and Situation. The site of St. Louis is on the high west bank of the Mississippi River a short distance below the mouth of the Missouri. As an early river town the site was particularly advantageous. As a modern railroad city its situation has proved to be one of the really superior centers in the Middle West. Were it farther south, near the mouth of the Ohio River, it would have been surrounded on three sides by the hill country of the Ohio Valley and the Ozark Highlands. *Cairo,* Illinois (12,123), occupies such a situation.

Commerce. St. Louis marks the northern extension of the Ozarks and is far enough north to be on the trade routes which skirt the northern margin of the hills of the Ohio Valley. These hills and the Great Lakes constitute the two sides of a great "funnel" through which the raw materials of the Western Plains must pass on their way to eastern consuming centers; Chicago dominates the northern and St. Louis the southern sides. St. Louis dips into the stream of commerce from the southern Great Plains and the western Gulf region, both great raw-material exporting regions. The vitality of large cities is dependent upon commerce and in this respect St. Louis is exceptionally favored.

Although the upper Mississippi and the Missouri are not so commercially active as the Ohio River, St. Louis has remained an important river port. Since the improved Mississippi-Ohio system was inaugurated in the early 1930s, the tonnage on all parts of the system has come to exceed a 100 million tons annually. The 9-foot channel from Chicago to the Gulf, and on the Ohio and Missouri rivers may conceivably bring about an increase over the present volume of trade on the upper Mississippi. World War II developments gave some indication of the increased use of the Mississippi system in the future.

Except for the important difference of Lake trade, St. Louis is similar to Chicago in its functions. Each lies at the Corn Belt margin of a large physical barrier to rail commerce. St. Louis commands the only water route and one of the three land approaches to the upper South. Professor Goode of the University of Chicago wrote years ago that the north-south trade of the Mississippi basin may eventually be as great as the east-west trade, and then Chicago and St. Louis will realize in full the advantages of their respective situations.

Manufactures. Census figures for *St. Louis* make it a city of 856,796 people but metropolitan St. Louis has a population of approximately a million. Immediately across the river are four satellites: *Alton* (32,550), *Belleville* (32,721), *Granite City* (29,465), and *East St. Louis* (82,295). The urban group may be generally characterized as of the heavy-industry class, with no particular speciality. Iron and steel are the leading industries, using upper Lakes ore and coal from southern Illinois and Oklahoma fields. One of the largest alumina processors in the country is located here. Oil refining, chemicals, meat packing, flour milling, airplanes, rolling stock, farm implements, leather and shoes, machine tools, and a variety of industrial machines are other important manufactures. Since the oil boom in southern Illinois, oil drilling- and processing-equipment manufacture was established at St. Louis.

The rise of new steel centers at Kansas City, Detroit, and in the Gulf South, and increased capacity in middlewestern steel centers has not brightened the hopes of St. Louis steel makers. The trek of shoe manufacturing to St. Louis has recently shown some indication of a return to the East. Glass manufacture has not gained greatly in importance since its establishment here early in the present century. Flour milling reached its peak about the time of World War I. But the prospects for the future of the St. Louis industrial area are by no means depressing. Although the expansion of industrial facilities by the government during World War II was mostly for such war goods as ordnance and explosives, the increased facilities in aircraft, iron and steel, petroleum refining, and chemicals was important and has been sustained since war's end.

Employment in the St. Louis district declined somewhat in 1947, but since then has steadily increased. The net value of manufactures has manifested a steady increase since the war began.[6]

Kansas City. Two states share the *Kansas City* industrial district: the Missouri section is much the larger (456,622); the Kansas section (129,553)

[6] *Annual Survey of Manufactures: 1952* (U.S. Dept. of Commerce, Bureau of the Census, Washington, 1953), pp. 62, 63.

FIGURE 14-11: *Boeing Airplane Plant, Wichita, Kansas*

No manufacturing industry was more geographically modified during World War II than the making of aircraft. This large plant is one of several built with federal funds for operation by an established manufacturer. Their continuing operation since the war has given them the appearance of permanent settlement. (Boeing Airplane Co.)

is less rapidly-growing. These twin cities stand, with Omaha, at the western margin of the Manufacturing Belt. No other large midwestern city has exhibited the vigor in population and industrial growth shown by Kansas City; the value added by manufacturing by both parts of the city nearly doubled between 1947 and 1952.

The new industrial facilities built by the government during World War II were principally for aircraft, ordnance, and petroleum-chemical manufacture; only ordnance has declined. Employment has kept up since the war. The principal factor in this continued activity is the decision by West Coast manufacturers to produce a large proportion of the aircraft in the Kansas City-Omaha districts (*Fig.* 14-11).

A significant addition to Kansas City has been the manufacture of primary iron and steel, a post-World War I development. By 1940, Kansas City led the nation in flour milling. In meat packing, the city ranks in the next group after Chicago. The dieselizing of railroads has not diminished the importance of railroad shops here. Branch assembly-manufacturing plants of Detroit auto makers have been established at Kansas City. Among mid-

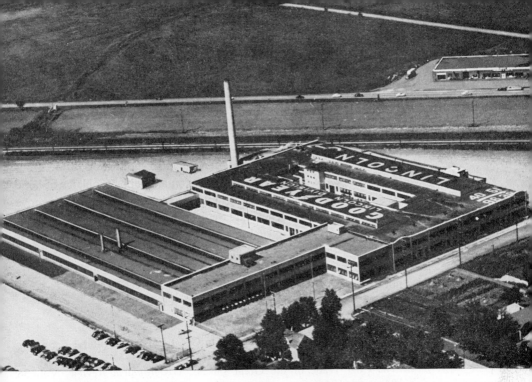

FIGURE 14-12: Goodyear Rubber Plant, Lincoln, Nebraska

Industry of several types has come to a great many of the smaller cities in the Corn Belt. Often the principal attraction is ample space and abundant labor. This plant manufactures mechanical rubber goods. (Goodyear Rubber Co.)

western industrial cities, Kansas City is one in which there is a paucity of machine-tool manufacturing.

Omaha. *Omaha* (251,117) has not displayed the vigor in industrial growth or in population noted in Kansas City. For many years it was primarily a railroad center, a stock market, and a milling city. World War II gave the city large facilities for the manufacture of aircraft; this industry did not subside after the war because of the Korean conflict and the decision to build planes here rather than concentrating on the West Coast. Industrial growth in Omaha since 1951 has not been in accordance with that between 1941 and 1951, although the decline was slight.

Oklahoma City. *Oklahoma City* (243,504) is in the Middle West but not a part of the Manufacturing Belt. This city and *Tulsa* (182,740) are near the margin of the Middle West, the Western Great Plains, and the South. Both cities have had similar records of growth; both have had an economy based largely upon wheat, cattle, and oil. Both received rather large industrial facility increase during the war for the manufacture of aircraft. Both cities have managed to continue in this aspect of manufacturing. *Wichita, Kansas* (168,279) is similar to the Oklahoma cities just described, with the oil industry lacking.

In a book of this compass, it is manifestly impossible to include all manufacturing centers. This is increasingly true because of the tendency for manufacturing to locate in smaller cities. Often the chief motivating factor in removal is to escape the costs of urban congestion and labor problems of large cities. With the dependence upon the motor-truck transportation, this move to smaller cities is easier. The increase in subcontracting in industry is a strong factor in encouraging such a recentralization. The Middle West has many small industrial cities which are not mentioned in this book, yet their industry oftentimes is a factor in the persistence of manufacturing in larger cities not far distant (*Fig.* 14-12).

BIBLIOGRAPHY

BALLERT, Albert G., "A Turn-around on a Great Lakes Freighter," *Economic Geography,* Vol. 25, No. 2 (April, 1949), pp. 146-155.
—— "The Coal Trade of the Great Lakes," *Geographical Review,* Vol. 38 (1948), pp. 194-205.
BROWN, Ralph, *Historical Geography of the United States* (New York, Harcourt, Brace, and Co., 1948), Chaps. 11, 12, 13, 14, 15.
COMSTOCK, H. B., "Magnesium," *Minerals Yearbook* (U.S. Dept. of the Interior, Washington, 1951), pp. 791-800.
CROSS, William P., *Floods in Ohio: Magnitude and Frequency,* Bulletin 17 (Columbus, Ohio Water Resources Board, 1946).
DURAND, Loyal, Jr., "The Lower Peninsula of Michigan and the Western Michigan Dairy Region," *Economic Geography,* Vol. 27, No. 2 (April, 1951), pp. 163-183.
HEWES, Leslie, "Northern Wet Prairie of the United States, Sources of Information and Extent," *Annals Assn. of American Geographers,* Vol. 41 (1951), pp. 307-323.
Lake Carriers' Association, *Annual Report* (Cleveland, 1953).
Missouri River Basin Agricultural Program, 81st Congress, 1st Session, House Document 373 (Washington, 1949).
MUNN, Alvin A., "Production and Utilization of the Soybean in the United States," *Economic Geography,* Vol. 26, No. 3 (July, 1950), pp. 223-234.
RODGERS, Allan, "The Iron and Steel Industry of the Mahoning and Shenango Valleys," *Economic Geography,* Vol. 28, No. 4 (Oct. 1952), pp. 331-342.
Transportation on the Great Lakes (U.S. Corps of Engineers, Washington, 1953).
WEAVER, John C., "Crop-Combination Regions in the Middle West," *Geographical Review,* Vol. 44, No. 2 (April, 1954), pp. 175-200.
WRIGHT, Alfred J., *Economic Geography of Ohio,* Bulletin 50 (Columbus, Division of Geological Survey, 1953).

CHAPTER 15

THE WESTERN GREAT PLAINS

PHYSICAL SETTING

THE WESTERN GREAT PLAINS is essentially the short grass portion of the physiographic province, Great Plains (*Fig.* 15-1). A glance at a physical map will reveal a high plains section of varying width extending along the eastern front of the Rocky Mountains for 1,300 miles. It includes some mountain outliers of the Northern Rockies, particularly in Montana. It is a dry region. In fact it has become something of a tradition to regard all of the land lying between the 20-inch isohyet and the Rockies as Great Plains.

Within one hundred years the Great Plains had been appropriated and settled, had reached a peak of production, and had experienced decline. Man appraised the carrying power of this grassland in a manner now held to have been unwise both for the individual settler and for the nation. As a result it has become a plundered province, and as a consequence many of the people had been caught in a serious economic situation. Most of the problems which now beset the people of this region are directly or indirectly the consequences of failure on the part of the heterogeneous population, which flocked to the Great Plains after the Civil War, to adjust their humid-farming practices to the conditions of this interior plains region.[1] Over-anxious settlers have learned to their sorrow that most of this great grassland is not plowland. In a manner of speaking, the Western Great Plains is a way-of-life and does not depend upon rigid delimitation for treatment. The western, the southern, and the northern boundaries of this great province are readily apparent, but the eastern boundary is not delineated as precisely. It is a transition zone that is determined by a combination of critical rainfall,

---

[1] See C. Warren Thornthwaite, "The Great Plains," in *Migration and Economic Opportunity,* by Carter Goodrich and others (Philadelphia, Univ. of Pennsylvania Press, 1936).

369

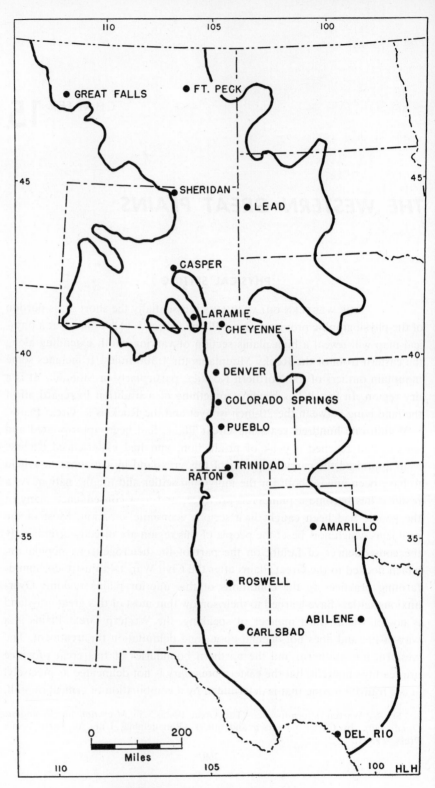

FIGURE 15-1: *Western Great Plains*

grass cover, and soil type. In the chapters on the Middle West, the portions of the lower, eastern Great Plains given over to the production of spring and winter wheat are treated as a part of that geographic region. In the present chapter there remains for consideration the higher western portion of the Great Plains where grazing occupies a larger part of the farm acreage than in the eastern transition zone.[2] This boundary recedes toward the west so far in northeastern Colorado as to nearly pinch off the northern portion.

The southern margins of the Edwards and Stockton plateaus of Texas give a definite limit to this geographic region in the south. In Wyoming, the western margin of the Great Plains swings past the opening to the geologically different but physiographically similar Wyoming Basin. The Canadian border is the northern boundary of this attenuated region.

Relief. The general concept of the flatness of these plains is for the most part valid. In many places, however, the generally level character of the region is broken by "badlands," mesas, or volcanic intrusions. East-flowing streams which rise in the Rockies have cut valleys through the water-deposited mantle. At several places along the front of the Rockies a lowland has been eroded, the largest part of this lowland is in northeastern Colorado and extending into southeastern Wyoming and western Nebraska, the Colorado Piedmont.

This Piedmont lowland situated at the narrow middle portion of the Plains, divides the Western Great Plains into northern and southern portions. The northern plains are dominated by the drainage of the Missouri River. The surface is somewhat lower and more rolling than in the southern portion. This was the only section of the Great Plains which was invaded by the continental ice sheet, the southern limit of glaciation approximating the present course of the Missouri River. The northern portion is characterized by numerous mountain outliers east of the Rockies and some hill country. Farther to the east is the more extensive "badland" topography. These badlands are the result of the very extensive erosion of relatively non-resistant sediments containing layers of more resistant sandstones and shales. In northwestern Nebraska there is an extensive sandhill area.

The principal difference in the terrain of the northern and southern plains is the broad belt of generally higher elevation of the High Plains along the front of the southern Rockies, a remnant of an older and higher surface formed by deposits of old streams from the Rocky Mountains. This older surface has been removed in the eastern or Low Plains. South of the

[2] *The Future of the Great Plains,* H. R. Doc. 144 (Washington, 1937), Fig. 2, opp. p. 23.

Arkansas River in eastern Colorado is an area of mesas which are in contrast to the monotonously flat Staked Plains of northern Texas.

Soils. The Western Great Plains are covered for the most part with a fairly deep and fertile soil. The soil-making materials were deposited during a very long period of erosion from the Rockies. This thick mantle of sediments has since been uplifted and the rivers have again eroded into the Plains, giving rise to broad terraces. North of Nebraska nearly all of the sediments which distinguish the High Plains have been removed.

Dark brown soils characterize much of the broad eastern zone of the Plains from Canada to Mexico. Lighter soils appear along the drier west. Within very small areas soil texture is extremely variable, ranging from clay soils to sandy loam. Soil diversity for the individual farmer is further complicated by the very large size of the individual holdings.

The soils are for the most part suitable in texture and fitted for crop agriculture when watered. Their ability to absorb and hold water varies widely and is, perhaps, their most critical quality from the viewpoint of agriculture. Soils with fine-textured surface materials generally hold water well but do not absorb it readily. Sandy soils can absorb water quickly but do not hold it well. Hence prolonged drought may affect crops on the heavy soils more seriously than those on lighter soils.

Of the four principal types of soil on the Western Great Plains, those of eastern Colorado are the most productive. They hold water fairly well under irrigation and produce a greater variety of crops, including sugar beets, alfalfa, and small grains. Under dry farming they produce cotton, wheat, barley, oats, and beans. Dairying and the feeding of sheep and cattle are important. There are numerous districts of sandy soil which preclude any profitable use. The largest by far is that of western and northern Nebraska, but there are smaller areas in the Colorado Piedmont and farther south in the valley of the Arkansas River. Wind erosion has damaged many parts of the Western Plains, but damage appears to be greatest in the northern and the southern ends of the region, where the sandy nature makes it difficult for the soil particles to group themselves into units large enough to prevent erosion.

Climate. The rainfall fluctuates so widely around a critical point for crop production that even a slight reduction in moisture affects crop yields seriously. The irregular but persistent recurrence of severe drought, wide fluctuation in temperature and in winds, and the general failure of settlers to adjust the farming practices of the humid East to these hazardous conditions are chiefly responsible for the problems which beset them. Market variations occur not only from year to year, but also from place to place; they also occur in irregular periods of several years and in major periods of many years' duration. Temperatures may vary seasonally as much as 100° F., even in the Texas portion of the Western Great Plains. More harmful than thermal variation, however, are the sustained high temperatures, sometimes continuing for three consecutive weeks. Livestock, dependent upon surface streams for water, suffer from both factors. Under such temperature conditions, wheat and corn are seriously damaged. In no other part of the interior United States are average wind velocities so high as in the Great Plains. The high rate of air movement increases evaporation and promotes dust-blowing on fields which are, or have been, cultivated.

The long-time effects of low rainfall, extreme variability in daily and seasonal distribution, low relative humidity, high winds, and the extremes of temperature have been to curtail the usefulness of the precipitation that falls. Hail insurance is commonly taken out on half of the wheat acreage on a representative farm or ranch in the Western Great Plains.

The Missouri is by no means the only river on the Great Plains which has periodic and disastrous floods. There are really two flood seasons each year: March and April when spring rains and melting snow on the grasslands, and in June when the melting snow on the mountains and the early summer rains combine to flood the streams. The program for flood control, navigation, and power development of the Missouri River System is the largest ever undertaken in North America. Six main stream dams are multiple-purpose. Eventually there will be a total of some 105 reservoirs on the tributary streams.

Vegetation. In the long history of the settlement of eastern United States, grass was a quiet factor in the environment, but with the migration to the Central Lowlands and the Great Plains, grass was dramatized. Hunters and trappers came first, then the cattlemen, but the sod was broken by the farmers who followed them closely. It was very old sod; centuries of buffalo and Indian occupancy had failed to deplete it. The grasses of the Plains were native to the land, differing in this respect from grasses introduced into the forested East.

The tall grasses of the eastern Plains country formerly crossed into the High Plains in western North Dakota, western Nebraska, and western Oklahoma. Now the original grass has been replaced by more or less unpalatable weeds and shrubs in all but the sand plains of western Nebraska.

Elsewhere the short grass turf dominated, and in some areas still does.

Buffalo grass in Wyoming, Nebraska, Kansas, Colorado, New Mexico, and Arizona; Grama grasses in Colorado and New Mexico; the Galleta grasses farther south and west, which made a sod that was able to support moderate grazing and hold the light-textured soils of the area with their fibrous roots. With overgrazing, these grasses gave way to less nutritious yellow snakeweed, flowering bailleya, and yellowish pingue. The range is thereby poorer but still can stand some grazing and will withstand wind. Eventually, overgrazing results in further deterioration of cover, the encroachment of plants such as Russian thistle, blueweed, and lambs quarters,—and wind erosion. The old sod which greeted the settlers may have had no superior in any part of the world. Its present forage capacity is from 30 to 50 per cent of its original value. It is lowest in the northern Plains and in the Dust Bowl areas such as southeastern Colorado and the Texas Panhandle. Revegetation has been underway for some years; western wheat grass, blue grama, and big bluestem are among the best for this purpose.

SETTLEMENT OF THE GREAT PLAINS

The movements of settlers onto the Great Plains and the subsequent expansions of grazing and cropping lands have occurred in times of abnormally high rainfall, or of high prices for beef and wheat or both. The Civil War had produced a shortage of cattle in the North, although Texas had great numbers to spare. An estimated 5 million head were driven from Texas northward over the plains to the railroads for shipment to the populous northeastern states.

For twenty years after the Civil War there was a relatively humid period on the Great Plains. There was also an eager westward movement of people; money was to be made in the raising of stock. During this time the northern Plains were filled with their first domestic cattle. By 1867 the first of the cow towns had been established at Abilene, Kansas, on the Kansas Pacific Railway, now the Union Pacific. The price of range steers rose from $7 in 1879, to $9.50 in 1880, and to $12 in 1881. The world boom in Great Plains beef was on.[3]

Settlement followed the lines of railroads, which were built at that time in the central and northern portions of the Plains. This encouraged the driving of cattle from Texas northward to Kansas shipping points. Later, herds were pushed into Nebraska, the Dakotas, and Montana, first to provide meat for military garrisons and Indian reservations, then to furnish

[3] In 1881 Gen. J. S. Brisbin published a book entitled *The Beef Bonanza; How to Get Rich on the Plains.*

a supply for eastern markets. Real and anticipated profits from cattle raising led to a phenomenal extension of ranching in the Great Plains. But changes in the Plains economy came fast.

In no other section of the United States has legislation been of such importance in determining the place and character of settlement. The Homestead Act of 1862 replaced the eastern-creditor land policy of Hamilton with the western-debtor land policy of Lincoln. From 1862 on, a man could have 160 acres of land from the public domain for the settling, although it is now known that in drier western parts of the Great Plains a farm of that size is far too small to support a family. He was required to put it under cultivation regardless of fitness. Not until 1909 was the size increased to 320 acres; in 1916 grants of 640 acres were made with the provision that they be grazed.

AGRICULTURE

Grazing. From the end of the Civil War until 1886 large herds of cattle grazed the Plains as one great pasture from Montana to Texas. With the drought years which began in '86 and with the enclosure of lands with barbed wire fence by homesteaders, the range became insufficient and cattle barons declined in importance. There was only slight increase in the number of cattle after 1890. In the range portion of the Plains states there were 12 million head in 1920 and 10 million in 1935. Yet because of continued and serious deterioration of the range, encroachment by homesteaders, and the drought of 1934, the Plains were estimated to have been seriously overstocked in 1935.

Today most of the cattle are owned by farmers who raise forage crops; the day of the vast cattle ranch with its famed brands is nearly over.[4] Herefords and Shorthorns are efficient consumers of the corn and other forage crops grown, and the pulp and molasses which are by-products of the beet-sugar refining industry. Even with the number of horses reduced 50 per cent, nine-tenths of the cropland is in forage crops and wheat.

Sheep are still very important on the Western Great Plains, but the greater number are grazed on the Western Slope of Colorado and in the valleys and mountain pastures of the Rockies. As Great Plains farm land is abandoned for one reason or another, the number of sheep increases.

No plow crop could be commercially important on the Western Great Plains until after the railroad had provided access to eastern markets. Unlike eastern farms, it was not uncommon for farm land to be mortgaged as

[4] There were several English and Scottish, and a few German and French interests in control of large herds of Plains cattle during the days of "cattle barons."

part of its first sale to the pioneers. There was too much emotion in the land sales which accompanied the movement of eastern people on the High Plains; farming alone could not always be made to show a profit. The crops, and the methods of growing them, were too often those of the humid East.

Wheat. Stock feeding was the basis of the farm economy; wheat did not at first play an important role. As a result of a series of dry seasons, development of a new type of wheat, the development of farm machinery, and the rise in the price of wheat, the commercial grain farming of the more humid eastern portion of the Plains spread westward to the Rockies.

Prior to World War I many farming communities had given up trying to make a living and had abandoned the land. Then the high prices for wheat of the First World War, together with a series of abnormally humid years, brought a great increase in wheat farming. Cornland and abandoned land went into wheat, rangeland was plowed for wheat. The price of wheat dropped just after the war, but the humid years continued for a time. Large-scale wheat farming kept on too. The cost of machinery had been so great that farmers felt that they had to keep on producing large crops in order to meet their obligations. This partly accounted for the continued large acreage in wheat despite the drop in price after the First World War. At this time the "suitcase" farmer entered wheat production, and the industrialization of wheat farming received an impetus (*Fig.* 15-2).

These were nonresident farmers who had purchased large areas of land and hired farmers in the vicinity to plow and seed them to wheat. The term has also been applied to business men of the Eastern Great Plains who leased or bought land on the High Plains for the same purpose. It was not unusual for a single farmer to put 3,000 to 5,000 or more acres in wheat; with a good crop once in five years he would break even or a little better; two crops and he would make money, providing the price of wheat was not down. This sort of wheat growing was condemned as speculation, and praised as furnishing paid employment for local farm hands during bad years.

It is wheat that has determined the size of most crop farms and it is this economy that has created much of the atmosphere of "temporariness" on the Western Great Plains. Paucity of cities and sparse rural population also contribute to this impression. The investment in barns and other farm buildings is low, although machinery investment is relatively high. Hog lots, corn cribs, silos, and poultry sheds have no place here. Instead of a silo, a trench is dug deep enough and long enough to hold a winter's supply of ensilage.

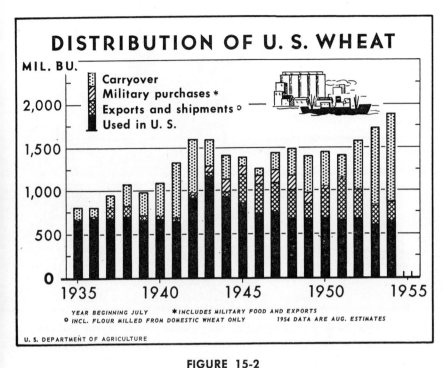

DISTRIBUTION OF U. S. WHEAT

MIL. BU.

Carryover
Military purchases *
Exports and shipments °
Used in U. S.

YEAR BEGINNING JULY   *INCLUDES MILITARY FOOD AND EXPORTS
° INCL. FLOUR MILLED FROM DOMESTIC WHEAT ONLY   1954 DATA ARE AUG. ESTIMATES

U. S. DEPARTMENT OF AGRICULTURE

FIGURE 15-2

For the full impact of this chart, compare it with *Fig.* 13-10.

This, covered with earth, serves adequately in this region of high winds, light snowfall, and no wood.

Generally speaking, the agriculture of the Western Great Plains exhibits two main north-south trending zones. The eastern one is a relatively narrow zone of specialized wheat farming, with some flax, sorghums, and stock feeding (*Fig.* 15-3). This zone is widest in the Dakotas and narrows south of Colorado. The western boundary varies with soil and moisture conditions Examples of this include the south Platte River Valley in Colorado where sugar beets, dry beans, potatoes, small grains, and livestock make the Fort Collins area a prosperous countryside. Farther south, east of Colorado Springs, there is an important bean-growing district. Still farther south is the Arkansas River Valley with its irrigated agriculture where melons are added to the usual varieties of irrigated crops.

The western zone, obviously, is interrupted by the districts noted above. It is primarily a grazing zone. Agriculture on the Great Plains, particularly in the south, has been criticized as being "out of balance." A major part of the cropland is planted each year in cash crops, such as wheat, sorghum

FIGURE 15-3: *Flax Combine, near Turtle Creek, North Dakota*

Mechanization in harvesting has proceeded even to such a geographically limited crop as flax. (Greater North Dakota Assn., Photo by SEBENS)

grains, and cotton. The acreage devoted to the production of forage crops not only is insufficient to give proper balance between soil-depleting and soil-building crops, but does not present adequate roughage for the area's livestock potential. Such a lack of balance in the "agricultural plant" results in considerable seasonal unemployment in agriculture. This is illustrated by data obtained during 1947, '48, and '49 at the Texas Technological College Farm at Lubbock. Grazing irrigated alfalfa pasture mixtures with beef cattle returned an average of $117 per acre, compared with $75.00 from the sale of the hay.

Influence of Irrigation. The impact upon Great Plains agriculture of the increase in irrigation made possible by the completion and activation of the Missouri Basin Development Program can only be estimated at this writing. There are, at present, no firm plans for the distribution of this water or for the allocation of cost to water users. Economists of the North Dakota Agricultural College estimate that changes in land-use through irrigation in that state will permit an increase of 127 per cent over the present number of farm units. About one-third of these farms will be straight irrigated farms with three-fourths or more of their land under irrigation. The

FIGURE 15-4: *Sugar-Beet Field, Colorado*

The generally prosperous landscape of the cropped portion of the Colorado Piedmont is evident in this beet field, with the Front Range of the Rockies in the background. (State of Colorado)

remaining farms will be rather equally divided between irrigated-and-live-stock farms and irrigated-and-dryland farms. In farms emphasizing livestock production, irrigated acreage will be about 10 per cent of the farm acreage. In those engaged in crop production, acreage will be divided in nearly equal proportions between irrigated and nonarable land.[5] In view of the fact that the Missouri Valley project embraces the northern half of the western Great Plains, the economy of this area is undergoing transition.

Colorado Piedmont. The largest and most densely populated agricultural region on the Plains is the Colorado Piedmont. This old erosion surface presents a broadly rolling terrain of from 5,000 to 7,000 feet in elevation, sloping to the east. The southern boundary is less regular than the others, grading into the Raton Mesa and the Park Plateau. Wind action has created a minor wasteland of dunes some twenty miles northeast of Pueblo. Otherwise the Colorado Piedmont is comprised of arable land within the limitations of a semiarid climate.

[5] Samuel C. Kelly, Jr. and Associates, *Irrigation in North Dakota* (Bur. of Bus. and Ec. Research, Univ. of North Dakota School of Commerce, 1954), pp. 14, 15.

Although the Piedmont, as the rest of the Western Great Plains, has steppe climate, the rainfall varies from 13 inches in the eastern portion to 20 inches farther west where elevations are two thousand feet greater. Extensive park lands and even some forest lands are to be found in the western portion. Waters of the North and South Platte and Arkansas rivers enable several parts of these valleys to be irrigated.

The agriculture of the Colorado Piedmont exhibits the three distinct types of Great Plains agriculture: irrigated crops, dry farming, and grazing lands. Approximately one million acres are irrigated, eight million acres are dry-farmed, and nine million acres are grazed.

Taken as a whole, the farming is mixed in type, with the acreage of hay, wheat, and corn ranking in that order on the cropped land. Barley and sugar beets are roughly a third as important in acreage as any one of the three chief crops. Vegetables, potatoes, and fruit are important only in the irrigated districts in the three river valleys that cross the Piedmont (*Fig.* 15-4). This region is the most important dairying section in Colorado or the Western Great Plains; it is as well one of the least important producers of range sheep. As sugar-beet refineries have been established, the pulp has become a companion feed with alfalfa for a growing lamb-feeding and beef-fattening industry.[6]

As specialization in wheat has declined, the increase in forage crops has not been commensurate with the increase in beef cattle and lambs. Extensive irrigated areas rarely present a picture of compact and uniformly cropped land; the farms of the Colorado Piedmont are no exception. Despite the apparent flatness of the landscape, the minor variations in terrain are enough to cause breaks in the uniformity of cropped land. The Piedmont is essentially a region of small landscapes, all irrigated, with broad expanses of wheat, barley, or range land intervening. Despite the fact that yields are greater in the irrigated land, the cost of transportation to markets has served to restrain the exuberance of irrigation enthusiasts (*Table* 15-1).

Among the larger irrigation projects are two which undertake to divert water from the western slope of the Rockies and by means of tunnels bring it to dry lands on the eastern side. One, a private venture, is the Twin Lakes Reservoir and Canal Company which diverts water from Roaring Fork on the western slope of Colorado to Crowley County farm lands on the east side. The largest, government-built, is the Colorado-Big Thompson project which diverts Pacific water from above Hot Sulphur Springs on the western

---

[6] Weld County in northeastern Colorado is reported to be the most important cattle-feeding county in the United States.

slope and by a 13-mile tunnel leads it to already-established irrigation lands on the east side of the Rockies.

Most recent and very comprehensive in scope is the project known as the Missouri Valley Plan. This envisages the conservation and use of the greatest river system of the Great Plains. The enormous Fort Peck dam on the upper Missouri was the first large unit under the proposed plan.

TABLE 15-1: Yields on Dry and Irrigated Land in Western Kansas, 1952

Crop	Dry	Irrigated
ALFALFA (tons)	1.	1.9
COTTON LINT (pounds)	190.	390.
GRAIN SORGHUM (100 pounds)	9.6	15.6
OATS (bushels)	15.6	18.3
WHEAT (bushels)	15.0	17.0

SOURCE: *Monthly Review*, Federal Reserve Bank of Kansas City, April, 1954, p. 8.

All irrigated communities have problems and expenses not common to humid areas. After irrigation has been practiced for fifteen or twenty years it not infrequently happens that over-alkalinity develops due to excessive evaporation. There is always the expense of securing surface water and of the maintenance of the canals.

TABLE 15-2: Trends in Irrigated Acreage, 1939-49

AREA	1939	1944	1949	Per Cent Change, 1939-1949
Colorado	2,467,548	2,698,579	2,872,348	16.4
Nebraska	473,775	631,762	876,259	85.0
Kansas	82,872	96,248	138,686	67.3
Oklahoma	4,437	2,237	34,071	667.9
New Mexico	436,402	5,534,640	655,287	50.2
Wyoming	1,284,027	1,353,873	1,431,767	11.5
United States	17,982,830	20,339,470	25,787,455	43.4

SOURCE: Census of Agriculture, Vol. III (1950).

To a greater extent than elsewhere on the Western Great Plains the Colorado Piedmont experienced an increase in land values during World War II. Airfields, depots for the military, ordnance plants, and conversion of plants to war work greatly increased the local market for farm products. Although most of the war contract work has ceased, the airfields and depots remain. The new Air Force Academy near Colorado Springs is another stimulant for Piedmont markets.

Other Irrigated Communities. Another irrigated district is the Arkansas Valley of southeastern Colorado. Agriculture here is similar to the Piedmont irrigated districts, with the addition of Rocky Ford cantaloupes, watermelons, peaches, pears, and more small grains and truck crops than are grown farther north. The value of all truck crops in this valley is not more than a fifth of the value of its sugar beets.

The Yellowstone Valley is the most important irrigated district in Montana's Plains region. It is centered around Billings and under conditions similar to the Colorado Piedmont, produces potatoes, sugar beets, alfalfa, wheat, garden peas, and corn. Berries are the only fruit that have commercial importance in the Yellowstone Valley. The alfalfa is fed to the cattle, dairy cows, and sheep which make the Billings area one of the two most important stock regions in Montana.

TABLE 15-3: Origin of Surface Water for Irrigation, 1949

| State | Per Cent of Enterprises Reporting | | | | |
	Lakes and Streams	Springs	Flowing Wells	Drainage Water	Sewage
COLORADO	84.2	5.6	3.5	6.6	.1
KANSAS	94.3	2.6	1.6	1.0	.5
NEBRASKA	86.8	2.0	6.4	4.5	.2
NEW MEXICO	91.0	7.5	.8	.6	.1
OKLAHOMA	89.7	1.7	—	8.6	—
WYOMING	90.9	5.3	1.7	2.0	.1

| State | Per Cent of Acres Irrigated | | | | |
	Lakes and Streams	Springs	Flowing Wells	Drainage Water	Sewage
COLORADO	84.4	1.6	2.3	11.7	—
KANSAS	95.4	.5	.8	3.2	.1
NEBRASKA	96.3	.2	.8	2.7	—
NEW MEXICO	96.7	2.9	.1	.3	.1
OKLAHOMA	99.6	.2	—	.1	—
WYOMING	93.0	3.6	1.2	2.1	.1

SOURCE: *Monthly Review,* Federal Reserve Bank of Kansas City, April 1954, p. 5.

Sugar Beets. Although sugar beets are grown in 22 western and north central states, California, Colorado, Idaho, Montana, and Nebraska produced about 70 per cent of the nation's crop in 1950 (*Fig.* 15-5). The

FIGURE 15-5: *Sugar-Beet Piling Machine, North Dakota*
In many irrigated areas in the western half of the United States the sugar beet is an important crop. In this photo sugar beets are being piled at a lower Yellowstone River valley community. (Greater North Dakota Assn., Photo by SEBENS)

most important single center of sugar-beet production in western United States is in the Colorado Piedmont, particularly in the South Platte River Valley. One county, Weld, produced nearly half of the states' total in 1950, and with three neighboring counties, accounted for more than three-fourths. Somewhat smaller beet districts are scattered along the Arkansas and Gunnison river valleys in Colorado. The second largest beet-growing area on the Western Great Plains is situated along the North Platte River in Wyoming and Nebraska. Beets are also grown farther east in the low plains along the Platte River and in the watershed of the Big Horn River in Wyoming.

Despite these concentrations of sugar-beet production, they are not the major crop in any of these districts. Beets have met the requirement of a high return per acre, imperative in irrigated regions. Beets are grown in rotation with small grains, alfalfa, and corn. Livestock-feeding operations are integrated into the farm program, with beef cattle and lambs being fattened, in part on the feed crops, sugar beet tops, beet pulp, and molasses.

Mechanization of growing and harvesting sugar beets have advanced, with the harvesting being more susceptible to mechanization. Most of this mechanization has taken place since 1944. In the Colorado Piedmont's most important beet area, 90 per cent of the crop was mechanically harvested in 1953. The Sugar Acts have not only influenced price but also have provided direct subsidy to growers.

Southern Great Plains Agriculture. The southern portion of the Western Great Plains in Colorado, New Mexico, Oklahoma, and Texas embraces a number of high plains or plateaus. Among them are the Edwards Plateau, Pecos Plains, Raton Mesas and High Plains of Texas also known as Staked Plains or Llano Estacado or Panhandle Plains. It is for the most part in contrast with the Northern Great Plains. It is higher, drier, and more dissected. Irrigated sections are less extensive; there is more grazing and less crop agriculture. In all of this southern region, more reliance is placed upon wells as a source of water for forage crops to carry the stock through winters and protracted droughts. Grain sorghums increase in importance south from Colorado, reaching their greatest concentration in the Texas Panhandle and eastern New Mexico. Two important varieties are kafir and milos; mechanization is well advanced. This is the western margin of the hard-winter-wheat region, embracing southeastern Colorado, western Kansas, and the panhandle of Texas and Oklahoma.

Cotton came to these southern plains rather late. Its production began after World War I, without irrigation. Since the 1930's cotton acreage has increased to about half a million acres, most of it in the Texas-Oklahoma Panhandle. Irrigation has become important. Mechanization of the cotton harvest is the prevailing practice.

Despite these three crops, and forage crops, rotation is difficult to practice in the Southern Great Plains. For one thing, yields hold up well without it; for another, fewer crops can be worked into a rotation system.

Much of the Southern Great Plains is devoted to grazing. There are few sheep in the panhandle, but the Edwards Plateau has great numbers of them. Where sheep are important there will probably be Basque sheepherders who have migrated here to follow their calling. Their covered wagons are a common sight in the Southern High Plains and in the mountain pastures. Despite the increase in the number of beef cattle in the Corn Belt, the cattle ranges of the Great Plains remain important. Ranches are large in the drier parts of the Plains; smaller holdings are generally found where water permits the growing of forage for fattening the animals. Year-long grazing is the practice from the Texas Panhandle southward.

FIGURE 15-6: *Lignite Strip Mine, near Hazen, North Dakota*
This state mines nine-tenths of all lignite in the United States. The big shovel in the foreground removes the overburden, while the smaller one mines the coal. (Greater North Dakota Assn., Photo by SEBENS)

MINERALS

Historically, the mining center of the Western Great Plains has been in the Black Hills of South Dakota where gold, silver, and lead have been mined since 1874. The largest gold-producing mine in the United States, Homestake Mine at Deadwood, has operated continuously, with time off during World War II. The Black Hills have had numerous other rich strikes, but none has persisted.

Potash has been mined near Carlsbad, New Mexico, since the 1930's. The deposits are as extensive and accessible as in the older Stassfurt field in Germany, and materially richer. The discovery of these New Mexican deposits caused the price of German potash to come down, with the result that the United States still buys much potash from Germany.

Bituminous coal and lignite are mined at several places on the Western Great Plains, notably western North Dakota, southern Colorado, near Great Falls and Lewiston, Montana, and just east of the Big Horn Mountains in Wyoming (*Fig.* 15-6). Coal is strip mined and is generally of rather low grade. Most of the lignite mined in the United States comes from North

Dakota. Gypsum deposits are worked at several places in western Kansas and southward to the middle Pecos Valley.

The oldest gas- and oil-producing field in the southern High Plains is the Panhandle Field. From its beginning in 1918, subsequent discoveries have extended it through Oklahoma into Kansas. For years it has been the largest gas field on the Great Plains, and for that matter, in the nation. The only important helium wells in the United States are within this large gas field, near *Amarillo* (74,246).

A more recent discovery is the southeastern New Mexico-Texas Panhandle oil field, producing in 1953 in excess of 25,000 barrels daily. Near many of these isolated oil fields on the lonely expanse of West Texas the production crews can be found living in neat little settlements provided by the producing companies.

In the Northern Great Plains of Montana, North Dakota, and Wyoming there also are recent commercial oil developments. The big Beaver Lodge and Tioga fields are beginning their developments in the vast Williston Basin, 118,000 square miles of prairie plains and "badlands" lying athwart the Montana-North Dakota boundary and extending northward into Canada. Although oil was first found in this basin in 1951, development has been relatively slow.

MANUFACTURING AND CITIES

In general there are two main types of manufacturing cities on the Western Great Plains, the commercial centers with a manufacturing "overlay," and the mineral-processing centers. *Denver* (415,786) is the only large city on the Great Plains, and as a manufacturer it has no peer in all the Great Plains. Denver began as a mining center, taking on important commercial functions as the Colorado Piedmont and the Plains developed, as well as its immediate Rocky Mountain region. It is the greatest sheep-marketing city in the nation, the result of the flocks on the "Western Slope," the Colorado Piedmont, and tributary sections, together with the rail accessibility to eastern markets.

Denver manufactures include nearly all of the food-processing and several of the mineral-processing industries of other Great Plains cities. There are also rubber products, instrument, leather, and porcelain factories. The industrial facilities allotted Denver during World War II were predominantly emergency in nature and none has continued as a major industry since the war. Several federal agencies have established offices in Denver since 1940.

FIGURE 15-7: *Steel Plant, Pueblo, Colorado*

This modern steel plant on the Colorado Piedmont uses iron ore from the Wyoming Rockies and coal from the Trinidad district to the south. Skip cars (foreground) travel up an inclined rail to feed ore, limestone, and coke in the proper proportions to the blast furnace. Two other furnaces can be seen in the background. (Colorado Fuel and Iron Corp.)

Other Piedmont cities are *Pueblo* (63,685), with primary iron and steel manufacture (*Fig.* 15-7), using ore from Sunrise, Wyoming, and coking coal from the Raton district in the southern part of the state. *Colorado Springs* (45,472) is primarily a tourist center, agricultural trading city, and base for the Air Force Academy.

Fort Collins (14,937) refines beet sugar, cans cherries and pickles, makes alabaster products, and manufactures cement. *Greeley* (20,354) refines sugar, makes dairy products, cans foods, and mills flour. *Loveland* (6,773) cans fruit and refines sugar. *Longmont* (8,099) refines sugar. *Scottsbluff* in Nebraska (12,858) refines sugar, packs meat, makes dairy products, and cans fruit. This district is one of the two largest irrigated areas on the Western Great Plains.

Bright silver towers pointing skyward over the fields near Tioga in northwestern North Dakota, represent the "first installment" of an industry new to the Northern Plains. It is a natural gasoline plant processing gases from the big Beaver Lodge and Tioga oil and gas fields. In the future, other plants of this type may be expected to develop throughout the Williston Basin wherever an oil and gas mixture is produced in volume enough to assure an economic scale of plant operation. In older districts, these natural gasoline plants are more numerous than refineries, and smaller in size, owing to the more-or-less local nature of the oil-field gases used. Such plants are found in Cut Bank, Montana, and in the West Texas fields. From them come butane, propane, dry natural gas, sulphur, and natural gasoline.

Despite the paucity of National Parks, the Western Great Plains have an important tourist industry. In the Black Hills, "Badlands" and on the plains, "dude" ranches, motels, and restaurants do a thriving business during the summer.

BIBLIOGRAPHY

BROWN, Ralph H., *Historical Geography of the United States* (New York, Harcourt, Brace and Co., 1948), Chaps. 20, 21, 22, 24.

"Crude Oil Exploration and Production," *Monthly Business Review,* Federal Reserve Bank of Dallas, Vol. 39, No. 9 (1954).

Farming Hazards in the Drought Area (United States Works Progress Administration, Division of Social Research, Washington, 1938).

MATHER, Eugene C., "The Production and Marketing of Wyoming Beef Cattle," *Economic Geography,* Vol. 26 (1950), pp. 81-93.

MUNN, E. N., "Protective Forestry," *Proceedings of the United Nations Scientific Conference on the Conservation and Utilization of Resources,* Vol. 5 (1951), pp. 143-146.

ROWAN, James F., "Mechanization of the Sugar Beet Industry of Scottsbluff County, Nebraska," *Economic Geography,* Vol. 24 (1948), pp. 174-180.

RUHLMAN, E. R., "Potash," *Minerals Yearbook, 1951* (U.S. Dept. of the Interior, Washington), pp. 1078-1094.

Rural Migration in the United States, Monograph 19 (United States Works Progress Administration, Division of Social Research, Special Reports, Washington, 1939).

The Future of the Great Plains, H. R. Document 144 (Washington, 1937).

"The Mohair Industry in the Southwest," *Monthly Business Review,* Federal Reserve Bank of Dallas, Vol. 25 (1950), pp. 193-201.

WEBB, Walter P., *The Great Plains* (Boston, Ginn and Co., 1931).

WHITE, A. G., A. T. COMBE, and A. L. CLAPP, "Petroleum," *Minerals Yearbook, 1951* (U.S. Dept. of the Interior, Washington, 1951), pp. 935-1052.

CHAPTER 16

THE ROCKY MOUNTAINS

PHYSICAL SETTING

THE GREAT PLAINS province is bordered on the west by the Rocky Mountains. In many places the mountain front is marked by narrow ridges or hogbacks which have been carved out of sedimentary rocks turned up against the mountain mass. In other areas, particularly in Montana, the approach to the mountains is indicated by outposts of smaller mountain areas such as the Little Rocky Mountains, Beaver Mountains, and the Big Snowy Mountains. In spite of these marginal features which mark the western border of the Great Plains, few physiographic provinces are as distinctly delineated. Certain Plains areas invade the mountains, and outliers of the Rockies are found on the Plains, particularly in Montana (*Fig.* 16-1). In a similar manner the land use of the two provinces is transitional at many places.

The Rocky Mountain System may be resolved into three provinces: Northern, Middle, and Southern (*Fig.* 1-2). As a whole, the Rockies have been a barrier to the movement of people and commodities, but their chief function in the development of the nation has been more positive. Upon occasion they have attracted settlement by their mineral wealth and by the agricultural possibilities of some of their valleys. In the latter phase of their development, there has been rather steady gain. In the former, there has been a great deal of fluctuation with the usual consequences in ephemeral settlement.

Trending as they do from northwest to southeast from Canada almost to Mexico, the Rockies have exerted a strong influence upon the pattern of settlement and upon the routes of commerce between the humid East and the drier West. The mountains provide water for the plains communities.

390

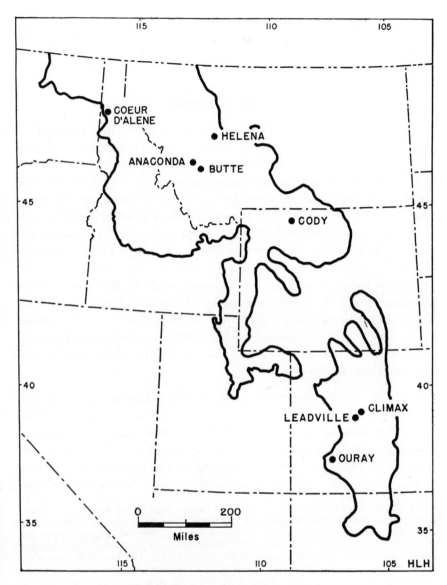

FIGURE 16-1: Rocky Mountains

as well as for the several intermontane valleys. They are so near the center of the great continental land mass that they have not increased appreciably the extent of the arid land in interior America. Their elevation not only enables them to supply water to many agricultural communities, but also to support extensive areas of timberland on their favorable slopes. Their height and grandeur have made the area a leading tourist center.

NORTHERN ROCKIES

These mountains differ from the Middle and Southern Rockies mainly in their lower elevations and predominantly linear arrangement of eastern ranges. They also have a greater longitudinal expanse.

In Idaho they are more closely spaced and there are no large intervening valleys. Near the Canadian border they appear to be just a mass of mountains with several well-defined glaciated valleys or trenches which provide easy accessibility, principally from the north and south. The over-all appearance of the Idaho and Montana Rockies is that of a high, maturely-dissected plateau with a few high peaks and massive ranges. Prominent among the narrow valleys are the Okanogan, Colville, Bitter Root, Pend d'Oreille, Purcell, Kootenay, and Rocky Mountain trenches. These have localized most of the people, both urban and rural. The best soils are here, the growing season is longer and the accessibility is easier, since most roads and railroads follow devious courses through the gaps between the Northern and Middle Rockies.

Minerals. The mineral wealth of the Northern Rockies is outstanding. Copper, silver, gold, zinc, lead, phosphates, mercury, arsenic, bismuth, manganese, chromium, and tungsten have all contributed to the fabulous wealth derived from the mining industry. Newest of these commercial minerals is chromium, the tough, heat-resisting alloying metal for steel furnace linings, armor plate, and high-speed machine tools.[1] Another critical war-

[1] A $15-million investment in chrome is at Monat, high in the Bear Tooth Mountains of Montana. In 1941 Monat was a sparsely wooded mountainside; its population was miner Monat and wife. The Japanese had choked off chrome from the Philippines; the Germans had blocked the Mediterranean route from Turkey's chrome mines; submarines imperiled shipping from South Africa. The Metals Reserve Corporation cleared away the mountainside at Monat, sank six levels of tunnels, and built a 12-story mill in the canyon. Production began in June to supply two-thirds of domestic needs.

A thousand workers moved in the new town. By late 1943, allied victories in North Africa enabled chrome to be shipped more cheaply than Monat could mine and mill it. The mill closed and the men went back to copper companies and other employers, and lower wages. Uncle Sam owns the largest "ghost" towns in the Rockies.

time alloy mineral mined in the Northern Rockies is manganese; the principal domestic source, Silver Bow County, Montana, produced about 5 per cent of the world's total during World War II.

Copper. But it is not from the strategic and vital alloying minerals that the Northern Rockies have gained their wealth; copper has been the principal mineral. The Butte, Montana, district has been, during its period of activity between 1882 and 1930, the greatest single producer of copper in the country, having yielded in about half a century more than $2 billion in copper, silver, gold, and zinc. Butte began its mineral career in 1865, with the discovery of silver, and for the next ten years or more silver was the leading mineral of the Northern Rockies. Butte remained the major silver producer in the state, although rich deposits were worked in five other mountain counties in Montana. During the early 1880's copper mining in the Butte district became so important that it surpassed silver. At first the ore was shipped to Swansea, Wales, for smelting, and the costs of transportation were so high none but the richest ores could be taken. Even after the first copper concentrator was built in Butte, the matte was still sent to Swansea for refining.

The first fully-equipped reduction plant was built at Anaconda in 1892; at the same time an electrolytic copper refinery was built at Great Falls on the Missouri River. During World War I a large wire and cable mill was built at Great Falls and since that time no step in copper refining has had to take place outside of the state. The rise of this great mineral industry in the development of the nation was like so many of the American resources, very fortunate in its timing.

Although Montana lost ranking in copper to the Southwest, its decline was not solely the result of circumstances in the immediate region. In an attempt to stabilize the copper market, the Copper Institute was formed by the leading American copper producers. The result has not been altogether satisfying either to domestic or to foreign purchasers of copper. Price could be stabilized, but the quantities of copper thrown on the market by new producers in central Africa could not. The copper surplus of the United States available for export has declined from a high of 36 per cent at the start of World War I, to 8 per cent in 1930, and to a deficiency in 1944. On the other hand, domestic refiners have long imported about 27 per cent of the copper consumed. In 1955, the *Butte* (33,251) copper workings were producing more ore as a result of extensive mining changes. The block-caving method is a form of shaft mining, unlike methods in the copper mines of Arizona, some of which were producing for the first time

FIGURE 16-2: *Bunker Hill Smelter, Kellogg, Idaho*

This is one of the many lead-zinc mining, smelting, and refining operations which take place in the Coeur d'Alene district of Idaho. Refined zinc from this plant is said to be the purest in the world, 99.99 per cent pure. In the foreground are tailings from operations of earlier days which it now pays to reclaim. (HENRY L. HUNKER)

in 1955. On the whole, it appears that the United States is favorably situated with respect to copper, having about 27 per cent of the world's supply within its own borders, and an additional 25 per cent under its financial control in other countries.

Lead and Zinc. Lead, silver, and zinc have long been joint products of copper mining as well as mined in their own right. The *Coeur d'Alene* district in northern Idaho produces more lead than any other western district; some 35 per cent of the nation's lead is mined in the Northern Rockies. Most of the lead is smelted at Bradley, Idaho, or at East Helena, Montana. Zinc is refined chiefly at *Kellogg* (4,913), Idaho, and at *Great Falls* (39,214) and *Anaconda* (11,254), Montana. By-products of this refining include arsenic and sulphuric acid (*Fig. 16-2*).

Forests. Although the Northern Rockies are by no means uniformly clothed with forests and are largely government-owned, they have important commercial lumbering. For the most part, these forests have not been exploited beyond satisfying local demand. The major exception is Idaho's white pine, the largest remaining stand in the United States. It constitutes more than two-thirds of the total lumber cut in the Northern Rocky Mountain province.

Floating logs out in flumes and the use of modern machines has enabled some of the difficult stands to be cut, but in many forested areas the chief source of income is from the tourist industry and related activities. With this in mind, the Forest Service is planting trees at the rate of a few thousand acres each year, scarcely a drop in the bucket considering the vast extent of land in every mountain county fit only for trees.

Agriculture. Taking the Northern Rockies as a whole, grazing is the major aspect of agriculture. Cattle and sheep divide the time between the mountain pastures and the winter feeding lots and alfalfa stacks of the valleys. Cattle and sheep are about equal in importance in the Northern Rockies, with most sheep in Idaho.

As soon as mining passed from the prospecting stage, crop agriculture began; the high prices for farm products which prevailed there stimulated it. Today the Northern Rockies rely upon three main crop regions: Boise, Coeur d'Alene, and Anaconda-Helena districts. The Boise-Payette-Weiser farming district is devoted primarily to hay, wheat, sugar beets, potatoes, and some apples, dairying, and livestock. The district farther north near Coeur d'Alene is much the same but with the addition of poultry, thus contributing to a more nearly self-sufficing economy. On the Montana side of the mountains, there is a compound farming region composed of the Anaconda, Helena, and Butte districts where agriculture is similar to that of western Idaho, but with greater emphasis upon hay and livestock. There is also greater emphasis upon dairying and the manufacture of butter, cheese, and canned milk. There are a few mountain valleys with dry farming and some with irrigated crops not included in these localized farming districts. Kalispell-Flathead Lake district is one of these; another is the Bitter Root Valley. Both of these are similar to the peripheral areas just described.

Manufacturing and Commerce. Although the Northern Rockies have perhaps a million and a half people, the region has very little manufacturing. However, its mineral industry gives rise to a vast amount of railroad traffic and some manufacturing. Most of the urban centers were originally mining districts and still function as such. They have become in turn trading centers for their respective farming districts. Virtually all are located on one of the main natural corridors through the mountain block.

FIGURE 16-3: *Hungry Horse Dam, Flathead River, Montana*

This dam in northern Montana is a unit of the Columbia River system for water control. Its power is being used by the first aluminum plant in the Rockies, operated by Anaconda at Columbia Falls, a few miles from the dam. The alumina is shipped to this plant from the middle Mississippi Valley. Power is also fed into the power pool of the Northwest. (U.S. Bureau of Reclamation)

In this respect they are generally in contrast with the towns of the Southern Rocky Mountain province.

Aside from the mineral reduction referred to earlier in this chapter, a growing oil-refining industry and fertilizer manufacture from a by-product of copper refining, there is little in the way of manufacturing. A foundry at Anaconda makes several million pounds of iron castings and 200,000 pounds of brass castings a year. Sugar refining is the principal industry based upon the farm products of the Northern Rockies. *Missoula* (22,485), Butte, Anaconda, *Helena* (17,581), and Great Falls have beet-sugar refineries. Most of the large lumber mills are at Missoula, *Kalispell* (9,737), and Polson.

The recently constructed Hungry Horse Dam (*Fig.* 16-3) will export power to the northwest power pool and to the new aluminum plant near Kalispell, Montana. Some water will be used for irrigation in the Flathead Valley.

Boise, Idaho (34,393), has had a great past in gold placer mining, but modern Boise prospers largely because of Arrowrock Dam, some 20 miles east of the city. The irrigated farming thus made possible has enabled the community to grow, in contrast with the many predominantly mining communities. The city's principal factory export is leather and its products. Some machinery, wood, stone, and clay products are made.

Tourist Industry. Reference has been made to the importance of the tourist industry in the Northern Rocky Mountains. Glacier National Park in the far north, is the largest and best-known of these public parks. Sun Valley, far to the south, is a different type of recreation center. It is railroad-owned and features winter sports and a luxury hotel service; it is the only large winter resort in the Northern Rockies.

MIDDLE ROCKY MOUNTAINS

Situation. The Middle Rocky Mountains comprise a varied group of landforms. Included are the Wasatch Mountains, Teton Range, Big Horn Mountains, Uinta Mountains, Absaroka Range, Snowy Range, Gallatia Range, Wind River Mountains, Big Horn Basin, Wyoming Basin, and Yellowstone section. It is essentially the mountain-rimmed Wyoming Basin with a Plains corridor between the Big Horn Mountains and the northern end of the Southern Rockies.

More transcontinental routes pass through the Middle Rockies than either of the other two mountain provinces. Elevations of 12,000 feet are

FIGURE 16-4: *Sheep Grazing, Aspen District, Colorado*

Nearly everywhere in the West livestock is important, whether it be grazing or irrigated land. For controlled migratory grazing on relatively poor pasture, sheep are dominant. These are in the Southern Rockies. (State of Colorado)

not uncommon in these mountain ranges, but their arrangement is conducive to east-west transportation routes. Even in the basins, elevations range upward from 6,000 feet. Volcanic activity in the Yellowstone National Park area is greater than for any other part of the nation.

The entire Middle Rocky Mountain area is dry except where the lofty ranges provide water for irrigation and human use. Although this province lies athwart the divide between Colorado River and Missouri River drainage, most of the province drains to the north. Mississippi River and Columbia River drainage are minor parts of the province.

Economy. Most of this region is arid and used for sheep raising. Transhumance is widely practiced; sheep are moved up to mountain pastures each summer and returned to feed in winter on alfalfa grown on irrigated fields. The canvas-topped shepherd's wagon is a common sight in many parts of the Middle Rockies.

Forests clothe many of the higher mountain slopes, but commercial lumbering is practiced in relatively few places. Mine supports and highway timbers are the principal wood products.

Minerals are not as important in the Middle Rockies as in either of its mountain neighbors. A good grade of bituminous coal is mined in southwestern Wyoming for Salt Lake City and other oasis cities, principally. Petroleum is found in the Wyoming and Big Horn basins.

Park City, Utah, in the Wasatch Range, has been one of the most important lead- and zinc-mining areas in the United States. In 1955 it seemed to be destined for "ghost" town status. As recently as 1951, Park City's output of recoverable metals was 23,438,400 pounds of lead and 20,417,100 pounds of zinc. The production in 1953 was approximately 5 million pounds of each. Local sources attribute the decline to lack of tariff protection to compensate for higher mining costs.

One small, new industry in the Park City area is the quarrying of a good grade of building sandstone. A ski-lift has been installed to encourage the winter tourist trade. But generally the lead and zinc miners have gone outside to other jobs; probably most of them have gone to Provo, Utah, to work for the steel mill or to the prosperous farms in nearby Heber Valley.

Manufacturing and Commerce. The cities of the Middle Rockies reflect the importance of the trade routes which pass through the Plains cor-

FIGURE 16-5: Berthoud Pass, Colorado

This pass (elevation 11,314 feet) is not only the principal one over the Continental Divide west of Denver, but it is also one of the important ski centers of the Colorado Rockies. (State of Colorado)

ridor between the Big Horn Mountains and the Laramie Range. *Casper* (23,673) is situated on the North Platte River at the northern extremity of the Laramie Mountains (in the basin of the same name). *Laramie* (15,581) is a transitional city lying between the Laramie Mountains and Medicine Bow Mountains; it might also be termed a Southern Rocky Mountain city. *Rock Springs* (10,857) and *Rawlins* (7,415) lie in the Wyoming Basin. The only manufacturing is oil refining.

Although several sections of the Middle Rockies have an important tourist industry, Yellowstone National Park is by far the most popular. Grand Teton National Park and Jackson Hole are just to the south. So-called "dude" ranches are found in many places throughout all three Rocky Mountain provinces, but there is a large concentration of them in Wyoming.

SOUTHERN ROCKY MOUNTAINS

The Southern Rockies have little in common with the Northern or Middle Rockies. The general pattern of mountains and basins is similar to a letter H, with three old lake plains nested along the center of the north-south axis: North, Middle and South parks, and farther south the San Luis Valley, all of them lying between the Front Ranges and the Park and Sawatch. Even within the Rockies themselves, there are numerous extensive areas of undulating land capable of supporting a grazing industry out of all proportion to the popular concept of a Rocky Mountain landscape (*Fig.* 16-6). Transportation routes follow the few deep gorges which mark drainage to the east, west, and south. The Royal Gorge of the Arkansas River is perhaps the most spectacular of these valleys. The extreme southern portion of the Rockies consists of two narrow elongated ranges which lose themselves on the eastern margin of the plateaus of New Mexico.

Minerals. Mineral exploitation in the Southern Rockies may have been more spectacular than in the northern section, but the importance of the mineral industries is currently far below its northern neighbor. Within the Southern Rockies minerals are less important than agriculture. Most of the "ghost" towns enumerated in surveys by the government are in this section. The amount of precious metals made the district around Central City one of the most flamboyant of all mining districts.

Scores of workings which have been abandoned pock the slopes of the ranges west of Denver (*Fig.* 16-7). The desolate landscape is occasionally enlivened by silver mines reopening when prices of silver or copper warrant. The discovery and operation of the mines near Leadville may be cited.

The gold boom began there in 1860; in 1863 it was deflated. In 1875 silver and lead were the basis for its next boom; in 1893 silver was derelict. In 1895 gold came back again, quietly. From mining properties have come such names as Leadville, Black Hawk, Central City, and Cripple Creek (gold); Ouray, Silverton, Telluride, and Creede (silver) in the San Juans.

Meantime coal mines were opened in both northern and southern Colorado. For some years these coal mines in the southern mountains and along the entire Piedmont have been first among the minerals of Colorado. The coal ranges in quality from subbituminous to anthracite; reserves are believed ample to supply the nation for five centuries. Although there is known to be a great deal of iron ore in the Colorado Rockies, ore for the iron furnaces at Pueblo is hauled from Sunrise, Wyoming; Colorado ore is expensively mined.

Molybdenum is mined at Climax near Leadville; the output of this one property constitutes about 80 per cent of the world's supply. Wolframite ore from Boulder County yields most of the tungsten produced in this country. Nearly 90 per cent of the nation's vanadium is also mined in this part of the Rockies. With the manufacture of automobiles, airplanes, high-speed machine tools, radio, and electronic equipment, these less common minerals assumed new values. Fluorspar, a calcium fluorine compound used in the manufacture of some steels and in the ceramic and chemical industries, is yet another important export from the Colorado Rockies, ranking fourth in the nation. Although some petroleum is produced in north central Colorado, most of the state's requirement is piped in from Texas. On Colorado's Western Slope oil shales promise much for the future.

Although not so important as the Northern Rockies, the Colorado section has been a producer of lead, zinc, and copper. With the gold and silver camps noted earlier, lead and zinc mining has become important. Since World War II, the low prices of these two minerals have resulted in serious unemployment. More than a third of the unemployed are lead and zinc miners in the Colorado Rockies, according to the Colorado Metal Mining Fund Board in 1954. The figures would be even higher were it not for the fact that skeleton crews are employed to prevent complete disintegration of the mines. Silverton, Telluride, Leadville, Ouray, and Gilman are among the communities affected. The contrast in unemployment between Colorado mining communities and those in the Middle Rockies is explained by the proximity of the latter to alternative sources of employment in agriculture, copper, and steel. Colorado mining towns are isolated and utterly dependent upon mining. All three Rocky Mountain provinces are sensitive to the federal government's policy toward gold and silver in the monetary system.

FIGURE 16-6: *Beef Cattle Grazing, Colorado*

This mountain pasture is on the Western Slope of the Colorado Rockies. (State of Colorado)

Agriculture. Grazing is the dominant phase of agriculture in the Southern Rockies. Transhumance is regularly practiced to take advantage of the vertical zoning of the vegetation; all of the plant zones are brought into use: sage brush and grass at the lower elevations, above that prairie grasses to about 8,000 feet, above this the open forest of pine, Douglas fir, larch, and lodgepole pine, and finally stunted vegetation above 10,000 feet. In all of the plant zones there is some vegetation suitable for sheep grazing at one time or another. Although there is no agricultural equivalent for the trench-like valleys of the Northern Rockies, the Colorado section has four extensive mountain "parks," which support many head of livestock, despite their aridity, elevation, and difficult approach. In North, Middle, and South Park, in the park-like San Luis, in the upper Arkansas, and lesser valleys, great numbers of Herefords and Shorthorns are grazed.

The range for cattle grazing is not so great as for sheep. The summer pastures for most of the cattle are on the foothills and lower slopes and the grassy parks. The dominant type of farm in all parks but the San Luis is forage-grazing, and will average from 1,500 to 2,000 acres in extent. As National Forest preserves were established in the surrounding mountains, the carrying power of the ranges was limited to safeguard the forest.

FIGURE 16-7: *Ashcroft, A "Ghost" Town*

Men with Geiger counters may pass through such "ghost" towns as this one at the margin of the Southern Rockies and the Colorado Plateau. (State of Colorado)

Since World War I, sheep grazing and the production of hay for shipment to other feeding areas have increased, while the number of cattle has decreased.

The fourth of the park lands of the Southern Rockies is the San Luis Valley, a broad bolson plain surrounded by high mountains except on the south, where the Rio Grande cuts a gorge just south of the Colorado-New Mexico line. Agriculturally this valley is more important than any of its northern park neighbors.

The economy of the San Luis Valley is based upon irrigated agriculture and the raising of livestock. The nature of the land-use varies with the availability of water and the racial background of the farmers. One county of 3,000 square miles occupies the northern half of the valley; except for irrigated sections along the mountain foothills on the west, it is given over to livestock ranching on a large scale.

The most populous irrigated sections are situated upon the alluvial fans made by the Rio Grande and its principal tributaries in the San Luis Valley. Iceberg lettuce is grown in the vicinity of Del Norte and along the flood plain of the Rio Grande canyon; the 8,000 foot elevation seems to aid in the development of crisp heads. The agricultural heart of the valley is in the Monte Vista-Center-Sargent region where alfalfa, potatoes, field peas, oats, hogs, cattle, and sheep constitute the basis of the farm economy. Pleasant farmsteads, adobe root cellars and the ever-present irrigation ditch set this region apart from the ranch-type of occupance farther south. Formerly hogs, and now lambs are fed upon field peas to bring top prices on Denver markets.

The southern counties have many Mexican farmers. More attention is given to such crops as broccoli, cabbage, cauliflower, garden peas, and potatoes. The summer pasturing of sheep on mountain grasslands has become an important phase of the farm economy in these southern counties, the flocks are wintered on alfalfa grown on the irrigated valley floor.

Agricultural development of the San Luis Valley has been limited by the amount of water for irrigation. A certain flow must be maintained in the Rio Grande River across the New Mexico border by international agreement. Storage dams have been built on the Rio Grande and tributary streams in the mountains; artesian wells supplement the water supply from mountain streams. Irrigation methods are generally simple; each year the ditches are plowed over and new ones built in the spring. Subirrigation is generally used with water seeping into the water table from the ditches. As in all irrigated regions, increasing alkalinity becomes an important problem.

Forests. Although approximately one-sixth of the area of Colorado is classed as national forest, this does not imply that commercial stands of timber are that extensive. The market for timber in the Southern Rockies is relatively large, owing to the demand of Denver and other cities of the Colorado Piedmont. Rocky Mountain forests have become an integral part of the flourishing tourist industry.

Manufacturing and Commerce. Within this province there is virtually no manufacturing beyond mineral reduction. Agriculture produces no surplus for manufacturing except in the San Luis Valley in the far south.

Leadville (4,081) processes zinc, lead, silver, and molybdenum ores. Molybdenum is the newcomer and enjoys something of a monopoly, since nearly 80 per cent of this alloying metal is mined at nearby Climax. This model town is rivaled in its creature comforts by no other mining center in the Rockies. In recent years, tungsten, tin, and pyrites have been recovered commercially.[2] Another mineral-processing center is the Cripple

[2] H. W. Davis, "Molybdenum," *Minerals Yearbook, 1953* (U.S. Dept. of the Interior, Washington), p. 785.

Creek gold district some 25 miles south of Leadville. In many of these old mining camps today's prospector is using his Geiger counter.

Alamosa (5,354) is the second-largest city in the Southern Rockies. It is the market center of the San Luis Valley and has developed dairy products manufacture, flour milling, meat packing, and vegetable freezing as a result of the Valley's agricultural productivity and access by rail to Pacific markets. Oil refining is the only industry outside of the foods group.

Tourist Industry. The Southern Rocky Mountains support an important tourist industry. One main reason is the spectacular nature of the alpine mountain landscapes. Another is the situation of the Southern Rockies with respect to main transcontinental trade routes. The Trail Ridge Road which crosses the Front Range west of Denver and again west of Estes Park is one of the thrilling automobile roads of the nation; Fall River Pass is above 12,000 and Berthoud Pass is above 10,000 feet. Rocky Mountain National Park, Gunnison National Park, and the Denver Mountain Parks are among the most popular on the continent. Pikes Peak, Longs Peak, and Mount Evans are well known to traveling Americans. Aspen, rich silver camp in the 1880's, has become a cultural center with music and educational programs, as well as a winter playground. A new highway has made part of the San Juans accessible to travelers.

BIBLIOGRAPHY

Bishop, O. M., and E. B. Miller, "Zinc," *Minerals Yearbook, 1951* (U.S. Dept. of the Interior, Washington), pp. 1319-1344.

——, and E. E. den Hartog, "Lead," *Minerals Yearbook, 1951* (U.S. Dept. of the Interior, Washington), pp. 738-759.

Critchfield, Howard J., "Land Use Levels in Boundary County, Idaho," *Economic Geography*, Vol. 24, No. 3 (July, 1948), pp. 201-208.

Drake, G. L., F. C. Simmons, and E. E. Matson, "Improvements in Logging Techniques in the United States," *Proceedings of the United Nations Scientific Conference on the Conservation and Utilization of Resources*, Vol. 5 (1951), pp. 234-242.

Geehan, R. W., "Molybdenum," *Minerals Yearbook, 1951* (U.S. Dept. of the Interior, Washington), pp. 856-864.

Hoffmeister, Harold A., "Middle Park and the Colorado-Big Thompson Diversion Project," *Economic Geography*, Vol. 23, No. 3 (July, 1947), pp. 220-231.

Lackey, Earl E., "Mountain Passes in the Colorado Rockies," *Economic Geography*, Vol. 25, No. 3 (July, 1949), pp. 211-215.

Meyer, H. M., and G. N. Greenspoon, "Copper," *Minerals Yearbook, 1951* (U.S. Dept. of the Interior, Washington), pp. 521-556.

CHAPTER 17

WESTERN INTERMONTANE AREA

PHYSICAL SETTING

THE PHYSIOGRAPHIC PROVINCES comprising the Intermontane Area exhibit a great variety of physical landscapes. In the present character of their occupance and in the history of their development, these areas have manifested many fundamental contrasts. This is accounted for in part by the availability of water resources in this generally arid region, and in part to institutional factors in settlement. Although newspapers in Salt Lake City refer to this area as the Intermountain Empire, its representatives in the Congress do not always vote as regional associates; they sometimes vote with their mountain neighbors. Yet there is ample reason for the treatment of these areas as one broad geographic region, despite the diversity.

In no other part of the United States is the proportion of federal-owned land so great (*Fig.* 17-2). It is by no means uncommon for private interests to be incensed at the public policies with respect to water, grass, forests, and power. Although public ownership does not mean that the discovery and exploitation of a mineral resource return no income to the state, the share varies with the resource.

Three large plateaus and basins comprise this vast Intermontane Area: the Columbia Plateau, Colorado Plateau, and the Basin and Range Province (*Fig.* 17-1).

Climate. The climate of the basins and plateaus of the Intermontane Area is the principal physical bond among its several sections. All of the area is dry, in part due to elevation, its interior location, the mountains which virtually surround it, and the poleward migration of the subtropical calm belt. It is classed as steppe for the most part, with desert conditions

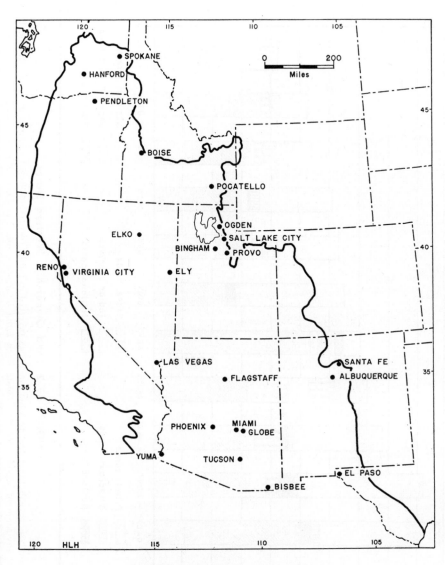

FIGURE 17-1: *Intermontane Area*

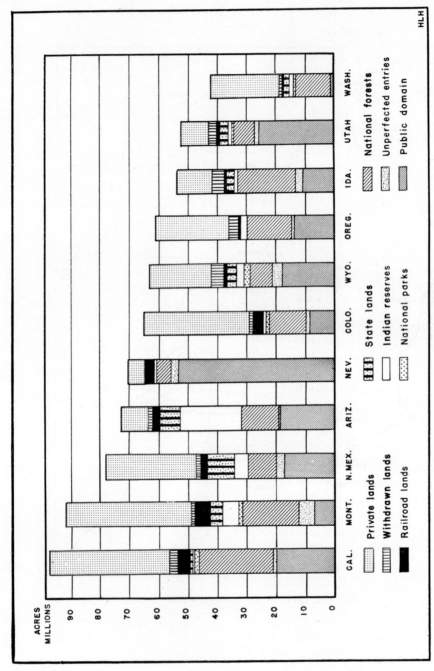

FIGURE 17-2: Land Ownership, Western States

This graphic analysis reveals the extent to which land has reverted to public ownership. Legal circumstances of settlement as well as the physical environment account for this. (Data from *Land Utilization and the Farm Problem*, U.S. Dept. of Agriculture, Miscel. Pub. 97, Washington, 1930) southward from the middle portions of the Great Basin. There has never been any doubt about its aridity; no cycles of humid climate attracted settlers unwisely as in the Great Plains. Yet there are indications of the arid climate being something of an asset as well as a liability, at least in certain districts.

These basins do not have so much rainfall as the Plains, nor is its distribution the same, except in New Mexico and Arizona, where a summer maximum exists that is as marked as on the Great Plains. All of the northern half of the province has a slight winter maximum. Precipitation is not uniform year after year, but there is none of the same pronounced cycles which characterize Great Plains climate. The northern portion receives from 10 to 18 inches, the amount decreasing toward the south. The cool temperatures of the relatively high altitude and latitude reduce evaporation in the northern portion.

The Cascades cast a rain shadow of considerable extent along their eastern margin on the Columbia Plateau; its effect is increased because of the low elevation of the Plateau near the junction of the Snake and Columbia rivers. Rainfall here is only 6 inches; most of the Plateau receives about 10 inches. Another district of low rainfall is the plain of the Snake River in southern Idaho where annual precipitation is from 10 to 13 inches.

The southern half of the Intermontane province is generally classed as desert, owing to the low rainfall and the generally high rate of evaporation associated with its latitude. In southeastern California, desert conditions prevail over an area extending as far east as the Arizona Highlands and south into Mexico.

Temperatures reflect the effect of altitude and the mountain periphery, particularly in the northern portion. The growing season is longest in the lower parts of the Columbia Plateau, where it is from 130 to 210 days, depending upon the altitude. Just west of this low center of the Plateau, in the folded ridges and valleys of the Yakima, east of it in the Palouse Hills, and southwest of it in the Deschutes Plateau, the growing season is from 80 to 200 days. Farther south in the Basin and Range Province, where elevations are greater, the growing season is from 80 to 150 days.

The extremes in elevation, from below sea-level in southern California to 7,000 feet above, and the very great variety of land forms and of soils, greatly affect the usefulness of rainfall. Night temperatures are lowered, and the growing season is shortened by the relatively high altitudes. Winds are noticeably less severe throughout this province than on the Great Plains, although wind erosion is a problem.

The proportion of irrigated land to the total area of the Intermontane region is very low indeed. Where irrigation is practiced it is not primarily in response to local need for the crops grown, but for distant markets both East and West.

Columbia Plateau. Westward from the Northern Rockies stretch nearly 200,000 square miles of lava-covered country which exhibits a great variety of landforms and soils. Continuing until recent times, geologically, fluid lavas have at a dozen or more intervals, risen to the surface through fissures and covered the then existing surface. In the Snake River Plain the flows are especially recent, as in Craters-of-the-Moon National Park.

The Columbia Plateau has older and more spectacular landscapes in the Walla Walla, Blue Mountain, and Payette sections (*Fig.* 1-2). At the point where the Snake River descends into the Columbia River, the elevation is about 500 feet; from this point the Plateau rises toward the west, north, and east. West of the lowland center of the Columbia River Basin are the Yakima ridges and valleys; on the north are the Channeled Scablands; on the east are the Palouse Hills; and on the south are the Blue Mountains. In southwestern Idaho is a dissected plateau known as the Payette section. The Grand Coulee project, heart of the water-control plan for the Columbia River system, was made possible during the Pleistocene Period when a gigantic ice sheet obstructed the course of the Columbia River, forcing the river to cut a new channel at a point in the present state of Washington about 150 miles from the Canadian border. When the ice receded, the river resumed its former channel, leaving its emergency outlet as an arid canyon some 50 miles in length. This abandoned channel is the Grand Coulee. The dam is, in a sense, a substitute for the glacier; the block of masonry is considerably longer than Boulder Dam but it is not so high. Power is being developed, irrigation made possible, and flood control furthered by this immense project. A steady flow of water down the Columbia will improve navigation and increase power output at Bonneville Dam, located where the Columbia breaches the Cascade Mountains.

The main objective of the Grand Coulee system is irrigation; all other benefits derived are supplementary. Water for irrigation purposes is pumped from Lake Roosevelt which reaches to the Canadian border 150 miles away. The water is pumped to an equalizing reservoir which feeds a canal to the irrigable portion of the Columbia Basin to the south, an area estimated at 1,200,000 acres of productive land, now mainly used for grazing and marginal wheat growing. The by-product of power from this and the Bonneville Dam has raised the Northwest's proportion of the nation's developed waterpower by about 20 per cent. The benefits of Grand Coulee accrue also through a firm flow at Chief Joseph, Rock Island, McNary, and the Dallas dams. All are on the Columbia downstream from Grand Coulee (*Fig.* 17-6).

The Channeled Scablands embrace a large area once dissected by the Columbia River during the period of ice-blocking. As a storage reservoir, the old channel of the Columbia is strategically useful in the consummation of the Columbia River Plan.

The Bonneville Dam does not lie in the Intermontane Area, but its development with the Grand Coulee project seems to make appropriate its treatment here. It facilitates transportation between the Columbia Basin and the Pacific Coast by enabling large ocean vessels to go as far as the Dalles of the Columbia River, and it has made possible increased power development.

Basin and Range Province. The second of the Intermontane provinces is the very extensive Basin and Range Province. It may be subdivided into five sections: Great Basin, Sonoran Desert, Salton Trough, Open Basin, and Sacramento Mountains in the far southeast.

The Great Basin embraces all of Nevada, most of western Utah, and a portion of southern Oregon and Idaho. This province is characterized by hundreds of roughly parallel fault-block ranges trending north-south. These structurally-tilted blocks of the earth's crust rise from 3,000 to 5,000 feet above the valleys which are partially filled with sediments carried from the mountains. Rapid runoff promotes extensive erosion which provides the sediments for deposition.

Drainage of the Great Basin is interior. A major stream, the Humboldt River, seeps into the ground before reaching a body of water. Ephemeral lakes are formed at many places in the Basin each year. If fresh water, as few of them are, they are called playa lakes; if salt, they are called salinas. In glacial times two very large lakes occupied the northern portion of the Basin, Lahontan in the west and Bonneville in the Great Salt Lake area. Lake Winemucca, Pyramid Lake, and Walker Lake are remnants of the former; Great Salt Lake, Utah Lake, and Sevier Lake cover only a small part of the area once occupied by Lake Bonneville. With the exception of Utah Lake, their basins and those of the short-lived ephemeral lakes are alkaline.

In the far southwest of the Great Basin is Death Valley, a depression only partially filled by sediments from the adjacent ranges. It is known chiefly for its altitude (270 feet below sea level) and for its inactive borax workings.

Immediately south of the Great Basin lies the Sonoran Desert section, similar to its northern neighbor but with more completely dissected ranges and wider valleys. It is drained by the Colorado River and its tributary, the Gila. Although it is more arid than the Great Basin, these surface streams permit some irrigated agriculture. The Salton Trough lies athwart the lower Colorado River where the international boundary divides the Colorado delta into more or less equal parts. Until the completion of the All-American Canal diverting water from the river into nearby Imperial Valley, water was brought in by way of the Mexican portion of the delta.

ECONOMY OF THE COLUMBIA PLATEAU

Forests and Minerals. There are no important commercial minerals mined in the Columbia Plateau, although mineral industries are represented by the aluminum-refining and fabricating industry in several Plateau cities. Forest land is found in some parts of the Plateau in Washington and Oregon, but virtually all of the lumber-products industry is based upon the white pine forests of the Northern Rocky Mountains.

Agriculture. The region was settled late in our history; the first major settlement was under the auspices of the Mormon Church. Their organized reclamation was based on irrigation and was by no means confined to the Salt Lake oasis. From New Mexico northward to Idaho, the Mormon pioneers founded and have maintained an irrigated agricultural economy, but the larger area by far is dry-farmed (*Fig.* 17-3).

Wheat. There are three major wheat-growing areas: the Palouse Hills, the Big Bend country, and the Snake River Plain. The Palouse area is a steeply rolling upland of loess soils which has been in the center of winter- and spring-wheat production in the Northwest. In this subhumid region, there are definite limits to the cropping system. Diminishing yields and erosion have forced some such rotation as the following on the 500-acre farms: sweet clover for the first and second years, winter wheat the third year, spring wheat the fourth year, fallow the fifth year, and winter wheat the sixth year. In the Palouse area wheat yields are much higher than the national average, 25 to 50 bushels as compared to 12 to 15 bushels.[1] Yields have been declining somewhat in recent years.

[1] See John H. Garland, "The Columbia Plateau Region of Commercial Grain Farming," *Geographical Review,* Vol. 24 (1934), pp. 371-379.

The Big Bend wheat district is north of the Palouse region and is in contrast chiefly because of its level to gently rolling terrain, its much larger farm units (1,600 acres), and the smaller proportion of cropped land. Mechanization of wheat farming took place earlier here than on the hilly Palouse. Crop failure is more frequent, fluctuation in cropped land much greater, and wheat farming is more of an industry in the Big Bend country of the Columbia than in the more important wheat region to the south. On the western margin, some wheat is being grown by irrigation. The yields (30 to 70 bushels per acre) in irrigated areas are generally higher than in the dry farming sections. Irrigated wheat constitutes 5 per cent of all northwestern wheat.

The third wheat-growing district is the Snake River Plain in southern Idaho. Some of the wheat grown in this valley is under irrigation. The proportion of land in fallow is therefore lower than elsewhere in the North-

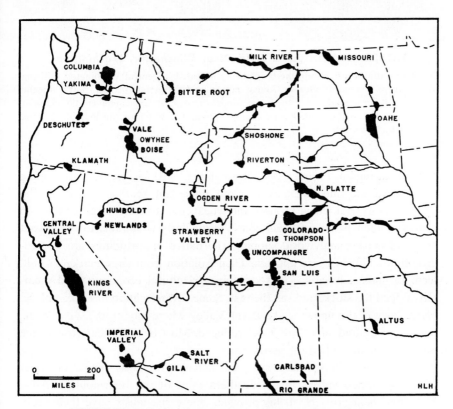

FIGURE 17-3: *Irrigation Projects, Western United States*

This is a generalized map of the major irrigation districts of the West.

FIGURE 17-4: Irrigated Field, Near Winchester, Washington

Beans and alfalfa are among the crops being irrigated in central Washington utilizing waters from the great Grand Coulee power and irrigation project north on the Columbia River. Canals bring the water south where secondary canals (in the picture) transport water to the field. Plastic tubing siphons the water to the individual rows. (HENRY L. HUNKER)

west wheat region. Farms are much smaller (100-175 acres), the cropping is more varied, and livestock is more important than elsewhere in the wheat regions. But wheat farmers and wheat industrialists have one thing in common: their means of livelihood is particularly vulnerable to the impact of world market and world supply. Alternative opportunities are exceedingly limited in these dry uplands. Their isolation from large markets would seem to make advisable a self-sufficing agricultural economy: feed themselves, feed the stock, and sell the rest. Some diversification has taken place, particularly in the upper Snake River Valley where hay crops, sugar beets, poultry, fruit, and sheep are now produced. Most of the wheat grown here is soft and better suited for pastry flour.

Fruit Crops. Unlike the great wheat acreage, orchards appear in rather widely separated valleys in the northern third of the Intermontane Area. Like the wheat growers of this province, these specialists have their problems of marketing a product so many thousand miles from its ultimate consumer. Fallow land in the orchard districts is not a sign of the cropping system as it is in wheat; rather it is evidence of reduction in fruit acreage and a temporary abandonment of farm land. Irrigation is practiced in virtually all of these orchard districts.

Across the ridges on the western margin of the Columbia Plateau, the Yakima brings water from the crests of the high Cascades to irrigate orchards of apple trees, 2 million of them. The Yakima Valley also grows cherries and vegetables and raises hogs. North of the Yakima Valley are other apple-growing districts; the Wenatchee Valley in Washington, and Okanogan Valley in British Columbia. South of the Yakima, across the Columbia River, is yet another, the Hood River Valley. These four districts also grow pears, potatoes, and vegetables, with diversification greatest in the Yakima Valley. Three smaller districts in Washington also specialize in apples: Spokane Valley, Touchet Valley, and the White-Salmon-Stevenson valleys on the east slope of the Cascades. Varieties of apples differ from district to district, but in general Winesap, Delicious, McIntosh, Yellow Newtons, and Spitzenbergs are the more numerous. Color distinguishes these apples from similar Eastern varieties.

Although high color, perfect fruit, and large size guaranteed by the co-operatives have made the job of the advertising copy writer easy, these fruit growers have their troubles. Two world wars cut off a large part of the export markets. Eastern fruit districts, in an effort to better their position, have adopted many of the marketing measures employed by northwestern fruit growers, with the result that their fruit has raised its competitive value. The cost of pipe, irrigation, control of insect pests, and scarcity of labor have all raised costs in these northwestern valleys.

Other Crop Areas. An important mixed agricultural district is the irrigated Snake River Valley in southern Idaho. Alfalfa, potatoes, wheat, sugar beets, and some fruit are raised in the eastern portion. Pocatello, Twin Falls, and American Falls are agricultural trading centers, each in an irrigated district. The American Falls dam irrigates what may still be the longest continuous irrigated section in the West. Farther west, near the Oregon boundary, there is less diversification; alfalfa leads, but apples are second. The root or apple cellar is a conspicuous feature of every community. The Idaho baking potato is probably as well known as the Washington apple. Potato production is about two-thirds that of Maine. This is the only one of the Columbia Plateau farming districts to have an important livestock industry. In these districts, as throughout most of the Intermontane country, sheep are more important than beef cattle. Transhumance is practiced with summer grazing on the high ranges and winter feeding on alfalfa grown under irrigation in the valleys (*Fig.* 17-5).

Peas have become an important field crop in the wheat-growing lands, particularly the Palouse district. Peas are tolerant of the low rainfall and are susceptible of mechanization. The crop is a legume and is important in this erstwhile one-crop wheat country, occupying land that otherwise would be in fallow. Within the pea-growing area there is some specialization; the Blue Mountain district raises peas only for local canning, whereas the Palouse area specializes in seed peas, ranking first in the nation.

Cities of the Columbia Plateau. There are few cities in the Columbia Plateau Province. All of them except the small city of Hanford, Washington, are basically commercial. Manufacturing industries have come to many of them, usually based upon the processing of agricultural surplus, timber or sometimes minerals. The economic capital of this "inland empire" is *Spokane* (161,721) near the eastern margin of the Plateau. Reversing its recent trend, Spokane increased in population by nearly one-third between 1940 and 1950. Flour milling, manufacture of timber products, mineral

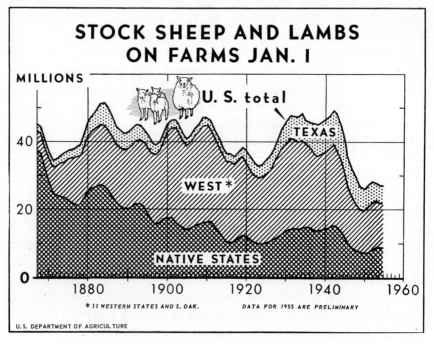

FIGURE 17-5

Western sheep are important both relatively and absolutely. Approximately half of the nation's sheep are raised on the plateaus and mountains of the West.

processing, vegetable freezing, and rolling aluminum contribute to a greater industrial diversity than is usual in Columbia Plateau cities.

Directly south of Spokane in the Big Bend country are Walla Walla, Washington, and Pendleton, Oregon. *Walla Walla* (24,102) is representative of livestock industry centers. Its manufacture of wool and leather goods are nationally famous. Hanford is the site of an atomic energy installation. *Lewiston* (12,985), in the more rugged portion of the Snake River Valley, is reported to have the largest white-pine mill in the world.

In the irrigated Snake River Valley of southern Idaho are *Pocatello* (26,131), *Twin Falls* (17,600), *Idaho Falls* (19,218), and *American Falls* (10,000). They have beet-sugar refining, flourmilling, fruit canning, and the manufacture of starch from culls of the famed Idaho Russet potato crop. Pocatello has varied this combination of industries with a large naval ordnance plant.

Future. A glance at *Fig.* 17-6 will reveal something of the pattern of future utilization of the Columbia River system. Power development and the attraction of manufacturing industries in the Northwest are often taken for granted by eastern people. Often the engineering and economic factors are favorable for water storage but political or regional conflicts sometimes prove insuperable.

Some industry has come to the Columbia Plateau and population has increased, but provision for supplementing the low natural flow of streams during the eight-months period of water storage depletion has remained in the planning stage for the most part. Grand Coulee Dam was completed before World War II, but since then only Hungry Horse Dam (*Fig.* 16-3) has been completed, and only Albeni Falls Dam started, in the plan for storing water upstream in the Columbia River system. It is reported that power requirements have nearly reached the limit with present storage capacity. The industrial centers of the Northwest, including both the Plateau and the Puget Sound region, now import all of the petroleum, most of the coal, and some of the electric power consumed.[2]

ECONOMY OF THE BASIN AND RANGE PROVINCE

Mineral Industries. A great variety and, in some instances, a great abundance of minerals are found in the Basin and Range Province. While gold and silver brought many people into these interior basins in early times,

[2] M. E. Marts, "Upstream Storage Problems in the Columbia River Power Development," *Annals Assn. of American Geographers,* Vol. 44, No. 1 (March, 1954), pp. 43-50.

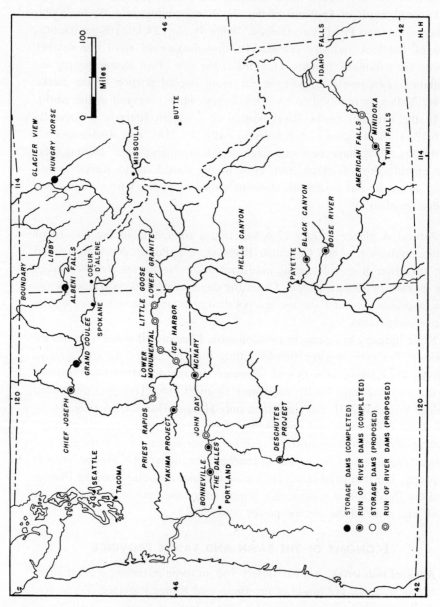

FIGURE 17-6: Columbia River Basin

STORAGE DAMS (COMPLETED)
RUN OF RIVER DAMS (COMPLETED)
STORAGE DAMS (PROPOSED)
RUN OF RIVER DAMS (PROPOSED)

Miles
0   100

Agriculture. The Salt Lake oasis is the largest irrigated farming district in the Intermontane Area; other oases in the Basin and Range Province are Reno-Carson City, parts of the Humboldt and San Juan basins, and Mesilla, Coachella, and Yuma valleys. Salt Lake oasis cities and towns extend for more than 200 miles along the front of the Wasatch Mountains in central Utah. The water for irrigation and urban uses comes from melting snow and the heavier rainfall of the lofty Wasatch range.

Salt Lake Oasis. After a 500-mile drive over the semiarid plains and plateaus on the east, to drop down the west slope of the mountains into the man-made green of Salt Lake City is indeed an experience. Wide streets, modern shops, and some high buildings bear testimony to the profits from commerce which had its beginning with Mormon outfitting in 1849.

The agricultural economy of this oasis sets it apart from all other irrigated districts of the Intermontane Area, not so much in the nature of the crops grown as the conditions under which they are produced and marketed. Co-operation stems from the early and continued efforts of the Mormon Church to arouse an enthusiasm for co-operative organization. Physical insularity, strong co-operatives, and a population of a quarter-of-a-million people have given to the oasis a self-sufficiency conspicuously lacking in all but the Mormon-irrigated communities. Here it amounts to a way of life. As in other irrigated communities, alfalfa and livestock constitute the principal emphasis of the agricultural economy; sheep, cattle, and hogs, rank in that order. Wheat, oats, barley, sugar beets, peaches, apples, apricots, vegetables, and dairy products also are produced.

To bring about an agricultural occupance such as obtains here, great capital investment has been required. The Mormon Church initiated most of the projects, but has retained control of only a few. The co-operatives have been strong enough to carry on the management of the diversified economy. The ruin of many irrigated communities throughout the West has been due to the general unfamiliarity with this type of farming and to overproduction. These pitfalls the Mormon pioneer irrigationists have largely avoided. During the period of inflated markets incidental to World War I, the oasis farmers did overspecialize. Since then, diversification of crops, re-emphasis upon craft industries of many kinds, and general belt-tightening restored self-sufficiency in the Salt Lake oasis. World War II completed the restoration and brought in more manufacturing.

Imperial Valley. Another irrigated area of major importance is the Imperial Valley in southern California· This portion of the Colorado River delta is irrigated with water brought in from the Colorado River. Two major improvements have been made: construction of the Hoover Dam near Las

FIGURE 17-8: *Hoover Dam, Colorado River*

Between the start and the completion of Hoover Dam on the Colorado River, the need for water in southern California had trebled. (U.S. Bureau of Reclamation, photo by HARRY MYERS)

Vegas, Nevada, and diversion of Colorado water by way of an all-American Canal which supersedes one which took an easier grade across part of the Mexican portion of the delta plain (*Fig.* 17-8).

The development of the Imperial Valley has been a spectacular project, first because of its size (450,000 acres), and second because of its remarkably sustained growth. This is the more to be wondered at since it has a desert climate with very high temperatures and an elevation of 246 feet below sea level. Lettuce and cantaloupes are the leading exports, with cotton ranking second, then citrus fruit, and finally dairy products. Remote as the region is, its hold on eastern markets seems to be reasonably secure because of its ability to market fresh fruits and vegetables as early as December.

Dairying in a region where there is no natural pasture must, of course, be a late development. The extraordinary growth of Los Angeles, San Diego, and other southern California cities during and since World War II has given rise to an expanding market for fluid milk and creamery products. Land values near these densely populated areas are too high to permit their utilization for dairying. Postwar increases in manufacturing for a peacetime market have greatly stimulated the sales of dairy products.

Salt River Valley. Not far away in the Salt River Valley of central Arizona is another irrigated district of more than average success. Construction of the Roosevelt Dam in 1910, some 70 miles northeast of Phoenix, enabled the extension of irrigated acreage (500,000) with water from the Salt River. The specialties of this district are similar to those of the Imperial Valley; long staple cotton is more important and dairying is much less important than in other irrigated communities throughout the Intermontane Area. Fruits of several kinds are also grown on an important scale.

Rio Grande. The physiographic diversity of the Rio Grande Valley seems to typify the nature of the Intermontane basins as a whole. For the first hundred miles, the Rio Grande flows east as a Rocky Mountain stream, until it enters the San Luis Valley, an extensive flat area of 7,500 feet elevation. As a Basin and Range stream it flows for 300 miles through a series of basins to El Paso at 3,800 feet.[3] The growing season ranges from 95 days in the northern San Luis Valley to 120 days at the Colorado-New Mexican boundary, and to 200 days in southern New Mexico. Clear sunny days are the rule throughout the entire valley. Rainfall averages 10 inches, with a slight summer maximum.

The southward extension of the Rio Grande depression, unlike the San

[3] Elephant Butte Dam, some 70 miles above El Paso, stores water to irrigate a long strip of floodplain to the south.

Luis Valley farther north, is a deeply dissected surface with little to commend it for agriculture. Just below the New Mexico boundary this section is
known as the Taos Plateau. Isolated Indian pueblos characterize its population distribution. Agriculture generally is of the subsistence type and is confined to the irrigated portions of the Rio Grande floodplain.

Still farther south in the valley, for perhaps 90 miles north and south,
Albuquerque, in the Middle Rio Grande Conservation District, is successor
to the many small irrigation systems which were scattered along this portion
of the valley. Cotton and alfalfa have become the leading crops in most of
the area, with the former now dominant. The hay has long been the basis
for feeding sheep and cattle pastured on the dry hills. A dairy industry is
being built on alfalfa as markets permit. Vegetables and fruit have been
grown for local consumption primarily; only melons and tomatoes have
secured much of an outside market.

Just above the mouth of the Rio Grande River are the irrigated citrus-
growing districts about Harlingen, Laredo, San Benito, and Brownsville
which were discussed in the chapter on the South. The number and importance of similar irrigated oases in the Open Basin country to the west are
increasing. Some of the labor-saving machines used in harvesting vegetables
are seen nowhere else. Fertile soil, sunshine and warm climate, controlled
water supply, and a rapidly-growing market are largely responsible for this
rapid development.

Cities of the Basin and Range Area. *Salt Lake City* (182,121), *Ogden*
(57,112), *Provo* (28,937), and *Logan* (16,832) are all located on the narrow, irrigated plain between the Wasatch Mountains and Great Salt Lake
(*Fig.* 17-9). No cities in all the Intermontane Area have grown more vigorously since 1941. The first phase of development was begun by the Mor-
mons a year before gold was discovered in California. The outfitting of
westward-moving settlers was followed by regular commerce over this
natural east-west trade route.

The coming of the Union Pacific Railroad ushered in the second phase of
development. Rail accessibility has put the Salt Lake communities in line
for a share of the trade that resulted from the development of the Pacific
Coast.

Although Salt Lake is the largest city, the location of Ogden, farther north
and closer to the canyon through which the railroads come from the East,
has made this the railroad center of the oasis. For slaughtering, flour milling, meat packing, and freight classification yards Ogden is superior to all
other cities on the oasis. Ogden stockyards handle sheep and cattle on a scale

FIGURE 17-9: *Salt Lake City*

Salt Lake City and its sister cities both north and south mark the oases which lie between the Wasatch Range and Great Salt Lake. (Salt Lake City Chamber of Commerce)

that makes it comparable to St. Louis. Salt Lake City is the principal trading center for all of the Mormon communities between Montana and New Mexico. It also serves much of the Intermontane Area. One of the largest merchandising warehouses in the United States handles everything a Utah farmer may need from steel "I" beams to pharmaceuticals.

Although Salt Lake City has long been a manufacturer of wool, steel products, and a score of commodities needed as food or other daily necessity, it was not until World War II that the district became one of the major manufacturers of primary iron and steel (*Fig.* 17-10). Iron ore for this great Geneva plant comes from Iron Mountain, 225 miles to the southwest. Limestone is quarried at Payseur, 35 miles distant. Bituminous coal of coking quality is mined in Horse Canyon, 120 miles to the southeast. Although built by the government to make plate for Pacific Coast shipyards, its conversion to peacetime production by a private corporation has been successful. The market still includes the West Coast industrial cities, but it is not for shipyards. Manufacturing has grown and greatly diversified in southern California, and the Salt Lake oasis profits from the increased industrial market.

FIGURE 17-10: *Steel Plant, Provo, Utah*

This integrated steel plant was built by the federal government during World War II. It has since come into private hands, has been expanded, and continues to make steel for the Pacific Coast, primarily. Ore, coal, and limestone come from southern Utah, see *Fig.* 3-2. The patterned farmland and nearby cities may be seen in the photograph, ringed by mountains of the Wasatch Range. (United States Steel Corp.)

Although by no means confined to the Salt Lake oasis, the tourist industry has long been an important aspect of Salt Lake City's economy.

ECONOMY OF THE COLORADO PLATEAU

Agriculture. One of the most important agricultural areas of these Intermontane basins are the valleys of the Colorado Plateau, most of them are in the northern portion, known as the "Western Slope" of Colorado. This portion of the Colorado Plateau embraces the drainage basins of two principal streams, the Colorado and Gunnison rivers. Although settlement began during the 1880's the relative isolation of most of these valleys has retarded their development. Here are deep valleys with productive soils and water for irrigation. The latitude and the relatively low elevation favor the growth of a wide variety of temperate-zone fruits for distant markets.

Grand Junction, a city of almost 15,000, is the principal market and commercial center of the Western Slope. It is situated at the junction of the Colorado and Gunnison rivers at an elevation of 4,600 feet (comparable to

Salt Lake City). The river plains produce large crops of sugar beets, hay, melons, grains, vegetables, and many kinds of fruit: apples, peaches, cherries, grapes, apricots, and strawberries. An impressive tonnage of these products is moved out over the scenic route of the Denver, Rio Grande and Western Railroad to Denver or Salt Lake City, and reshipped to eastern markets. Yields are good and the prospect of rapidly growing markets in the urban areas of the Pacific Coast would seem to give these interior valleys a bright future.

Another of these specialized valleys is the Uncompahgre, irrigated with water diverted from the Gunnison River by means of the six-mile Gunnison Tunnel. Crops grown are much the same as in the Grand Junction area. Along the upper reaches of the valleys both sheep and cattle are grazed. The Western Slope, for all of its intensive crop agriculture, remains the most important sheep range in Colorado.

South of the very deeply dissected canyon country of the Western Slope in Colorado and Utah, the Plateau is much less dissected and therefore less formidable. The Indian Country may be said to lie between the San Juan and Little Colorado rivers on the Plateau of northern New Mexico and Arizona. Its general inaccessibility has undoubtedly contributed to the persistence of its ancient Indian occupance, as well as to the sparse white settlement. Down from the highest Plateau elevations with a mountain-like climate and ponderosa pine forests, through the middle elevations with piñon-juniper woodland type of forest, through scanty grasslands of the lower elevations, and to the arid flats or washes is the vertical setting for several centuries of human occupance.

For many, mostly whites, the moderate temperatures, 15 inches of rainfall, and piñon-juniper woodland of the middle elevations offered the more inviting and accessible home. For most of the 40,000 Indians, Navajos and Hopi, the scanty grassland and the dry washes with infrequent water sources, constituted the basis of an economy and a home. Periodic trips to the timbered elevations for nuts and for wood have been persistent aspects of a pastoral-agricultural life. Unfortunately, periodic trips to the nation's capital now also appear to be a necessity for the satisfaction of these Indian agriculturalists.

Forests. The saw-timber stands of ponderosa pine on the highest elevations have become the basis for the most important commercial lumbering in the Southwest. Inaccessibility retarded the development of this industry until fairly recent times.

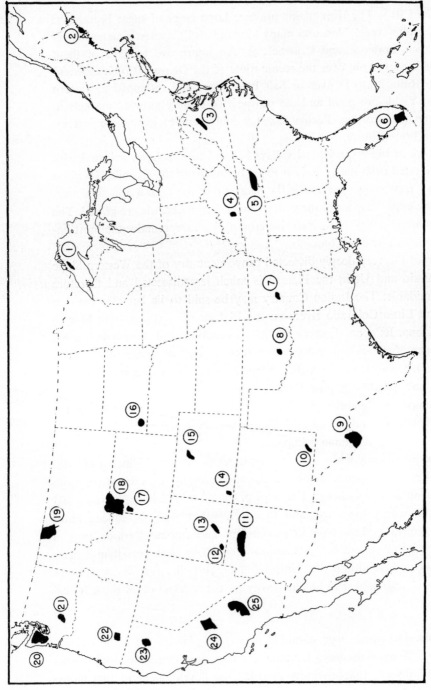

FIGURE 17-11: National Parks in the United States

(1) Isle Royale, (2) Acadia, (3) Shenandoah, (4) Mammoth Cave, (5) Great Smoky Mountains, (6) Everglades, (7) Hot Springs, (8) Platt, (9) Big Bend, (10) Carlsbad Caverns, (11) Grand Canyon, (12) Zion, (13) Bryce, (14) Mesa Verde, (15) Rocky Mountain, (16) Wind Cave, (17) Grand Teton, (18) Yellowstone, (19) Glacier, (20) Olympic, (21) Mount Rainier, (22) Crater Lake, (23) Lassen, (24) Yosemite, (25) Sequoia

428

FIGURE 17-12: *Oil Refinery, Rifle, Colorado*

This demonstration or pilot shale oil refinery of the Colorado Bureau of Mines has passed into private hands. It is the nation's first commercial producer of oil from the very extensive shale deposits of the Western Slope of Colorado and adjacent states. (Bureau of Mines, U.S. Dept. of Interior)

Minerals. The minerals of the Colorado Plateau have become relatively important only in recent years, although they have long played a minor role in its economy. The most extensive by far are the vast beds of oil shales in the northern part of the Plateau in Colorado. A government-owned pilot plant for distillation of shale has recently been superseded by a much larger and more advanced type of plant for oil shale treatment. The future will be determined largely by the trend in petroleum discoveries elsewhere and by the company which leases or buys this facility (*Fig. 17-12*).

Northward from Grand Junction are extensive beds of bituminous and some anthracite coal. Utah coals dominate the Intermontane market for bituminous coal. South of this city are deposits of copper, lead, zinc, silver, and vanadium, presently of minor importance.

Latest of the minerals to stimulate the economy of the Colorado Plateau is uranium. The United States continues to be dependent on foreign sources for the major portion of its uranium supply, but domestic production ranks this country second only to the Belgian Congo. Most of the domestic supply comes from the Colorado Plateau, with some from the Black Hills

429

and from the phosphate deposits of Florida, Utah, Idaho, Wyoming, and Montana.

While the uranium deposits of the Colorado Plateau are not as high in quality as that of the Belgian Congo, their extent is much greater than was realized even in 1952. Most of these deposits are of the carnotite type, although pitchblende (80 per cent uranium oxide) is being mined a few miles west of the Plateau in the Marysville, Utah, section.

While most of the mining once was from rims of canyons, or through inclined shafts, many mines have begun to sink vertical shafts, some as deep as 600 feet. There are approximately 530 mines on the Colorado Plateau, most of which employ fewer than ten men. In 1954 these mines shipped some 10 tons of ore daily; the Atomic Energy Commission states in 1955 that production is doubling every 18 months. Among the mines are such companies as Lehigh Coal and Navigation Company, Climax Molybdenum Company, and Anaconda Copper Mining Company; there is nothing provincial about the uranium industry.

There were in January, 1955, 9 mills for processing this ore located on the Plateau, and the A.E.C. indicates that additional mills will be built at Moab and Hite, Utah, and at Bedrock, Colorado. Most of the mills process from 200,000 to 300,000 tons of ore each year and employ from 150 to 250 men. The mills in Colorado handle mostly vanadium-uranium type ores, while the mill at Grants handles limestone deposits.

Population of the Plateau cities and towns has increased since 1950; Grand Junction has increased one-tenth; Montecello one-fifth; Rifle and Durango one-third; Moab one-and-a-half times. The Bureau of Business Research of the University of New Mexico estimated the 1950-1953 increase in population in McKinley and San Juan counties, New Mexico, at 18 and 56 per cent, respectively. In addition to mining, the development of natural gas reserves in San Juan County has been important.

BIBLIOGRAPHY

BROWN, Ralph H., *Historical Geography of the United States* (New York, Harcourt, Brace and Company, 1948), Chap. 26.

GRANDSTAFF, J. O., "Adaptation of Livestock to New Environments," *Proceedings of the United Nations Conference on the Conservation and Utilization of Resources,* Vol. 6 (1951), pp. 424-427.

HOFFMEISTER, Harold A., "Alkali Problem of Western United States," *Economic Geography,* Vol. 23, No. 1 (Jan., 1947), pp. 1-9.

Irrigation Agriculture in the West, Miscel. Publ. No. 670 (U.S. Dept. of Agriculture, Washington, 1948).

LEMONS, Hoyt and Rayburn TOUSLEY, "Washington Apple Industry: Its Geographic Basis," *Economic Geography,* Vol. 21 (1945), pp. 161-182.

MARR, Norman, "The Columbia River Basin," *Canadian Geographical Journal,* Vol. 25, No. 2 (Aug. 1952), pp. 68-83.

MILLER, Elbert E. and R. M. HIGHSMITH, "Geography of the Fruit Industry of the Yakima Valley, Washington," *Economic Geography,* Vol. 25, No. 4 (Oct., 1949), pp. 285-295.

PARKER, Margaret T., "Tucson: City of Sunshine," *Economic Geography,* Vol. 24, No. 2 (April, 1948), pp. 79-113.

Water for Utah (Utah Water and Power Board, Salt Lake City, July, 1948).

WRIGLEY, Robert, Jr., "Pocatello, Idaho, As a Railroad Center," *Economic Geography,* Vol. 19 (1943), pp. 326-336.

CHAPTER 18

PACIFIC VALLEYS AND RANGES

ALTHOUGH WHITE SETTLEMENT began on the Pacific Coast nearly a century after that on the Atlantic, it was only a little more than one hundred years ago that the former experienced the first of a series of fundamental changes which have made the rest of the nation acutely aware of the Pacific realm. Upon a nation whose economic characteristics largely reflected the resources of the humid eastern-half, came successive impacts of Pacific resources: gold, fish, timber, and petroleum. These resources were not all unique to the Pacific Coast, but each proved to be a powerful stimulus to the economy. So, too, was the agricultural system fashioned on a dry subtropical climate, cheap Oriental labor, and co-operatives. And finally, the stimulus of an industrial transformation which resulted from new sources of energy and the extraordinary growth in population.

The Pacific Valleys and Ranges is still an area with great empty spaces, is still a land of extractive industries, and with a "colonial" as well as intensive agriculture (*Fig.* 18-1). The many specialized districts in which the transformation has been epochal remain as exceptions to the over-all economy.

Lying west of the Intermontane Area, this province extends for nearly 1,400 miles along the Pacific margin of the continent. Topographically, it is a complex land of high mountains and broad valleys. The major features are the Cascade-Sierra Nevada Mountains, the Coast Ranges, and the Klamath Mountains. Framed by these mountains are two productive lowlands: the Central Valley of California and the Puget Sound-Willamette lowland. The treatment of this large area is divided into the Pacific Southwest and the Pacific Northwest, regions whose economic development is for the most part a contrast.

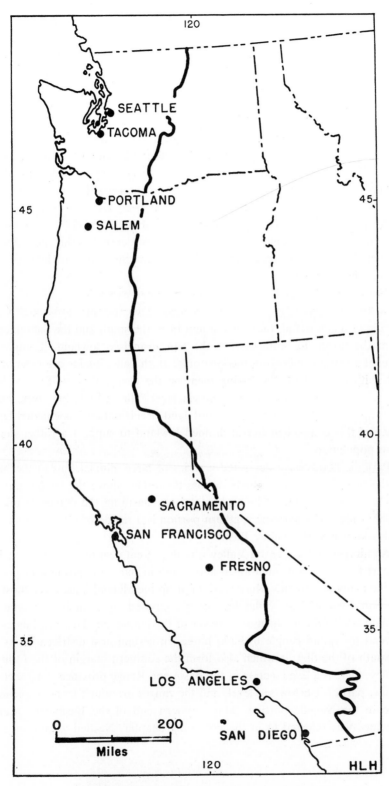

FIGURE 18-1: *Pacific Valleys and Ranges*

PACIFIC SOUTHWEST

Relief. The Pacific Southwest comprises five physical regions: Sierra Nevada Mountains, Central California Valley, Klamath Mountains, the Coast Ranges, and the Los Angeles Basin. The Sierra Nevadas constitute a great, tilted mountain-block approximately 400 miles long by 125 miles wide. The short abrupt slope is toward the Great Basin on the east, and the long gentle slope is on the west. The high Sierras on the east provide a natural water reservoir for the dry valleys to the west. In the foothill section on the long western slope, the upland has been dissected so thoroughly as to leave no extensive flatlands. The availability of water for irrigation has enabled the hill lands to support a fairly dense farming population, specializing mainly in fruit. Many districts have unused land interspersed among the farms.

The Central Valley is in reality a great trough extending some 400 miles between the Coast Ranges and the Sierras. Two streams flow toward the middle of this lowland, the San Joaquin from the south and the Sacramento from the north, to unite east of the San Francisco lowland. Tributaries enter the San Joaquin from the east only. Both valley plains are essentially flat, with rolling lands bordering them on the east and west. East of San Francisco Bay the valley floor is at sea level. The meandering rivers have built up natural levees on the swampy land. Reclamation has enabled large areas of this convenient but ill-drained lowland to support a rather dense farm population.

Periodic floods have deposited a series of large alluvial fans at the base of the Sierras, extending almost across the valley above the headwaters of the San Joaquin River. These alluvial fans constitute the choice farmland of this valley. The extreme southern portion is a region of inferior drainage and is known as the Tulare Basin.

An airview of the Central Valley reveals a great deal of wasteland, owing in part to the swamps mentioned above and in part to deposition of gravel by the tributary streams which have built up the alluvial fans. Over most of the San Joaquin Valley the limitations imposed by a subhumid type of climate add to the wasteland character of the landscape. There is, however, a trend for urban people to build homes in certain arid districts.

South of the Sierras which also form the southern margin of the Central Valley, there is a large section of the Basin and Range province. This section is low, part of it below sea level, and the ranges are much less conspicuous than in the Nevada portion. This southern end of the Basin and Range province was referred to in the preceding chapter. Nestled within an area of short mountain ranges is the Los Angeles Basin, third and last of these Pacific Coast lowlands.

Climate. Although California has a Pacific location, its climates are in part continental in character. The Marine West-Coast type of climate prevails on the northern Coast Ranges of California and above; it also occurs on the lower elevations of the Sierra Nevadas, whereas the Mediterranean climate prevails in most of the Central Valley. The Coast Ranges of California are lower than in the Northwest, thus limiting the amount of rainfall, and the more southerly latitude results in higher temperatures. They are characterized as subhumid, with 10 to 20 inches of rainfall, occurring almost entirely during the winter season. The upper valley of the San Joaquin has steppe climate throughout most of the area; in the far southwest of the Central Valley, in the rainshadow of the Coast Range, desert conditions obtain. The Coast Ranges have the Mediterranean climate except for the middle Salinas Valley and the Carrizo Plain which are steppe. South of the Central Valley, the mountains have Mediterranean, and the lowlands of the interior have desert climate.

In many of the lowlands agriculture would be impossible were it not for irrigation. Mild winters and clear hot summers, modified at many places by Pacific breezes, have attracted the motion-picture industry and the tourist. The climate became a permissive factor in the manufacture of airplanes during World War II when San Diego performed some of the plane-making operations out-of-doors.

Soils and Vegetation. The soils of the alluvial fans which comprise most of the eastern half of the San Joaquin Valley are very productive when watered. In the Sacramento Valley further north the soils are much less uniform and have large areas of sand and gravel deposited by the flood waters of the Sacramento River. The San Joaquin Valley likewise has many sandy districts. In the Los Angeles Basin the alluvial fans are similar to those of the San Joaquin Valley.

In the Pacific Southwest, limited sections with mature soils and young alluvial fans are the foundation of its agricultural prosperity. In the extreme southern end of the Great Valley there are extensive areas of lacustrine plain which are often inundated by flood waters. In the Tulare Lake plain several thousand acres have been reclaimed by an elaborate system of pumps and drainage ditches which impound the flood waters for irrigation during the dry season. The vegetation on a few of the moister ranges is Mediterranean scrub forest. Elsewhere the low rainfall has limited the vegetation to chaparral on some ranges and bunch grass and creosote bush on the dry lowlands of the interior.

Forests. Under such circumstances of relief and climate, commercial lumbering might seem to be unlikely, but the great latitudinal and altitudinal ranges have combined to give California important stands of timber. Although California ranks next after the states of the Pacific Northwest in commercial lumbering, it is by no means so important in the state's economy. In 1951 the timber cut was entirely softwood (4,546,393,000 board feet). In addition the National Forests returned to the state some $2.5 million as additional income, exceeded only by Oregon.[1]

Commercial lumbering is confined to the rainy northern half of the state: redwood in the Coast Ranges north of San Francisco, with ponderosa pine, sugar pine, and western white pine from the Sierra Nevada and Klamath mountains. Moisture-bearing winds from the Pacific do not bring rain to the Central Valley and the Los Angeles Basin where the growth of trees, even in the most favorable places, is Mediterranean scrub forest. The same winds enable the Sierra Nevadas to support tree growth on their western slopes.

Labor shortage over a period of many years, relatively inaccessible mountain forests, and two northern neighbors specializing in lumbering, have combined to limit its development in California. So long as the western slopes of the Sierras are timbered, water storage is made easier and the tourist industry enhanced by the tree growth.

Fisheries. The Pacific Southwest has a much larger fishing industry than the Northwest (862,149,000 pounds as against 204,987,000 pounds), and the varieties, methods of fishing, and the disposition of the catch differ. Despite the importance of this California industry, it is not without its problems. The principal varieties caught are, in order: sardine, tuna, salmon, and mackerel.

The sardine catch has fluctuated greatly; in 1935 it was 1,168,213,000 pounds, in 1945 it was 849,971,000, and in 1951 328,894,000 pounds. Since all sardines are packed, the effect upon the packers is obvious. The tuna catch has held up better, but competition with the Japanese industry has been serious. The fishing grounds have spread as far as the west coast of South America. Lower labor costs, floating canneries, and absence of alternative opportunity for the Japanese have made it difficult for Americans to compete. Peru now markets some canned tuna in this country.

The most recent addition to California's fishing is the mackerel. By 1935

[1] *Agricultural Statistics* (U.S. Dept. of Agriculture, Washington, 1952), p. 799.

the catch of mackerel in the Pacific surpassed the Atlantic. Since that year, however, the mackerel catch has steadily declined, from 146,427,000 pounds (1935) to 33,518,000 in 1951.

When the fishing industry is at capacity, approximately 18,000 are employed. The seasons for the several varieties spread the work rather uniformly throughout the year. The two principal fishing ports, Los Angeles and San Diego, are modern; the boats and methods are up-to-date. Yet fluctuations are so severe as to make California fishing a sick industry. Japanese and Italians do most of the fishing, and their catch is landed and processed on Terminal Island, principally.

Agriculture. The oldest agriculture of the Pacific Valleys and Ranges is in California. It began with the transplanting of Mediterranean crops and methods from the Old World by Spanish missions. Now California's agriculture has become a giant industry; it ranks first nationally in total crops and has long since outgrown local and even national markets. The fact that California has been one of the three leading agricultural states in the nation for the past 45 years, is due to a number of circumstances, among them the climate and the soils of this large state, the rapid growth and the nature of the population, and the agencies developed by man to offset natural and economic disadvantages. It is a common error to think of California as having a simple agricultural economy based on an abundance of certain factors peculiar to that region alone; actually there are few if any agricultural districts in the United States which have experienced such revolutionary changes in crops and in marketing procedures.

The listing of ranking farm products is impressive in its importance but no less so in its variety.[2] It is the circumstances under which these products are grown and marketed which make California agriculture distinctive. Something of the major frame of reference is in order here. The total area of the state is nearly four times that of Ohio, yet cropland is but one-third greater. Approximately 36 per cent of California is classed as farmland, but only one-third of this is cropland. Two-thirds of this cropland must be irrigated. The acre-value of this cropland is high, comparable to the eastern Corn Belt. The highest over-all wage rate in the United States is paid to the farm labor on these arable acres, yet the over-all output per man-hour

---

[2] In order of market value, California's farm products are: fruits, truck crops, dairy products, cattle, cotton fiber, eggs, poultry, potatoes, and barley (1952). Truck crops also rank first in the nation. Specifically dominance is in asparagus both fresh and processed, cantaloupes, carrots, celery, lettuce, spinach, sugar beets, prunes, peaches, pears, grapes, lima beans for processing, tomatoes for processing, and turkeys.

FIGURE 18-2: *Harvesting Squash Seed, California*

California valleys grow a large part of the vegetables and flowers for commercial seed houses. In this photograph squash seeds are being harvested by means of a mechanical behemoth attended by field hands. (*Steelways,* American Iron and Steel Institute and WEISSNER Studio)

is the lowest of any comparable area; in certain districts the output is high. Under such conditions it seems odd that 75 per cent of the farms are fully-owned by the operator.

Labor. Throughout its history, California has had to contend with an inadequate supply of labor. Orientals were brought into the area in substantial numbers. Subsequently other types of labor were introduced as the demand for workers changed. Ultimately California achieved its greatest fame in the crops which made such heavy demands upon labor. The native white farmers who once operated large ranches and wheat farms gave way, in part, before gardeners specializing in the production of fruit in the irrigated districts of southern California and in some areas of the Central Valley (*Fig.* 18-2).

The Chinese from railroad gangs, together with thousands of others imported to work in fruit during the nineteenth century, displaced the native white labor in the fruit districts. A few East Indians and some Japanese came in at this time. California's distance from markets and its water costs had to be offset by cheap labor; it was believed at the time her crops were not susceptible to mechanized production. But this solution of the cheap labor problem brought others in its stead. In 1882 Chinese were excluded by law. With the passage of the Dingley tariff in 1897, sugar beets were given strong support everywhere in the United States, but particularly in California, where beets took over part of the former wheat and orchard land.

Forty times as much labor was required on a beet-sugar plantation as on the larger wheat ranch. This time it was Japanese labor upon which the new crop was based. But the Japanese did not long confine themselves to work on sugar-beet plantations. They spread from the beet fields to take up land for themselves in districts then regarded as submarginal by the white farmers. No land that could be watered could be regarded as hopeless by the Japanese. They made strawberries an important crop in California agriculture. It fitted into the seasonal labor requirements of the sugar beet.

When, in the 1920-1930 period, farmers in the San Joaquin Valley began to raise long staple cotton, Mexicans and, later, Negro hands came in to work in the fields. Today cotton is mechanized, it has also greatly increased its acreage. The superior quality of the fiber, heavier yields, and declining prices for local farm products tended to stimulate the growing of cotton. The acreage in cotton in California in 1920 was 1,500 acres; in 1952 it was 1,320,000 acres. The yield in California is 573 pounds per acre; in Georgia the yield is 330 pounds. Local labor works in the cotton harvest between the grape harvest in September and the early thinning of sugar beets after the New Year.

Agriculture has embraced still another influx of outside labor. White labor came in from the drought-stricken Great Plains of Texas and Oklahoma during the 1930's. This was in addition to the annual influx of migrant white workers who have long motored to the West Coast orchards to harvest fruit. With conditions arising from this last influx of outlanders, such contributions to literature as *Grapes of Wrath* and *Ill Fares the Land* have been concerned.

The essence of the agricultural problem of California is in the consequences from the attraction of outlanders to work for wages low enough to enable California to compete with eastern producers for eastern markets. There are said to be more than two hundred crops which can be successfully grown in California. Not all can be profitably grown, however. The crops in which California has seen fit to specialize are those in which some modification of the plantation system of production can be employed to keep costs down. This has meant that other races were brought in still further to reduce the labor cost. One observer has said that California has "factories in the field." [3] He refers to the fact that the laborers do not regularly live on the land they work; there is a predominance of the large-scale units of production, a thousand acres or more; complete dissociation of the management function from labor; seasonal employment, organization of growers, packers, and to a degree, of labor. Many features of the rural landscape where farming has long been a way of life are missing in California. Every change of crop emphasis in California's agriculture during the past hundred years is represented by vestiges of the formerly dominant economies in the landscape prevailing today.

These practices of depending upon stoop labor are in process of change, however. Mechanization is making headway. In 1945, 30 per cent of California's sugar beets were harvested by machine; in 1950 it was 87 per cent. Cotton in the San Joaquin Valley is also succumbing to mechanization; the prospect there is for 90 per cent mechanization. Yet these two examples represent but a small part of the total labor force required.[4]

Judging from the studies that have been made, California has had somewhat better living conditions than other states in the inspected camps where migratory workers live. Since the World War II it is reported that restrictions have been relaxed to the detriment of the camps involved. Few states are entirely free from the practice of using migratory labor, but California probably relies upon this type of labor to the greatest extent.[5]

Farm Size. It is to be expected that a state which has passed through such contrasting agricultural economies would have extremes in the size of its farms. The Central Valley began with ranches and dry farming, whereas the Los Angeles district had the mission type of farmstead. Today approximately two-thirds of California's farmland (not just cropland) is in large units of 1,000 acres or more, but two-thirds of the farmers are found on the remaining third of the farmland. Most of the large holdings are in the Central Valley.

The impact of World War II, the subsequent increase in population, and rapid industrialization are making important changes in California's agriculture; mechanization of crops, even some heretofore depending upon stoop labor, will tend to increase the size of the operating units in time.

[3] Carey McWilliams, *Factories in the Field* (Little, Brown and Co., Boston, 1938). See also *Migratory Labor in American Agriculture* (Report to the President, Committee on Migratory Labor, Washington, 1951).

[4] For the nation as a whole, between 1940 and 1950 agricultural production increased 27 per cent, but labor requirements declined 5 per cent. This is suggestive of some far-reaching consequences.

[5] The significance of a passing of "a way of life" in farming communities is great. Geographers and others interested in the regional-economic complex will find it of interest to read Carey McWilliams, *op. cit.*

Irrigated farming is increasing in the Central Valley, particularly; this in time will doubtless modify the acreage of a representative farm.

Marketing. Most California farm products have long been marketed under the direction of co-operative organizations. Co-operative controls have extended to picking, grading, packing, and merchandizing. In some instances production controls have been practiced successfully. In this manner, California growers have been able to offset the additional transportation, water, and labor costs. Local markets have been growing rapidly, thus easing the problem of finding an outlet. Industrialization has caused wages to rise and they, in turn, have hurried mechanization.

Sacramento Valley. The Central Valley of California has the possibility of becoming one of the world's great agricultural areas. Embracing a little more than a third of the state, it is roughly 400 miles long and 45 miles wide (*Fig.* 18-3). It may be resolved into three subdivisions: Sacramento Valley in the north, San Joaquin Valley in the south, and a closed basin in the far south known as the Tulare Lake plain. Although some of the Sacramento Valley is irrigated, many circumstances under which agriculture is carried on here are in contrast with those of the drier San Joaquin Valley. There is less urban pressure on rural land in the Sacramento.

The Sacramento has a much larger volume of water than the San Joaquin; rainfall in the northern valley is greater, but summers are dry and temperatures are high; pastures regularly burn out during the summer. Soils here are somewhat poorer than in the San Joaquin; extensive areas are unused. In the northern portion of the Sacramento Valley a livestock economy prevails. Orchards are increasingly important toward the south, mainly pear, peach, and prune. Hops are a minor crop.

On the reclaimed relatively-alkaline river plains north of Sacramento the Japanese have grown a variety of rice for their own consumption and for export to Oriental markets. The land devoted to this crop has increased; in 1953 it amounted to 412,000 acres, yielding 70 bushels per acre. Mechanization has proceeded in all phases of rice growing, particularly during and since World War II. Prospects for irrigated farmland in the Sacramento Valley are believed to be about 4 million acres, including the land now irrigated. The delta lands of the mouth of the Sacramento River will total 700,000 acres. The proximity to large urban markets of *Sacramento* (137,572), *Stockton* (70,853), *Alameda* (64,430), *Oakland* (384,575), and *San Francisco* (775,357) has induced an important truck- and fruit-farming concentration on the delta lands about San Francisco Bay.

This vegetable-growing section has far outgrown its immediate market, and is the nation's greatest exporter of fresh and canned asparagus, beans,

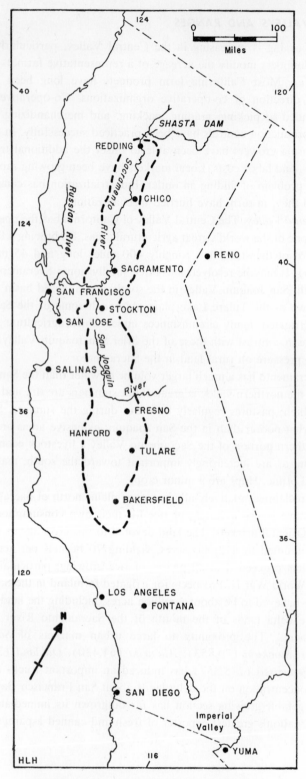

FIGURE 18-3: Central Valley of California

and peas. It is also a part of the prune, apricot, almond, pear, walnut, and flowers culture of the valleys in the Bay area. The importance of the Japanese labor in this economy has long been recognized locally, but the compulsory mass evacuation of the Japanese during World War II brought it forceably to the attention of eastern consumers. This is one of the major districts where the combination of opportune timing, land, labor, and capital applied to intensive farming has given rise to the expression "factories in the field."

San Joaquin Valley. Although the volume of water in the Sacramento River is much greater than that of the San Joaquin, the latter valley offers greater agricultural possibilities if watered. The San Joaquin River rises in the Sierra Nevadas, as do all of its tributaries. Great alluvial fans mark the entry of each tributary on to the lowland. In the south, above the headwaters of the San Joaquin, these alluvial fans almost cross the entire valley plain. It is upon these fans that most of the land presently irrigated is localized. Proposed increases in irrigated land also involve these fans, nearly all of them being on the eastern side. Heavy snowfall in the Sierra Nevadas is the principal source of water; the Coast Ranges receive less than half as much precipitation as falls on the Sierras.

Potential irrigated acreage will be something like this: American River and the lower San Joaquin River valleys will embrace some 3.5 million acres; the upper San Joaquin, east side, some 5.75 million acres; foothills and mountain valleys of the Central Valley some 2 million acres.[6]

In addition to the water from the mountains, there is a canal paralleling the San Joaquin River which brings water from the lower Sacramento River. Ultimately, the Central Valley project will bring tremendous increases to the water supply of the San Joaquin Valley. The rate of population growth, and particularly the industrial growth (California now ranks sixth in the nation in factory employment) makes this water supply a major issue in California.

One of the important irrigated districts lies between the King and the San Joaquin rivers, centering around *Fresno* (91,669). Vineyards, citrus orchards, cotton and potato fields occupy the largest acreage. Figs, apricots, peaches, and plums are important specialties. Fresno raisins have national fame. Hops are grown as a supplementary crop.

In driving through the Central Valley cropland one is never allowed to forget that it has been reclaimed. Interspersed among the green oases of intensive farming are brown remnants of winter pasture where soil or water

[6] *Ten Rivers in America's Future* (Report of the President's Commission, Washington, 1951), Vol. 3, p. 82.

conditions limit the extension of irrigated land. Thousands of cattle graze the brown foothills of the Sierra Nevadas.

Los Angeles Basin. There are a number of coastal lowlands and valleys which support agriculture. The most important of these lowlands is that of the Los Angeles Basin. This southern California agricultural district is critically deficient in water, yet produces nearly one-third of the state's total farm products. Where water is available, virtually all of the land is in some kind of crop.

Much use of the lower Colorado River has been made to irrigate the farmlands of the Los Angeles Basin and of the Imperial Valley farther south. In the Basin and Range Province, about 150 miles below Hoover Dam, the Parker Dam creates a reservoir known as Lake Havasu, designed to provide storage for pumping into the Colorado River Aqueduct of the Metropolitan Water District which comprises Los Angeles and twelve other cities in southern California, with a population of between 3 and 4 million.

One of the important diversion dams is the Imperial Dam across the Colorado River nearly 100 miles south of the Parker Dam. It diverts water to the Gila Project Canal for use in Southern Arizona, and to the American Canal supplying water to the Imperial Valley. Owens Valley water is also brought into the Los Angeles Basin. With these waters, the small farms (10 acres or less) produce grapes, apples, walnuts, celery, tomatoes, lima beans, poultry, and dairy products for the increasing local market and for the eastern states.

But even this pleasant and prosperous countryside has its problems. The local mountain streams are of little consequence. Wells are dug increasingly deep as the homes spread out into rural areas. The ditch, a standard feature of most irrigation districts, is not common in the Los Angeles Basin; most of the irrigation water is pumped. In order best to adapt the crops to local water and temperature conditions, there is vertical zoning within each valley. Lemons are the least hardy and therefore occupy the slopes midway between the valley floor and the height limit of irrigation; thus they are able to profit from the air drainage and avoid most frost. English walnuts and sugar beets occupy the valley floor where cool air settles and deep-rooted crops will not tolerate the underground water. Oranges are grown both above and below the zone for lemons, except where local conditions determine otherwise.

But these local problems are by no means the only ones. It is 3,000 miles from eastern markets, and transport costs have steadily risen since 1944, although some rates have declined. Rival districts which specialize in subtropic fruits have developed. The demand for frozen fruits and vegetables has enabled other districts to market their off-season products, to the disadvantage of the Los Angeles Basin growers. The rapid growth of manufacturing industries in the Los Angeles Basin has sent land values higher, thus pricing some land out of agricultural use. Competition for labor has likewise raised costs of farming. Because of this, intricate machines are to be seen in action in the fields (*Fig.* 18-2), but even with their use, stoop labor is a requirement.

Coastal Valleys. There are other smaller though important agricultural districts in California; many of them are in the valleys of the Coast Ranges. Some of these smaller districts have almost enough rain for their crops, while others have to rely wholly upon irrigation. The three most important of these mountain valleys are just south and north of San Francisco: Santa Clara, Salinas, and Russian. One of the more important is the Santa Clara Valley, with San Jose as its chief city, one of the world's fruit capitals. Under pump irrigation, prunes, apricots, pears, grapes, white cherries, peaches, and English walnuts are grown for national and international markets. Although these crops dominate the valley, others are grown; plums, olives, citrus fruit, and figs have a place in the highly developed agricultural economy of the Santa Clara Valley. Artificial drying of the fruit has supplanted natural sun drying; the major part of the crops are canned, however.[7]

Another important valley south of San Francisco is the Salinas. This longer and drier valley parallels the Santa Clara, opening directly into Monterey Bay. Like so many other districts in California it has had a great variety of nationalities living there: Spanish, Mexican, Peruvians, Basques, English, Danes, Swiss, and Portuguese. They have successively sought to make a living from cattle raising, sugar beets, pecans, head lettuce, and dairying.[8] From a few cars of head lettuce in 1921, it has become a great triple-harvest export. A new hardy strain, huge icing plants, and a desirable product have given rise to 5 million crates of winter lettuce, 4 million crates of spring, and 6 million crates of summer lettuce. The decline in sugar-beet acreage in 1951 and 1952 seems to have been arrested in 1953.

Three counties along the coast north of Los Angeles have mountain valleys which support commercial agriculture. Ventura, Santa Barbara, and

---

[7] For an excellent account of the development of this economy, see J. O. M. Broek, *Santa Clara Valley* (Utrecht, 1932).

[8] During two world wars the Salinas Valley was the scene of guayule production as a source of rubber. In his 1930 report on the project, the then Major D. D. Eisenhower cited an increase in rubber yield from this plant, from 400 to 2,200 pounds per acre over a nine-year period. The industry has not become established in the Salinas or any other valley in the United States.

FIGURE 18-4: *Citrus Orchards, Ventura County, California*

North of Los Angeles the citrus orchards cover the low hills which rise inland from the narrow coast plain. An intercover crop is grown to be turned under for green manure; it also serves to protect the soil from washing and retains a high proportion of all rainfall. A tract of acres in lemons has lost a total of only a few hundred pounds of topsoil over a period of 14 years. (U.S. Soil Conservation Service. JAY ALLISON photo)

San Luis Obispo counties are the most important (*Figs.* 18-4, 18-5). Citrus and deciduous fruits, beans, and wheat are most important. These counties have thus far remained attractive rural sections with many residential districts.

Farther south along the coast between Santa Barbara and Los Angeles, are the Oxnard Plains, one of the nation's centers of lima-bean production. Irrigated crops include sugar beets, oranges, lemons, and walnuts. Nearby are produced most of the domestic-grown flower seeds.

North of San Francisco the Russian River Valley is the principal oasis among the valleys of the Coast Ranges; its specialization is fruit. Petaluma Valley raises poultry, and the Napa Valley grows grapes. Most other valleys in the southern Coast Ranges are too dry for crops.

Mineral Industries. Two minerals have accomplished spectacular things for California: gold in the second half of the nineteenth century, and oil

FIGURE 18-5: Avocado Orchard, Santa Barbara County, California

Along the coast is this orchard of six-year-old avocados, planted on the contour. Between the rows seeded barley conserves soil and moisture. (U.S. Soil Conservation Service)

in the twentieth century. Minerals brought thousands of people to California, where timber and farm lands brought hundreds to the Pacific Northwest. By comparison with the present century's experience with oil in California, the gold rush during the past century no longer appears spectacular. In 1899 Los Angeles began its hectic career as an oil producer, although abortive attempts had been made earlier. All other land uses were ephemeral if oil was suspected; orchards, lawns, public property, and even the floor of the Pacific coastal waters surrendered to the oil derrick. Production jumped from 4 million barrels in 1905 to 330 million barrels in 1950; for a quarter-century California has been one of the three leading mineral states.

There are three main petroleum-producing districts in the state, the leading one being the upper San Joaquin Valley with a yield of 146,117,000 barrels (1950). Second-ranking district is the Los Angeles Basin with 118,681,000 barrels, and third is the Coastal Lowland with 62,829,000 barrels. Only Texas exceeds California in petroleum production. In natural gas California ranks after Texas and Louisiana.

The metal-mining industry is by no means so important, although in gold and silver California ranks second and third, respectively. These two account for two-thirds of the metals mined. Lead, zinc, and copper rank relatively low. In fireclays the state ranks fifth; in slipclays it is third. In cement (manufactured) California's 26 million barrels rank it second only to Pennsylvania. One major steel maker near Los Angeles uses iron ore from Eagle Mountain (831,445 tons in 1950), in southern California. A rather wide variety of minerals are extracted in the state, but most of them are not on the tonnage basis.

Manufacturing in California. In 1950 the state, which historically has sold agricultural products to the nation, had a market value of farm products totaling $2.5 billion; for that year the net value of the state's manufactures was $4.2 billion. For many years its manufactures were based upon the conversion of its agricultural surplus and the timber from its forests. Even after the discovery of petroleum, California relied upon eastern manufacturers for most of its needs.

World War II was a turning point in its industrial development. New industrial facilities expansion financed by the federal government made an impressive addition to the state's capacity.[9] These emergency payrolls brought many thousands of persons to California during the war years. Many of them remained on the Coast after the war was over. The Korean conflict kept some plants in production that otherwise might have closed. Between 1929 and 1950 the percentage increase in the net value of manufacturing in California rose more rapidly than in New York or Pennsylvania, oldest leaders in manufacturing.[10]

In 1952 California ranked sixth in net value of manufactures, after New York, Ohio, Pennsylvania, Illinois, and Michigan, in that order. For the year 1951 the growth in net value was $800 million. The impact of such industrial growth as this upon other aspects of the state's economy is significant. Among the most important increases between 1946 and 1952 were in the manufacture of electrical machinery (three-fold), transportation

[9] *The Geographic Distribution of Manufacturing Facilities Expansion, 1940-1944* (War Production Board, Washington, 1945), p. 23.

[10]

NET VALUE OF MANUFACTURES
($1000)

State	1929	1947	1952
New York	4,974.	9,667.	13,101.
Pennsylvania	3,431.	6,947.	9,673.
California	1,349.	3,995.	6,960.

SOURCE: *Annual Survey of Manufactures* (U.S. Dept. of Commerce, Washington, 1952), p. 44.

FIGURE 18-6: Orange Products Plant, Ontario, California

Not all California citrus fruit is sold fresh. (Exchange Orange Products Co.)

equipment (almost three-fold), machinery, primary metals, and fabricated metals, each about doubling its net value. Such long-established industries as petroleum refining, foods, lumber, stone, clay and glass, and apparel showed modest increases (*Fig.* 18-6).

Some of the reasons for these industrial gains include the large increase in California's population (1930, 5,677,251; 1950, 10,586,223), tendency for some eastern manufacturers to recentralize their operations, the proportionately large share of government-financed industrial facilities allotted to California, and the greater amount of water and of power available for manufacturing.

An area which had been deficient in primary steel-making capacity achieved new integrated facilities at Fontana, east of Los Angeles, and in the San Francisco district. California metal fabricators can also buy steel from another new source, Provo, Utah. Primary steel mills are apt to attract industries to them which use their product, and California's mills are no exception.

Despite the increases in the state's manufacturing, factory employment as a percentage of total population in Los Angeles and even in San Francisco remains lower than for New York City or Chicago.

San Francisco (775,357) was, for most of its history, the largest city in California and its principal manufacturing district. Although Los Angeles was much the larger city by 1940, the Second World War caused its population to increase nearly one-third, while San Francisco gained only one-sixth, still a substantial gain.

Oakland (384,575) gained at a greater rate than its big neighbor. *Berkeley* (113,805), the last member of the triumvirate, gained 40 per cent. *Richmond* (99,545), farther north on the Bay, gained 400 per cent in its population. The population and industrial gains in the San Francisco urban area may be attributed to the acceleration of forces which have long been important; it seems quite likely that there will be a continuing expansion of the cities in the Bay area.

A glance at a map reveals the compound harbor of San Francisco, with the city of San Francisco at the northern tip of a long, hilly peninsula; the city is accessible by rail only from the south. The splendid protected deepwater harbor separates San Francisco from its mainland neighbors, Berkeley and Oakland. World War II activated the economies of smaller cities to the north and northeast. The several divisions of the armed services took over ports for their individual development. The bay is so large that it was not bridged until 1937.

As one of the Pacific port cities with access to the Central Valley and the middle interior of the United States, the commerce of San Francisco has developed upon a wide range of outgoing and incoming products. The rise of Seattle and of Los Angeles have done little to affect this aspect of San Francisco's economy. The San Francisco port group handles about one-fourth of all United States' Pacific Coast tonnage, a significant tonnage in view of the export of heavy tonnages of wood, petroleum, and seafood through other specialized ports.

The discovery of gold in the Sacramento Valley in 1849 startled the little town of 800; within two years time it had a population of 25,000. During the century that has passed, petroleum discoveries and the tremendous increase in the farm productivity of the Central Valley have made the role of these ports vital. The Valley has enabled San Francisco to secure its position as financial, commercial, and industrial center for the Central Valley.

A recitation of the factory products of San Francisco-Oakland industries gives a fair conception of the diversity of its manufactures. They are: chemicals, clothing, food, machinery, metal products, paper, petroleum products, primary iron and steel, rubber, textiles, and transportation equipment. World War II with its government-financed industrial facilities gave San Francisco a total little more than half as much as Los Angeles. By industries, San Francisco got three times as much in shipyards, almost nothing in aircraft, primary steel, or in machinery; a fifth as much in chemicals; and a fourth as much in food products as the southern California city. This contrast is significant; the war effort did little to change the nature of the district's industrial economy.

Los Angeles. Los Angeles has been described as the largest city for its size in the nation; the pun is not without its significance. Los Angeles proper is scarcely distinguishable from the several suburban cities which make up the metropolitan area, with more than one-third of the state's population. The Los Angeles area is not a single broad plain but rather five more-or-less united lowlands, separated by dissected hills and low mountains, and bound together by a network of highways and railroads. Although described as having a Mediterranean climate, the variations between such places as Long Beach and San Fernando is marked. This complex terrain contributes to the smog problem.

Its population has had a rapid growth since World War I, particularly during the past two decades. The city of *Los Angeles* (1,970,358) has most of its industry along the railroads which follow the Los Angeles River south to the harbor. Much heavy industry is here, including 35 meat packing plants, rubber factories, oil refineries, automobile assembly plants, and steel fabricating plants. The suburban cities include *South Gate* (51,293), *Long Beach* (250,767), *Compton* (47,991), and *Torrance* (31,834). On the east are several small cities and many towns beyond the city limits; among these *San Bernardino* (73,827) and *Riverside* (56,571) are the most important (*Fig.* 18-7).

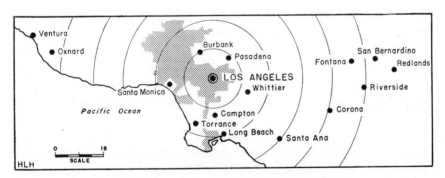

FIGURE 18-7: Los Angeles Urban Cluster

Within this framework one of the nation's most important industrial districts is developing. Although most of the industrial plants are south of the urban core, several other cities have factory payrolls. Concentric circles are at 10-mile intervals.

FIGURE 18-8: Goodyear Rubber Plant, Los Angeles

Such types of manufacturing as this rubber-tire plant could not locate in the Los Angeles area until large quantities of water were guaranteed. This meant that the city must reach out to the mountains and eventually to the Colorado River. At mid-century most types of large industrial consumers of water are represented in the Los Angeles area. (Goodyear Tire and Rubber Co.)

On the north are *Alhambra* (51,359), *Glendale* (95,708), *Burbank* (78,577) and *Pasadena* (104,577). West of Los Angeles is *Santa Monica* (71,595). Los Angeles with its seemingly limited hinterland has undergone more than just a growth in population.

The variety of factory products is great; clothing, food products, machinery, metal products, motion pictures, petroleum products, rubber tires and mechanical rubber goods, primary metals, and transportation equipment. Employment in aircraft manufacture during World War II exceeded that of Detroit's automobile employment. The county and city of Los Angeles makes more rubber tires than any city except Akron (*Fig.* 18-8); assembles more automobiles than any except Detroit; ranks third in food preparation, and fourth in clothing manufacture.

Although employment is high in aircraft manufacture, the industry is for the most part only the making of air frames and the final assembly of the plane; motors, both piston and jet, are primarily products of the Manufacturing Belt in the east. Despite the large pool of labor experienced in

FIGURE 18-9: *Kaiser Steel Plant, Near Los Angeles*

Utah coal and southern California iron ore meet in this integrated steel plant east of Los Angeles. The mill was built during World War II; it is laid out on an 1,800-acre site in a fertile valley, with rolling mills, open hearths, blast furnaces, and tinplate mill shown in the picture. Something of the importance of water may be seen in the fact that this plant is reported to consume only 1,100 gallons of water per ton of steel as compared with the industry average of 65,000 gallons. (Kaiser Steel Corp.)

the aircraft industry in southern California, the facilities for construction, and the climate permitting work out of doors, the Korean conflict and preparation for war between 1947 and 1955 did not restore this industry to California in its wartime proportions. The war-built plants in the Middle West took over a major share of these contracts; California in 1955 accounted for one-third of the industry, all in the southern California area. The aircraft industry reflects the changes resulting from congestion and mounting land values by expanding in peripheral locations.

Fontana's new integrated steel plant (California ore and Utah coal) makes nearly two-thirds of the primary steel in southern California; this is a small fraction of the total steel production, but it is attracting steel fabricators to it (*Fig.* 18-9). It is significant that in addition to automobile assembly, California is getting an important share of parts manufacture; the Ford Company, for instance, has made it a policy to relate parts contracts with retail sales, geographically. Automatic and calculating machines, earth-moving machines, oil field equipment, electrical and electronic equipment, and machines for the motion-picture industry are important aspects of the machinery category. Such war-time industries as shipbuilding, the manufacture of explosives and ordnance have not remained active. The extraordinary increase in population affords the best reason for industrial growth. Water is believed to be adequately provided for in the years of industrialization ahead by means of the Central Valley Project which will bring water from northern California as well as utilize all of the water resources of the entire southern half of the Central Valley and the mountain periphery.

PACIFIC NORTHWEST

As with the Pacific Southwest, the Northwest lies between the dry interior plateaus and the Pacific Ocean. Although variously delimited by those who have written on the Northwest, we shall consider this region as comprising the Cascade Mountains, Olympic Mountains, Oregon Coast Ranges, Siskiyou Mountains, and the Puget Sound lowland section, including the Willamette Valley. There is a narrow coastal plain bordering the Coast Ranges, generally from two to three miles in width, except on the central Washington coast when it widens to thirty.[11]

Relief. The Cascade Mountains rise in a gentle slope from the Puget Sound lowland. Their general appearance resembles a dissected plateau of about 7,000 feet elevation, with a number of volcanic peaks rising above the general level of the province; only one exceeds 10,000 feet, Mt. Rainier, elevation 14,415 feet.

The Oregon Coast Ranges consist of folded and faulted mountains with a relatively uniform summit level. These ranges are breached by several rivers, among which are the Umpqua, Rogue, Klamath, Chehalis, and Columbia. There are few good harbors along the west side of this mountain province; streams which cross it are able neither to open up a considerable hinterland nor to offer promising harbors. Unlike the Atlantic Coastal Plain, this narrow plain has but one important drowned river, the Columbia. Less important bays are found at Grays Harbor, Washington, and Tillamook and Coos in Oregon. South of the Oregon Coast Range, and connecting them with the Cascades are the Calapooya and the Siskiyou Mountains which cross into northern California. The Puget Sound-Willamette lowlands lie within the mountain frame indicated above.

[11] For a detailed study see Otis W. Freeman and Howard H. Martin, *The Pacific Northwest* (New York, 1954).

Climate. Due to the breaks in the Coast Range which permit marine influence to penetrate much of the interior lowland, a large part of the Pacific Northwest has a marine West Coast type of climate. For about nine months of the year, the marine influence gives rise to overcast skies, moisture-laden winds, and winter rainfall. In summer these winds are heated by the land, thus giving relatively dry summers. This sequence is common to the coastal lowlands as well as to the interior valleys. On the higher elevations along the Coast and the Olympic ranges rainfall varies from 50 to 180 inches a year, whereas on the lowlands of Oregon it averages from 17 to 35 inches. Only on the highest eastern mountains is there much snow; in many spots it remains on the ground throughout most of the summer.

Throughout the Pacific Northwest, differences in elevation and in distance from the Pacific cause important variations in climate. The difference between the windward and the leeward sides of mountains profoundly affects the climate. Differences in latitude along the Pacific margin have the minimum effect upon climate. Temperatures west of the Cascades, except in high altitudes, are moderate. Freezing weather regularly occurs, however, and occasional summer temperatures of 95° are recorded. In the Puget Sound-Willamette lowland the growing season averages seven months; along the coastal lowland it is even longer. The presence of warm and cool air masses gives rise to cloudy days in winter and to regular and heavy fogs along the coast. For ocean shipping and airways over many of the lowlands, the fogs are an important hazard.

Soils. The Puget Sound lowland is for the most part gently rolling to hilly, with brown soils of various textures, in large part underlain by a porous sand or gravel layer. Glacial deposits are more common in the northern portion where outwash plains and morainal deposits give an intricacy to the soils pattern and render many sections unfit for plow crops. The soils and drainage of the Willamette Valley are more favorable for agriculture. The nearly-level to gently-rolling valleys are surrounded by hilly foothill lands. Soils are moderatively productive, being silty or heavier, for the most part. There is no equivalent of the porous layer found in the Puget Sound lowland.

Forest Industry. The effect of the mountain and valley terrain upon climate has been noted; its effect upon vegetation is obvious in *Fig.* 9-2b. Because the effect of these environmental conditions upon vegetation is greater from east to west than from north to south, vegetation zones are similarly oriented. On the whole, natural conditions have favored forest growth in the Pacific Northwest above all other regions of the United States. Three-fifths of the total area of Washington and Oregon west of the high Cascades is classed as forest land, only one-tenth of which is noncommercial in character. The settlement and subsequent history of these states bear testimony to the dominance of forests in their economy. With more than half of the old-growth saw timber remaining in the United States, these two states probably receive more national attention than any previous timber storehouse.

One hundred years after New England white pine initiated the commercial lumbering industry on this continent, the lumberjack reached the Pacific slopes. During these hundred years many important changes had come to the business of felling trees and moving them to the sawmill. Had it not been for these changes in the industry, Pacific forests could not have become available at the time. Forests of the Northwest were mostly in mountainous country; the trees were enormous, both as to height and bulk, and in much of the forested region there was no snow and ice to simplify moving out the logs. There was only a small local market for the timber and no alternative use possible for the land. The eastern lumberjack from Minnesota who worked the Pacific forests found his day relatively short because machines designed to save labor at every stage in the lumbering process were soon on the scene. The part-time worker was no more; living conditions were entirely different; the camps took on the appearance of permanent towns, with women, children and schools; instead of horses and their French Canadian drivers, there were tractors and trucks. In the Pacific Northwest, lumbering became a large-scale industry.

In Washington the forests consist largely of Douglas fir, ponderosa pine, yellow pine, hemlock, and on the higher elevations, spruce and fir. Oregon has much the same trees, and in addition, Port Orford cedar, sugar pine, and redwood in the southern part of the state. It is the last great forest. It contains such notable specimens as the world's tallest trees and oldest living trees known (three thousand years).

The Douglas fir region in the western part of Oregon and Washington covers an area somewhat larger than Ohio (50,000 square miles), with five-sixths of it in forestland. The Douglas fir dominates, with some hemlock, cedar, and true fir. Two-fifths of this timber is contained in the Willamette National Forest. Taken as a whole, this great timber region is estimated to contain about one-third of the remaining sawtimber in the United States. Douglas fir forests have been uniquely susceptible to bad fires. Dry summers and predominance of resinous trees create an acute hazard all summer.

Because of its rough terrain and because a huge volume of privately-

FIGURE 18-10: *Lumber Mill, Springfield, Oregon*

Wood and its products continue to be the most important single type of industrial product in Oregon. (Weyerhaeuser Sales Co.)

owned timber was readily accessible to water transportation in the Puget Sound, Grays Harbor, and Columbia River territories, only a moderate amount of cutting of Willamette National Forest timber was made prior to 1940.

Lumbering began in Washington because a great deal of the best timber there was within fifty miles of tidewater, and accessibility to ocean ports was necessary, inasmuch as most of this timber was then being cut for export. The Puget Sound lowland was the scene of the first important lumbering operations, with half a dozen towns springing up on the Sound. At the same time this timber was being cut, the older Atlantic and Gulf states were still cutting great quantities of pine. At no time in its history has the Pacific Northwest been the only major logging region.

Oregon developed more slowly than Washington (*Fig.* 18-10). The need was less pressing and the timber for the most part was less accessible to tidewater ports. In both states the mills were close to the timber supply. Most of the area of both states is east of the Cascades, but the timber and the population have been localized on the west side. Washington has remained the more important forest-industry state, yet there is scarcely a community in western Oregon whose prosperity does not depend upon the wood-products industry. The lumber industry is the basis for the state's principal manufacturing group. Oregon's commerce is also largely concerned with wood; the leading exports (domestic and foreign) are in order: lumber, flour, wheat, paper, and canned goods (including fish). Of all wood cut in Washington and Oregon, 88 per cent is for lumber, 7 per cent for pulp and paper, and 5 per cent for plywood. Coos Bay now leads in lumber export.

Fishing Industry. Although fishing and the canning of fish products constitute an important industry in the Northwest it no longer dominates the industry of the Pacific Coast of the United States. In 1945 Alaskan and British Columbian waters and canneries surpassed those of Washington and Oregon. The importance of fishing along this Northwest coast began long ago with the salmon industry. Nearly every harbor on the Northwest coast has a fishing fleet, but Seattle, halibut center of the world, has more fishing craft than any other port, and the bulk of the fishery products ultimately clear through this port. Fishing craft of many kinds, repair establishments, and huge warehouses for storage are concentrated about Salmon Bay terminals. Canneries, icing plants, warehouses, and reduction works constitute the landscape of an important fishing port. Fifteen thousand fishermen and 1,300 cannery employees are reported to be engaged in this industry in Washington and Oregon alone.

Salmon has been overwhelmingly the major part of the catch. In recent years the catch has been somewhat more varied; halibut and oysters are relatively minor, though increasingly important. The spawning habits of the salmon make them easy to catch in prime condition on their way to the fresh-water spawning grounds. Each spring and summer salmon move up the many streams emptying into the north Pacific Ocean for their only spawning in the lake or river in which they were born four to nine years before, depending upon the variety of salmon. The start of this tremendous migration varies with the distance the fish have to go. The parents soon die after the final act of reproduction. The length of stay in fresh water varies from a few months to two years or more; likewise the period of life in the Pacific varies from two to six years depending upon the kind of salmon. In size and color the salmon will vary; the red-meated salmon has been the best seller, but pink- and white-meated varieties have surpassed the more expensive red within the past twenty years.

The construction of Bonneville and Grand Coulee dams cut off 800 miles of Columbia River and 100,000 square miles of watershed as spawning grounds for these famed salmon. Proposed additional dams on the Snake have been held by some to seriously reduce the remaining spawning grounds. Salmon "ladders" have been at least partially successful in permitting salmon to by-pass the dam on their way to spawning waters in the upper streams.[12] They are impossible at Grand Coulee dam.

World War II interrupted Japanese encroachments upon salmon fishing in the Pacific Northwest and in Alaska, tuna fishing off California and Mexican waters, and the canning industry based upon these and other seafood. Japanese success in these ventures was apparent to any observer of the grocers' shelves in the United States. With increased interest in Pacific waters and the memory of the unemployment in the United States during the 1930's, it is not unthinkable that some measures will be taken to end the sometimes legal practices calculated to scuttle the United States Pacific fisheries. Although fishing in Oregon is not so important as in Washington, at several places it is a major industry. On the Columbia River fishing is important at Astoria, Warrenton, and the Dalles. On the Pacific Coast the principal fishing ports are Tillamook, Newport, Reedsport, and the towns on Coos Bay. Salmon is the leading catch, with halibut, pilchards, steelhead trout, shad and oysters important in that order. Pilchards are processed for oil and fertilizer; it is the most recent of developments in Oregon fishing.

The halibut industry reached its peak catch in Pacific waters in 1915, but it has far outdistanced its North Atlantic competitor, New England. It employs one-tenth as many wage earners as the salmon industry, markets half of its catch as fresh fish and freezes the rest, ranges hundreds of miles from port for fishing, and uses the modern equivalent of a single line instead of the quantity methods of the salmon industry. Seattle is the principal halibut port, despite the northward migration of the major catch.[13]

Agricultural Industry and Districts. Only the north states on the Pacific Coast developed as a climax to the westward movement of people across the continent. Settlement in the Pacific Southwest began on the coast and moved eastward. The conditions under which agriculture was established

[12] The Bonneville Power Administration released these data concerning the fish to make use of these fishladders:

Year	Chinook	Blueback	Silver	Steelhead trout
1938	271,799	75,000	15,185	107,003
1940	391,595	148,808	18,822	185,174
1942	403,938	39,845	2,547	92,131
1944	238,191	15,071	4,073	93,047

[13] Ranking fish in the catch of Washington (1950): salmon, halibut, shad, cod, mackerel, herring, shrimp, and oysters. In Oregon: salmon, sturgeon, halibut, oysters, cod, smelt, and herring. *Geographic Atlas* (New York, 1953), p. 160.

in the Northwest were not greatly different from those of the Old North-west Territory a century earlier, from which many had migrated. For their respective times, both were tardily settled, although unlike the Ohio Coun-try, the Oregon Country did not attain a population of 2 million within the first generation of its occupancy. After nearly a century it now barely approaches that figure. Settlement spread from Portland southward along the Willamette Valley, later moving north to the Cowlitz and Chehalis valleys onto Puget Sound lowland, but it has remained primarily an agri-culture country. Today 80 per cent of the farmers live on these three low-land areas.

Four years after the discovery of gold in California, Seattle was estab-lished. During the early years of the export of farm products from the Northwest to California, they brought collector's prices in the markets of dry California. The Northwest, after a time, caught up with this California demand for the staples of life; lumber soon supplanted food products as the prime export from the Puget lowland. California's agriculture became more nearly self-sufficient after this boom period of imports.

Most of Washington's farm land lies outside the Pacific Northwest, and is found east of the Cascades in the great rolling wheat lands of the Palouse Country, but two-thirds of the farms are in the lowland bordering Puget Sound. The region appears to have more cut-over land than plowland; a great deal of the area is unused; swamps, tidal flats, cut-over land with the stumps remaining, and large sections of obviously poor soil are prominent in the landscape of the northern portion of the Puget Sound Lowland.

White River Valley. The agricultural heart of western Washington is the White River Valley, part of a J-shaped system of valleys, with Seattle at the end of the vertical completed by the Duwamish Valley, Sumner at the turn, and Tacoma at the end of the hook which is made by the fertile valley of the Puyallup. The floor of the White River Valley is a plain of black, alluvial soil relatively free from the gravel common to much of the lowland of western Washington. The hills on either side are abrupt, have poor soil, and are partly timbered.

Today, the White River Valley and adjacent lowlands have localized a large part of the urban population of western Washington. City markets and canning plants have enabled the farmers of these lowlands to develop an agriculture based on dairying, poultry, vegetables, cranberries, and plums; small fruits and berries ripen all summer. In midsummer, when work on the cropped land slackens, the sour-cherry belt along the hills of the valley sides brings in migratory labor from as far as east of the Lakes states and as far south as California. Local authorities assert that there are no "grapes of wrath" harvested in Washington's migratory labor camps. Seventy years ago the lowland was a series of pioneer clearings.

One of the problems of the White and Puyallup Valley farmers has been the role of the Japanese in land ownership and plant management. The nature of the urban market has accounted for the type of crops grown; the need for a great deal of cheap hand labor is obvious.[14] The removal of the Japanese from Pacific valleys during World War II put this and other fruit and vegetable districts in the position of being so shorthanded that crops were not all harvested.

Willamette Valley. The Willamette Valley is the best of the three districts making up the interior lowlands of the Pacific Northwest. This valley contains about 55 per cent of the farms in the entire state of Oregon. Agriculture here is highly diversified, with general farming predominant usually centering around dairying or farm sheep, with a good deal of cash grain and legume-seed production. Many specialized fruit farms produce prunes, cherries, pears, and apples. Truck farms are primarily concerned with onions, celery, peas, beans, and tomatoes; this is one of the heaviest producers of strawberries in the United States.

The Willamette Valley's farming calls for thousands of transient harvest hands each summer. Near Athena, 22,000 acres of green peas need thousands of pickers; Salem's sweet cherries need 10,000 extra hands; the harvest of the entire nation's filbert crop, walnuts by the thousands of tons, four million bushels of pears near Medford in the Rogue Valley, sugar beets at Nysea, and hogs centering about Independence use 25,000 extra pickers. The voluntary co-operative labor of the Corn Belt would be no solution for the labor shortage of the Pacific Coast. The increase in manufacturing industries since World War II has aggravated this shortage.

Other Districts. Lying between Puget Sound lowland and the Willamette Valley is some hilly country bordering the Columbia and Cowlitz rivers. Although it is not a good agricultural region, the Portland market has induced some dairying, poultry, and vegetable gardens. Most of the Portland market is supplied by farms farther south in the Willamette Valley.

Just south of the Columbia there is a country of rolling hills which lies between the Cascades and the Blue Mountains. It is situated in the great Columbia lava flow. The climate is hot and dry in summer, moderately cold in winter. Dry farming (wheat) predominates, with a few irrigated districts. The uncultivated sections support large herds of sheep and cattle.

In the region west of the Coast Range there are districts in which special-

[14] Washington's farm market value of crops in 1949 was $510 million, with fruit, wheat, dairy products, cattle, truck crops, and eggs the ranking products.

ized dairy farming for cheese production and those in which poultry farming for eggs are increasingly important. Farther south in Oregon, in the valleys of the Umpqua and the Rogue rivers, specialized fruit and vegetable farming is carried on with general farming. In the Umpqua area, prunes, peas, cherries, apples and small fruit; in the Rogue, pears are most important.[15]

Minerals. The Pacific Northwest is not one of the important mineral centers of the United States, nor is it likely to be. A good grade of bituminous coal is mined on the Puget Lowland at Bellingham and at several minor centers in the interior. Semianthracite is mined in small quantities on the west side of the Cascades. Oregon has bituminous coal mined at the Coos Bay field in the southwestern part of the state. There are representatives of a number of other mining industries in the Northwest. Among them are Washington's antimony, cobalt, manganese, mercury, copper, lead, and gold. No one of these is a major industry. Washington's mineral industries are about twice as important as in Oregon, where coal, antimony, gold, mercury, and nickel are mined.

Manufactures. Despite the increase in the amount and the variety of manufactured products in the Pacific Northwest since 1939, and the great power developments east of the Cascades, this phase of the region's economy is still characterized by the dominance of its two long-standing industries; wood and its products, and foods. Aluminum, aircraft, heating equipment, primary iron, wool textiles, and leather are also manufactured in the region. Washington has a net value of manufactures half again as great as Oregon, and its factory products are of greater variety.

Portland and Tacoma manufacture furniture. Sawmills are widely scattered over the Puget Sound and Willamette lowlands. One specialized wood product is the packing case for the wide variety of canned foods exported from the two states.

Aluminum. The aluminum industry has come since 1940. In 1944 approximately half of the nation's aluminum was made in these two states, although not all in the region here treated as the Pacific Northwest. Tacoma, Vancouver, and Wenatchee have huge, war-built plants. The vast power requirements are met by turbines at Bonneville Dam in the Cascades, and at Grand Coulee on the Columbia Plateau (*Fig.* 18-11). Texas has risen to a position in aluminum production comparable to the Northwest, but thus far northwestern aluminum plants continue the same level of production.

---

[15] Oregon, farm market value of crops, 1949, $366 million: cattle, dairy products, wheat, fruit, and truck crops.

Aircraft. Seattle began the manufacture of airplanes during World War I. Boeing made them in his native city, near the supply of suitable spruce for the frames; engines were imported from eastern manufacturers. He specialized in transports and bombing planes, and was forced to depend upon exports to countries of western Europe to supplement his market in the United States. Despite exports, this company had to give up plane manufacture at one period and turn temporarily to furniture. World War II gave this industry a tremendous boost. Twelve thousand workers were employed in this one plant. Two wars have given the airplane industry the stimulus which has made it a major industry (*Fig.* 18-12). Both Boeing and Douglas also operate aircraft plants in the Middle West.

Shipbuilding. Portland, Seattle, Bremerton, Vancouver, and Tacoma were all-important shipbuilding centers during World War II, but with the coming of peace, these shipyards closed.

Cities. Most of the cities of the Pacific Northwest are situated on Puget Sound; the principal exception is Portland on the Columbia River. Seattle, Tacoma, Port Angeles, Bellingham, and Everett are predominantly commercial cities through which moves a heavy tonnage; Portland has all to itself the trade of the Columbia River basin, in itself a great exporter. Eight other ports are small and specialized.

Domestic commerce is by far the larger part of trade of these port cities. As a group, they are primarily export in their function. Dominant commodity is wood, as shingles, woodpulp, newsprint, and lumber. Some Canadian timber exports also move through these ports. The military activity in Alaska, the new aluminum industry at Kitimat, British Columbia, and the new oil pipeline from Alberta to the Pacific have combined to make these waters more active commercially. Wheat and flour, fish products, refined copper, aluminum, aircraft, ships, fruits and vegetables are prominent in Puget Sound exports.

Seattle (467,591) dominates the middle route. The immediate hinterland of Seattle developed later than California, and its industries were more restricted. No gold or oil discovery caused it to boom. As the principal port for Alaskan trade, it experienced the major share of its commerce with the United States; it continues to do so. Within the past fifty years, the proportion of United States' foreign trade with Asiatic countries has increased two-and-a-half times; Seattle shares heavily in this.

The industrial district of Seattle lies along the Duwamish flats south of the city, around Lake Union, and at Ballard, on suburban Salmon Bay. Above these industrial and commercial lowlands the city rises on its hills

FIGURE 18-11: Generators, Bonneville Dam, Columbia River

Emphasizing the mounting power demands in the Northwest, all ten generators at Bonneville Dam are operating at full load (518,400 KW) in the daytime. (Bonneville Power Administration)

in a series of more or less discontinuous districts. Embayment and hills have given Seattle something of the appearance of San Francisco. Residents assert that Seattle has leveled more hills than any other city in the United States. Elevations vary from 12 to 500 feet.

The nature of manufacturing is not such as to bring about much interplant dependence or a high net value. A small primary steel tonnage has not attracted much manufacturing to the city. Aircraft is the only important metal fabricator, and the motors are brought in from the eastern states. The leading manufactured products (net value) are: foods, lumber and wood products, machinery, paper, primary metals, and transportation equipment.

Seattle's location between Lake Washington and the Sound, within sight of high mountains on both east and west, contributes to its advantages as a tourist and recreation area.

Portland (373,628), a hundred miles from the Pacific, is connected with it by a channel of sufficient depth to accommodate most ocean-going vessels. Three-fourths of this commerce is domestic coastwise; few foreign vessels visit this port. The character of the water-borne freight is representative

FIGURE 18-12: *Boeing Airplane Plant, Seattle, Washington*

World War I brought the beginning of the aircraft industry to the Pacific Coast, but it was not until World War II that it gained top rank among the Coast's industries (employment). This company also operates large plants in the Middle West. (Boeing Airplane Co.)

of the prewar economy of the region. Portland ships nearly twice as much wheat as Seattle. Wool shipments rank second only to Boston. The export of timber and its products exceeds that of Seattle.

Access to the farmlands of the lower part of Puget Sound Lowland and the productive Willamette Valley and much of the northern portions of the Intermontane Area and the Rockies has kept Portland most important in agricultural commerce.

In addition to food products and wood, Portland has achieved some importance in the manufacture of clothing and wool textiles, chemicals, transportation equipment, and machinery. Oregon boasts of leading every state west of the Atlantic Seaboard states in the manufacture of woolen worsted textiles, and wool, worsted, and linen yarn. (Her western valleys support goats yielding about half of all mohair wool in the United States.)

Smaller cities in the valley include *Salem* (43,140) which manufactures local and Belgian flax fiber into thread, yarn, and twine. *Eugene* (35,879) makes wool blankets, knit goods, and suitings. Medford, south of the Willamette Valley, makes a variety of leather goods.

Pacific Prospect. The prospect is of special interest for any area which has experienced such a growth as that of California. The number of people who can go to such a place for retirement or employment is very much greater than at any time prior to the 1940's. They can go at an earlier age than ever before; they may find employment. The duration, location, and nature of World War II greatly stimulated the growth of the Pacific Coast, in both commerce and manufacturing. The postwar years have not greatly diminished this for California, although this is not true of the Northwest.

With a present population in excess of 10 million, a projected population of 15 million by 1960, the availability of water and the price of land became of increased interest and concern. The great Central Valley Project, when completed, will bring water from northern California to the San Joaquin portion of the Central Valley. This will take care of California's water problem (*Fig.* 18-3). Increased population and manufacturing are causing land values to soar. Labor has always been short and it is relatively more scarce today.

Industrial locations may appreciate or deteriorate in desirability; both are happening in parts of California. Industry which was established in California during the war emergency suffers as a result of the gradual decline in some contracts and abrupt cancellation of others. Not all California industrial locations have been rational, but many turned out to be fortunate. One cannot leave a study of this great province with the feeling that the door of opportunity is closing in even the most congested sections of California. Site disadvantages can be overcome, albeit expensively. The "dead hand of the past," obsolescence, has not been laid on California manufacturing facilities. This growth phenomenon is not just a boom. The Northwest has had a more conservative growth during the same years. Water and labor shortage affect many parts of the Northwest, too, but in somewhat different ways.

For the Pacific Valleys and Ranges and indeed for the Intermontane Area as well, the rapidity and scale of population and industrial increases of mid-century give every aspect of being permanent. The degree of change and the rate at which it occurred are measures of the changing state of the arts as well as an accelerated "westward movement."

BIBLIOGRAPHY

BOKE, Richard L., "River Development in the Central Valley of California," *Proceedings of the United Nations Scientific Conference on the Conservation and Utilization of Resources,* Vol. 4 (1951), pp. 137-141.

BROWN, Ralph H., *Historical Geography of the United States* (New York, Harcourt, Brace and Co., 1948), Chaps. 25, 27, 28.

"California Cotton Rush," *Fortune,* Vol. 39 (1949), pp. 85-89.

Central Valley Project, California (Bureau of Reclamation, U.S. Dept. of the Interior, Washington, 1950).

CLAIRE, Justinian, *The Sheep Industry,* Supplement to Federal Reserve Bank of San Francisco, *Monthly Review,* Sept., 1950.

EISELEN, Elizabeth, "The Central Valley Project, 1947," *Economic Geography,* Vol. 23, No. 1 (Jan., 1947), pp. 22-31.

FREEMAN, Otis W., and H. H. MARTIN, *The Pacific Northwest* (New York, John Wiley and Sons Inc., 1953).

HEWES, Gordon W., "The Fisheries of Northwestern North America," *Economic Geography,* Vol. 28, No. 1 (January, 1952), pp. 66-73.

"Industrial Los Angeles," *Fortune,* Vol. 39 (1949), pp. 76-83.

Ten Rivers in America's Future (The Report of the President's Water Resources Policy Commission, Washington, 1950), Vol. 2.

Types of Farming in California, Analyzed by Enterprises, Bulletin 654 (Univ. of California, Berkeley, 1941).

Western Power and Fuel Outlook, Supplement to Federal Reserve Bank of San Francisco, *Monthly Review,* Nov., 1950.

WILSON, Curtis M., "Port of Monterey and Vicinity," *Economic Geography,* Vol. 23, No. 3 (July, 1947), pp. 199-219.

ZIERER, Clifford M., "Tourism and Recreation in the West," *Geographical Review,* Vol. 42 (1952), pp. 462-481.

Part Three

GEOGRAPHIC REGIONS OF
CANADA, ALASKA, AND HAWAII

CHAPTER 19

CANADA

INTRODUCTION

PROBABLY the most important factor in the development of Canada is the desire and intention of becoming a nation; the approach to the economic geography of Canada is therefore national. Within this major frame of reference the economic subdivisions are used to the extent that the national economy permits. It is sometimes asserted that Canadians are endeavoring to establish a nation in defiance of the geographic circumstances under which they live. Boundary-makers have been accused of plying their trade without concern for the solvency of the regions they create.

The intent of the respective nations is paramount in all instances where the international boundary cuts across a region of relatively uniform natural endowments. The impact of this friendly boundary between the United States and Canada has been and remains a fundamental factor. Canada's most valuable timber, most useful waterways, and warm and fertile soils are near this boundary, likewise the major concentration of economic life in the United States. But everywhere this border marks a fundamental difference between its two sides. Even in the Spring Wheat region the boundary is responsible for the greatest of all differences, a market for wheat. Similarity of physical conditions are permissive in their influence; the compelling factor is the intention of the people occupying the land.

Situation. Canada lies in much the same latitude as Europe. Its situation with respect to the Atlantic and Pacific oceans has some elements of frustration. Its Atlantic margin trends at right angles to that of the United States and that of the prevailing paths of ships on the western European-eastern United States run.

Along the eastern periphery flows the cold Labrador current which appreciably impairs the usefulness of Canada's Atlantic coast. Along the Pacific margin the mountains present a continuous barrier; the Alaskan Panhandle reduces the Canadian contact with the Pacific Ocean. Most large Canadian rivers debouch into Hudson Bay, the Arctic, or the North Atlantic, thus limiting the usefulness of several streams.

Canada embraces the qualities associated with continentality: great distances, extremes of climate, a variety of landforms, and a variety of resources. Its situation between the western European countries, the United States, and the Soviet Union have combined to give Canadians a "continental" attitude toward the common problems.

The mere size of Canada, its climatic extremes, and its great distances have imposed conditions of settlement so exacting as to make the 14 million population numerically inadequate for the task of settling and developing such a large and varied area.

Instead of accessibility to the warm Gulf of Mexico and the Mississippi River, Canada has the inhospitable Hudson Bay and Mackenzie River. The landform provinces of the United States are in most instances common to Canada, although in a different pattern. The great bulk of the Appalachian Highlands lies south of the border; the Canadian portion extends from the St. Lawrence River to the Maritime Provinces on the Atlantic. The two nations jointly share the great Central Lowland province, the heartland of the continent. The Laurentian Upland is predominantly Canadian; only the Adirondacks and the Superior Upland are south of the border. The Northern Rockies of the United States continue on to Alaska, with higher elevations and fewer passes.

The Intermontane Area of the United States narrows and increases in elevation north of the border. The Coast Ranges of Canada are higher and more rugged than they are in the United States. The Cascades lose identity in the Canadian Coast Mountains.

Population. The significance of these physical facts is determined by the people who live in Canada, in part by their numbers and in part by the nature of their economy. In terms of the land area and the variety and abundance of earth resources, Canada is underpopulated. Its growth to the 14.6 million in 1953 has been cyclical; high points coincided with the American Revolution, the Irish famine, railway construction, the settlement of the western heartland, and the midcentury industrialization of Canada.

Between 1940 and 1953 Canada's population increased by 25 per cent. The only province to decline during this period was Saskatchewan which

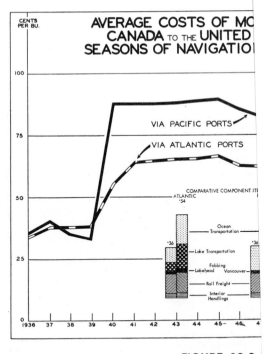

AVERAGE COSTS OF MC
CANADA TO THE UNITED
SEASONS OF NAVIGATIO

FIGURE 19-2

(Board of Grain Commissioner

In Chapter 2 there was some discussion o
agricultural regions shared by the two natio
indicate the conditions under which Canadi
its characteristic economy. Canada, too, had
took place much later than in the United St
came, shortly after the formation of the confe
pact of the agricultural frontier so important
nation.[1] Wheat did for Canada in the econo
what cotton had done for the United States (
ference in timing has made a great deal of dif
tory of the respective nations (*Figs.* 19-1, 19-

Despite the limiting factors of climate, soil
in employment in all provinces except Britis
highest proportion is in the Prairie Province
production gives rise to manufacturing. Cott(
cane and beet, tobacco, and the subtropical

[1] See V. C. Fowke, *Canadian Agricultural Policy*

---

just failed to hold its own. Sixty-two per cent of all Canadians are urban dwellers, although only two cities are in the million category: *Montreal,* 1.4 million; and *Toronto,* 950,000 (1952). The geographical distribution has not changed greatly since 1940. The most densely populated parts of the Dominion are in order: Prince Edward Island (43.96 per sq. mi.), Nova Scotia (31.23), New Brunswick (18.65), Ontario (10.94), and Quebec (6.68). The movement of Canadians to the United States continued even during World War II; in 1951, 26,000 came to the United States; of these 3,000 were classed as professional.

TABLE 19-1: *Population and Area, Canadian Provinces, 1951*

Province	Population	Area (sq. mi.)
ONTARIO	4,597,542	348,141
QUEBEC	4,055,681	523,860
MARITIME PROVINCES	1,256,710	50,400
BR. COLUMBIA	1,165,210	359,279
ALBERTA	939,501	248,800
SASKATCHEWAN	831,728	220,182
MANITOBA	776,541	219,723
NEWFOUNDLAND	361,416	147,994

SOURCE: *The Canada Yearbook,* 1954, p. 120.

CANADIAN INDUSTRY

A basic difference between the economies of Canada and the United States is the contrasting role of agriculture. Only 3.5 per cent of Canada's area is classed as arable, with an additional 2.5 per cent in meadow and pasture. Forest and woodland occupy 35 per cent of the area; the remainder, 59 per cent, is largely wasteland for one reason or another.

The manufacturing of the United States was first based upon a surplus of agricultural products; this continues as one foundation for its manufacturing. Commerce in the United States has likewise been concerned with farm products to an important extent. The nation's farms have long been a very important part of the market for manufactured goods. The reclamation of dry and of wet lands for agricultural purposes has been, and still is, an important frontier. While Canada shares all of the above factors of growth, it is on a much smaller scale. A study of the Canadian economy will therefore contribute to the perspective of the United States economy and vice versa.

Agriculture. To the extent that Canada shares the crop-specialty regions of the United States, the physical conditions under which these crops are

ANALYSIS OF CANA
BY SE
CROP YEARS

PER CENT

VIA UNITED STATES ATLAN

VIA CANADIAN PACIF

VIA CHURCHILL

* CROP YEAR END DATE

FIGU

This analysis of Canadian wheat exports
of this commerce in grain, see also *Fig*
Canada)

grown are similar; natural factors ⌐
do not change at the international b
ditions under which crops are produ
There is therefore a continuity in the
graphic regions reflect the nationa
Figs. 2-5, 1-3).

For the most part, the agricultura
with that of the United States, so fa
Whereas the great Central Lowlands
of crop-specialty regions, there is no
in climate within Canada are seldom
gion, chiefly because climatic condi
seldom encountered. Then too the ⌐
limiting factor in the development ⌐
much of the heart of Canada.

types of transformation-type industries in the United States. In Canada
even wheat and tobacco are for the most part sold for other nations to
process. In both countries dairying has attracted an important milk-process-
ing industry.

The major factors in accounting for the high wages and mechanization
of farm work in the United States stem from the extraordinary increase in
urbanization and the fact that the crops were susceptible of mechanization.
Canada is undergoing a similar experience, although on a smaller scale.

TABLE 19-2: Occupational Structure of the Gainfully Employed, 1950

UNITED STATES		CANADA
62,000,000	*total*	5,000,000
Per cent		*Per cent*
16	Agriculture, forestry, fishing	23
26	Manufacturing	20
24	Trade, commerce, and transportation	22
27	Service	19
1	Mining	2
5	Construction	8

SOURCE: *The Canada Yearbook; 1954*, p. 697; *Statistical Abstract*, 1954, p. 198.

Forests. The economy of Canada as a whole and of at least three of its
major geographic regions reflect the importance of forest resources in the
economy, including its manufacturing and commerce. The major frame of
reference for the Canadian forest industry merits some attention. The current rate of growth is estimated by the Forest Service as being 14 cubic feet
per acre, with a possible 28 cubic feet under better management. For the
United States forests the figures are 33 and 57 cubic feet respectively.
Although the total forested area of Canada is estimated as 1.45 million
square miles, only .43 million are classed as accessible and fit for ultimate
lumbering. In other words the proportion of commercial to total forest in
Canada is 34 per cent; for the United States it is 68 per cent.[2] These facts
do not deprecate the importance of the forest industries in the Canadian
economy, but they establish a suggestive frame of reference.

Minerals and Mineral Industries. A preview of Canada's minerals was
given in Chapter 3; it remains for us to relate them with Canada's regions
and to the circumstances under which the mineral economy has developed.
Nearly all minerals have to be extracted from the ground and from the

[2] *Trees: Yearbook of Agriculture* (U.S. Dept. of Agriculture, 1949), p. 745.

rock which encompasses them. This makes imperative the use of great quantities of heat and power. Canada is inadequately supplied with metallurgical coking coal, and the coal fields are remote from the market. Most of Canada's coal is on the Great Plains; it is generally low-grade. The best bituminous coal is found in long narrow deposits west of Calgary and paralleling the Rocky Mountain front. Canada's coal reserves are estimated to be 3.7 per cent of the continent's. Fortunately the Appalachian Plateau coal fields are not far distant and the Great Lakes provide low-cost transportation part of the way. An important part of the bituminous coal used for Canadian coke plants is from Canadian-owned coal mines in West Virginia and other Plateau states. Domestic and imported tonnages of coal are about equal. The amount of hydroelectric energy and the distribution of the water-power sites are of tremendous value to Canada.

Petroleum and natural gas have also become important sources of Canadian heat and power for industry. The very important discoveries and subsequent development of petroleum and gas fields in the plains of Alberta since 1947, has given both the Provincial and Dominion governments a decided "lift" in economy. The timing of the exploitation could hardly have been more fortunate from the point of view of Canadians.

Probably the greatest petroleum discovery in Canada up to mid-1955 is the Pembina field, 70 miles southwest of Edmonton, where estimated reserves are about a billion barrels. Other major fields include Sturgeon Lake, Smiley field in Saskatchewan (the first important light crude), and Rosslea field in Manitoba. The rate of growth in 1953-54 was about twice that of the United States. At some future date the 20,000 square miles of Athabaska tar sands may be mined for oil extraction. These sands are 200 miles north of Edmonton.

A third important industrial mineral is copper, and Canada is well supplied with it. It occurs with nickel in the Sudbury district in the proportion of about two pounds of copper for each pound of nickel recovered. Other important copper sources are, at Noranda-Rouyn, Lynn Lake, Gaspé Coppe, Horne, and Flin Flon. Canada ranks fourth in world copper production.

Recently in western Labrador important deposits of high-grade iron ore, accessible by strip mining, have been discovered and are being developed into a significant source.

Nickel from the Sudbury district in southern Ontario constitutes about three-fourths of the world's production. The market for most of this ferroalloy is not far distant in the United States' Manufacturing Belt; the Canadian use of nickel for steel manufacture is growing. Canada is the second-largest producer of zinc; their largest producer is in the southern Canadian Rockies near Trail, B. C. (*Fig.* 20-23). In cobalt production, Canada ranks fourth, with most of it mined in southern Ontario, at Cobalt. For many years this was Canada's great silver source; now most silver comes as a joint product of lead, copper and gold mines. From the Sudbury district also comes one-half of the world's platinum.

A relatively new mineral, uranium, is extracted from pitchblende at Port Radium on Great Bear Lake. This is one of the most isolated of Canadian mining districts. Men and supplies are flown in, and the ore is shipped out by water during the summer to the railhead at Waterways, Ontario, thence to the refineries near Toronto on Lake Ontario. Another "new" metal is titanium, mined just north of Havre St. Pierre on the St. Lawrence River.

Recent explorations between Regina and Radville in Saskatchewan, indicate sylvite ores from which potash may be extracted. The deposits lie from 3,000 to 7,000 feet below the surface; no operations today are at such depths.

The market for these Canadian minerals is largely in the United States. Most of the risk and investment capital has come from the United States, particularly since 1940. This is true both for the mining and manufacturing industries.

Manufacturing. Many of the conditions under which Canadian manufacture took place differ from those in the United States, the difference in timing being one of the most important. Lacking cotton fiber and the individual enterprisers interested in the establishment of a cotton-textile industry at that time, an early start was not a factor in the development of Canadian manufacturing. So, too, the exchange built up as a result of cotton sales to England were lacking. The dearth of a domestic market was another important factor in accounting for Canada's tardy industrialization. With the United States manufacturing districts so near, and with Great Britain paying for Canadian raw materials with factory goods, additional reasons for tardy development are apparent. Canada's membership in the Empire, and later in the Commonwealth, has been only partial compensation for the relatively small population, and hence relatively limited market at home. The nature as well as extent of the Canadian market for factory goods differed from that in the United States. Since the middle of the nineteenth century, the tariff of the United States has kept many Canadian factory goods out; the Reciprocal Trade Agreements have lowered somewhat the provisions of this tariff.

To contend with this situation, Canada has resorted to a number of devices in order to promote manufacturing, one such device is known as Empire Content, adopted early in the 1930's. It provides that Canadian branch plants of the United States (or other country) may label their factory products "Product of Canada" if the required proportion of manufacturing costs are attributable to Canada. Thus the product has access to the Canadian and Commonwealth markets on the same terms as a wholly-Canadian-made commodity. The greater part of the United States' investment of some $8 billion in Canadian industry is in such branch plants. In 1950 some 2,500 or about one-fourth of all Canadian factories were to a large degree owned by interests in the United States. A number of Canadian concerns also have large manufacturing plants in the United States and have much capital invested here.

In 1946 Canadians spent $832 million for increased industrial facilities; in 1951 it was in excess of $2 billion. In view of the close industrial bonds between Canada and the United States, this increasing industrialization is especially significant. In addition to the actual increase in factory production, there are important accompaniments which result from urbanism and higher wages. The changes have altered somewhat the main pattern of Canadian manufacturing, but the growth trend is more significant. During World War II, economic co-operation between Canada and the United States resulted in the manufacture of new types of products in Canada by Canadians. The postwar period of an industrially-retarded Japan and Germany gave Canada a welcome market opportunity. By 1955, with Japan, Western Germany, and Great Britain having greater industrial facilities than in 1939, Canada's factories find a market harder to get. There is no evidence of curtailment thus far.

Canada ranks eighth among the world's steel-making nations, with a 1953 production of 3.4 million tons. During the same year Canada mined about 5 million tons of iron ore, placing it sixth among iron-mining nations. During this year the United States sent 2.3 million tons of iron ore to Canada and bought from her 1.2 million tons. In the same year, Canadian exports of pig iron to the United States totaled 11,000 tons, while imports from the United States amounted to 8,500 tons. This is a phase of the international integration of the primary iron and steel industry.

The use of hydroelectric power is relatively more important to Canada than it is to the United States (*Fig.* 19-3). One of the largest hydroelectric installations in the world has been completed in British Columbia's coastal mountains, Kitimat, the basis for a gigantic, integrated aluminum-smelting and refining center. The most recent power development is taking place at the International Section of the St. Lawrence River where agencies of the

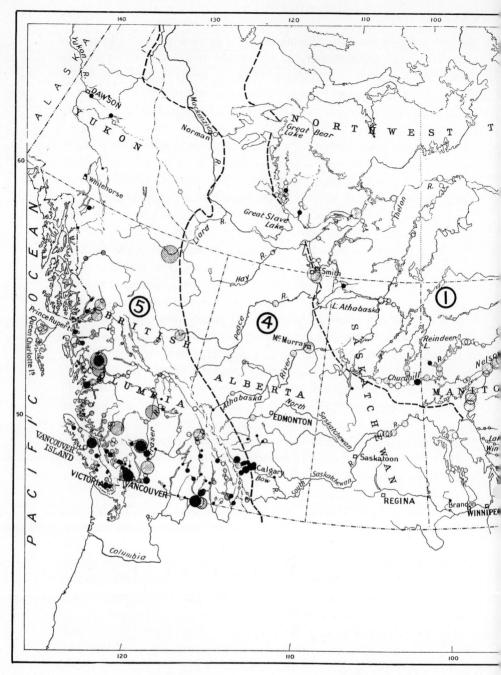

FIGURE 19-3: *Water Powers*

Developed water power sites (black discs), undeveloped water power sites (shad
Shield, (2) Appalachian, (3) St. Lawrence Lowland, (4) Great Plains, (5) C
Resources, Ottawa)

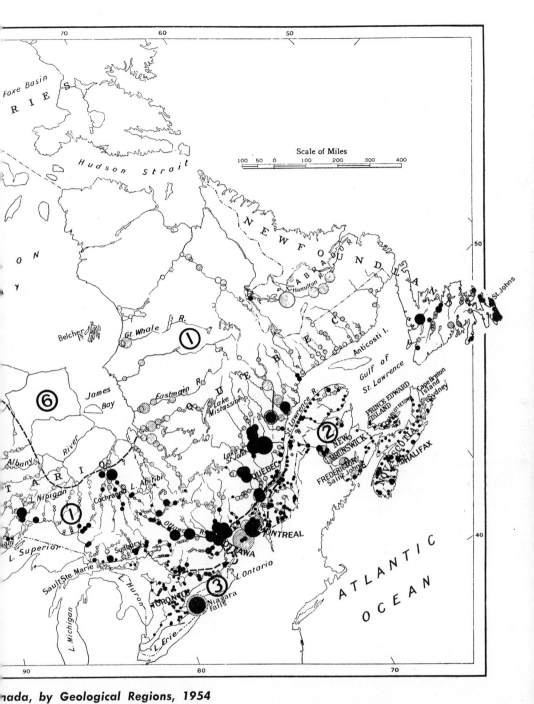

nada, by Geological Regions, 1954

s), and boundaries of geological regions (--) are shown for: (1) Canadian
eran, and (6) Hudson Bay Lowlands. (Dept. of Northern Affairs and National

481

two nations are co-operating in the installation in an area now power-deficient.

TABLE 19-3: *Manufacturing in Canada*

Net value, 1950

Pulp and paper	$511,142,983
Electrical	206,769,220
Sawmills	239,225,162
Machinery (not elec.)	171,257,491
Nonferrous—metal smelting	202,711,781
Automobiles	284,785,098
Rubber products	134,061,761
Iron and steel, primary	154,542,373
Apparel, women's	91,469,056
Printing and publishing	129,018,312
Breweries	105,073,118
Apparel, men's	103,346,165
Railway rolling stock	82,389,000
Bakery products	98,412,581
Slaughtering and meat packing	107,701,364
Petroleum products	107,371,118

SOURCE: *The Canada Year Book, 1954,* p. 647.

CANADA'S TRADE

Main Phases in Canada's Development. There have been three main phases in Canada's development as an economic power. The first was the development of specialities for world trade, fostered by Great Britain until World War I when it became apparent that Britain was unable to continue indefinitely with this market support; this situation was officially recognized at the Imperial Conference in Ottawa in 1932. A second phase for Canada was a trend toward self-sufficiency made possible through the enactment of tariffs and the payment of bounties of one sort or another to stimulate Canadian industries. A third phase has been an unplanned but increasing interdependence with the United States for deficiencies in raw materials and market. In effect, the first two have served to supplement the third.

Export duties have been levied only on such commodities as will move anyhow. As a result of legislative attempts to gain prosperity, and of the increasing population, there has been a trend toward self-sufficiency throughout the populous parts of Canada. This is despite the emphasis upon furs, softwood, wheat, pulpwood, dairying, and minerals. These successive export specialties clearly reflect the role of the United States market, and to an extent, the role of Canada in the British Commonwealth of Nations.

For Canada, the net result of Britain's insistence upon paying for raw materials with factory products has been increased domestic production and dependence upon the United States for its imported factory goods. Economic domination by the one nation over the other is by no means in the total ratio of their respective populations, nor does it exist in all forms of economic endeavor; each nation has absolute advantages as to resources. Early in 1944 the two governments agreed upon the general policy of postwar Reciprocal Trade Agreements, similar to that of pre-war days. The one factor that looms over the reciprocal development is that Canada numbers but 14.6 million people. Students of political geography may well observe this important example of economic and political harmony in the development of a continental heartland, cross-currents to the contrary notwithstanding.

Relative Standing. Canada ranks third among the nations in the value of its trade, yet it ranks fortieth in population. In 1950 the value of Canadian-United States trade was surpassed by the trade between no other two nations. Each year since 1948 the United States has bought more Canadian goods than all British Commonwealth countries combined. In 1941 the United States took one-third of all Canadian exports; in 1951 it took three-fifths of the total. In turn Canada buys 70 per cent of all merchandise imports from the United States. After allowing for price differences, Canada's annual product in 1950 was 40 per cent higher than in 1940.[3] Canadian imports from the United States embrace a very wide variety of commodities, including raw materials for industry and manufactured goods and luxuries. In 1950 imports of machinery led, followed by petroleum products, and coal. What cannot show in such a statistical record of imports and exports between Canada and the United States are the international industrial bonds, including integration, which relate individual industries on both sides of the border. More will be said of this later.

Of the rather narrowly-specialized group of exports, the United States takes 80 per cent of the newsprint, which with wood and wood products constitutes Canada's leading export group. The second-ranking export group is agricultural products; this does not take into account the fact that a large part of the wheat is exported through the United States ports. Approximately half of this agricultural group is animal products: live cattle, fish, furs, and hides. Third-ranking group is minerals; 90 per cent of Canada's mineral

[3] In 1948 Canada exported an average of $241 in goods per capita, while imports were $205 per capita. In the United States for the same year, the figures were $94 and $140 respectively.

production is exported. Of the total mineral export, nickel, silver, and copper dominate; gold, lead, zinc, iron ore, and petroleum follow in order. The last two will soon be exported in much greater quantities. More important than these visible items of export are the millions of dollars spent in Canada by tourists each year.

Tourism as a Factor in Canadian Trade. Although it is difficult to assess definitely the direct and indirect results of tourism, it seems certain that the greatest single source of dollars for Canada is from visitors, nearly all of them from the United States. This flow of people across the border is primarily a summer phenomenon, although all seasons are represented. The ease of crossing the border, and the proximity of the most densely populated parts of the respective countries, has made the crossing a commonplace event. Although most Canadian regions are concerned with tourists, the Maritimes, St. Lawrence Valley, Ontario Peninsula, and Pacific Mountains and Valleys are the most popular. Entry is by ocean liner, lakeboat, ferry, railroad, airplane, and automobile. No other country can match this flow of tourists.

Individual families, church, educational, and recreational groups may return to the same place each year. Scientific groups frequently meet in convention in Toronto or Montreal. Branch plants bring sales meetings; the mining corporations hold international board of directors meetings in Canadian cities. Technical "task forces" frequent both urban and frontier areas in the development of minerals. The pressure of young people upon the institutions of higher learning, particularly professional schools, has reached the place in the United States where many seek admission to Canadian universities. Thousands of United States citizens have bought property in Canada and commute to their work in Detroit, Buffalo, or other cities.

On the other hand, the Canadian Parliament has upon occasion "viewed with alarm" the departure of college and university graduates for employment in the United States. French-speaking citizens of Canada have come in large numbers to the New England states. On a smaller scale the same thing has happened in the Pacific Northwest. The more moderate climate, and factory payrolls, attracted many from north of the border during and after World War II. With the industrialization of Canada has come an impetus to the flow of people as well as commodities across the border.

BIBLIOGRAPHY

See bibliography at end of Chapter 20.

CHAPTER **20**

CANADIAN REGIONS, RESOURCES, AND INDUSTRIES

CANADA may be resolved into seven geographic regions, each distinguished by a degree of homogeneity in its economic life. These regions are: Maritime Canada, Newfoundland, St. Lawrence Valley and Ontario Peninsula, Laurentian Upland, the Prairie Provinces, Pacific Mountains and Valleys, and the Arctic Plains.

Most of these regions border the United States and it is along a narrow zone near the border that the principal Canadian centers of population are found. The economies which have developed within each of these regions vary widely and their relation to the trade of Canada is significant, especially when the creation of a homogeneous nation is the goal. Increased trade with the United States directly does not impair the integrity of these Canadian geographic regions.

MARITIME CANADA

Physical Setting. Nova Scotia, New Brunswick, and Prince Edward Island are included in the geographic region traditionally known as The Maritimes (*Fig.* 20-1). In the development of Canada, these lands have had the longest history, yet they have not, in modern times, served as the "front door" to Canada. Shipping has sought the inland ports, upstream along the St. Lawrence River. The most economical port to use is generally the one requiring the shortest land haul.

There is little in the physical environment of New England which has contributed to its high degree of urbanism except its situation with respect to the productive lowlands of the Great Lakes and the breaches in the Ap-

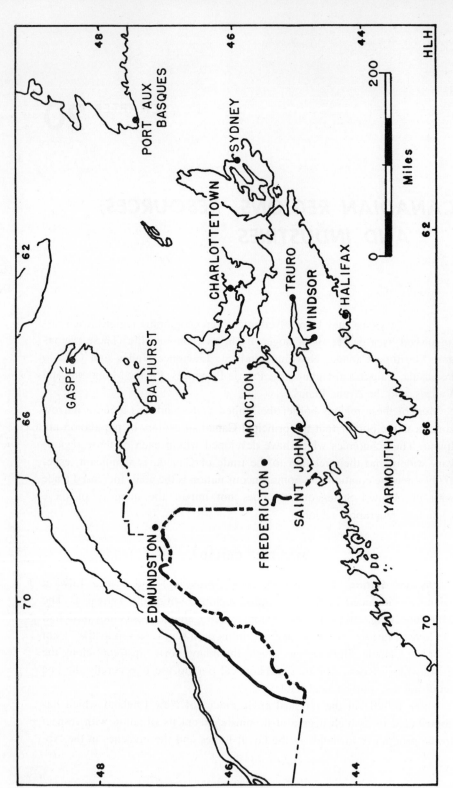

FIGURE 20-1: *Maritimes*

Miles

0 200

palachian Highlands. Canada's Maritimes have no such location. They may have profited more from their relation to northeastern United States than from their location with respect to the interior of Canada. During the anxious periods of the economic depression of the 1930's and the subsequent war, Canadian newspaper editorial comment displayed increasingly the feeling that Canada's future lay in continental development. These editorial comments were by no means confined to the most "worldly" [1] of Canadian provinces, the Prairies.

Relief and Soils. Viewed on a relief map, the Maritimes appear as a northern extension of the Appalachian Highlands, set apart from the main bulk of the Highlands only by the caprice of the boundary-makers. These uplands, together with the associated peninsulas and islands which make up the eastern promontory of North America, have a situation with respect to Canada which contrasts with that of New England to the interior of the United States. The Canadian portion of the Highlands does not preserve the well-defined subdivisions of the Appalachians which characterize the area south of New York State. In eastern Canada, including the Maritimes, the Appalachian System is represented only by the moderate highland areas of the New England-Maritime Province (*Fig.* 1-2). The five physiographic sections comprising this Province are Gaspé, New England Upland, Seaboard Lowland, Nova Scotia, and Newfoundland.

Although this region is essentially a fairly rugged and inaccessible area, it has some reasonably fertile districts; among these cultivated valleys are the St. Johns of New Brunswick, the Annapolis and Cornwallis of Nova Scotia, and smaller valleys in eastern Quebec. Generally, the Canadian portion of the Appalachians is forested, has swift streams, and numerous lakes; it is scarcely an inviting land for agriculture. Glaciation scraped off the higher places and filled the valleys; the net result generally was disastrous for both; in New England a similar process frequently benefitted the valley, since the glacial till had a somewhat smaller proportion of boulders.

Climate. The location of the Maritime on the eastern "hump" of North America gives them two main types of climate: the marine climate of southern Nova Scotia, mildest of all parts of the Maritimes, and the continental type of most of the remainder. Differences in elevation (100-2,700 feet) in the continental portion are great enough to warrant subdivision.[2] For the farm crops grown in this area, the British Meteorological Service

[1] Worldly in the sense that international-affairs coverage is unusually complete in the newspapers of Prairie Province cities, a consequence of the wide range of nationalities represented among the population.

[2] D. F. Putnam, "The Climate of the Maritime Provinces," *Canadian Geographical Journal*, Vol. 21 (1940), pp. 135-147.

has adopted 42° F. as the critical temperature limit. The growing season varies from less than 150 days in northern New Brunswick to 190 days in southern Nova Scotia. Most of the 35 to 50 inches of precipitation occurs during the winter six months, although there is no pronounced seasonal maximum.

Forests and Lumbering. New Brunswick and Nova Scotia have most of the commercial timber in the Maritimes, with the former having a stand half again that of Nova Scotia. In general, Maritime forests resemble those in New England. Coniferous stands dominate: red and white spruce, balsam, the mixed hardwood and softwood type in which white pine and hemlock occur, and some black spruce and cedar which occur on poorly drained land.[3]

Even in New Brunswick and Nova Scotia, less than 20 per cent of their timbered land supports merchantable timber. Despite the minor position of Maritime forests in Canada's forest industry,[4] the industry plays an important role in the life of the local farmers. Winter employment and the sale of wood from their own woodlots are frequently the principal sources of cash income.

Agriculture. One of the two important agricultural areas of the Maritime Provinces is Nova Scotia. At one time Nova Scotia was the front door of Canada. In 1800 Nova Scotia, or New Scotland, appeared to have a future as promising as Massachusetts, which is not much more than half as large. Its location on the Gulf of St. Lawrence places it nearer England; its harbors are never frozen; it is nearer to the Grand Banks fishing grounds. Massachusetts has no agricultural area so large as the combined Annapolis-Cornwallis valleys. The mineral wealth of the Canadian province is more varied and more abundant than Massachusetts. At the conclusion of the American Revolution, New England Loyalists flocked into Nova Scotia to give it the same type of stock which dominated in Massachusetts during its early years. In spite of all these favorable circumstances, Nova Scotia supports only half a million people, engaged in fishing, agriculture, lumbering and a little manufacturing. It has been passed by in the nation's development because of its remoteness from the continental heartland which produces the major part of Canada's exports and consumes a large part of its imports.

[3] W. E. D. Halliday, "A Forest Classification for Canada," *Forest Service Bulletin* 89 (Canada Dept. of Mines and Resources, 1937), pp. 1-50.

[4] At Lepreau, near St. John, New Brunswick, on the north shore of the Bay of Fundy, Canadian and United States interests completed a mill in 1955 costing $75 million, with a capacity of 350,000 tons of newsprint and kraft paper annually.

Even the ports of northeastern United States ship more Canadian products than the Maritime ports.

The famed lowland of the Annapolis-Cornwallis valleys in western Nova Scotia is the largest area of good farm land in all the Maritimes. It stands as an arable island in the glacially-scraped rock surface of Nova Scotia, most of which is woodland or cut-over forest. The valleys parallel the western coast, separated from the Bay of Fundy by a narrow ridge known as North Mountain, rising from 400-600 feet above the valley floor. The combined valleys are nearly one hundred miles in length, vary in width from three to ten miles, and open at each end to the Bay waters. The reddish sandstone soils are in contrast with the lava and granites of the bordering ridges. The growing season averages 190 days, from April 22 to November 3, with a frost-free period of 145 days. Although it is the first part of the Maritimes to warm up in the spring, the Bay of Fundy gives these valleys the same advantages that the Great Lakes give their lee shores: late spring budding and late autumn frosts which make possible the successful apple orcharding which is the most important source of farm income. Approximately half of the apple crop of all Canada comes from these valleys, little of which can be sold in Canada. Such a specialty is possible only because of a highly developed export market in western Europe, particularly in Great Britain which takes most of the two-million-barrel production.

Despite the emphasis upon apples, the farmers are as nearly self-sufficient in foodstuffs as possible. Small grains, hay, and root crops for the stock, and vegetables for the table have made these valley farmers perhaps as prosperous and contented as those described in Longfellow's poem on the Acadians. At the open ends of the valley, where the world's highest tides flood the narrow flats, the farmers have built dikes to reclaim the rich alluvial soils.

In most aspects of the agricultural industries, New Brunswick is similar to Nova Scotia. In the total acreage and in the value of field crops, the value of land and buildings, and in the net income of the farm operators, New Brunswick is slightly ahead of Nova Scotia, although, of course, the Maritimes are at the bottom of the list of Canadian provinces. The Maritime Marshland Rehabilitation Act, 1948, sets up an organization for the construction and maintenance of canals and ditches needed to reclaim about 100,000 acres of wet land, principally in New Brunswick, but found in all three sections.

Fishing. In fishing, New Brunswick ranks third among all Canadian provinces, being exceeded only by British Columbia and Nova Scotia. This is true for both salt-and-fresh-water catch. The economy of Nova Scotia began with fishing and lumbering, first white pine and the other softwoods. Today deep-sea fishing and lobster fishing remain as an important basis of the economy. *Digby* (1,657) is the main port for what is probably the world's greatest scallop fishing fleet. *Yarmouth* (8,106) has an important tuna fishing fleet.

Minerals and Manufacturing. Nova Scotia produces two-thirds of the coal mined in Canada, from seams located on and near tidewater. The Sydney field on Cape Breton Island which occupies 200 square miles, is bounded on three sides by the sea. On the east side of Nova Scotia, in Pictou County, the seams exceed twenty feet in thickness. Tidewater coal and iron from the ore beds in Newfoundland meet at the furnaces of *Sydney* (31,317), where the manufacture of iron has been relatively a major industry. That it has remained small is largely due to the propinquity of the United States. Furthermore, the St. Lawrence is frozen part of the year, and the construction of a rather meandering national railroad to connect the province with the interior has not overcome its isolation. *Halifax* (85,589), *Amherst* (8,620), and Truro manufacture the items associated with service industries and export some chocolate, petroleum products, and sugar.

The basic contrasts in the economy of New Brunswick and of Nova Scotia is revealed in the importance of their respective mineral and manufacturing industries. The minerals industry of New Brunswick is about one-fifth as important (employment) as that of Nova Scotia. A high-grade gypsum is quarried near Hillsborough, and there is a small oil and gas industry near Moncton.

Both Nova Scotia and New Brunswick have declined in population since 1940, in each case about 40,000. Although the rural population of the two sections is comparable (300,686 in 1951), the urban population of New Brunswick is about two-thirds that of its eastern neighbor (215,011 as against 344,011). Manufacturing is more concentrated in New Brunswick which has eight cities with manufactures of at least $1 million annually; Nova Scotia has 18 such communities.

Installed horsepower of prime movers and the net value of manufactures, are comparable, but New Brunswick trails Nova Scotia in the number of industrial wage earners and wages paid. The principal manufactures are pulp and paper, sawmill products, processed fish, sashes and doors, air-conditioning equipment, and foods. During the past twenty years manufacturing in New Brunswick has increased, while Nova Scotia has remained

FIGURE 20-2: *Port of Halifax*

By virtue of their location, climate, and Old World atmosphere, the Maritimes have profited greatly from the tourist industry. The Nova Scotian Hotel (center) is a conspicuous feature of the Halifax waterfront shown in this photograph. The aircraft carrier H.M.C.S. *Magnificent* is in the foreground. (Canadian National Railways)

nearly static. Most of the manufacturing industries named above are concentrated in *St. John* (50,779) and *Moncton* (27,334).

Tourism. A combination of comfortable summer climate, Old World atmosphere, and fair seasonal accessibility by automobile from the urban centers of southeastern Canada and New England have promoted an important tourist industry for many parts of the Maritimes (*Fig.* 20-2). The degree of isolation which characterizes the region has tended to preserve something of the settlement forms and culture of the French, Scottish, German, and New England ventures in occupying the land.

Descendants of the French Acadians from the original settlement in the Minas Basin have prospered along the Bay of Fundy coast southwestward from Grand Pré. Kentville, Wolfville, Bridgetown, Annapolis Royal, Digby, and Weymouth are pleasant towns along what is locally known as the longest Main Street (80 miles) in the world. Germans from the Palatinate came to the more rugged east coast of Nova Scotia where all the features of a fishing economy make this a tourist objective. The largest town is Lunenburg, where offshore and Grand Banks fishing dominates the economy. In this district the economy has changed very little over the years.

From Yarmouth to Barrington and at Shelburne along the rugged southeast coast, the settlers were Loyalists from New England and the Middle Atlantic colonies. These first settlers built substantially in their adopted land; today it is an antiquarian's delight. The economy demands a frugal livelihood based upon fish, fish products, and tourists. Along the north shore is another colonial American town, Pictou, founded by settlers from eastern Pennsylvania and Maryland, just before the American Revolution. Settlers from Scotland followed some years later. Something of the inaccessibility which still characterizes these districts is suggested by the fact the Canadian Pacific Railway does not enter Nova Scotia by way of the land bridge, Chignecto Isthmus, but crosses northern Maine to St. John, New Brunswick, on the Bay of Fundy. Tides in the Bay are so high that railroad car ferries are impractical.

Airlines from Boston and Montreal serve St. John's, with branch lines to Yarmouth, Halifax, and Sydney, but air connection plays a minor part in the economy of Nova Scotia.

NEWFOUNDLAND

Youngest of the ten political provinces of Canada, the Island of Newfoundland and the Coast of Labrador have a varied political history and an economic life marked by great fluctuations. Admission into the Canadian confederation made no change in the boundaries of Newfoundland and its territorial possession across the straits of Belle Isle. This easternmost part of the North American continent has long played an important part in the affairs of the United States and of Canada (*Fig.* 20-3).

Physical Setting. This island is about the size of the state of Ohio. It lies at the mouth of the Gulf of St. Lawrence separated from Cape Breton Island and Quebec by the cold waters of the Gulf. It lies also on the main transAtlantic air routes to Great Britain and western Europe. Air fields are maintained at Gander on Newfoundland and at Goose Bay on Labrador.

Terrain. The entire coastline of this roughly triangular island is exceedingly irregular due to submergence of an ancient mountainous upland. Glaciation has modified the terrain as a result of scraping the uplands and deposition in the lowlands. The surface of Newfoundland is a rolling plateau, sloping from a maximum elevation of 2,000 feet on the west to about 700 feet on the east; parts of the southern margin are lower. Long Range, the

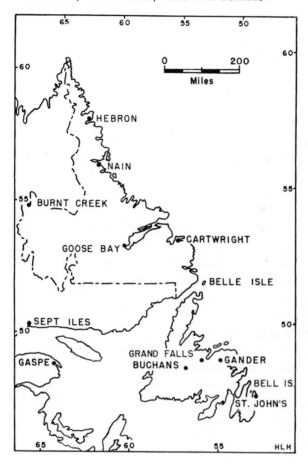

FIGURE 20-3: *Newfoundland*

one mountain range in Newfoundland, parallels the west coast. Resistant rocks and glacial scouring have combined to give the island poor thin soils and poor drainage. There are no major streams to offer access to the interior of the island.

Climate. Newfoundland's climate is in no small part the result of its situation upon the lee coast of the continent at a place where the cold Labrador Current flows along the eastern shore. Ice or ice water is therefore a part of the environment throughout the year. Although no harbor is frozen in winter, there is much floating ice. Winds from the south bring warmer air in from the vicinity of the Gulf Stream, thus causing fogs which abound along these coasts. In winter the cold air masses from the mainland bring continental conditions to insular Newfoundland. There is extreme variability to weather conditions due to the prevalence of cyclonic and anti-cyclonic phenomena. Although winters are long and cold, the extremes of temperature are not comparable to the interior of North America.

At the more favored places, the growing season is seldom over one hundred days. Although there is very much less fog in the interior of the island than along the coastal waters, there is too little sunshine for most temperate zone crops. Nearly all of the population lives along the eastern and southern coasts despite the cloudy weather and frequent rains.

The effect of this climate upon tree growth has been to prevent its reaching commercial size along the east coast and elsewhere to attain heights generally under 50 feet and a diameter of 12 inches. Fairly dense forests of black spruce, balsam fir, and a few other varieties of fir, pine and juniper occupy much of the interior of the island. Glacial scouring has resulted in extensive areas of no tree growth, locally known as "barrens." Virtually no timber is exported, but pulpwood and newsprint have become established at two places, Corner Brook and Grand Falls.

Population. Except for the Exploits River Valley in the east, virtually all of Newfoundland's population (361,416) lives along the coast. The principal city, *St. John's* (67,749), and the shores of Conception Bay, localize nearly all of the people in the far southeast. The south coast has few people except on the peninsula between Placentia and Fortune bays. The long narrow peninsula on the northwest is very sparsely populated except in the southern portion.

Agriculture. There are few districts of good soil, and they are all located in the western part of the island. The people who live along the eastern and southeastern shores are accessible to fishing grounds. The agriculture of Newfoundland is in the nature of a residuum; fishing has always dominated the economy of Newfoundlanders. Newfoundland has reacted as have so many parts of the world where nature has endowed them with a resource adequate for sustenance: specialized in the one favored livelihood and bought the necessities.

About 66,000 acres of the island support some sort of agriculture today; this is about one-fifth of 1 per cent of the total area. Most of this cropped land is as widely scattered as the fishing villages which dot the indented eastern and southeastern coasts. The landholdings of the 35,743 farmers are very small; nine-tenths of the units are under four acres.

The important crops are hay and potatoes; a few acres of cabbage and turnips are also grown. The livestock raised includes sheep (89,000),

cattle (23,000), goats (12,000), swine (11,000), and poultry (346,400).[5]
Dairying is retarded in its growth by the lack of urban markets; St. John's
depends upon the nearby Avalon Peninsula for nearly all of its dairy
products.

Most of the intervillage communication is by boat. The single railroad is
narrow-gauge and runs between Port au Basque and St. John's; it does
little to promote a commerce in farm products. The interior of the island
is almost sterile. During the depressed years of the 1930's, when Newfoundland was in the process of seeking new sources of employment, a survey
reported that more farmland could be found in the Gander and Humber
valleys in the northeast.

In 1947 there were 6 fox farms and 80 mink farms, a marked decline
since 1915, the peak fur-farming year. Trapping of beaver, mink, and fox
has also declined.

Fishing Industry. Newfoundland's cod-fishing industry is world famous
and has been the dominant source of the island's livelihood since the first
permanent settlement. The fisheries on all coasts of the Island of Newfoundland, the Coast of Labrador, and the deep-sea fishing on the Newfoundland
Banks include nearly all varieties of fish found in the cold waters of the
North Atlantic.

Since the low period of the 1930's, the trend is toward a greater variety
of fish caught and products marketed. Salted codfish has declined from 71
per cent of all fishery exports in 1938 to 55 per cent in 1948. Herring,
lobster, salmon, bream, and haddock exports have increased during the
same period. Employment by fishing districts has changed. The Census in
1945 listed 30,953 persons as fishermen; those engaged in inshore fishing
increased, and those engaged in deep-sea and Coast of Labrador fishing declined. Freezing has helped Newfoundland diversify its fish exports; cod,
herring, and haddock fillets are the most important increases.

Hair seals have been a fairly important adjunct to cod fishing; the present catch is about a third of that during the peak years late in the nineteenth
century. During the spring, before cod fishing begins, several hundred sealers
go north to kill seals on the ice floes northeast of Newfoundland. The oil
from the fat is used for soap making, and the skin is used for leather.

Minerals. There are four minerals mined commercially in Newfoundland, island and mainland: bituminous coal, lead, zinc, and iron ore. Iron

[5] *The Canada Yearbook, 1950* (Dominion Bureau of Statistics, Ottawa), p. **451**
(Data is for 1945).

FIGURE 20-4: *Apparel Plant, Newfoundland*

Since Newfoundland became a part of Canada, efforts have been made to attract industry. Among those which have been established is this modern mill, a response to labor primarily. (Dept. of Mines and Resources, Newfoundland)

mining on Bell Island in Conception Bay is the principal support for the 4,000 persons living there. The Wabana Mine produces hematite ore from beds that extend out under the Bay. The seam is so wide that electrically-operated shovels can be used to load the broken ore into mine cars from which it goes directly into steamships. This ore is relatively high in phosphorus, the reduction of which is an added expense. In 1945 the mine exported 1,704,000 tons to nearby St. John's, to Great Britain and to Germany.

Zinc and lead ores are mostly American properties and constitute but an infant industry thus far. The extraction center is near Red Indian Lake in the interior of the island. Interest in copper, silver, nickel, chromium, and vanadium has continued but nothing of a commercial nature has been reported.

Bituminous coal is known to exist in the remote St. George's Bay area on the west coast. Although reportedly abundant, there is very little market for this coal on the island. Domestic heating is with wood, and there is but little industry. Cape Breton Island ships coal to St. John's more cheaply than Newfoundland can.

FIGURE 20-5: *Newfoundland Machine Shop*

Machine shops are generally found near the factories which use machinery. This modern machine shop suggests the success Newfoundland has had in attracting some new industries. (Dep't of Mines and Resources, Newfoundland).

Commerce and Manufacturing. Mention was made earlier of Newfoundland's situation with respect to the trans-Atlantic air routes. Steamship routes have much the same pattern. Few of the ships stop at Newfoundland ports, and the opportunity for employment of local persons on the great airfields is limited; the fields are almost self-sufficient "colonies" of outlanders.

Within very recent years, Newfoundland's government has aggressively sought new manufacturing industries and has met with some success. Among the new plants are those making pulp and paper, cotton textiles, leather goods, machine shop products, sea food, and fish products (*Figs.* 20-4, 20-5).

ST. LAWRENCE VALLEY-ONTARIO PENINSULA

The major part of Canada's population, agriculture, manufacturing and commerce has been concentrated on two lowland areas of southern Canada, the St. Lawrence Valley and peninsular Ontario. It is this part that has drawn the fire of those who assert Canada is trying to create a great nation in defiance of geographic circumstances. These populous lowlands are sep-

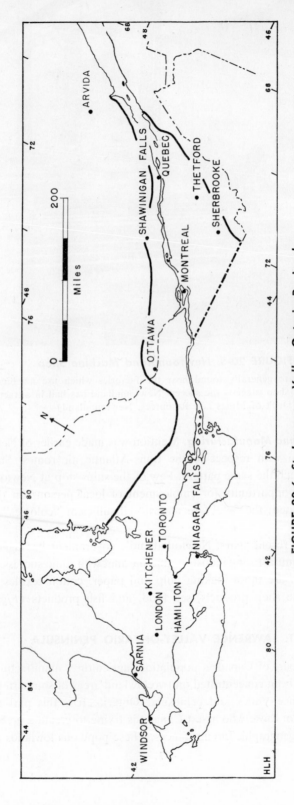

FIGURE 20-6: St. Lawrence Valley-Ontario Peninsula

This map qualifies as a map of Canada's Manufacturing Belt. It also shows the locale for the Great Lakes-St. Lawrence Seaway.

arated by a southern extension of the Laurentian Upland which reaches the St. Lawrence River at the International Section.

Physical Setting. The St. Lawrence Valley lowland is an attenuated low-lying plain stretching on both sides of the river from Quebec City to the Thousand Islands. This plain averages 50 miles in width, and embraces an area slightly smaller than the state of Ohio. The Laurentian Upland borders the lowland on the north; the Appalachian Highlands border it on the south. The northern border is much more definite.

The Ontario Peninsula, a northward extension of the Central Lowland Province of the United States, is in reality a compound peninsula with its several parts well located to serve as passageways between the St. Lawrence Valley and the Great Lakes basin, and between the lake plain of New York and the eastern lake section of the Middle West (*Fig.* 20-6).[6]

The peninsula dips deeply into the flow of traffic between eastern and western Canada, a position quite likely to appreciate in importance with the completion of the St. Lawrence Seaway. Unlike the St. Lawrence River, the accessibility of this peninsula is not confined to the summer months. Ice in the Great Lakes affects the commerce of the peninsula much less than the frozen St. Lawrence affects Montreal.

Soils. Most of the St. Lawrence Valley is a series of nearly level plains thickly covered by glacial deposits. Some of the soils are among the best in Canada, with the upper (western) portion of the valley more favored than the lower section. Old lake plains are numerous in the upper Valley. Although rather more of the lowland is south of the St. Lawrence, the major part of the rural and nearly all of the urban population are on the north side. This is so for several reasons, among them the great accessibility to central and western Canada and to power sites on the rivers descending from the Laurentian Upland.

In many respects the soils of the peninsula are similar to those in the St. Lawrence Valley. The Peninsula is covered with a thick mantle of glacial deposits and is comparatively free from lakes and swamps. Along the north shore of Lake Erie the drainage is poor; a narrow belt of poorly-drained lake plain also borders Lake Huron and Lake Ontario.

Climate. The climate of the St. Lawrence lowland is typically east coast continental. The growing season averages 130 days. Winters are long and cold; the St. Lawrence is frozen nearly six months of the year somewhere along its course. The lower Valley has a maritime influence similar to south-

6 J. R. Whitaker, "Peninsular Ontario: A Primary Regional Division of Canada," *Scottish Geographical Magazine,* Vol. 54 (1938), pp. 262-284.

FIGURE 20-7: Farm Hamlet, Quebec

French Canadians have come in large numbers to the United States, particularly to New England. One reason for this may be evident in the rough land shown in this photograph of a farm hamlet on an arm of the St. Lawrence River in Quebec. (Canadian National Railways)

ern Labrador. Precipitation is rather evenly distributed throughout the twelve months, with the summers dry enough to permit the maturing of small grains.

The situation of the Peninsula between Lake Huron on the west, Lake Erie on the south, and Lake Ontario on the southeast has an important effect upon its climate. Although the region is located in the path of prevailing cyclonic activity and the weather varies greatly throughout the year, the marine influence upon temperatures along the Lakes shores has an important effect upon agriculture.

Late spring budding and late autumn frosts characterize the Lakes shore belts. A frost-free period of 170 days obtains along the shores of the Great Lakes in the south, in the north along the margin of the Laurentian Upland it is 115 days. In this portion of the humid continental (short summer) climate, the average precipitation is relatively evenly distributed throughout the year.

An important vacation industry has been developed upon the cool summer climate and the water. The ten million Americans concentrated in

FIGURE 20-8: *Thetford Asbestos Mines, Quebec*

This is one of the Quebec asbestos mining districts which give Canada top ranking in this commodity. (Asbestos Corporation, Ltd.)

cities on both sides of the border find the St. Lawrence Valley and peninsular Ontario an easily accessible vacationland.

Isolation. The lower St. Lawrence Valley is relatively isolated. Most of the settlements are in or near the river which affords a means of transportation only in summer. Snows remain on the ground for a long time; automobile traffic is difficult. The low temperatures also contribute to isolation. Perhaps as important as any reason is the willingness to be isolated which the French-speaking habitant seems to accept.[7]

The St. Lawrence River orients the roads, the farms, and the villages. The so-called "long-lot" farm has developed as a consequence of subdivision for inheritance and because of the desirability of river frontage, wide and deep though the St. Lawrence is (*Fig.* 20-7). From the river, these rural settlements appear to be a more or less continuous village, partly as a result of the closely-spaced, substantial farmsteads, but due more to the general absence of the usual characteristics of the north, forests and wasteland.

[7] Roderick Peattie, "Climate in the Lower St. Lawrence Valley," *Geographical Society of Philadelphia Bulletin,* Vol. 21, No. 1 (Jan., 1923), pp. 31-36.

The relative isolation of this section has promoted the hold of the church upon the habitant and upon the economy which he has single-mindedly maintained. There have been few French settle in this lowland since the original nucleus of some 6,000 came, but the birthrate and the reluctance to disperse widely have given rise to four million French-speaking Canadians, by no means all farmers, however. Three-fourths of these live in southern Quebec and Ontario, while another million have migrated to New England. Both urban and rural French-speaking Canadians have perpetuated not only the language, but the customs, traditions, and political attitudes of a former France. These qualities, together with the Norman architecture of the older houses, give to most districts an Old-World atmosphere. Peattie attributes the fact that the original 6,000 French Settlers did not remain a wreck of an old people lost in the flood of an Anglo-Saxon nation to their isolation, birthrate, and to the Catholic Church.[8] No such isolation obtains in the peninsula of Ontario. Its towns and cities are not localized by a river. The population is predominantly English-speaking. Although the Great Lakes ports and channels are frozen in winter, the network of transportation lines on the Peninsula is much denser than farther east. Rail and highway traffic between western New York and the lower Lakes margin adds to Ontario's year-round commerce. Currently the Peninsula is in the process of industrialization.

Agriculture. The French farmers in the St. Lawrence Valley have made dairying their principal source of income. Where urban markets permit, they sell fluid milk, otherwise it is cheese or butter. Exports of these latter two commodities to western Europe rather than the United States has been the result of tariff restrictions principally. In an attempt at self-sufficiency, they raise tobacco, potatoes, oats, wheat, hay, buckwheat, rye, barley, flax, beans, peas, and strawberries. It is not the mere variety of the crops, but rather the conditions under which they are grown and disposed of, which makes this valley distinctive in North American agriculture.

Although as nearly self-sufficient as climate and soil permit, these farmers have always specialized in something. They produced virtually all of Canada's wheat crop until the railroad opened up the prairies for settlement and wheat. Since then they have specialized in dairying, despite the difficulties in developing an export market. Canadian exports of cheese to the United States in 1952 were about 10 per cent of her total cheese exports. Butter is nearly twice as important as cheese. Its market has been virtually

[8] Roderick Peattie, "Isolation in the Lower St. Lawrence Valley," *Geographical Review,* Vol. 8 (1918), pp. 102-118.

assured from the start. Less dependence was placed upon exports, and in England butter met with less competition from the continent.

Southern Ontario is the leading agricultural region in Canada. On almost every basis for measuring agricultural productivity, it ranks first. It is first in the net income of farm operators, in value of farm capital (buildings, machinery, and livestock), average value of farmland, value of the fruit grown, tobacco, dairy cows, swine, sheep and poultry, and in the making of cheese. It is second in the value of all field crops, and third in the acreage in field crops. Despite these impressive statistics, the representative farm on the Peninsula appears somewhat less prosperous than similar types of farms across the border in Michigan's lower peninsula or in northern Ohio.

As will be seen in *Fig.* 2-5, northwest of the major axis of the Ontario peninsula, the agriculture is predominantly raising of livestock, beef cattle, swine, dairy cattle, and poultry. Southeast of the axis there are some specialty districts, with livestock persisting in all of them. Tobacco is the specialty crop extending inland west from the Prince Edward Peninsula. The Niagara Peninsula is the most important fruit-growing district in Canada. In addition to vineyards, truck and market gardens, apple orchards also are important. This region extends around the western end of Lake Ontario to Toronto. Elsewhere a dairy combination prevails, with livestock being variously represented. Immediately across from Detroit a mixed-crop agriculture obtains, with sugar beets, corn, tobacco, swine and truck crops. Forest products became a part of the farm economy well back from the shore of Lake Ontario and continue onto the Laurentian Shield.

Minerals and Power. There is no important mineral industry within the Lowland. The largest asbestos mines in the world are located at the southern margin of the former, in the Appalachians, at *Thetford Mines* (15,095), Vimy Ridge, Black Lake, and at *Asbestos* (8,190) (*Fig.* 20-8).

Modern electric generation and transmission have brought the vast power resources of the Laurentian Upland to the cities of the St. Lawrence Lowland. The province of Ontario has built power plants and sold the power to private consumers for many years at a rate substantially lower than that charged across the border. This has attracted some industries seeking cheaper power.

On the St. Lawrence River, at the International Section, there has long been serious consideration of the development of hydroelectric power. In 1954 the final plan to harness the St. Lawrence at the International Section was implemented by joint action between Canada and the United States and the construction of dams was begun. Present canals around the series

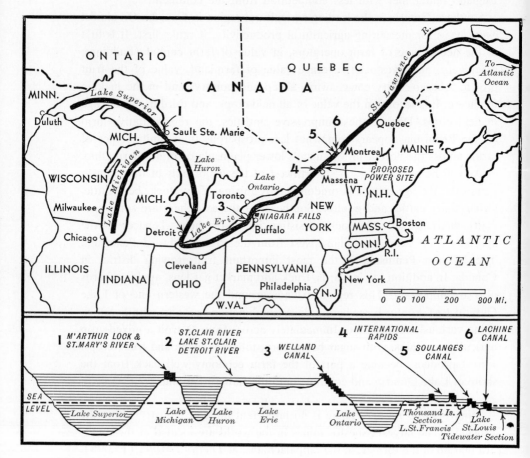

FIGURE 20-9: *Great Lakes-St. Lawrence Seaway*

The Great Lakes-St. Lawrence Seaway will be a major factor in the economic development both of the area it serves and of the seaboard states where its competitive influence may be felt. Its location between the manufacturing belts of the United States and of Canada is of increasing significance as foreign sources of iron ore and alloying metals play a larger part in the foreign trade of both countries. (Adapted from a map drawn for *The New York Times* by LUCAS MANDITCH)

FIGURE 20-10: *Shawinigan Power Plant, Maurice River, Quebec*

The southern Ontario-Quebec lowland is industrial Canada. Its need for power has resulted in the construction of many such installations on tributaries of the St. Lawrence as the one pictured. This need for power has also given rise to two recent treaties with the United States, one providing for a redevelopment of Niagara Falls power, and the other for development of power sites along the International Section of the St. Lawrence River between Ontario and New York. It is this navigational bottleneck between Montreal and Prescott which keeps large ocean vessels on one side and Great Lakes freighters on the other. (Shawinigan Water and Power Co.)

of rapids are limited to vessels drawing 14 feet of water. When the navigation portion of the St. Lawrence project is completed, the new draft will be 29 feet. In 1950 this section of the St. Lawrence, with the present canals, handled in excess of 14 million tons of cargo. Large as this tonnage seems to be, it represents approximately 3 per cent of the tonnage moved on the Great Lakes. Present United States plans for navigation improvements include only two of the Great Lakes, Ontario and Erie (*Fig.* 20-9).

Manufacturing and Cities. The oldest and still an important industrial district in Canada is the middle St. Lawrence Valley between Montreal and Quebec City. Included in this district are *Three Rivers* (46,074), *Shawinigan Falls* (26,903), and *Sorel* (14,961).

The basic factors in the industrialization of this region are its accessibility to the interior of Canada and to the United States by water and by rail; access to the Atlantic by ocean vessels; the abundance of water-power sites and of forests, and the concentration of the Province's population along the St. Lawrence River (*Fig.* 20-10).

Although there has long been a variety of commodities manufactured there, essentially industrial diversification is a recent achievement. Manufacturing productivity is concentrated in large plants and in a few places. Ranking factory products are, in order: foods and beverages, textiles (excluding clothing), paper and its products, iron and steel products, nonferrous metal products, wood products, and chemicals.

Three of the cities are important ports, Montreal, Three Rivers, and Quebec. The following table gives some idea of their port traffic.

Table 20-1: Major St. Lawrence River Ports, 1952

	MONTREAL, MAJOR TONNAGE	
Inward	*Commodity*	*Outward*
2,509,705	Grain	4,187,520
951,414	Bit. coal	—
104,171	Gasoline	1,635,829
336,629	Flour	833,447
801,417	Fuel oil	295,142
311,104	Crude oil	—
204,717	Gypsum	54,750
206,366	Iron Ore	202,414
6,942,228	Total	9,143,377
	THREE RIVERS	
1,394,779	Pulpwood	—
370,925	Bit. Coal	—
430,349	Grain	653,024
—	Newsprint and paper	144,910
4,015	Lumber	1,969
20,799	Sulphur	—
2,466,077	Total	872,329
	QUEBEC	
544,542	Pulpwood	268
365,644	Bit. Coal	1,835
245,527	Gasoline	571
448,059	Fuel Oil	2,903
1,887,108	Total	1,133,067

SOURCE: *The Canada Yearbook, 1954,* pp. 823.

Ontario leads Canada in the net value of its manufacturing, but by no means all of it takes place in peninsular Ontario. Ontario is increasing its lead in manufacturing (1953) and most of the increase is localized in the southern peninsula. Although possessing no important mineral resource, its position between the minerals of the Laurentian Shield and the industrial markets of the United States has promoted Ontario manufacturing (*Fig. 20-11*).

The crescent-shaped belt of industrialized country between Toronto, Hamilton, and Niagara Falls might be termed Canada's newest manufacturing "belt". In this 100-mile crescent live nearly two million people who are experiencing the most rapid rate of industrialization in Canada. Ontario was the only province to gain substantially in population between 1940 and 1950.

Although many of the cities of southern Ontario are not widely known south of the border, the listing of industrial concerns that are expanding in this region reads like a *Who's Who in Industry* for the United States and Great Britain, with the former predominating. Jet engines, automobiles, aircraft, synthetic rubber, primary iron and steel, chemicals, electrical machinery, and textiles are among the products manufactured in this industrial region.

FIGURE 20-11: *Nickel Refinery, Port Colborne, Canada*

After a 10-day growing period on one of the electrolytic tanks at this refinery, a 138-pound cathode of pure nickel is replaced by a thin starting sheet of nickel on which another cathode will be built up. (International Nickel Co. of Canada)

Montreal. At the head of ocean navigation (Lachine Rapids) on the St. Lawrence River is Montreal, largest Canadian City and one of the great ports of North America. It has a situation which commands not only the St. Lawrence Valley, but the Ottawa and Champlain lowlands also. Its site is on the southeast side of Montreal Island, some 30 miles in length and 8 in width.

Nearly three-fourths of its population (1,021,500) are of French extraction, making it the second-largest French-speaking city in the world. Despite this, the dominance in commerce and in manufacturing rests in the hands of English-speaking Canadians. Montreal has always been a trade center. Since early French voyageurs roamed the forests for furs, Montreal has been an exporter. After furs came soft wood, wheat, pulp and paper, with dairy products and minerals in supporting roles.

In some ways Montreal resembles the export cities of the upper Lakes. Immense grain elevators, long docks, acres of warehouses, and large ocean freighters are common along Montreal's miles of water front. Despite the fog and ice of the Gulf of St. Lawrence, Montreal and Quebec are favorite ports for passengers from both sides of the border. The great handicap has been the fact that the St. Lawrence is frozen several months of the year.

Wheat is Montreal's big export by water, although upon occasion wood pulp and paper surpass it. Even so, an estimated one-fifth of Canadian wheat is exported by way of United States' Atlantic ports, the winter ports for Canada. Grain shipments by way of Hudson Bay have not affected Montreal; Vancouver's grain exports have greatly increased, although not all at Montreal's expense. The changed position of Britain in the world's wheat market has accounted for some decline in the volume through Montreal.

As the largest city of Canada and its greatest port, Montreal exhibits many of the characteristics of New York City's economy. Commercial dominance has promoted financial dominance. Its large banks, insurance companies, and industrial concerns rank among the world's largest. People come from many parts of the United States as well as from the provinces to attend its universities.

The combination of a beautiful location at the foot of Mount Royal, the French population, and both English and French perspicacity in encouraging tourists, have brought to Montreal and the St. Lawrence Valley one of its greatest sources of income.

The manufacturing of Montreal includes many service industries, owing to its great size. Meat products, shoes, cotton and wool textiles, flour, beverages, tobacco products, paper, cement, rolling stock, and wood products have been made there for a long time. More recent manufacturing includes aircraft, chemicals, petroleum products, rubber tires, electrical equipment, and industrial machinery. A tariff has promoted the steel group, particularly electrical, industrial, and agricultural machinery manufacture.

Sorel refines titanium from the Allard Lake mines in the lower St. Lawrence Valley. Shawinigan Falls refines aluminum. Three Rivers is an exceedingly important paper manufacturer.

Quebec (164,016) is not a smaller edition of Montreal. Its commerce is about one-fifth as great. Its manufacturers are primarily of the service type, but with more pulp and paper and aluminum manufacture.

Ottawa (202,045), the national capital, is not a St. Lawrence River city but is included in this section because of propinquity and its economy. The principal manufactures are pulp, paper, and lumber products.

Toronto. The dominant industrial city of the Peninsula is Toronto (675,754). It is also the home port for the major part of the Canadian Lakes fleet. Although not comparable to the largest Lakes ports in the United States, Toronto handles about 5 million tons of freight through its modern and well-equipped port. The principal commodity is wheat, most of it for transhipment.

The Peninsula's highways and railroads are used for the transportation of freight from western New York State to Detroit and Chicago. The industrialization of the Peninsula is accelerating this type of commerce. Toronto has 4,000-odd factories making an increasingly diversified line of products, among them being automobiles, machinery of many types, truck trailers, chemicals, leather goods, wood products, and wool clothing.

At the middle of the industrial crescent is *Hamilton* (208,321), the chief steel-making center of Canada, and with some heavy machinery manufacture. *Niagara Falls* (22,784) at the other end of this industrial belt is a part of one of the continent's greatest electrometallurgical and electrochemical districts. Relatively cheap power, brine, and nearby market for these products for industry have been the chief location factors.

London (95,343), midway between Detroit and Hamilton, manufactures auto parts and machinery. *Windsor* (120,049), across the Detroit River from Detroit, manufactures automobiles, auto parts, pharmaceuticals, textiles, and foundry and machine-shop products. Many of the city's residents are employed in Detroit and neighboring cities. *Sarnia* (34,697), at the southern end of Lake Huron, is the most important oil refining center in Canada (*Fig.* 20-12).

FIGURE 20-12: *Imperial Oil Refinery, Sarnia, Ontario*

In addition to the industries based upon the mineral resources of the Laurentian Shield, some cities of the Ontario peninsula have developed the petrochemical industry based upon Alberta oil. (Imperial Oil Co., Ltd.)

LAURENTIAN UPLAND

Role in the Development of Canada. In a manner of speaking, the Laurentian Upland or Shield has been one of the most important provinces in the development of Canada. Its importance lies not in the warmth of its welcome to agricultural, forestry, or mining pioneers, but rather in its effectiveness as an obstacle to the development of the central plains of Canada.

This Upland embraces an area larger than all of the Lakes states south of the border. Spreading in all directions from Hudson Bay, the Upland reaches the Atlantic on the east, the Great Lakes on the south, and the Central Lowlands on the west and southwest. It constitutes about five-sixths of the provinces of Ontario, Quebec, and Manitoba.

Our study of the United States has revealed that a subdivision does not develop apart from other subdivisions; its character is determined by the remote as well as the immediate environment. In the United States the frontier passed rapidly westward; in Canada it could not. While the St. Lawrence Valley was attempting to develop an export agriculture based upon wheat, furs, and wood, westward-moving pioneers emerged from the St. Lawrence lowlands to encounter not the prairie grasslands of the lower Lakes states, but the barrier of the Laurentian Upland, and the international boundary. Canada's prairie plains had to wait for the railroad to make settlement possible. The Laurentian Upland, therefore, affected the timing of occupance of the interior.

Thus when Canada was first supplied with a great wheat surplus, it was near the close of the nineteenth century. It is hardly possible to exaggerate the importance to Canada's economic development of the prairie wheat country; it marked the beginning of an epoch in which this province did for Canada what the cotton-growing states did for the United States. The principal factor in the vital difference in "timing" was the Laurentian Upland.[9]

Physical Conditions. This largest of Canadian physical divisions is a great rock-and-water plain, for the most part below 1,500 feet in elevation. At places in eastern Quebec and in Labrador it rises to 4,000 feet. The ancient rocks of the Laurentian Upland have been glacially scraped, leaving many low hills of bare granite in the north and deposits of assorted materials farther south. The ice also deranged the surface drainage, leaving thousands of old lake plains scattered over the surface. Only the remnants of these ancient lakes remain today, but the surface of the Upland is perhaps one-fourth water. The outer margin of the Upland is marked by several large lakes: Great Bear, Great Slave, Athabaska, Winnipeg, and the upper Great Lakes along the International border. Large areas of muskeg country and ill-drained lacustrine plains still further reduce the amount of arable land. Where such land is found, it generally is an old lake plain with fertile but light soil. South and west of James Bay is an extensive clay belt on which an agricultural occupance has begun. The climate of the Upland varies widely from the humid continental with short summers to the subarctic.

Forests and Lumbering. The forest industry of the Laurentian Upland has experienced two phases: the early commercial lumbering of saw logs, and the more recent wood-pulp industry. The cutting of saw timber has moved west to the forests of British Columbia, but the Laurentian forests have become of great economic importance as a source of paper-making material. For many years Canadian wood pulp has surpassed in importance

[9] For a full treatment, see W. A. Mackintosh, "The Laurentian Plateau in Canadian Economic Development," *Economic Geography,* Vol. 2 (1926), pp. 537-545.

FIGURE 20-13: *Pulp Operation, Terrace Bay, South Central Ontario*
The combination of wood and water is basic to the economy of eastern Canada.
(Ontario Dept. of Travel and Publicity)

that of the United States. Today the United States imports most of the pulp
it consumes, chiefly from Canada. The Laurentian forests supply virtually
all of this Canadian export. Jack pine, poplar, spruce, and balsam predominate, and upon these woods the pulp industry has been built. With
more than adequate water-power resources for this giant consumer of cheap
power, ample timber, the world's largest consumer of pulp and paper just
across the border, and the absence of alternative opportunity for employment, Ontario and Quebec may be expected to look to the perpetuation of
this industry so vitally affecting Canada's position in the economic structure
of world trade (*Fig.* 20-13).

Water-Power Resources. It has been fortunate for Canada that the bulk
of her water-power resources are localized in Ontario and Quebec, the
provinces of greatest need. Neither province has commercial coal fields,
the power-consuming pulp industry is here and the major part of Canada's
agricultural and industrial population is along their southern margin. No
other Canadian water-power districts are so near the large United States
markets. The International section of the St. Lawrence River is one of the
greatest potential water-power districts in the world. On the north shore of

the broad estuary of the St. Lawrence a northern tributary, the Saguenay, has tremendous power resources. Smaller but important power sites are located on the following Laurentian rivers: Thunder Bay on Nipigon River transmits power to Fort William and Port Arthur; Abitibi Canyon on Abitibi River transmits to Sudbury 250 miles farther south; Far Falls on English River, Pat Rapids on Albany River, and smaller installations are located on Mattgami, Spanish, St. Marys, Montreal, Kaministiquia, Seine, and Winnipeg rivers.

Water power plays a very important role in Canadian exports; wood pulp and paper are jointly Canada's greatest export and they consume a tremendous amount of electric power. Another high-ranking export group is minerals, with an equally great demand for electric power. Nickel, copper, lead, zinc, aluminum, and iron processing all are localized on the Laurentian Upland or immediately below it. Seventy per cent of Canadian steel is the product of electric furnaces.

Agriculture. Despite the impetus given agriculture by the early period of commercial lumbering, by the construction of railroads, by the rise of important mining districts, and by paternalistic Provincial governments, agriculture on the Laurentian Upland has generally been fragmentary and transitory. A combination of agriculture and lumbering spread from the lowlands of the St. Lawrence River and Ontario Peninsula. In such a region as the Upland arable land is limited, and then restricted to small tracts, generally inaccessible. Settlement was a consequence to lumbering, and such agriculture as developed was in response to these lumbering communities. With the passing of lumbering in the lower portions of Ontario and Quebec, farming waned and settlements generally declined. The soils in some districts were rich enough, but so light that a few seasons' rainfall carried them away. The long and very severe winters, the short and moderately warm summers (July is the only month in which freezing temperatures have not been recorded in the James Bay clay belt), and the general inaccessibility of the Upland combine to make farming very hazardous. As highways are constructed, the tourist industry spreads farther into the Upland; mineral districts are being opened in many places; where new varieties of staple crops have been developed, yields have generally been higher than in the southern lowlands, but the future of agriculture is limited at best.

About one hundred miles north of the city of Quebec and a like distance west of the mouth of the Saguenay River lives an isolated agricultural community on the Lake St. John lowland. Fifty thousand French Canadians carry on a generally self-sufficing agriculture similar in its major aspects to that carried on in many isolated communities in Central Ontario. The pressure of rural population upon farm land in the St. John lowland has led the church to foster colonists moving north into the James Bay region to establish new communities.

Probably no more than 5 per cent of the clay belt is being used. As with most farming districts in eastern Canada, there is a close relationship between agriculture and lumbering. As a source of income it has enabled the marginal type of farm to persist.[10]

Minerals. Before 1900 the Canadian Pacific was the only railroad across the Laurentian Upland. Within the next fifteen years another east-west line and a few short connecting lines were built to ports on Lake Superior, Lake Huron, and Georgian Bay; in 1932 the line from Cochrane was extended to a new port, Moosonee, on James Bay. Railroads enabled settlement to proceed, although in a somewhat tentative manner. Conceived as agricultural railroads, their construction led to the development of some of the vast mineral resources of the Laurentian Upland.

It is somewhat easier to identify Canadian mining districts on the Laurentian Upland with minerals in general, rather than one specific mineral. For instance copper is mined with other and more valuable minerals, such as platinum and nickel (*Fig.* 20-14). Gold, silver, lead, and zinc are likewise mined jointly with other minerals. Thus Flin Flon, Copper Cliff, Falconbridge, and Sudbury all produce copper and a variety of other minerals. On the other hand, the Allard Lake district in southeastern Quebec is the largest known deposit of ores bearing titanium. Port Radium on Great Bear Lake mines pitchblende, yielding uranium and radium. Yellowknife, Kirkland Lake, Larder Lake, and Porcupine are primarily identified with gold.

Iron is known to exist in many places, but proximity to high-grade ores in the United States has until rather recently retarded Canadian development. Steep Rock Lake, 100 miles north of the Minnesota border, is one of two iron-producing districts on the Laurentian Upland; the other is in western Labrador, Burnt Creek.

Manufactures. The Laurentian Upland has but little manufacturing. Most widespread are the sawmills and the pulpmills. The distribution of sawmills on the Upland resembles a "pothook"; from the Ottawa Valley the

---

[10] See Angus Hills, "Rural Settlement in the Great Clay Belt of Northwest Ontario," *Annals Assn. Amer. Geographers,* Vol. 38 (1948), pp. 61-2; and J. R. Randall, "Settlement of the Great Clay Belt of Northern Ontario and Quebec," *Bull. Geographical Soc. of Philadelphia,* Vol. 35 (1937), p. 53-66.

mills extend as far as the eastern end of Lake Superior, thence north toward James Bay. About half of Canada's mills are on the Laurentian Upland. The stands of timber, the available water for power and for transportation, and the great markets in the United States promise a long future for this industry. Unlike the mineral districts, there is an anonymity about the major lumber and pulp centers.

Arvida on the Saguenay River some 20 miles above the head of navigation, manufactures both alumina and aluminum (*Fig.* 20-15). Using electric power from the Shipshaw River, bauxite from British Guiana and Jamaica, and cryolite from near Ivigtut, Greenland, Arvida is one of the greatest producers of aluminum on earth.

Fort William and Port Arthur are the twin ports on the north shore of Lake Superior. They are the outlets for much of the wheat grown in the Prairie Province and are distributing points for the vast territory of northwestern Ontario with its mineral districts. They are primarily wheat exporters; lakefront elevators store nearly 100 million bushels, and wheat exports to the St. Lawrence are at the rate of 200 million bushels a year. Iron ore from Steep Rock Lake was first exported from Port Arthur and has continued to flow in increasing tonnages.

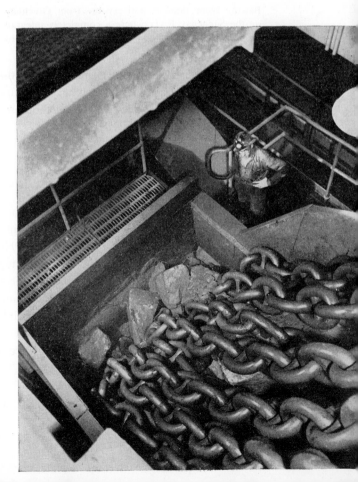

FIGURE 20-14: *Nickel Crusher, Northern Ontario*

This massive crusher reduces nickel ore to smaller particles in the Frood-Strobie Mine. After passing through the crusher the ore is ready for hoisting to the surface for further processing. Mines range in depth from 500 to 5,000 feet. (International Nickel Co. of Canada)

FIGURE 20-15: *Aluminum Plant, Arvida, Eastern Quebec*

Bauxite from Jamaica and cryolite from Greenland meet electric power at Arvida on the Saguenay River where a completely integrated plant makes about half of all Canadian aluminum. (Aluminum Co. of Canada Ltd.)

The nature of the imports indicate something of the frontier character of these port cities: mining machinery and supplies, agricultural machinery, barbed wire, canned goods, and the thousand-and-one items needed in a vast hinterland now being developed.

PRAIRIE PROVINCES

Situation. The Central Lowlands and the Great Plains physiographic provinces narrow as they extend northward into upper Canada. At the latitude of middle Hudson Bay, the Great Plains are pinched out by the expanding Central Lowlands and the southern portion of the Arctic Rockies (*Fig.* 20-16). The geographic region Prairie Province occupies nearly all of the Central Lowlands and the Great Plains as far as the Peace River Plains. The region does not possess the uniformity which is suggested by the name.

The eastern portion of this Prairie Province includes many old lake plains

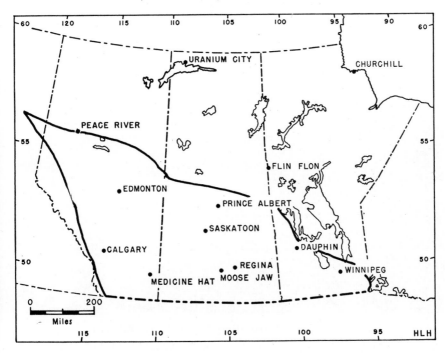

FIGURE 20-16: *Prairie Province*

left by the retreating continental ice sheet. The largest of these lacustrine plains is known as Lake Agassiz, which probably was as large as the combined basins of the present five Great Lakes. The southern portion is now drained by the Red River of North Dakota, Minnesota, and Manitoba. Lake Winnipeg, Lake Winnipegosis, and Lake-of-the-Woods are the more important existing remnants of Agassiz. The lacustrine plain is characterized by the fine materials deposited on the lake bottom and in the deltas of the erstwhile tributary streams; in the main good soils have been developed on these deposits.

The western boundary of these lacustrine plains is a series of distinct uplands and escarpments known as Riding Mountain, Touchwood Hills, and the Missouri Coteau. Beyond, the plains rise in higher steps to 4,000 feet at the base of the Rocky Mountains. Most of the surface has been covered with glacial deposits in which a few swift streams have eroded deep valleys.

Climate. These plains lie within the regions of humid continental (short summer) and cold steppe climates. The characteristics of the continental

FIGURE 20-17: *Harvesting Sugar Beets, Alberta*

The sugar beet has become an important crop in the subhumid interior plains of Saskatchewan and Alberta. As in the United States, the permissive factor in the beet industry is tariff protection. (Alberta Government Photo)

interior are very much in evidence. Most of the annual precipitation occurs in summer. Winter and summer temperatures average lower and higher, respectively, than in eastern Canada; sensible temperatures, however, reflect the dryness of the region.

Although elevation increases to the west, distance from the cold Hudson Bay is likewise greater. In Alberta the influence of the warming chinook (a mild, drying wind) blowing through gaps in the western mountain barrier is frequently experienced. This wind melts the snow and raises the temperature in a remarkably short time, so that winter snows seldom lie long on the ground. Eastward from Alberta, the temperatures are somewhat lower in winter and the chinook influence is not so pronounced. It has been said that spring advances from the Peace River district (56° North) toward the southeast, and that winter begins in Manitoba and advances northwestward.

Wheat-Growing Prairies. By all odds the best known and most important section of these western Canadian plains is the spring wheat-growing

FIGURE 20-18: Combining Oats, Southeastern Alberta

Oats is an important crop in the Prairie Province (Massey-Harris, Ltd.)

prairies west from Lake Winnipegosis to the Peace River and southward to the drier plains country of southern Alberta.[11]

When Canada took over the government of the Territories from the Hudson Bay Company in 1870, there were only a few thousand acres of improved farm land in the entire area of the three provinces, nearly all of it being in southern Manitoba. Eighty years later there were some 43,-767,000 acres in field crops alone and only 7 million acres in Manitoba. Despite these impressive figures, the prairies experienced a number of agricultural crises; the most severe was that between 1929-1938, when the world depression coincided with drought in the wheat lands.

When the Canadian and Provincial governments were speculating upon the extent of prairie settlement, a report from the hand of a government appraiser, Captain John Palliser, characterized most of the southern portion of Alberta and Saskatchewan as unfit for agricultural settlement be-

[11] See Henry M. Leppard, "The Settlement of the Peace River Country." *Geographical Review,* Vol. 25 (1935), pp. 62-78; C. A. Dawson, and R. W. Murchie, *The Settlement of the Peace River Country* (Toronto, 1934); Craig Duncan, "The Saskatchewan River Basin, Canada: A Geographical Appraisal of the Water Resources," doctoral dissertation, The Ohio State University, Columbus, 1955.

FIGURE 20-19: *Beef Cattle Grazing, Near Edmonton, Alberta*

The beef cattle industry dominates livestock in Alberta. (Alberta Government Photo)

cause of its aridity. Bounded roughly by Calgary, Saskatoon, and Morden, this triangle has become known in Canada as the Palliser Triangle.

Appraisal of the carrying power of these plains has varied with the rainfall cycles in which the appraisals were made. In good years, and most years have been favorable for wheat growth, these wheat farmers have repeatedly made good crops. Enough capital was accumulated to build and stock many a permanent farmstead for a mixed type of farming (*Fig.* 20-17).

As dry cycles succeeded humid, the limitations noted in the Palliser report became evident. In 1937 the yield of wheat in the Saskatoon area dropped to 2.6 bushels per acre. Drought and a world depression marked the end of sole dependence upon wheat.

Realignment of Prairie Economy. Attempts to solve the problems of the Prairie Province farmers have been made by Provincial and National governments. When England adopted a protective tariff in the late 1930's, Canada received as a benefit the imposition of 6 cents per bushel duty on non-Commonwealth wheat entering Great Britain. This gave a minimum of aid to Canadian wheat exporters. During the past 15 years the population has declined in the Prairie Province, particularly in Saskatchewan.

Despite this decline in population there had been a transformation in the agricultural economy of the Prairie Province. In the acreage and the value of field crops, Saskatchewan was first among Canada's ten provinces in 1953; Alberta was third. Spring wheat was still the leading crop (23,045,000 acres), but oats was second (7,535,000 acres), barley third (6,082,000), and rye, flaxseed, hay and alfalfa combinations followed with 5,453,000 acres (*Fig.* 20-18). In beef cattle, Alberta and Saskatchewan each almost equalled Ontario, the ranking province (*Fig.* 20-19). Sheep in Alberta nearly equal the number in Ontario. Swine and dairy cows understandingly lag behind in the Prairie Province. The only province to surpass Saskatchewan in the net income of farm operators was Ontario; Alberta was third. In the value of "farm capital" (value of farm buildings, machinery, and livestock), Saskatchewan was second and Alberta third.[12]

In the Peace River Valley between Fort St. John and Dawson Creek on the west, Lesser Slave Lake on the east, Fort Vermillion on the north, and well below Grande Prairie on the south, there is the northwestern extension of Prairie Province.

Agriculture. It has been wheat-growing country for more than a generation, but mechanization of farming practices and new varieties of wheat have brought about an increase in acreage, and the introduction of livestock has been an accompaniment of this agriculture. The heart of the wheat country lies between Peace River, Spirit River, and Grande Prairie. On all margins livestock has become a part of the farm economy. The part that livestock plays in the economy is often semicommercial. It is self-sufficing in the Dawson Creek (west) area and south of Grande Prairie.

Mineral Industries. Since the early 1940's the Prairie Province has been undergoing other important changes in its economy. Oil and gas discoveries have resulted in an important mineral extraction industry, particularly in Alberta.

The oldest field is Turner Valley which in 1942 produced nearly all of Canada's oil (*Fig.* 20-20). Even in 1952 this field accounted for 40 per cent of Canada's oil. The Leduc field is replacing it as the greatest producer in Canada. The biggest producer of asphaltic oil is the field near Lloydminster. A rich deposit of "liquid bitumen" has been discovered at Waterways, in northeastern Alberta. The Athabasca oil sands is placed on the map only for reference. At the present rate of one barrel of oil for each

[12] Manitoba ranks fifth among the 10 Canadian provinces in most of the categories listed above. This is due to a number of reasons, among them poor drainage and soils, rocky terrain, and low population concentration.

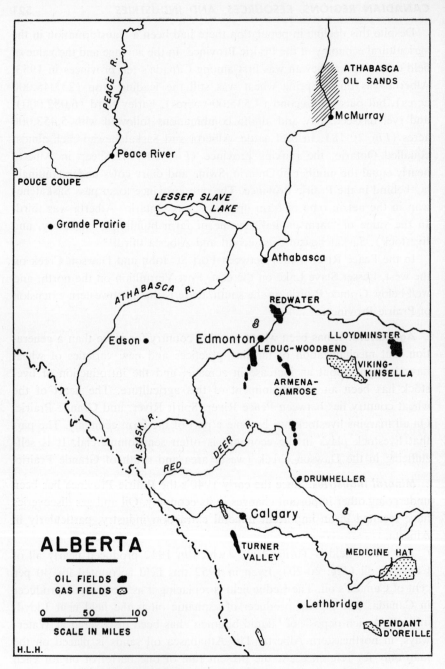

FIGURE 20-20: *Oil and Gas Fields, Alberta, 1954*

Since World War II the oil industry has become important in the wheat-cattle country of Alberta. (Dept. of Mines and Minerals, Province of Alberta)

FIGURE 20-21: *Oil Refinery, Edmonton, Alberta*

Edmonton is near the center of Alberta's growing petroleum industry. Pipelines have reached both the Pacific and Great Lakes ports. Shown here is a catalytic cracking unit of one of the four multi-million-dollar refineries in the Edmonton district. The manufacture of petrochemicals is well established nearby. (Alberta Government Photo)

ton of sand quarried, it is not commercially feasible. It is, however, probably the greatest source of oil known on the earth.

Oil and gas pipelines have been built to the Pacific Coast, to Superior, Wisconsin, for Lakes shipment, and to Montreal. The Pacific Coast cities on both sides of the border are eager to have access to the natural gas as an industrial and domestic fuel. Despite Provincial and National controls over oil and gas resources, Alberta is experiencing a mild boom in the oil and gas industry.

A newcomer to the Canadian oil industry is the Williston Basin extending across the border into North Dakota and eastern Montana. Salt is obtained from brine wells near Lindbergh, and Waterways, Alberta, and at Unity, Saskatchewan; the Prairie Province produces only 1 per cent of Canada's salt; Ontario dominates the industry. Clay is found in relatively small quantities in all three of the prairie provinces.

Manufacturing and Cities. The largest city in the vast plains of central Canada is *Winnipeg* (235,710). It is situated in the neck of a great funnel embracing the prairies and plains, with the north side of the funnel being the Laurentian Upland and the south side being the International border. Through this "neck" pass the railroads which have picked up vast tonnages of wheat, oats, barley, rye, flaxseed, and animal products produced in the Prairie Province. Locally, Winnipeg is trade center for the important Red River Valley.

Farther west and north are the principal collecting and distributing cities which service the economy of the Canadian plains region. Some 400 miles northwest of Winnipeg is *Saskatoon* (53,268), market center for the greatest wheat-growing region in all Canada. Its elevators, and flour mills, flaxseed-processing plants, stockyards, and packing plants rank among Canada's greatest. *Regina* (71,319) engages in similar processing and distributing activities but on a smaller scale.

Edmonton (159,631) has added to the grain trade and livestock industry, the dairy-products industry, the rapidly increasing oil and gas industry, and a representative of the petrochemical industry (*Fig.* 20-21). *Calgary* (129,060) lies farther south and west near the front of the Rockies in a region where scanty rainfall favors the livestock industry rather than wheat farming. A relatively small steel mill is this city's latest industry of consequence.

Lethbridge (22,947) is growing primarily because of the St. Marys-Milk River irrigation project just getting underway, whereas *Medicine Hat* (16,364) farther to the east appears to be static.

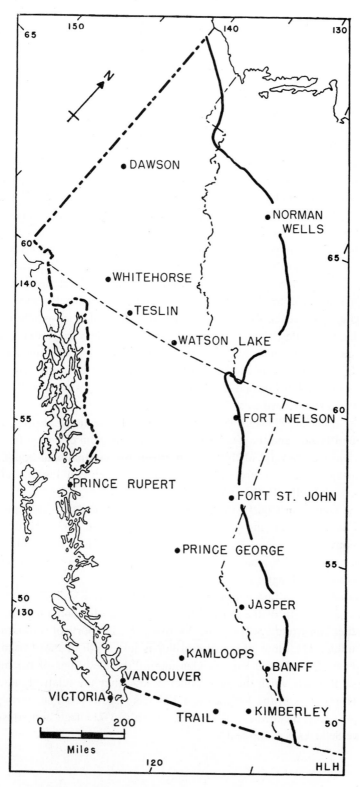

FIGURE 20-22: *Pacific Valleys and Ranges, Canada*

PACIFIC MOUNTAINS AND VALLEYS

Physical Setting. West of the Great Plains Province is a large area of high mountains and intervening valleys (*Fig.* 20-22). Whereas in the United States the Rockies, Intermontane Area, and Pacific Valleys and Ranges were discussed separately, in Canada the differentiation between these physiographic provinces is by no means so apparent nor have the divisions so clearly been reflected in geographic regions. The Canadian portion of the Northern Rocky Mountains, the Interior Plateaus, and the Canadian Coast Mountains, for instance, are treated as a single geographic region (*Fig.* 1-3).

The Canadian portion of the Northern Rockies comprises the eastern section, Canadian Rockies, which extend north to the territorial boundary with a uniform eastern front. Immediately to the west are the Purcell, Selkirk, and Columbia Range sections of the Northern Rockies. In them are glaciated, trench-like valleys similar to those noted across the border in the United States. The easternmost of these valleys is Rocky Mountain Trench which extends for almost a thousand miles. The Purcell, Selkirk, and Okanogan trenches to the west are about a third as long. The Selkirks are more heavily forested than the Canadian Rockies section. The Arctic Rockies extend northward into Alaska.

The Interior Plateaus comprise three main sections: Fraser Plateau, Stikine Plateau, and the Yukon Plateau. They range in elevation from 2,500 to 3,500 feet. Several of them just north of the international boundary are important for agriculture. A second group lies between Jasper and Prince Rupert 300 miles farther north.

The Canadian Coast Mountains section is the northern continuation of the Cascade Mountains in the United States. On the Pacific border are the Vancouver Range and the Queen Charlotte Islands. The Inland Passage section of coastal Canada is the drowned counterpart of the Puget Sound section in Washington.

Natural passes through the Pacific Mountains and Valley region are not many. Just north of the border there is a series of mountain passes which together constitute a sort of corridor to the Pacific ports of southern British Columbia. The other principal corridor is just south of the Alaska border southeast from Prince Rupert. Considering the elevations of the mountain ranges through which the passes offer access, they are relatively low; Kicking Horse Pass in the Rockies is 5,399 feet; Crowsnest Pass farther south is 4,461 feet; Yellowhead Pass in the north is 3,711 feet; and Allison Pass in the Selkirks is 4,486 feet.

Climate. The climate of the Pacific Mountains and Valleys is very diverse, in keeping with such a large mountainous area on the windward side of the continent. The marine west coast or temperate marine-type of climate includes all of the Pacific littoral where elevations are not too high. The greater part of the interior plateaus may be termed moderate continental. Some is cold steppe.

Forest Industry. The forests of coniferous and softwood trees of Washington and Oregon continue northward into Canada. The Canadian Coast Mountains in British Columbia have the densest and most luxuriant stands in the Pacific Mountains and Valleys. These are the continuation of the Cascade Mountain forests. On Vancouver Island and the Queen Charlotte Islands are found most of the Douglas fir and Sitka spruce which in Washington are on the coastal ranges. A heavy stand of western red cedar and western hemlock is found on the humid slopes of the Canadian Coast Mountains, where the treeline ranges from 5,000 feet in the southern portion to 3,000 feet in the north.

From the western slopes of these coast mountains comes about 85 per cent of the timber cut in the Pacific Mountains and Valleys. Here are the largest lumber mills and the pulp and paper mills. On the drier interior slopes east of the Canadian Coast Mountains, comes 13 per cent of the commercial timber cut in Canada. The stands on these interior slopes are lighter, with openings and park areas. Ponderosa pine grows on the drier, lower slopes; at higher elevations are Douglas fir and species requiring greater rainfall. Despite the great timber stands, British Columbia in 1953 suffered fewer acres loss by fire than any eastern province except the Maritimes, in part due to the resistant Douglas fir. The timber cut of British Columbia is something over half of the total national production. In pulp and paper production British Columbia ranks fourth, after Quebec, Ontario, and the Maritimes.[13]

Fishing Industry. Canada's share of the Pacific Coast fishing industry is second only to Alaska in the catch of salmon and halibut together. Not all parts of the Canadian Pacific are engaged in the same type of fishing. Not all years are equally important in the total catch. Salmon is the principal fish caught, accounting for over half of the total value. The chinook salmon is the least important part of the annual pack on this coast, yet is the most desirable. Herring, together with anchovies and pilchard, account for about

[13] World newsprint production, 1951: Canada 4,820,000 tons, followed by the United States with 826,000, Sweden 299,000, and Finland 297,000. *The Canada Yearbook* (*1954*), p. 478.

FIGURE 20-23: *Fishing, British Columbia Coast*

Fishing continues to be one of the two most important sources of livelihood for Pacific coastal communities. (British Columbia Government Travel Bureau)

one-fourth, and halibut, sail, and flounder for about one-tenth of the marketed value of the British Columbia catch. Tuna, clams, crabs, and oysters provide additional income for the fishing industry of this coast.

Almost all fishing in British Columbia waters is within sight of land. There are no very large boats such as are used in California fisheries. The representative fishing boat is a seaworthy craft, with all navigational aids and with modern mechanical gear, often making long runs along the coast. Marketing procedures are as modern as the equipment (*Fig.* 20-23).

Most of the salmon catch is canned, although some is frozen and some sold fresh. Fresh and frozen halibut and shellfish are also marketed. The fishing industry is seasonal and fluctuating; life in the tiny hamlets perched on piles near the canneries is likewise seasonal. Although mechanization has reached a high point in the canning industry, many migrant white and Indian workers move into company houses or private shacks during the canning season.

Agriculture. Drowning has almost eliminated the land that is flat enough for crop agriculture along the margin of the Canadian Coast Mountains. On the southern and eastern portions of Vancouver Island are districts

FIGURE 20-24: *Lower Fraser River Valley, British Columbia*

The scale of the plateaus between the Canadian Rockies and the Coast Ranges is much smaller than its counterpart in the United States, but there are important specialized districts. This valley supports a diversified and prosperous agriculture. (British Columbia Government Travel Bureau)

supporting a commercial agriculture. One of the largest and the most important of the 12 districts which are scattered through the southern portion of the province is the delta and lower valley of the Fraser River. With some modifications, the agriculture of all of these districts is similar to that of the lower Fraser.

Mixed farming with dairying, hops, poultry, apples, peaches, and small fruit, potatoes, and truck crops constitute the basis of the farm economy in the lower Fraser Valley (*Fig.* 20-24). The markets are nearby Vancouver, Victoria, and New Westminster. Conspicuously lacking is the self-sufficing character of most mountain valley communities in the Appalachian Highlands (*Fig.* 20-25).

East of this Fraser district are 6 others, all on the Canadian Pacific Railroad and several not far distant from mining centers just north of the International boundary. From west to east the more important are the Penticton district in the Okanogan Valley, Grand Forks district on the International border, Nelson district in the Kootenay Lake Valley, and the Cranbrook and Fernie districts. Farther north and generally parallel to the southern

FIGURE 20-25: *Fraser Valley Orchard*

This orchard in blossom is viewed against the background of the Canadian Coast Mountains. (British Columbia Government Travel Bureau)

group, is a second group of similar agricultural districts, including Lilloet, Kamloops-Revelstoke, and Golden-Windermere. Despite the seeming isolation, there are ready markets for the produce of these districts.

The third group of agricultural districts extends eastward from Prince Rupert along the Canadian National Railroad through Prince George and Tete Jaune Cache to Jasper. Where drier conditions prevail, as in the Kootenay district, sheep and range livestock are more important than fruit or truck crops.

Minerals. British Columbia ranks fourth among the 10 provinces in the value of its mineral production, not far behind Alberta. This western province has a mineral economy based upon a dozen or more minerals, but with lead, zinc, silver, sulphur, and copper dominant. This province leads Canada in the production of barite, cadmium, bismuth, antimony, tungsten, and tin, but in none of them is the industry very important.

Sullivan, one of the world's largest lead and zinc mines, is located at Kimberley on the eastern margin of the Purcell Range, in the Kootenay Valley. This mine sends concentrates to its huge smelters and chemical works at Trail (*Fig.* 20-27). The sulphides yield sulphur which is used in the preparation of superphosphate fertilizer for domestic markets and for export. Nearly all of Canada's lead and 58 per cent of the zinc comes from this Sullivan mine. This province leads Canada's silver production, virtually all of it coming as a by-product from the refining of base metals.

On Vancouver Island are the only mining industries on the British Columbian coast. Iron ore, copper, and bituminous coal mines are active. The Trail-Nelson district just above the Idaho border is a mining district for lead, zinc, gold, copper, and silver; in 1953 many of these mines were inactive. Due east of Nelson, at Fernie and at Crowsnest are bituminous coal-mining districts. Altogether, the Pacific Mountains and Valleys region has an important mineral phase to its economy. The joint products of its mining have proved to be a stabilizing factor.

Cities and Manufacturing. The distribution of population in this large region has been determined by the commercial mineral deposits, the distribution of arable land, and its accessibility. Three-fourths of the population live in the southern third of the province.

Vancouver (344,833) is Pacific Canada's largest city and the nation's fourth-largest (*Fig.* 20-28). It is situated on the delta plain of the Fraser River on Burrand Inlet. The city was planned as the western terminal of the Canadian Pacific Railroad in the 1880's. It is still the most important commercial city in western Canada. Its agricultural trade territory extends up the Fraser and Thompson rivers. Vancouver's manufacturing largely accounts for the province ranking third (net value) in Canadian manufacturing. The principal products are, in order: sawmill products, processed fish, pulp and paper, ships, meat, fruit, and vegetable products, fertilizers, butter and cheese, and petroleum products.

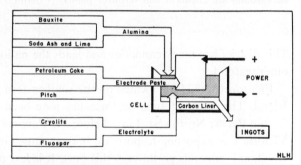

FIGURE 20-26: *Manufacture of Alumina and Aluminum*

This diagram shows the steps taken in the manufacture of alumina and aluminum in an integrated plant such as the one at Kitimat, British Columbia, some 400 miles north of Vancouver. The bauxite ore used is mined on the West Indian island of Jamaica; power for the plant is generated at Kemano, 50 miles from the smelter. Production of aluminum is now 88,500 tons annually with an increase to 330,000 tons planned for 1959. (Adapted from chart in *New York Times,* June 26, 1955)

FIGURE 20-27: Metallurgical Plants, Trail, British Columbia

One of the world's greatest nonferrous metallurgical centers is in the Canadian Rockies. The river in the foreground is the Columbia. The large plants in the center are lead smelter, lead refinery, zinc plant, and sulphuric acid plant. On the river terrace in the background are chemical and fertilizer plants. (COMINCO Photo)

This district has many canneries and leads the nation in processing fish and other seafood.

Victoria (51,331) is located on the southeastern peninsula of Vancouver Island. The Strait of Juan de Fuca has long been an important waterway for the Pacific Northwest. Long before the Panama Canal was constructed, Victoria was exporting to ports on both oceans. Great quantities of wheat, wood, and minerals go through this port. It is less of an industrial city than its size would suggest. The presence of the Provincial government buildings, the climate, and the nature of the people contribute to an English city atmosphere. *New Westminster* (28,639) is an important lumber and fish exporter on the lower Fraser River.

The problems facing these and other cities similarly situated in the Puget Sound area, on both sides of the border, have led several of them to form an international organization known as the Pacific Northwest Trade Association, similar in some respects to the New England Council noted earlier in this book. Representatives from Vancouver, Victoria, Bellingham,

FIGURE 20-28: *Port of Vancouver*

The great Pacific port of Canada is Vancouver on the Fraser River delta. As with other Pacific ports in the Northwest, its commerce is primarily export. A recent addition to the commerce of this region is oil from Alberta fields. (Aero Surveys Ltd.)

Tacoma, and Seattle have asserted that this group of cities compete with California port cities rather than with one another.

The prime objective of this "operation bootstrap" is to secure markets, not necessarily additional manufacturing facilities. The latter will come in due course, but only if there is an increased market for the products. The new oil pipeline from Alberta has given rise to refining, storage, and shipping facilities in cities of the Fraser delta.

Other Cities. Prince Rupert (8,546) is a town planned originally as a rail terminus utilizing the principal corridor through the central and northern Canadian mountain system. It has failed to live up to expectations as a grain-exporting port. Only the nucleus of the planned city has been built. Normally its economy is based upon salmon and halibut fishing and processing. During World War II the United States armed services so expanded facilities in Alaska that Prince Rupert underwent a boom.

A second boom is currently modifying the local economy; unlike the war, this will affect the fortunes of Prince Rupert for years to come. The new, integrated aluminum plant at Kitimat some miles to the south put thousands of construction workers in the Prince Rupert area. The new plant annually produces 550,000 tons of aluminum, more than doubling the 1948 aluminum production of Canada. Construction workers on the plant and on the railroad were transient, but the installation itself greatly increases the working force of the district.

The Nechako River has been dammed to make it flow westward from the British Columbia lakes. A tunnel takes the water under the Coast Range and drops it into the deep Gardner Canal (fiord) at Kitimat. Power costs are reported to be little more than half those of Bonneville Dam on the Columbia.[14] Power output is approximately that of Bonneville, Shasta, and Wilson dams combined. A pulp mill and a chemical plant have been built here to use surplus power and provide cargo for the returning bauxite-ore boats (*Fig.* 20-26).

Trail (11,430) lies west of the Selkirk Mountains and just north of the United States border (*Fig.* 20-27). Its economy is based upon mineral industries. In 1895 Trail got its first copper smelter; its first lead smelter was built in 1900; and in 1910 ores from the famed Kimberley district (Sullivan Mine is the largest) were brought in and upon them the present economy is largely based. Approximately 11 per cent of the world's lead, 10 per cent of the zinc, and important quantities of gold, silver, cadmium, and bismuth are produced by the Trail industries. Power for these operations comes from the Kootenay River, near Nelson, some 27 miles away. Bituminous coal from Crowsnest Pass mining district, 280 miles distant is used to supplement water for power. Fertilizer was first made in Trail in 1930, utilizing the sulphuric acid from the copper smelters.

Tourists. The national parks of the Pacific Mountains and Valleys region embrace but a small fraction of the spectacular mountain scenery. The largest parks include Tweedsmuir Park, Waterton-Glacier International Peace Park, Banff National Park with its Lake Louise, Jasper Park, Kootenay Park, Mount Revelstoke Park, Strathcona Park on Vancouver Island, and Yoho National Park. The relative distance of these parks from the largest United States cities has kept down the patronage. Another example of international co-operation is the Evergreen Playground Association, formed by the cities of the Puget Sound area to advertise tourist attractions on both sides of the border.

[14] The head (of power) at Shipshaw in Quebec is 208 feet, at Niagara Falls it is 165 feet, at Grand Coulee it is 350 feet, but at Kitimat it is 2,580 feet.

ARCTIC PLAINS

North of the Prairie Province and the bulk of the Laurentian Shield, there is a vast empty land of plain, tundra, and occasional scrub forest. Physiographically it embraces the Arctic Plains and Mackenzie Lowlands of the Central Lowland, and the Arctic Archipelago Province. The principal stream is the north-flowing Mackenzie River with its extensive delta. The eastern portion of the Arctic Archipelago is fringed by highland and fiorded coastline.

Second in size to the Mississippi among North American rivers, the Mackenzie flows in a meandering course between the Mackenzie Mountains and the Arctic Rockies until it crosses the plains to debouch into the Arctic Ocean. Since the headwaters thaw before the lower reaches of the river, floods are severe and common in the early summer.

Climate. Although temperatures in summer reach 80° F. occasionally, the winter of long nights and subzero temperatures may last for eight months. Winter temperatures average —55° to —60° F. in the lower Mackenzie Valley, and —30° to —50° F. in Baffin Land. Its winter receives the attention of the American press below the border upon occasion. During the construction of the Alaskan Highway in 1941-1942, the combined maneuvers of Canadian and United States forces during 1950, the construction and maintenance of the DEW line of radar defense stations, and the occupation by the armed forces of Thule base on northwestern Greenland are among the reasons for this interest.[15]

Vegetation and Animal Life. The treeline swings southeastward from the lower Mackenzie to a point on Hudson Bay near Churchill. However, some trees are found in sheltered places above this line, even on Arctic islands in the Archipelago. In the Barrens Section of the Laurentian Shield several hundred varieties of flowering plants have been found.

Over the Arctic Plains as a whole, the animal life is surprisingly varied. It includes buffalo, moose, bear, wolf, fox, musk ox, rabbit, lynx, mink, fisher, and martin. In many places the grazing is good enough to support these wild animals together with growing herds of caribou and reindeer. Several varieties of ducks, geese, and other northern fowl are also found here. Along the Arctic margin, the Eskimo has managed to eke out a living from the sea. The introduction of the herds of reindeer by the government

[15] DEW, that is, Distant Early Warning.

was intended to change the emphasis from exports to a modification of an earlier economy of self-sufficiency in foodstuffs.

Minerals. Half of the handful of white people now resident in this great area are engaged in some form of mining. Gold, silver, pitchblende, and petroleum have been commercially produced here. Exploitation of some of these minerals waited upon airplane transportation for location and development. Mention was made in the last section to pitchblende on Great Bear Lake; in very recent times silver has also been mined here. Between 1920 and 1925, and again in 1941, oil was extracted at Fort Norman on the Mackenzie River. In 1943 a pipeline was constructed to White Horse, Yukon Territory, 400 miles distant. In 1945 this project of the United States Army, Canol, was abandoned. In 1948 some of the pipe and most of the equipment was moved to Edmonton, 600 miles to the south, where it was used to refine crude from the Turner Valley-Le Duc fields.

There were in 1950 approximately 10,000 people living on the Arctic Plains, half of them are Eskimos living for the most part between the Mackenzie River and Hudson Bay. Nearly all of the 4,000 Indians live farther inland, below the tree line. There are about 2,500 white people living along the periphery of the region, at Great Bear and Great Slave Lakes. No account can be given of those who man the line of radar stations.

BIBLIOGRAPHY

ARCHIBALD, E. S. and Wm. DICKSON, "Prairie Farm Rehabilitation," *Canadian Geographical Journal,* Vol. 28, No. 2 (Feb., 1944), pp. 53-63.

BEALL, H. W., "Some Modern Aspects of Forest Fire Control in Canada," *Proceedings of the United Nations Scientific Conference on the Conservation and Utilization of Resources,* Vol. 6 (1951), pp. 40-43.

BEDARD, Avila, "Forestry in Quebec," *Canadian Geographical Journal,* Vol. 28, No. 6 (June, 1944), pp. 258-280.

BELL, Ralph P., "Canada's Aircraft Industry," *Canadian Geographical Journal,* Vol. 24, No. 3 (March, 1942), pp. 113-145.

BROWN, L. Carson, "Cobalt Blooms Again," *Canadian Geographical Journal,* Vol. 47, No. 1 (July, 1953), pp. 25-35.

BURPEE, L. J., "Prince Edward Island," *Canadian Geographical Journal,* Vol. 33, No. 5 (Nov., 1946), pp. 192-217.

COOPER, S. G., "The Canadian Woollen and Knit Goods Industry," *Canadian Geographical Journal,* Vol. 33, No. 4 (Oct., 1946), pp. 174-185.

CRAICK, W. A., "Manufacturing in Western Canada: Fifty Years' Development," *Canadian Banker,* Vol. 57, No. 2 (Spring, 1950), pp. 47-61.

FOWKE, V. C., *Canadian Agricultural Policy* (Toronto, Univ. of Toronto Press, 1947).

FRENCH, Conrad O., "Cattle Ranching in British Columbia," *Canadian Geographical Journal,* Vol. 26, No. 6 (June, 1943), pp. 298-306.

FULLERTON, D. H., "Eighty Years of Foreign Trade," *Canadian Geographical Journal,* Vol. 35, No. 3 (Sept., 1947), pp. 106-121.

GODBOUT, J. A., "Agriculture in Quebec," *Canadian Geographical Journal,* Vol. 28, No. 4 (April, 1944), pp. 157-181.

GODWIN, Gordin, "Forests and Forestry in the Canadian Economy," *Forestry Chronicle,* Vol. 24, No. 4 (Sept., 1948), pp. 245-251.

GOUGH, John, "British Columbia," *Canadian Geographical Journal,* Vol. 35, No. 1 (July, 1947), pp. 2-35.

GROSE, Rex E., "Manufacturing in Manitoba," *Canadian Geographical Journal,* Vol. 46, No. 3 (March, 1953), pp. 84-110.

HARE, F. Kenneth, "Climate and Zonal Divisions of the Boreal Forest Formation in Eastern Canada," *Geographical Review,* Vol. 40, No. 4 (Oct. 1950), pp. 615-635.

HASTINGS, R. J., "Bulbs on Vancouver Island," *Canadian Geographical Journal,* Vol. 28, No. 4 (Oct., 1943), pp. 178-185.

HOAN, Daniel W., "The St. Lawrence Seaway, Navigational Aspects," *Canadian Geographical Journal,* Vol. 36, No. 2 (Feb., 1948), pp. 52-69.

HOOKE, A. J., "Alberta, Nature's Treasure House," *Canadian Geographical Journal,* Vol. 35, No. 4 (Oct., 1947), pp. 154-177.

JOHNSON, Charles W., "Relative Decline of Wheat in the Prairie Provinces of Canada," *Economic Geography,* Vol. 24, No. 3 (July, 1948), pp. 209-216.

KEENLEYSIDE, H. L., "The Forests of Canada," *Canadian Geographical Journal,* Vol. 41, No. 1 (July, 1950).

—— "Recent Developments in the Canadian North," *Canadian Geographical Journal,* Vol. 34, No. 4 (Oct., 1949), pp. 156-176.

KERR, Donald, "The Climate of British Columbia," *Canadian Geographical Journal,* Vol. 45, No. 4 (Oct., 1952), pp. 143-157.

LLOYD, Trevor, "The Mackenzie Waterway, A Northern Supply Route," *Canadian Geographical Journal,* Vol. 25, No. 3 (July, 1943), pp. 415-434.

LONG, H. G., "Prairie Irrigation," *Canadian Geographical Journal,* Vol. 33, No. 4 (Oct., 1946), pp. 152-159.

MACFARLANE, R. O., "Manitoba," *Canadian Geographical Journal,* Vol. 35, No. 3 (Sept., 1947), pp. 124-152.

McGUIRE, B. J., and H. E. FREEMAN, "How the Saguenay River Serves Canada: The Making of Aluminum," *Canadian Geographical Journal,* Vol. 34, No. 5 (Nov., 1947), pp. 200-225; also Vol. 42, No. 4 (Oct., 1951), pp. 144-163.

——, "Wealth from the Canadian Shield," *Canadian Geographical Journal,* Vol. 38, No. 5 (May, 1949), pp. 198-227.

MERCER, G. A., "Newfoundland," *Canadian Geographical Journal,* Vol. 36, No. 3 (March, 1948), pp. 104-129.

MOORE, Ralph R., "An Economic View of Alberta," *Canadian Geographical Journal,* Vol. 47, No. 5 (Nov., 1953), pp. 174-193.

"Newfoundland, An Economic Survey," *Monthly Review,* Bank of Nova Scotia, New Series, No. 37 (1949).

PHILIPPS, Fred H., "New Brunswick," *Canadian Geographical Journal,* Vol. 40, No. 1 (Jan., 1950), pp. 12-43.

PUTNAM, D. F., "The Climate of the Maritime Provinces," *Canadian Geographical Journal,* Vol. 21, No. 3 (Sept., 1940), pp. 135-147.

————, ed., Canadian Regions (New York, Thomas Y. Crowell, 1952).

REEDS, L. G., "Land Utilization in Central Ontario," *Economic Geography,* Vol. 22, No. 4 (Oct., 1946), pp. 289-306.

ROBINSON, J. Lewis, "Agriculture and Forests of Yukon Territory," *Canadian Geographical Journal,* Vol. 31, No. 2 (Aug., 1945), pp. 54-72.

ROBINSON, M. E. and A. C. ROBINSON, "The Pas: Crossroads of the New North," *Canadian Geographical Journal,* Vol. 45, No. 2 (Aug., 1952), pp. 54-63.

ROBINSON, M. J. and J. L., "Fur Production in the Northwest Territories," *Canadian Geographical Journal,* Vol. 32, No. 1 (Jan., 1946), pp. 34-48.

RUMMY, G. R., "Settlements on the Canadian Shield," *Canadian Geographical Journal,* Vol. 43 (1951), pp. 116-127.

"The St. Lawrence Seaway," *Commercial Letter,* The Canadian Bank of Commerce, Toronto, March, 1955.

"Types of Farming in Canada," *Farmers Bulletin* No. 77 (Dept. of Agriculture, Ottawa, 1939).

WALKER, John F., "Mining Development in British Columbia," *Canadian Geographical Journal,* Vol. 45, No. 3 (Sept., 1952), pp. 114-132.

WEBB, F. T., "The Canadian Pulp and Paper Industry," *Canadian Geographical Journal,* Vol. 31, No. 6 (Dec., 1945), pp. 284-299.

WHITAKER, J. R., "Distribution of Dairy Farming in Peninsular Ontario," *Economic Geography,* Vol. 16, No. 1 (Jan., 1940), pp. 69-78.

WOLFE, Roy I., "Summer Cottages in Ontario," *Economic Geography,* Vol. 27, No. 1 (Jan., 1951), pp. 10-32.

WRIGHT, Jim, "Saskatchewan," *Canadian Geographical Journal,* Vol. 24, No. 3 (March, 1947), pp. 108-136; also Vol. 45, No. 1 (July, 1952), pp. 14-33.

WYLIE, N. V. K., "Newfoundland, An Historical Sketch," *Canadian Geographical Journal,* Vol. 38, No. 4 (April, 1949), pp. 148-175.

CHAPTER 21

ALASKA

INTRODUCTION

FOR THE MOST of the hundred years that Alaska has been identified with the United States, its natural resources have been the basis for its colonial-type economy. Fish, minerals, furs, and timber have been the basis for a lavish return on the investment in the Territory. World War II made the United States and Canada aware of the strategic location of Alaska in the Pacific theater of operations and also with reference to the trans-Arctic air routes. This awareness was somewhat late in being realized. In 1941 there was no direct highway or railroad connection between Alaska and the United States, despite the fact that Seattle is only about 500 miles distant from southern Alaska (*Fig.* 21-1). By 1943 the United States Army Engineers had completed the Alaska Highway from Fairbanks to the northern terminal of a highway at Grande Prairie, Alberta (*Fig.* 21-2).

With a globe and a piece of string one may see the Aleutian Islands in their true perspective with reference to the Pacific borderlands, more specifically the United States, Canada, Alaska, Australia, and the Orient. On the globe one may observe that the Aleutians extend in a great arc westward from Alaska toward the mainland of Asia. Pearl Harbor is not on the shortest steamer route from San Francisco to Tokyo; rather such a route follows the Pacific Coast of Canada, Alaska, and the Aleutians. Dutch Harbor is some 5,000 miles from San Francisco but only 2,500 miles from Tokyo. Names not common on American lips since the days of the Alaskan gold rush were in common usage during the war. United States military and naval bases at Fairbanks, Sitka, and Anchorage in Alaska, and at Unalaska and Kodiak, probably the best sites in the Aleutians, were feverishly completed in 1942. Only three miles of open sea separates islands belonging to the United States and the U.S.S.R. The postwar years have witnessed but

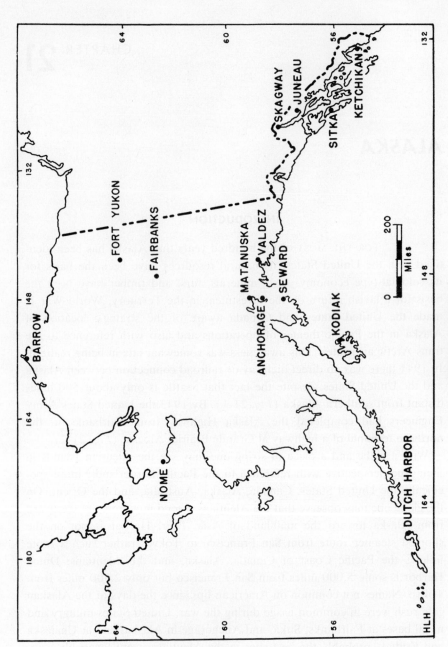

FIGURE 21-1: Alaska

slight easing in the tension over Pacific developments. Japan has become an ally of the Western World; the U.S.S.R. has become an enigma and therefore a problem. Most bases of the armed forces have been inactivated or abandoned, but some remain active. Population of Alaska has soared from 80,000 in 1940 to 128,643 in 1953.[1] Canada and the United States have maintained the Alaska Highway and conduct joint operations of a military nature in the Arctic. But the recent interest in Alaska by the armed services has in no sense changed the fundamentally colonial character of the Territory's economy, although it is by no means a part of the "white man's burden" as seen by Kipling.

Alaskan fisheries, mines, and furs have produced more than $2 billion in products, all at relatively small cost to the United States. Absentee ownership means that most of the profits from the several enterprises leave the Territory; only wages and taxes remain, and not all of these; migratory labor must be recruited for a number of enterprises. This largely accounts for the seeming anomaly of great industrial growth without commensurate social gains in the producing communities. Despite this, there is relatively great trade per capita, actuated in part by the need for imports of food, machinery, fuels and the like, and in part by the absence of any widespread desire to be self-sufficing in economy.

PHYSICAL SETTING

Relief. Although Alaska's shape is such that it embraces a longitudinal and latitudinal expanse comparable to that of the United States, its area is only about one-fifth that of this country.

Pacific Mountain System. Three major mountain systems enter Alaska from Canada, Canadian Coast Mountains are represented by the Alaskan and Aleutian ranges; the Rocky Mountains are represented by the Arctic Rockies; and the Coast Ranges of the Pacific Northwest are represented by the Alexander Archipelago, St. Elias, Chugach, Kenai, and Kodiak ranges. Framed by the former two mountain sections are the Central Alaska Uplands and Plains drained by the Yukon and Kushkokwim rivers. Between the Alaska Range and the Kenai-Chugach ranges are the much smaller Alaska Basins. The Chugach Mountains include many peaks of more than 10,000 feet elevation. Some of the large glaciers reach the sea, making an impressive sight; of more than local fame are the Bering Glacier and the Columbia Glacier near Valdez. In the Alaska Range is Mount McKinley,

---

[1] In 1940, it was 72,524; in 1930 it was 59,278. Civilian whites number about 72,000, Eskimo some 17,000; Indian about 11,000, and Aleuts about 7,000.

FIGURE 21-2: *The Alaska Highway*

The Alaska Highway was built as a defense measure, but during the postwar years it has become a useful road for trucks for year-round service. During the winter months the engines of these trucks are never stopped during the 1,600-mile run. (Bureau of Public Roads, U.S. Dept. of Commerce)

highest in North America (20,300 feet), rising higher above its plain than any peak in the world. Southwestern Alaska has both active and extinct volcanoes; most spectacular has been Mt. Katmai which in 1912 blew away its summit area during a three-day period of violence. An adjacent forested valley has since been known as The Valley of Ten Thousand Smokes, owing to the innumerable fumeroles.

The Alaska representative of the Arctic Rockies is the Brooks Range. North of these mountains are the Arctic Plains, Alaska's representative of the great Central Lowlands of the United States and Canada.

Southeastern Alaska. From the State of Washington north to Alaska's south boundary, the Pacific Coast is steep and broken. Glaciation and submergence of the coastal margin have given it curious indentations known as fiords. The fiords (locally known as canals) vary in length from 100 to 200 miles, and in depth from a few hundred to two thousand or more feet. For a thousand miles along this coastline there is an inland passage to Alaska. From a steamer one has spread immediately before him the Alpine landscape of lofty snow and ice fields, breaking fronts of glaciers, and

542

waterfalls. Level land is so rare that agriculture, even grazing, is out of the question; the few towns have had to blast their sites from the mountain slopes or are supported on piling above the Pacific. Accessibility to the interior of Alaska or to British Columbia is limited to a very few places and under anything but favorable circumstances. Perched upon these precipitous slopes, the few towns must draw upon the resources of the Pacific and upon a few minerals of the coast ranges for their livelihood. The panhandle of Alaska is more accessible by coastal steamer than by any other means. The mountains have no natural corridors through them except water.

Climate. Alaska has been termed the "weather factory" of North America. In 1941 the United States began to observe the weather conditions of Alaska and distribute the data as a basis for the safe and intelligent development of airways. Among the phenomena studied are the curious Alaskan gales or "williwaws." The knowledge of Pacific weather conditions are to the United States and Canada, what those of the Atlantic are to the countries of western Europe.

Lying north of the Pacific Ocean with a vast expanse of land to the east and separated only by Bering Strait from the still much larger land mass of Siberia, the main portion of Alaska is covered during the winter by relatively high atmospheric pressure. Just to the south there usually exists a trough of low pressure, the Aleutian Low. Through this "pressure valley" pass a great many cyclonic disturbances which enter North America on their west-to-east movement. The high Canadian mountains frequently cause a stagnation of air in the Gulf of Alaska which may last for weeks.

Central Uplands. The Central Uplands ranging in height from 2,000 to 4,000 feet has an extreme range of temperature during the year: from —76° F. to 100° F. is not uncommon. Rainfall is very low, ranging from 10 to 18 inches, much of it occurring during the summer months. The growing season varies from 75 to 100 frost-free days. At Fairbanks, about one hundred miles from the Arctic Circle, there is an average of 120 days of zero weather, and 234 days when the temperature drops to freezing at night. The total number (theoretical) of hours of sunlight per year is as great as in the Dakotas and plant development is rapid.[2] Snowfall is light

---

[2] At the winter solstice, sunrise and sunset officially occur at about 9:03 A.M. and 2:54 P.M., respectively. At the summer solstice, they are, respectively, 2:09 A.M. and 9:54 P.M. Length of the period of sunlight does not mean that many hours of sunshine however. Very few sunshine data are available, but for Juneau, with a possible 17 hours of sunshine during the long summer days, there are actually fewer per year than at Boston. Boston's yearly total of sunshine is more than twice that of Juneau.

and is needed to supplement the low summer rainfall. Postwar military training operations have stimulated interest in Alaskan climate.

Arctic Plains. The lowlands along the Arctic and the Bering coasts have even less precipitation than the interior upland, generally from six to eight inches. Extremes of temperature are less severe than in the interior, both in summer and in winter.

Southeastern Alaska. This is one of the smaller climatic provinces, but by all odds the most important to the 30,000 or more whites living along this narrow strip of marine west coast climate along the Pacific margin. Rarely does a harbor freeze; the summers (50°-55° F.) and even the winters (20°-25° F.) are not greatly different from the coast of Washington. Precipitation is heavy, from 50 to 200 inches annually, depending upon the location. Fogs and generally poor visibility make this continental margin hazardous for airmen and for navigation of the Inside Passage. It is in this type of climate that the United States has its principal economic stake.

ECONOMY

Forests and Lumbering. The forest industry is not the most important aspect of the Alaskan economy, but stand of timber is so great that it is discussed first. Most of the commercial stands of timber are found along the windward mountainous coast, from sea level to 2,500 feet the stand is most dense. Heavy rainfall rather than extremes of temperature have prevented much diversity in this forest. Western hemlock predominates (73 per cent) with Sitka spruce (21 per cent), western red cedar (3 per cent), and Alaska cedar (3 per cent). Approximately three-fourths of this timber is within three miles of the coastline.

Strictly saw timber is limited; most of the timber is fitted for pulp. There are two large National Forests in which the stumpage is appraised and the cutting contracted to private companies. Tongaro National Forest embraces 16 million acres in southeastern Alaska. The Chugach National Forest between Prince William Sound and the Kenai Peninsula, has some 5 million acres. In 1951 a total of 61,892,000 board feet were cut and sold to the United States and to the Orient.

Fishing Industry. Alaska has the most important of the world's salmon fisheries. Many harbors, many fish, and access to the United States market has been a potent combination. Absence of alternative opportunity is also a factor, despite the fact that outside labor is essential in some aspects of this industry (*Fig.* 21-3). The Japan Current with its wealth of sea vegetation and animal organisms upon which millions of fish feed flows southward off the coast. Fish in Alaskan waters are several times as important as off the Atlantic Coast. However the salmon catch shows a steady decline over the years, despite control measures enacted by the government. Commercial salmon fishing began in Alaskan waters in 1878; by 1900 it had surpassed the salmon catch of the Columbia River. Although Alaska's salmon catch has declined, it still is first in the world and constituted two-thirds of the total Alaskan catch in 1953.

TABLE 21-1: *Fisheries, Catch by Section, 1953*

Section	Fishermen	Vessels	Boats	Quantity (1000 lbs.)	Value ($1000.)
ALASKA	11,906	1897	4773	296,966	39,299
PACIFIC COAST STATES	25,528	3308	7444	1,018,016	97,411

SOURCE: *Statistical Abstract of the United States, 1954,* p. 736.

Five species of salmon are caught in Alaskan waters; in the order of the 1951 catch they are: pink, red, chum, coho, and king. The most desirable varieties are the red and king. Salmon were canned in 1,922 canneries with 3,484,468 cases (48 one-pound cans). In addition 13.5 million pounds were frozen, 4 million mild cured, and 56,000 sold fresh.[3]

In order to ensure an adequate spawning season, the fishing season has been restricted by the United States Government. Alaskan canneries are perforce located on the steep-sided coastal margin. The Chicago packing plant technique has been applied to every step in the preparation of salmon for the market. The use of a machine, the "iron Chink," has largely supplanted the Oriental upon whom the industry once depended; it has not entirely supplanted him, however, for a large number of laborers have to be imported for the canning season, an estimated 18,000 out of the total of 30,000 wage earners in the industry. The peak year, 1936, witnessed a pack in excess of 8 million cases of 48 one-pound cans each.

Most of the North American halibut are caught in the Pacific between Puget Sound and Dutch Harbor in the Aleutians (*Fig.* 21-4). As with the salmon catch, halibut fishing is controlled; open season is from May 1 to May 28 or to June 25, depending upon the area. Of the 18.5 million pounds of halibut caught in 1951, the Alaskan fleet landed 4.5 million pounds at British Columbian ports.

Twenty-four herring plants handled 28 million pounds of that species

[3] *Annual Report of the Governor of Alaska, 1952* (Washington, 1952), pp. 39-47.

FIGURE 21-3: *Fish Cannery, Cordova, Alaska*

This cannery of the New England Fish Company is representative of this important Alaskan industry. Building sites are virtually nonexistent, for plants and homes alike. Much of the labor is migratory. (Photo by GUY-HAROLD SMITH)

in 1951. Fourteen of these plants are in southeastern Alaska, and ten in the central part. Clams totaling 670,706 pounds were processed in 14 plants in central Alaska. Eleven plants processed 2.5 million pounds of crabs. The shrimp catch totaled 1.5 million pounds, all in southeastern Alaska. No oysters were harvested in 1951.

Furs. The two main Pribilof Islands, St. George and St. Paul, some 200 miles north of Unalaska, localize the greater part of the Alaskan seal and fox-fur industry. In 1951 there were 60,689 fur sealskins taken from these two islands, 50,573 from St. Paul and the remainder from St. George Island. These skins were shipped to the St. Louis, Missouri, fur auction. Under the controlled program, the average take in sealskins during the past ten years has been 62,953. The Pribilofs also accounted for 900 fox skins in 1951. These rocky, moist, windswept islands are excellent for this fur industry. The fur of these foxes is finer, thicker, and longer than most; in addition it has a blue undercoat that is peculiar to foxes in very few parts of the world. The Pribilof Islands are so young that the volcanic soil supports only grass.

FIGURE 21-4: Naknek, Alaska

This community is located on the Naknek River, in the Bristol Bay area. (GEORGE B. KELEZ, Fish and Wildlife Service)

In addition, trapping of wild animals is important. In 1951 the following were reported: 260,000 muskrat, 22,000 mink, 18,000 beaver, 9,000 marten, 8,000 weasel, 4,000 fox, 2,000 otter; other fur-bearing animals were trapped, but the foregoing were the great bulk of the harvest. The Territorial government has established wildlife refuges for the moose at Kenai Peninsula, sea otter at the Aleutians, brown bear at Kodiak Island, and the musk ox at Nunivak. Governmental controls over seals and sea otters seem to be effective. Seals have reached a population of 3 million approximately, from a low of 200,000 in 1911. The luxurious skin of the sea otter cannot be taken; the animal was almost decimated some years ago. Efforts to increase their number appear to be moderately successful.

The markets for Alaskan seal and fox skins is at St. Louis, where the same kinds of furs are brought in for tanning from several parts of the world. New York City then takes almost all of these skins for tailoring into apparel.

Agriculture. In 1938 Alaska imported about $5 million worth of food that could have been produced in Alaska, so far as soil, climate, and types of crops are concerned. Yet the complaint most often heard from the

547

Matanuska Valley colony concerned the lack of market for their agricultural produce. These two seemingly incompatible statements may be entirely true. Circumstances which have contributed to this arise largely from the following: Alaska's area of about 600,000 square miles supports but two significant areas of crop agriculture, the Matanuska Valley in the Pacific margin, and the Tanana Valley in the interior; most of the Territory's population lives in the southern panhandle and the region adjacent to the mouths of the Copper and Matanuska rivers. Many of these people are closer to the farms of Washington than to Alaska's. Local transportation is for the most part inferior to that of the United States. Again, there are few if any destitute whites in the Territory; only the Indians and natives are poor.

Such an agricultural principle as "Feed the family, feed the stock, and sell the rest" does not fit the crops, the role of livestock, or the wishes of most Alaskan farmers. The farmers are in the minority; relatively high wages prevailing in all industries, as well as the inhospitable farming environment, conspire to make a self-sufficient type of agriculture physically and economically out of the question. The development of agricultural specialties is consistent with the facts enumerated above. If and when the freight-carrying airplane becomes an economical means of transport in Alaska, a new agricultural regime may dawn for Alaska's farmers. So long as every major industry has to import labor from "outside" every summer, farming is not apt to attract many recruits.

Agricultural Areas. There are two relatively important and two much less important farming districts in Alaska: Matanuska Valley, Tanana Valley, Kenai Peninsula between Cook Inlet and the Kenai Mountains, and parts of the Kuskokwim and Yukon valleys. For grazing purposes there are many different kinds of pasture lands, totaling perhaps 40,000 square miles or about the size of Ohio.

Matanuska Valley. The only federal government-sponsored agricultural colonization in many years took place in the Matanuska Valley during the depressed 1930's. In this valley the summers are cooler than in the Dakotas, despite the longer day. Several weeks of growing temperatures prevail before the seeds germinate, due to the cold ground. Spring is therefore not the beginning of life in the Matanuska Valley. The usual summer day maximum is perhaps 70° F., and the summer night minimum is generally between 45° and 60° F. The dependable growing season even for hardy crops is usually ended by September.

For hardy crops there are 123 days of growing season; for tender crops there are only 105 days. Rainfall occurs all through the year, with the maximum in July and August. Thunderstorms are rare. In winter, which may begin in October, the sun is so low that much of the sunlight is cut off by the Chugach Mountains bordering the southern margin of the Matanuska Valley. Snowfall is light, from 20 to 40 inches; its depth on the ground is modified materially by the occurrence of the periodic Knik or Chinook wind.

The Matanuska Valley project is divided into 250 farming units varying in size from forty to a hundred acres, for the 190 families living there in 1944. The Matanuska Corporation cleared the rather dense forest of cottonwood, alder, birch, spruce, and willow. By 1944 there were some 7,000 acres cleared for farming purposes. All necessary purchases were financed by the federal government. Clearing the land, constructing communications, and organization of co-operatives were all aided by the government. Twenty years after this initial venture, the Matanuska Valley presents a rural landscape which may be a preview of what many Alaskan communities will be like in the future. A tent community has become a settlement of 180 well-built log houses of from six to eight rooms. Each home has a substantial red-painted barn. Berries, white potatoes, cabbages, oats, peas, hay, poultry and dairy products are produced in quantities great enough for export to the towns along the railway. In 1943 the greatest increase in farming had taken place in dairying; there were 700 dairy cows, mostly Holstein and Guernsey. Milk was selling at $6.20 per hundred pounds. The hay used to feed these herds and about an equal number of swine (there are very few beef animals) was usually a mixture of oats and pea vines or of vetch and oats, yields averaging about three tons of dry hay per acre. Due to its low price, barley is often used for corn in poultry and stock feeding. Alfalfa and soybeans will not do well in the Valley. Among the small grains, oats yield about 45 bushels, barley 23 bushels, and spring wheat 22 bushels per acre. White potatoes yield well. Nearly all of the buying and selling are done through the Matanuska Valley Farmers Cooperative Association.

To process some of these products, the Association has established a vegetable-canning plant, a cold-storage plant, and a creamery. These together with the hospital, power plant, warehouses, school, trading post, and the offices and residences of the administrative officers constitute a landscape very much in contrast with other Alaskan and many United States rural areas. No other agricultural community has had such federal backing, not excepting the Federal Resettlement projects in the United States.

Tanana Valley. By no means so important as the Matanuska Valley is the farming district around Fairbanks in the Tanana Valley. The Agricultural Experiment Station is located here. Oats, barley, potatoes, dairying, and berries are the important commodities. Physical conditions are in contrast with the Matanuska Valley. Winters are colder, summers are warmer, and both seasons are drier in the Fairbanks area.

Prospects. In 1939 there were 623 farm units in operation in Alaska; in 1950 there were 525. Acreage in land farmed in 1939 was 1,775,752; in 1950 it was 421,799. Yet during these years, the value of these farms (including equipment used in farming) rose from $3,841 to $6,544. The acreage of every crop except potatoes has declined since 1939; barley from 654 acres to 55; oats from 527 acres to 333; and wheat from 527 acres to 204.[4] Reasons for the decline include a continued high rate of civilian employment by the armed forces installations; the acreage is too limited to justify the degree of mechanization obtaining elsewhere; and the dissatisfaction with farming here, now that the depressed years have passed. Wind erosion has been a relatively serious problem for most of the period of occupancy in the Matanuska Valley. The armed services buy as much as possible from the Alaskan farms, but despite this "captive" market, acreage has declined. Perhaps the efforts of the Alaska Development Board to establish new industries in the Territory will meet with some success and the economic base of the economy will be broadened.

Mineral Industries. Seventy-five years have elapsed since the first gold prospectors stormed Alaska. In 1880 Wrangell was the center of a migration headed for the gold of Canada's Cassia district. The same year Juneau had its first gold mining in the Silver Bow Basin.

Juneau again boomed in 1896 when gold production on Klondike Creek in the Yukon country of Canada began its phenomenal rise. Skagway came into being as an outfitting depot and within a year had 15,000 population. The first stampede in Alaska itself was along Anvil Creek near Nome, in the summer of 1898, reaching its climax in 1900. Fairbanks had its first gold rush in 1902, and thousands of prospectors came in from the Klondike, from Nome, and up the trail that today is followed by the Richardson Highway. Less spectacular gold fields became known at intervals up to World War I.

The picks, shovels, and pans of the early prospector soon gave way to the sluice box and later to hydraulic placer mining. This type of mining dominated World War I; by 1950 the proportion had risen to 96 per cent placer

---

[4] *Statistical Abstract of the United States, 1954,* p. 944, and *1952,* p. 661.

mining and 4 per cent lode mining. Placer mining has been brought to a high degree of refinement in Alaska, despite the handicap of frozen ground and dry summers. This type of operation is used in most parts of Alaska, the principal exception being the southeastern part of the Territory. Lode mines are located for the most part in southeastern Alaska and the Willow Creek district near Anchorage.

Placer mining can be practiced only during the short summer, and even then the ground may be frozen as much as two hundred feet under the insulating cover of muck and other materials. Literally scores of miles of water pipes are used to thaw out the ground and to bring water from great distances for the mining operation. Bulldozers, draglines, and huge dredging machines dig, wash, and recover the gold from about nine million cubic yards of gravel per day. Wages must be high to attract men to these isolated places; and for such brief periods, the capital investment in equipment is high; obviously the whole process necessitates large-scale treatment of gravels if there is to be any profit. Similar methods are employed in California gold operations, but at half the cost. The individual operator still works the smaller, rich placer deposits, however, and will in all probability continue to do so.

TABLE 21-2: *Mine Production of Gold, Silver, Copper, Lead, Zinc, and Coal in Alaska, in Terms of Recoverable Metal, 1946-1953*

YEAR	GOLD (lode & placer) (fine ounces)	SILVER (lode & placer) (fine ounces)	COPPER (Sh. tons)	LEAD (Sh. tons)	ZINC (Sh. tons)	COAL (Sh. tons)
1946	226,781	41,793	2	115	—	
1947	279,988	66,150	12	264	25	
1948	248,395	67,341	16	329	22	
1949	229,416	36,056	4	51	2	
1950	289,272	52,638	6	149	6	420,000
1952	250,000	35,000	1	21	1	494,000
1953 value	$8,837,000	$30,000	—	$7,000	—	$3,767,000

SOURCE: *Minerals Yearbook, 1950,* p. 1366; and *Statistical Abstract, 1954,* p. 947.

Although Alaska has one of the two extensive deposits of good coal on the Pacific borderland, the tonnage mined was of relatively little consequence prior to the Matanuska Valley settlement during the 1930's. Population increase during and since World War II accelerated coal production. The quality of some of Alaskan coal is up to United States Navy standards; a good grade of anthracite is also found.

During 1950 some 420,000 tons of bituminous and subbituminous coal were mined in Alaska, mostly from Matanuska Valley near the coast, and the Healy field in the interior not far from Nenana. The Alaska Railroad obtains its coal from the Matanuska fields. Strip mining of coal has been practiced for several years, but most of the coal obtained thus far has come from underground mines.

Silver is largely the product of gold mining (76 per cent) and of lead mining (24 per cent). Most of the silver comes from bucket-line dredging operations in the Fairbanks and Howe districts. Most of the lead comes from one mine in southeastern Alaska. Zinc and lead are also products of gold mining. Tin is mined at Lost River on the Seward Peninsula; it increased during 1951, but the tonnage is small. Platinum is mined in the Goodnews Bay district, but no data are released by the government. Sand and gravel have become important commodities since the beginning of defense-establishment construction.

Commerce and Manufacturing. Except in a very limited sense, the isolation of Alaska did not pass with the completion of the highway through Canada, the wartime construction of the first great highway in the Territory, the Alaska Highway. Prior to that time the Richardson Highway between Fairbanks and Valdez on the coast, was the only major road. The Glenn Highway between Anchorage and the Richardson was built next. Since then the Taylor Highway has been extended from the Alaska Highway to Eagle on the Yukon River. Seward has been connected to Anchorage, and the Hawley Sterling Highway connects the Kenai Peninsula, with its promise of farming, with the main Territorial highway system. Cordova and Mount McKinley Park have each been connected to the highway system. Nearly all of southeastern Alaska is quite without connecting highways. Juneau, the capital, and Ketchikan, the salmon-canning center, are isolated except by steamer and airplane. Trucking is regularly scheduled over the Alaska Highway throughout the year.

The Alaska Railroad is 470 miles in length from its southern terminus at Seward, on Resurrection Bay, to Fairbanks. In addition there are branches from Portage to Whittier, carrying mostly military traffic, the Matanuska branch to Palmer and Jonesville, carrying coal, farm products and machinery, the Eielson branch from Fairbanks, military traffic, and the Suntrana branch from Healy, with coal traffic. At the coast, military traffic moves through the port of Whittier and commercial traffic goes through Seward. The railroad operates freight and passenger steamers, towboats, and oil barges on the Yukon and Tanana rivers. Revenue freight transported during 1952 totaled 1,355,080 tons, of which coal shipments constituted 654,072 tons.

FIGURE 21-5: *Newest Thing in Alaskan Transport*
This giant cross-country motor freight train is used in transporting cargoes of freight to isolated areas of northern Alaska. (R. G. Le Tourneau, Inc.)

For most of Alaska's towns, the steamer is the only way to get about. The Alaska Steamship Company provides service to all sections of maritime Alaska, from Ketchikan to Kotzebue. The Alaska Railroad operates boats and barges on the Yukon and the Tanana rivers. But it is to the airplane that many Alaskans look to give a measure of accessibility, both local and international.

Fourteen airlines fly scheduled air routes within Alaska, including the Aleutian Islands; nearly all of them fly the mail as well as passengers and cargo traffic. The official map showing Alaska air routes gives some concept of the significant location of Alaskan cities with respect to Canadian cities and those in the United States. There are three major concentrations of Alaskan airways: Juneau in the southeast, Anchorage in the south, and Fairbanks in the interior. Northwest Airlines flies the Chicago, Edmonton, Whitehorse, and Anchorage route to the Orient. Northwest also flies the Portland, Vancouver, and Anchorage routes. Canadian Pacific Air Lines flies the Edmonton, Fort St. John, Whitehorse, and Fairbanks route. Another Canadian airline company flies the Prince Rupert-Ketchikan route. There are no U.S. certified "cargo-only" carriers operating in Alaska.

TABLE 21-3: *Intra-Alaskan Air Carrier Traffic, 1949-53*
(*including scheduled and nonscheduled routes*)

Revenue passenger miles	
1949	61,185,000
1951	55,222,000
1953	34,732,000
Cargo ton-miles	
1949	8,217,000
1951	2,736,000
1953	1,706,000
Mail ton-miles	
1949	389,000
1951	817,000
1953	1,161,000

SOURCE: *Annual Report of the Civil Aeronautics Board, 1953* (Washington, 1954), p. 48.

Among the 130 landing fields some of the Territorial airlines perform a very personal type of service for isolated communities or families. Over the route between Juneau and Fairbanks green vegetables, eggs, fruit, and other perishables are regularly flown. These figures do not take into account the traffic flown in aircraft operated by the armed services.

The foreign trade and the trade with the United States which moves by steamer goes through the port of Seward; in 1952 receipts at this port were 468,000 short tons; the shipments were 15,000 tons, with some 350 vessels entering and leaving the port during the year. Alaskan imports from countries exclusive of the United States in 1952 were $993,574; exports to such countries were $3,041,956. These figures are about average for the years between 1945 and 1952.[5]

Cities. Alaskan cities and towns are localized in three districts: the panhandle in the southeast, Cook Inlet, and Prince William Sound. Until World War II *Juneau* (5,956) was the only modern city in the Territory and the largest one. It got its start in gold mining; today it is the Territorial capital. *Sitka* (1,985), the old Russian capital, makes its living from fishing. *Ketchikan* (5,305) is the southernmost Alaskan town and is headquarters for the halibut fishing fleet, accounting for nearly three-fourths of the 45 million pounds caught each year on the Pacific Coast. Each year its salmon fishing fleet supplies the nine local canneries with salmon for over one-half

[5] *Statistical Abstract of the United States, 1954,* p. 950.

million cases of 48 cans each. Several million pounds of halibut, salmon, and cod are frozen in Ketchikan each year.

Fifteen miles south, on Annette Island, is the *Metlakatla Indian settlement* (867) which for more than a generation has set an example in co-operation. A sawmill, salmon cannery, hydroelectric plant, water system, boat yards, and model town are the result of co-operative action by these people, aided principally by the United States government's grant of exclusive fishing rights near the island.

The remaining towns of the panhandle area include *Wrangell* (1,263), *Skagway* (758), *Douglas* (699), and *Petersburg* (1,619). All engage in fishing and some lumbering. Petersburg has a large fish-freezing warehouse. Douglas has one of the few iron foundries in Alaska. Cities of Cook Inlet district are more or less intimately related to the Government-owned Alaska Railroad and the resettlement project in Matanuska Valley, not far from *Palmer* (900).

Anchorage (11,254) is the Territory's largest city, largely a consequence of World War II. It has the shops and offices of the Alaska Railroad, although its terminus is at *Seward* (2,114) farther south. Gold mining was the first stimulus for Anchorage, followed by fish canning and a share of the coal trade.

Seward is unique for Alaska in that it is primarily a port and lacks the usual mining, fishing, and fur interests. Palmer is the administrative center for the Matanuska Valley settlement. It has creameries, a canning plant for vegetables, as well as the usual warehouses and port facilities. Its tributary area has not displayed vigorous growth since World War II.

Valdez (560) on Prince William Sound, has an excellent harbor and is the terminus of the Richardson Highway to Fairbanks. Furs are regularly exported. *Cordova* (1,165) has had a mineral and trading background but today depends upon lumbering, salmon- and crab-canning, and clam digging. Far to the west, on the remote Seward Peninsula, is *Nome* (1,876). There is no harbor here to facilitate off-shore shipping. Its reliance is upon the gold and other mining of the region.

Fairbanks (5,771), in the interior on the Tanana River, is the focus of an airline network and terminus of the Alaska Railroad and the Alaska Highway (*Fig.* 21-6). Gold mining has been a major element in its economy from the beginning. Today this is a highly mechanized industry. The great dredges handle huge tonnages in order to make profitable the venture in a short season and low recovery per ton of material.

The University of Alaska at nearby College, the Agricultural Experiment Station, and two large air bases tend to enliven Fairbanks. The inter-

FIGURE 21-6: *Fairbanks, Alaska*

Fairbanks is the metropolis of interior Alaska. The University of Alaska and the Agricultural Experiment Station are nearby. An indication of the city's northerly latitude is the shadow of the bridge over the Tanana River. (United States Air Force)

national airport is a busy place, even though it operates thus far on a temporary basis, pending completion of facilities.

Alaska's Prospect. Comparison of Alaska with countries in northern Europe or with the Soviet Arctic tend to disparage American attempts at Arctic occupation. As Alaska's Governor Ernest Gruening has stated, "The Alaskan economy rests none too securely on two industries, both absentee-owned and both dependent upon migrant labor." The attempt to bring more manufacturing to the Territory has met with qualified success. In 1952 there were two pulp mills under construction there—first representatives of that industry. One aluminum plant was in the planning stage. Service industries have expanded, owing to the thousands of servicemen currently stationed in the Territory.

While administration should be simplified when Alaska is made a state in the Union,[6] labor will still be short; freight rates are high because the costs are high, and the climate can play no such part in attracting people as in

[6] It is reported that more than fifty federal agencies have some control in Alaskan affairs.

California. The prospect of pressure on farmland in the United States is not likely to make farmers look to Alaska. The prospect is for a continuing colonial economy, with perhaps four rather than two basic industries, fish, minerals, pulp, and possibly smelting and refining of imported bauxite ores.

BIBLIOGRAPHY

EITEMAN, WILFORD J. and A. B. SMUTS, "Alaska, Land of Opportunity—Limited," *Economic Geography,* Vol. 27, No. 1 (Jan., 1951), pp. 33-42.

HANSON, Herbert C., *Agriculture in the Matanuska Valley, Alaska* (U.S. Dept. of the Interior, Division of Territories and Island Possessions, Washington, 1944).

MILLER, E. Willard, "Agricultural Development in Interior Alaska," *Scientific Monthly,* Vol. 73 (Oct., 1951), pp. 245-254.

RANSOME, A. L., "The Mineral Industry of Alaska," *Minerals Yearbook, 1951* (U.S. Dept. of the Interior, Washington), pp. 1385-1409.

ROCKIE, W. A., "Pitting on Alaskan Farmlands, a New Erosion Problem," *Geographical Review,* Vol. 1 (Jan., 1942), pp. 128-134.

———, "Picture of Matanuska," *Geographical Review,* Vol. 32 (1942), pp. 353-371.

STONE, Kirk H., "Populating Alaska: the United States Phase," *Geographical Review* (1952), pp. 384-404.

Study of the Alaska Tundra with Reference to Its Reactions to Reindeer and Other Grazing, Report No. 10. (U.S. Dept. of the Interior, Fish and Wildlife Service, Washington, 1945).

CHAPTER 22

HAWAIIAN ISLANDS

INTRODUCTION

IT PROBABLY TOOK World War II to make the rank and file of the United States citizens aware of the island frame of reference which makes the Hawaiian Islands significant to the United States. The war which dramatized the situation and the physical attributes of some of these hundreds of island groups in the Pacific has been followed by the establishment of trusteeships by the United States, Australian, New Zealand, British, and French governments. The problem of occupying strategically important islands has been replaced by the necessity of maintaining their economic well-being. This is no mean obligation that has been assumed.

The Hawaiian Islands are nearest to the United States of these island groups, yet they are 2,000 miles distant. Almost as far again to the southwest are the Marianas, Carolines, and Marshall Island archipelagoes, all under United States trusteeship. A more familiar land beyond these islands is the Philippine Republic, once part of the so-called American Empire.

The Hawaiian Archipelago extends over an area comparable to Wyoming, with a land area of approximately 7,000 square miles, the equivalent of Connecticut and Rhode Island combined. The situation of the Hawaiian Islands in the vast Pacific Ocean, with respect to the United States, has steadily grown in importance since the war, in part due to the rising Asian problem. Within the relatively brief span of fifty years, this group of Pacific Islands has become an important factor in maintaining the United States and Canada as leading world powers (*Fig.* 22-1).

From the very beginning, the Hawaiian Islands were able to relate their agricultural economy to the North American market directly. There was no period of agricultural self-sufficiency after the United States took over the

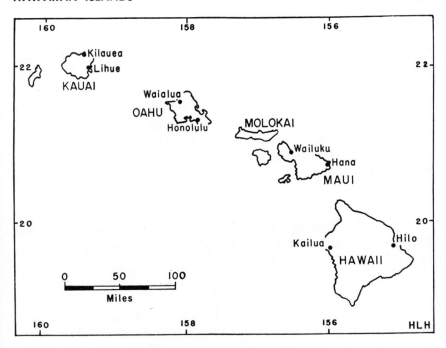

FIGURE 22-1: *Hawaiian Islands*

islands in 1894; the plantation system had developed before the change. Both the productivity and the trade-per-capita have risen rather steadily since 1900.

PHYSICAL CHARACTERISTICS

Situation. The islands of the Hawaiian group lie at the southeastern extremity of a much more extensive group of smaller islands some 1,400 miles north of the equator and 2,000 miles west of California. They lie on the steamer and air lanes to Australia and the southwest Pacific, rather than the direct routes to Japan and China, as is sometimes supposed. Their main strategic importance derives from their situation with respect to the Aleutian Islands, the Panama Canal, and the western coast of North America, a fact which has greatly appreciated in importance since the development of air power.

Relief. Although their combined area is not great, the Hawaiian Islands have a wide diversity of landscape features, owing in large part to their volcanic origin. The largest islands represent volcanic mountains built up by the accumulation of lava and other materials. This chain of mountains is partly surrounded by coral reefs. Live volcanoes, snow-capped peaks, palm-fringed beaches, and fern forests contribute to a variegated natural setting.

The island of Hawaii, nearly twice the size of the remaining islands, has two volcanoes of approximately 13,000 feet and some lower ones. Most of the area of the several islands is unfit for crop agriculture because of the rugged terrain. Plain-like areas are found at various altitudes, but many of the lava slopes are barren wastes. Extensive coastal plains are rare; the only one of considerable extent is on the south shore of Oahu. In addition to the rugged features resulting from volcanic deposition, erosion has created districts of very rough topography. There is little vegetation to soften the outlines of this terrain over most of the islands. Most parts of the islands are dry. On the whole, the terrain of much or most of the Hawaiian Islands can scarcely be termed inviting to agricultural occupance; 8 per cent may be classed as arable.

Climate. The climate of these islands is primarily a consequence of their location between 18° and 22° north latitude, on the poleward margin of the belt of northeast trades. The marine influence and their low latitude give to all except elevations a uniformly warm climate with generally dry summers and moist winters. There are some places where this seasonal distribution does not hold, however.

This type of climate has been a factor in attracting Chinese and Japanese nationals in large numbers from their homelands. The rugged relief of the Islands makes directional as well as altitudinal differences in local climate. Areas on the lee side of the mountains are similar to San Diego, California; windward sides have heavier and more evenly distributed rainfall, depending upon the elevation. Lee coasts particularly have a variable rainfall from year to year; these differences may be very great. Much of the winter rainfall on lee slopes is the result of storms known as "kona."

POPULATION

Out of a population of about half a million, 184,611 are Japanese, 32,-376 are Chinese, 114,793 are Caucasian, 86,091 are Hawaiian, and 61,071 are Filipino. About 70 per cent live on Oahu; Honolulu alone has a population of 248,034. Despite this diversity of racial groups, the Hawaiian Islands have been something of a model of peaceful human relations.

ECONOMY

Agriculture. The economy of the Hawaiian Islands is basically agricultural and likely to remain so. When admitted into the Union as a territory, Hawaii had an established economy and a fairly dense population. The market of the United States permitted the Islands to pursue their agricultural specialties. They have purchased much in the way of foodstuffs from the mainland.

Agriculture has become important despite the fact that only about 8 per cent of the 6,423 square miles is arable. Meadows and pastures of all kinds occupy about 40 per cent, and woodland about 25 per cent. Acreage devoted to crops in 1949 was as follows: total sugar cane 221,542, with 108,-298 acres harvested; pineapples 51,018; coffee 3,403; corn 752; taro 591; sweet potatoes and yams 279; rice 170; and potatoes 108 acres.[1] About one-fifth of this cropland is in the hands of the so-called "big facilities."

Crops generally follow a vertical pattern of land-use zones. Rice and taro grow mainly on the flood plains and deltas; taro as now grown is mainly a remnant of its former importance. On the next higher lands bananas and vegetables are grown. Sugar cane dominates the lower mountain slopes, some as high as 2,000 feet. Most of the pineapples are at a somewhat higher elevation than cane but generally not above 2,500 feet. Cotton is grown in the middle altitudes, as is coffee on the island of Hawaii. There is no crop agriculture above this zone. Government and private forests occupy much of the land in the highlands that is put to any use.

Sugar Cane. Sugar cane is grown mainly on Hawaii, Maui, Oahu, Lanai, and Kauai. There are 16 of these sugar plantations on Hawaii, 10 on Maui, 7 on Oahu, and 5 on Lanai. Plantations vary in size from 1,000 to 15,000 acres, with the planting staggered so that about 10 per cent of the area is planted each year. Cane is grown from sections of the stalk cut from the tops of ripe cane. From this one planting there will be five ratoon crops, six harvests in all. The permeable soil, the extremely heavy water requirement of the plant, the absence of surface streams, and the scanty rainfall combine to make irrigation imperative on more than half of the total cane acreage. The crop needs the maximum of sunshine, hence much is on the sunny, lee slopes. Topographic conditions make irrigation costs high;

[1] The market value of agricultural products, 1950, was: cane sugar $110 million, pineapples $75 million, truck products including all potatoes $9 million, beef cattle $7 million, dairy products $5 million, and coffee $1 million. *Statistical Abstract of the United States, 1952,* p. 658.

FIGURE 22-2: *Sugar-Cane Plantation, Hawaii*

Many towns have grown up around sugar plantations. Experiment stations, fertilization, irrigation, and relatively high-priced labor have made the Islands' sugar plantations among the most scientific in the world. (Hawaii Visitors Bureau)

on a representative plantation the annual costs for irrigation may be as high as $300,000 (*Fig.* 22-2).

Despite mechanization of much of the work on a sugar plantation, the labor requirements are still very great. A major problem is to secure adequate labor on the isolated plantations. As a consequence, the management is apt to be very paternalistic; housing and recreational devices have been used to attract a body of dependable labor. Most of the foremen have been recruited from among the Filipinos and the Japanese. The exchange of labor between cane sugar and pineapple growers has been possible; the pineapple growers have used some of the idle labor during the slack summer cane season.

Hawaii's one-million-tons production is slightly less than the production of cane sugar by Puerto Rico, and greatly exceeds that of continental United States 564,000 tons). The cane yield per acre in Hawaii is 75 tons; in Puerto Rico 30, and in Louisiana 20 tons, and this despite the fact that the conditions under which it is grown in Hawaii are by no means ideal. The winters are too cool, water is scarce, rotation is not practiced, fertilizer must be applied regularly, and labor is short. Dry exposures are often deliberately chosen; the maximum sunshine raises the sugar content of the cane. Experimentation has resulted in better methods and varieties. Hawaiian sugar enters the United States duty free; U.S. ships move it to the States.

Pineapples. Although pineapples are the second-ranking crop in the Islands, their aggregate acreage is half that of sugar cane.[2] Pineapples are a luxury rather than a staple food; they have no tariff protection, yet the Islands produce more than three-fourths of the world's crop. As with cane, this crop needs a great deal of manual labor; the same types of imported labor are used to care for it. The tolerance of pineapples with respect to soils, temperature, and rainfall is greater than cane; as a consequence production has spread to several parts of the archipelago. Improvements have been made in the plant and in the methods of growing it and canning it. National advertising on the mainland has succeeded in taking pineapples out of the purely luxury class. Despite this, the Hawaiian pineapple industry has fluctuated at times with the changes in purchasing power in the United States.

As with cane production, the same paternalistic methods have been in vogue; the same companies exercise control over more than half of all pineapple acreage. Most of the pineapples not canned in Honolulu are canned on the plantations.

The principal producing districts are Maui, Molokai, Lanai, and Oahu. Here under varying conditions of rainfall and temperature, the slips of pineapple plants are set in the ground in early autumn. By inserting them through holes in heavy moisture-proofed paper several feet wide, weeds are kept down and moisture conserved. After a period of about twenty months, the fruit is harvested. A first and second ratoon crops are grown, harvested at yearly intervals; neither ratoon crop is as abundant as the plant crop. Labor during the harvest is nearly all manual; at this time additional labor is recruited from the idle cane plantations. Unlike the sugar crop, pineapples are destined for many parts of the world. The 13.7 million cases packed in 1950 constituted 80 per cent of the world output (*Fig.* 22-3).

Fishing. The development of an important fishing industry does not seem compatible with the shortage of plantation labor; in fact the industry fails to meet the domestic demand for seafood by about 20 per cent. The industry is virtually confined to the island of Oahu. On the northwest coast of Oahu a fishing fleet of about one thousand craft is engaged in inshore fishing. The catch is largely a variety of tuna. Fishermen of Japanese ancestry man

---

[2] 1950 cane acreage was 109,405, pineapples 51,018, cotton 3,403, corn 752, taro 596. *Statistical Abstract of the United States, 1952,* p. 605.

most of the boats. Although deep-sea fishing has made some headway and the waters are believed to be abundantly stocked, there is no immediate prospect of an increase. Good harbors are rare; the waters are very deep, and alternative employment is increasing; these are not conducive to fishing.

Quarrying. The only mineral industry on the Islands is quarrying stone and making of lime and cement. Combined tonnage for 1950 was only 9,000 short tons.

Commerce and Manufacturing. There is much commerce among some of the Islands and the mainland. Total exports in 1950 amounted to $236,432,730 of which the United States took $228,353,010. Total imports amounted to $349,627,410 of which the United States supplied $340,411,-393. This figure for exports does not include some $30 million spent by tourists in the Islands. Unlike Alaska, Hawaiians finance a large part of their capital requirements, including the shipping industry. Proceeds from agricultural land leases are a relatively important source of income to the Territorial government.

Although the Census lists 474 manufacturing establishments in 1950, factory employment of 17,000 is largely confined to canning pineapples,

FIGURE 22-3: Pineapple Canning Plant, Hawaii

This view of the production line in a pineapple canning plant in the Islands gives an excellent sidelight on the labor supply for this great Hawaiian industry. (Hawaiian Pineapple Co.)

sugar refining, cotton textiles and apparel. The operation of utilities for factory goods has been increased as a result of the relatively large defense establishment maintained there by the United States.

THE ISLANDS

Oahu. Oahu with an area of 604 square miles, is second in size to Hawaii, but its population density of 378 per square mile places it far ahead of any other island in the archipelago. The mountain topography of Oahu embraces the same type of varied landscape common to the other islands. The mountain slopes are forested to their tops. There is less barren land. On the southern margin there is a broad coastal plain, the largest of its kind on all of the Islands. The indented shoreline forms a few excellent harbors, among them is Pearl Harbor, a few miles from the city of Honolulu. Rainfall varies from 27 inches at Honolulu to 139 inches yearly on the windward east coast. The largest forest reservations are on Oahu. The soils of Oahu, as are those of the other islands, are composed of weathered lava and coral limestone; they are naturally fertile but in use require liberal fertilization, owing to irrigation and absence of rotation.

With approximately one-fourth of its area in crops, Oahu has the largest proportion of arable land of the group. Seventy per cent of this cropland is devoted to sugar cane, 22 per cent to pineapples, with the remainder used for truck, rice, and other minor crops. Although the Kaneohe district raises tomatoes, potatoes, peas, cabbages, and some tropical vegetables not grown on the mainland, more than half of the fresh vegetables and fruit consumed by the large Honolulu market is imported from California. Despite the apparently optimum conditions of climate and soil for many of these crops, the heavy rains on the gardened slopes cause destructive erosion. The colonial type of agriculture has a strong appeal for so many subtropical and tropical people who are great food importers. There are many more dairy cattle and fewer beef animals and swine than on the other large islands.

Sometimes referred to as the "hub" of the Hawaiian Islands, Oahu is well-situated to engage in the lucrative interisland trade. The largest city in the Pacific is *Honolulu* (248,034), on Oahu. Other important cities on this island are *Waialua* (8,369), *Schofield Barracks* (5,000), and *Pearl City* (2,663). These urban centers constitute the largest market in all of this Pacific area. Manufacturing industries are not important. Most of the sugar is refined on the mainland. Canning of pineapples, production of utilities, and the fabrication of consumer goods for residents and tourists make up the bulk of Oahu's manufactures.

FIGURE 22-4: *U.S. Marine Barracks, Kaneohe, Hawaii*

This military post is evidence of the strategic situation of the Hawaiian Islands in the defense system of the United States. (Official Marine Corps Photograph)

Hawaii. This large island is about twice the area of all others in the Hawaiian group. Its two largest volcanoes, Mauna Loa and Mauna Kea, make it a conspicuous island. Although mountainous, its shore line is more regular than any of the smaller islands. Of its 4,000 square miles only 4.8 per cent is in cropped land. Population density is less than one-eighteenth as great as on Oahu.

Hereford cattle, horses, mules, sheep, goats, and a few swine and poultry make Hawaii the most important livestock area in the Islands. The requirements of the plantations in the way of draft animals and meat are largely met by this island. On the eastern coastal plain of Hawaii are large sugar-cane plantations. Smaller concentrations are on the south coast. The only coffee grown in the Islands is produced in the central and western (Kona) part of the island of Hawaii at altitudes of from 1,500 to 2,500 feet. The industry is largely in the hands of the Japanese who operate farm units of from 5 to 15 acres. Most of the 15 million pounds of this coffee is exported to the mainland for blending purposes. As in all other intensive farming operations in the Islands, there is a shortage of labor during the harvest season; these coffee farms import labor from the pineapple growers during their slack season.

FIGURE 22-5: *Moana Hotel, Waikiki Beach, Hawaii*

This hotel caters to the important tourist trade which has developed between the Islands and the mainland. (Hawaii Visitors Bureau)

At one time rice was an important crop on Hawaii; today the rice crop is only 650,000 pounds; the Islands import 85 million pounds from the mainland, mainly for the Oriental population. Like coffee and cotton, rice is largely in Japanese hands. Cotton is grown on a small scale, less than 500 acres.

Hilo (27,198) on the northeast coast is the largest city on Hawaii, and second-largest in the Islands. Its fishing and canning industries rank next after Honolulu.

Other Islands. Kauai and Maui have some sugar, rice, and pineapples. Grazing is the only form of agriculture on dry Niihau. Molokai has some crop agriculture, including pineapples.

The future of the Hawaiian Islands has been reappraised since the beginning of World War II. The profitable but colonial status of the Islands may soon be modified by admission to statehood. In itself, such a political change should have little effect upon the economy of the Islands. The shifting commercial emphasis to the Pacific Ocean countries on the part of the United States only serves to strengthen the military and naval appraisal of the Islands' location. It is probable that with statehood will come a less complex control over its affairs. Transportation (particularly interisland) rates may be lowered.

BIBLIOGRAPHY

GUILLOU, René, "Mechanization of Tropical Farming in Hawaii," *Proceedings of the United Nations Scientific Conference on the Conservation and Utilization of Resources,* Vol. 6 (1951), pp. 191-195.

HAAS, W. H., ed., *The American Empire* (Chicago, Univ. of Chicago Press, 1940).

WILSON, James N., "Pineapple Industry of Hawaii," *Economic Geography,* Vol. 24, No. 3 (July, 1948), pp. 251-262.

Part Four

PROSPECT

CHAPTER 23

PROSPECT

IN A TEXT on the regional geography of the United States and Canada, much must be left to the reader by way of establishing perspective for the facts presented. The Air Force, by examination, is able to determine the absence of "depth perception" in an individual seeking to take pilot training. This information saves lives and property as well as instruction. Unfortunately there is no such device for measuring so promptly the mental perception of an individual. A prime function of student-teacher relationship is the determination of the relative importance of all the facts which bear upon a given situation.

The foregoing chapters have been concerned with the geographic foundations of the well-being of the United States, its territories, and Canada. This has proceeded from the viewpoint of both the principal economic activities and the major geographic regions. No matter which is the approach, there is much evidence of change in the manner and place of economic production. Growth and decline are found in each industry and in every region.

The expression "foundations of national well-being" suggests something of the backward look. The term *geographic regions* suggests something that has been established. It is primarily for this reason that this book includes chapters with the functional viewpoint. One would be naïve to believe that the problems of the economy of any region are solely the product of that region, that their influence is confined to it, or that the solutions lie wholly within it, or for that matter, even in the nation. The rapid growth in interdependence among nations means that virtually no economic activity in the United States or Canada is free from the consequences of developments in similar activities in other parts of the world.

As an aid in establishing some perspective for the facts presented in this book, this concluding section will attempt to sketch the prospect for major economic activities by outlining some of the over-all conditions under which the American economy functions.

Every major economic activity functions within a frame of reference of its national organization. The four chapters of Part I attempted to establish this for agriculture, the mineral industries, manufacturing, and commerce. There is yet another set of conditions under which the national organization must function. What has been observed in the chapters on principal economic activities and in the several regional chapters must all be influenced by an over-all set of conditions. These major considerations include the increase in population, the size and character of the labor force, social and industrial technology, and government. Each of these will be mentioned briefly with examples of their geographical impact drawn from the foregoing chapters.

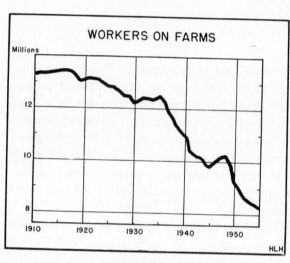

FIGURE 23-1

More food is grown in the United States for more people by fewer farmers. *Fig.* 2-7 should be studied in connection with this chart of the workers on farms.

Population Increase. Beyond noting man's distribution, the national occupational structure, and his role as a producing agent, little specific attention has been paid in these chapters to man as such. The major events that will profoundly affect the future economy of the nation are concerned with man and have already taken place. In 1954 there were a record 4,060,000 babies born in this country. Only ten years ago the Bureau of the Census predicted a static population within a few years and the country generally was planning with this in mind. In 1955 the economic population for the next twenty years was already in existence. What are believed to be conservative estimates of the population in 1955 give 165 million; in 1965, 190 million; and 1975, 220 million.

Between 1955 and 1975 the number of young people reaching marriageable age will increase. By 1965 the birth figure should increase as children born in the years of the baby "boom" since 1942, begin to establish families. During the next ten years there will be a 20 per cent increase in population, and the next twenty years an increase of 40 per cent.

Labor Force. The availability of this increased population for the national labor force will not increase at such a rate, however. During the next ten years the population available for work will increase from 6 to 10 per cent, depending upon the proportion of work-age young people entering college and university. For the next twenty years the increase in the working force will be from 20 to 30 per cent.

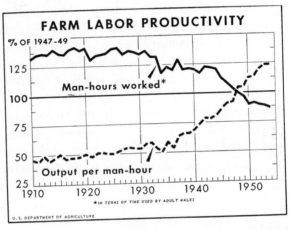

The manner in which this working force is used is, of course, constantly changing. We are apt to speak of this loosely as the technological evolution; its study is beyond the field of economic geography, but many of the con-sequences have defi-nite geographic implication (*Fig.* 23-2). Technological changes generally include social-technological changes as well. An attribute of most Americans is the propensity to want to increase profits, and during the past fifteen years the social-technological changes have probably had greater effect upon our economy than the strictly technological changes. At any rate, the tendency is to underestimate their influence.

FIGURE 23-2

The dramatic aspect of this agricultural change in the United States is suggested on this chart of farm labor productivity. For examples of increasing mechanization in agriculture which makes this possible, see *Figs.* 11-3 and 13-5. Someone has termed this the "magnificent decline in agriculture."

Social Technology. In this social-technological category come the many changes in business organization and management which bring about increased production and have definite geographic expression. Many of them have been noted in this book, for instance the backward and forward integration in the primary steel industry. Another is the rise of larger business units. The recentralization of manufacturing facilities during World War II is another example, one with greater geographic impact than any other. From labor's viewpoint there are several examples, including changed standards of work and of pay. Looking ahead to the annual-wage concept of contractual relations, the geographic implications seem to be important, taking the form of increased integration and subcontracting among larger producing units.

Another aspect of this social technological evolution is concerned with training the working force or that part of it concerned with the implementation of industrial technology. Industry has gone far in the expenditure of money and human effort to secure new sources of needed raw materials and in great research laboratories maintained by industry to promote economies in production by means of new processes and new products. On the other hand, providing human resources of industry has generally been neglected by those whose future depends upon them. An estimated 27 per cent of the work-age young people are expected to attend a college or university. Although these institutions have been financed by churches, private fortunes, and by the proceeds of the sale of public lands, these sources of revenue are proving to be inadequate and some other source of income must be found. What is next after land? Many in and out of industry feel that manufacturing industries must promote this phase of the general welfare. A number of large manufacturing concerns have taken steps to close this gap between the future need for such trained men and women and the educational facilities available for their training.

Technological Change. Technological changes may take the form of increased use of machinery, economy of raw materials including power, and changes in production techniques. A review of some of these changes would include the relative increase in the use of powered equipment. Between 1935 and 1945 the population of the United States increased by 10 per cent, while total energy consumed rose by 70 per cent. Between 1945 and 1955 the annual consumption equivalent to 6.0 tons per capita rose to 10.0 tons per capita. Even fuel men have their version of the Malthusian law. Another example is the perfection of the by-product coke oven, the openhearth and the electric furnaces which combined to free the primary steel industry from dependence upon a certain type of coal and a concentrated market. The continuous strip rolling mill, on the other hand, lowered costs in rolling steel and thus strengthened the competitive position of some established steel

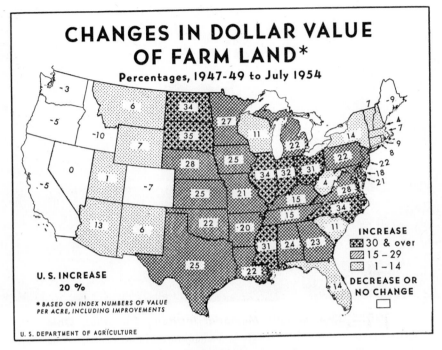

CHANGES IN DOLLAR VALUE OF FARM LAND*
Percentages, 1947-49 to July 1954

INCREASE
30 & over
15 – 29
1 – 14

DECREASE OR
NO CHANGE

U. S. INCREASE
20 %

* BASED ON INDEX NUMBERS OF VALUE
PER ACRE, INCLUDING IMPROVEMENTS

U. S. DEPARTMENT OF AGRICULTURE

FIGURE 23-3

Changing use of land for agriculture is only one of the factors which have brought about the changes shown on this map. Compare it with *Fig.* 23-2.

centers. The movement of primary steel manufacture thus was arrested, not accelerated.

In the mining industry, too, technological changes have reduced the number of men working underground, lowered the permissible quality of the coal or ore mined, and enabled smaller deposits to be worked economically (*Fig.* 9-3). In agriculture, the single beet seed, hybrid corn, new varieties of wheat and of cotton not only increased the yield, but in some instances enabled the production of these crops to enter regions or into crop combinations formerly denied them. Quick freezing of fruits and of vegetables also made it possible for some hitherto noncommercial districts to get into production. Between 1940 and 1946 in the United States, real product per man-hour in agriculture showed a rise of 56 per cent, as against 9.5 per cent expected. This gain has been maintained since 1946, when an upward trend of 1.5 per cent per year has been experienced (*Fig.* 23-2).

The above examples were drawn from the list of things now accomplished. Looking into the future, there is yet another long list of technological

FIGURE 23-4: Battelle Memorial Institute, Columbus, Ohio

This institute does sponsored research for manufacturers in many parts of the United States and some foreign countries. Originally concerned with research in iron, its activities have grown to include research in a wide variety of industrial and agricultural production. It is the largest private research organization in the nation, and with its European divisions, the largest in the world. This photograph shows the parent plant, and largest facility.

changes the main features of which are known today. Among them are the commercial use of iron-bearing taconite and jasper, oil shale, titanium, automation in factories, and the commercial use of atomic energy.

There is of course some opposition to many of these technological changes on the part of organized labor, vested interests, and even the federal government. The introduction of these changes may abruptly lower the value of a human skill, the value of land, or the number of people directly employed. Despite some opposition, the future will have more of it, no matter what the cost. Furthermore, the rate of increase will undoubtedly accelerate as more people are trained in the understanding and appreciation of pure and applied science (*Fig.* 23-4).

Government. Government has become an important factor in economic change. For twenty years the American farmer, miner, and manufacturer have had an increased market for their products arising from war or from an aspect of our foreign policy. Committed to the principle that only the productive can be strong, and only the strong can be free, the United States, particularly, has sought to aid in increasing the production of, and finding markets for, friendly nations. This has made it both more difficult and easier for domestic producers to sell abroad, depending upon the country and the product. It is one more factor in competition that appears to be growing in importance.

The government is firmly committed to a policy of protection, subsidy, and investment in manufacturing and commercial facilities. Exploitation of resources itself is held to be a normal process; only "mal-" or "over-"exploitation is evil, and some legislation has been enacted to that end. River control, power development, irrigation, and soil conservation programs have become accepted parts of the economy of the United States and of Canada. Commodity price controls play an important role in determining agricultural land utilization. In any assessment of the future of these two countries, whether in war or peace, government has become one of the most important forces in their respective economies.

BIBLIOGRAPHY

CLARK, Colin, "World Resources and World Population; *Proceedings of the United Nations Scientific Conference on the Conservation and Utilization of Resources,*" Vol. 1 (1951), pp. 15-26.

MOORE, Wilbert E., *Industrialization and Labor, Social Aspects of Economic Development* (Ithaca, Cornell University Press, 1951).

MUSKAT, Morris, "Advances in the Efficiency of Oil Recovery," *Proceedings of the United Nations Scientific Conference on the Conservation and Utilization of Resources,* Vol. 3 (1951), pp. 40-45.

PUTNAM, Palmer C., *Energy in the Future* (New York, D. Van Nostrand Co., 1953).

RALSTON, O. C., "The Future of the Light Metals, With Special Reference to Titanium," *Proceedings of the United Nations Scientific Conference on the Conservation and Utilization of Resources,* Vol. 2, pp. 252-254.

Resources for Freedom, Report to the President by the President's Materials Policy Commission (Washington, 1952).

SALTER, R. M., "Techniques for Increasing Agricultural Production," *Proceedings of the United Nations Scientific Conference on the Conservation and Utilization of Resources,* Vol. 1 (1951), pp. 83-91.

SEQUENS, Jiri, "The Conservation of Non-ferrous Metals," *Proceedings of the United Nations Scientific Conference on the Conservation and Utilization of Resources,* Vol. 2 (1951), pp. 252-254.

SMITH, Guy-Harold, ed., *Conservation of Natural Resources* (New York, John Wiley and Sons, Inc., 1950).

SULLIVAN, John D., "New Processes for the Utilization of Low Grade Ores," *Proceedings of the United Nations Scientific Conference on the Conservation and Utilization of Resources,* Vol. 2 (1951), pp. 146-152.

WOOTEN, H. H., and Erwin J. UTZ, "Reclamation of New Lands for Agriculture, Potentialities and Problems in the Development of Irrigation and Drainage," *Proceedings of the United Nations Scientific Conference on the Conservation and Utilization of Resources,* Vol. 6 (1951), pp. 602-604.

ZIMMERMANN, E. W., *World Resources and Industries* (New York, Harper and Bros., 1951).

Index